ABOUT THE AUTHOR

Dr. Thomas N. Garavan is an academic at the University of Limerick, where he lectures on a range of subjects including human resource development, training and vocational education, human factors and safety, safety and health legislation and strategic management. His research interests include the analysis of how organisations structure and deliver training, HRD networks, the influence of managerial values on human resource development, the predictions of safety culture climate, continuing professional development and the effectiveness of graduate training and development programmes. He is a Fellow of the Irish Institute of Training and Development and a member of the American Society of Training and Development. He is editor of the *Journal of European Industrial Training*, associate editor of *Human Resource Development International* and co-author of *Training and Development in Ireland*, *Cases in Irish Business Strategy and Policy*, and the two-volume set *Entrepreneurship and Business Start-Ups in Ireland*.

THE IRISH HEALTH & SAFETY HANDBOOK

2ND EDITION

Thomas N. Garavan

Specialist Contributors

Ronan Carbery
Eamon Collins
Michael Copus
Ruth Corless
Ambrose Downey
Thomas Dalzell
Con Egan
Michael Gaffney
Brian Greenford
Eoin McCann
David McGuire
Alan Murphy
Claire Murphy
Fergal O'Brien
Philip Thornton
Fergus Walsh
Lorraine Whelan

www.oaktreepress.com

OAK TREE PRESS
19 Rutland Street, Cork
www.oaktreepress.com

ISBN 1 86076 189 5

Printed by ColourBooks, Dublin.

CONTENTS

PART TWO
BEHAVIOURAL DIMENSIONS OF
HEALTH AND SAFETY

PART THREE
MANAGING HEALTH, SAFETY
AND THE ENVIRONMENT

PART FOUR
RISK MANAGEMENT

PART FIVE
OCCUPATIONAL HEALTH AND HYGIENE

ACKNOWLEDGEMENTS

The second edition of this handbook has evolved and changed in a number of significant ways. These changes have come about as a result of the significant legislative programme at EU and national levels and the growing interest in health and safety as a subject of academic research. The legislation section is significantly updated to reflect new statutory provisions in such areas as working time, parental leave, sexual harassment, bullying and maternity leave. There have also been some significant case law developments in areas such as employers' duty of care, occupiers' and vicarious liability and the interpretation of important provisions of the Safety, Health and Welfare at Work Act, 1989. Key sections on occupiers' liability, environmental standards, risk assessment and control, safety culture and climate, occupational health and hygiene are significantly enhanced and modified to reflect recent developments in theory, research and practice.

The author would like to thank a large number of people who provided specialist contributions, support and direct assistance during the production of the second edition of this handbook. Michael Copus, Thomas Dalzell, Ambrose Downey, Con Egan, Eoin McCann, Brian Greenford, Alan Murphy, Fergus Walsh, Fergal O'Brien, Eamon Collins, Ruth Corless, Claire Murphy and Philip Thornton who provided contributions in areas such as environmental management, electrical safety, occupational hygiene, risk management and loss control, health and safety legislation, safety statements, behavioural aspects of health, safety and welfare, sexual harassment and bullying. These contributions are reflected in several chapters within this handbook.

The author would like to thank the following at the University of Limerick for their support and encouragement: Professor Noel

Whelan, Dean, College of Business; Joseph Wallace, Head, Department of Personnel and Employment Relations; Professor Donal Dineen and Professor Paddy Gunnigle, College of Business; and Dr Thomas Kennedy, Head, Department of Accounting and Finance.

The author specifically thanks a number of professional colleagues for their continuous support, encouragement and friendship: Dr Michael Morley, Noreen Heraty, Professor Patrick Flood, Dr Sarah Moore, Sarah McCurtin, Tom Turner, Daryl D'Art, Claire Gubbins, Helena Lenihan, Juliet McMahon, Colette Noonan, Anne Morgan, Ricky Cullen, Fergal O'Brien, Gerard Fitzgerald, Anna Cunningham, Briga Hynes, Patricia Fleming, Professor Barra O Cinnéide, Carole Hogan, Anet Burke, Aidan Lawrence, Jack O'Sullivan, Anne Murphy, Breda Flaherty, Brid Burke, Amanda Cahir, Noreen Clifford and Pat Casey. Others who provided assistance to the author and contributors include John Kennedy, Safety Inspector, HSA; Gerry Higgins, Michael Gaffney, David McGuire, Haaris Sheikh, Christine Cross, Francis McNamara, Lorraine Morgan, Elaine Purcell, Eithna Egan and David O'Donnell.

The author's heartfelt thanks go to Kim O'Neill, University of Limerick, who typed the manuscript and who kept track of the numerous changes made as the book took shape, Mary Cunningham who completed the bibliography and tracked down all of the missing biographical items and Claire Murphy who helped to edit the text.

Dedicated to

Garavan Family: Thomas Sr., Jim, Patrick Joseph, Gerard,
Mary B. and Rita.

Daly Family: Margaret (Garavan), Mary (Lyons),
Anne (Donoghue), Teresa Angela, John Joseph and Edward.

In memory of

James Garavan, John Garavan, Bridget Garavan,
John Daly, Margaret Daly and Michael Joseph Daly.

List of Cases

LIST OF FIGURES

LIST OF TABLES

Introduction

HEALTH AND SAFETY IN IRELAND: AN OVERVIEW

INTRODUCTION

The establishment and maintenance of a healthy and safe work environment for all employees is now generally accepted, as not only desirable, but a necessary component of a contemporary human resource management approach. It is justifiable in both business and humanitarian terms. Occupational health and safety issues underpin many aspects of human resource management. Job design, quality of working life programmes, recruitment and orientation, training and development, performance management and payment systems all involve in some shape or form occupational health and safety issues.

During the last 20 years, health, safety and welfare issues moved up the HR agenda in Ireland with the enactment of comprehensive health and safety legislation. The costs of accidents at work and diseases, both physical and psychological, incurred as a result of work activities, are now calculated in terms of medical and hospital costs, time lost, replacement costs, rehabilitation and workers' compensation payments, retirement and superannuation entitlements. There is an increasing awareness of management failures to pay greater attention to the health and safety of employees. This awareness has translated into criminal charges and the payment of financial compensation for some companies.

Recognition of the immensity of these costs to employers and the prospect of cost reductions through healthier and safer workplaces and work practices has led to the introduction of more comprehensive safety management initiatives by Irish organisations. A range of statutory regulations, designed to achieve both compliance with specific rules and the encouragement of proactive approaches to safety, has supplemented these safety management initiatives. Strategic approaches to health and safety, as in other HRM areas, are designed therefore to ensure that occupational health and safety issues are paramount in the minds, and plans, of senior managers and HR decision-making processes.

THE EXTENT OF THE SAFETY AND HEALTH PROBLEM IN IRELAND

Exact statistics on the numbers and costs of accidents, injuries and diseases in Irish industry are difficult to secure. The context of health and safety and the environment in Ireland is a complex one. A number of issues stand out:

- It is estimated that there are approximately 1.7 million people in employment. This represents an increase of over one million in a ten-year period.

- The statistical evidence indicates that, of the 1.7 million in employment, almost one-quarter of employees are working in conditions that present serious physical risk, specifically in employments such as construction, mines, quarries, farming and the heavy manufacturing sector.

- The nature of health and safety as an area of practice has changed significantly. There is evidence of a generally greater level of focus on health and safety issues at workplace level and a broadening of the scope of health and safety to include more complex and less tangible issues such as stress, repetitive strain injury (RSI), bullying and various forms of harassment.

- The nature of work itself has changed. The evidence points to the emergence of new forms of employment including contract work, teleworking, sub-contracting, functional flexibility and often forms of atypical employment. The SME sector has also experienced significant growth. The evidence points to a generally lower standard of safety and health in this sector compared to multinational and foreign-owned companies. Many of the newer business activities have given rise to many new challenges in areas such as work stress, ergonomics, work/life balance and repetitive strain injury.

- Significant changes have and continue to occur in the legislative area. Specific influences here include the strong role played by the EU in formulating regulations and directives related to safety and the environment, equally and diversely, and the emergence of public safety as a key issue.

- The psychological relationship between employer and employee has changed significantly. Specific issues relevant here include the emergence of employability values amongst both employees and employers, higher levels of educational attainment, greater awareness and knowledge amongst employees about health, safety and environmental issues and the emergence of specialist providers of safety services. These changes place significant responsibilities on employees, employers and the state regulating mechanisms.

The statistics on accidents, fatalities and insurance costs present a relatively depressing picture in Irish and European terms. The most recent comparative statistics produced by Eurostat (1998) identify a number of important trends:

- The Irish three-day-plus accident rate measured on the standard per 100,000 in employment indicates that Ireland is second only to Sweden, suggesting that it is the second safest place in Europe to work.

- The data on fatal accidents in the workplace is, however, the second highest in the EU. Portugal has a higher rate of fatalities; 5.9 for Ireland versus 7.7 for Portugal using a standardised accident metric.

- Musculo-skeletal disorders are reported as the most common health problem affecting workers within the EU. This problem manifests itself most significantly in sectors such as construction, transport and health/social welfare. Stress/depression and anxiety is the second most common health problem and is most pronounced in health/social sectors and education.

- The Eurostat data reveals a number of significant variations in accident rates based on gender, age and accident frequency.

- Young persons aged between 18-24 are most at risk of suffering an accident. This category typically works less than 20 hours per week and works as shift workers or night workers. They are 20-50% more likely than average to have an accident.

- Women are less accident-prone than men. However, the EU data reveals that the number of accidents in sectors that employ women is increasing at a significant level.

- The European average absence rate per accident is 20 days and, in respect of three-day-plus accidents, it stands at 31 days.

- Ninety-three per cent of employees return to the same job after an accident. A small percentage change to a different job (3%). 2% of employees have to reduce the number of hours worked and a very limited number never work again.

- Fourteen per cent of employees who have an accident are likely to have more than one accident in a 12-month period. Some commentators suggest that this lends support to the view that some employees are more accident-prone than others.

Employees in the 55-64 age groups are more likely to suffer occupationally-related ill health.

Other statistical data on safety in Ireland reveal the following trends:

- In Ireland, 62 per cent of all accidents result in an insurance claim. This is significantly higher than the European average.

- On average, 5,000 reportable three-day accidents per annum are reported to the HSA.

- There is an average of 60 fatalities per annum in the Irish workplace.

- Approximately 600,000 work-days are lost per annum due to accidents and sickness.

- The estimated average claims cost in Ireland is 2.5 times more than in the UK.

- Employers' liability insurance is three times higher in Ireland than in the UK.

- The financial cost to the economy of accidents in the workplace is estimated at €3.3 billion per annum or 6 - 7 per cent of GNP.

- It is estimated that more than 20 times more days are lost to the economy due to poor health and accidents at work than due to industrial disputes.

- The average cost of an accident in Ireland is estimated at €336.89.

- The employee most at risk is foreign, or a young/new recruit or is over 40, or is a temporary worker, and is employed in a firm that employs less than 50 people whose management priorities are short-term objectives.

- Many high-risk sectors exist within the economy. A general perception exists, and the statistics support a view, that the high-risk sectors have not changed or improved significantly. Many of the fatalities and serious accidents occur in areas such as farming, construction and fishing.

- There is strong evidence of under-reporting of workplace accidents. In 1997 it was estimated that only 26 per cent of accidents accounted for in the labour force survey were reported to the HSA.

- There is strong evidence that the number of employers' liability insurance claims has increased. The Irish Insurance Federation estimates that 10,175 claims were initiated in the year 2000, which represents an increase of 10.5 per cent on the previous year. The gross cost of the claims in 2000 stood at €199 million (IR£157 million). In contrast the number of public liability claims decreased; however, the gross cost of such claims increased by almost 9 per cent to €217 million (IR£171 million). **Table 0.1** presents a three-year summary.

Table 0.1: Three-year Employer Liability Claims, Premiums and Losses

	1998	1999	2000
Claims Lodged	9,270	9,211	10,175
Gross Written Premiums (IR£ m)	123	127.5	140
Gross Incurred Claims (IR£ m)	14.7	138	157
Loss (IR£ m)	45	34	52

An IBEC study reported in 2001 reveals that employer liability premiums have increased by 40 per cent in a one-year period. The Irish Insurance Federation posits three reasons for this increase in premiums:

- There is significant inflation in terms of the claims made by employees in personal insurance cases.

- The case of *McGreaney* vs *Monaghan County Council* (2001) HC changed the basis on which actuaries should value future income returns on compensation awards. The High Court decision mandates that, when assessing the likely future income from compensation awards, actuaries will have to base their calculations on a return of 2.5 percent rather than the previously accepted 4 per cent.

- It is also argued that lower interest rates resulting in lower investment income has forced insurers to charge larger premiums.

THE DEVELOPMENT OF OCCUPATIONAL SAFETY, HEALTH AND WELFARE IN IRELAND

Early developments in health and safety awareness and prevention in Ireland, like corresponding developments in the United Kingdom and United States, were largely due to the pressure of social reforms, and the associated Humanitarian movement, in the late nineteenth century. These concerns centred on the hazardous working conditions and initially increased risks associated with new manufacturing and mining industries and in particular the use of child labour. Governments were, initially, very reluctant to pass protective health and safety legislation, considering that the management of health and safety was essentially a "management prerogative". The absence of regulations, and the costs of protecting employees, resulted in a situation where many organisations paid little attention to even the most obvious physical hazards until forced to do so by the emergence of health and safety legislation.

A variety of different professions began to express an interest in health and safety issues during the 1970s and 1980s, each bringing particular perspectives and models of causes and solutions. Often the perspectives they advocated were in conflict with those of other professionals. Deves (1989) suggests that each professional group aims "to cultivate their own specialities, [their] interest groups are powerful and . . . [they] guard their turf jealously". Legislative developments, especially in the late 1980s/1990s, served to ensure their continuous interest in health and safety issues, usually as consultants to industry or governments.

The main professions involved in health and safety in Ireland include the medical profession, occupational epidemiologists, industrial hygienists, ergonomists, industrial psychologists and more recently, occupational sociologists. Management, unions and the legal profession have maintained an interest in health and safety issues. Each professional group represents a different perspective and will be considered in this overview because each has something to offer.

The task of the human resource manager in the health and safety field is thus made extremely complex, in co-ordinating and conciliating between these different professional groups, to ensure the most cost-effective approach to a growing range of health and safety issues. Current issues, which highlight the differing diagnostic and management approaches of these professions, include repetitive strain injury (RSI), otherwise known as occupational overuse syndrome (OOS); stress; sick building syndrome (SBS) and exposure to chemicals and dangerous substances. These issues are considered in later chapters of this handbook.

The Medical Model of Health and Safety

The medical profession was not traditionally involved in workplace issues such as accidents and disease. However, due to the negative effects of industrialisation, the medical profession was more likely to be consulted by managers and government agencies, searching for ways to reduce the growing financial and human costs of industrial accidents.

Medical specialists generally focused on the identification of the direct physiological effects of work on employee health. Such aspects of employee behaviour as over-exertion, the handling of toxic substances and the dangers of using machinery preoccupied early occupational medicine practitioners. Links between the handling of toxic substances and the development of allergic skin rashes could be relatively easily determined and treated with appropriate medication. Trained to diagnose such relationships and prescribe appropriate interventions, medical approaches to health and safety gained in popularity in organisations.

The so-called "medical model" has been challenged by recent health and safety studies of stress, occupational overuse syndrome, and sick building syndrome. It is in general argued that medical or physical approaches are narrowly focused or are unable to adequately explain causes or to devise suitable preventative strategies. Spillane and Deves (1987), for example, argue that medical diagnoses tend to favour managerial perspectives of the "malingerer", or even worse, to enhance employee feelings of "patienthood"; in other words, it promotes the idea that employees are encouraged to feel that they are helpless victims of work-caused illness. This can foster excessive employee dependency on medical specialists, and lead to ongoing treatment rather than encouraging a rapid return to work duties. This is a problem reported by many Irish organisations.

Occupational Epidemiology

An important component of occupational medicine, occupational epidemiology, explores the frequency of the occurrence of phenomena of interest in health care, and relates measures of their frequency to their determination. Epidemiologists research "epidemics", or the incidence of disease and illnesses in workplaces, and attempt to establish their causes and solutions. Occupational epidemiologists use large-scale scientific studies to determine causal relationships between work behaviours and occupational accidents and diseases. Much of their research concentrates on studying the incidence of health and safety problems such as asbestosis, toxic reactions, skin diseases or industrial deafness, and suggesting ways of preventing their occurrences. The epidemiologist's contribution is criticised for its overconcern with physical relationships and secondly, its pathological (or sickness) emphasis.

Industrial Psychology

The application of psychology to the workplace and its use as an explanation of accidents and diseases brought a different perspective to their causes and treatment, emphasising behavioural rather than simply physical approaches. Applications of industrial psychology to health and safety include studies into worker stress and repetitive strain injury or occupational overuse syndrome. Rather than simply relating these symptoms to the physical nature of the work, industrial psychologists take a broader view and postulate that accidents and diseases may be partly caused by individual, psychological reactions to stressful, boring or repetitive work processes, as possible examples (Donald and Carter, 1993).

Industrial psychology is, however, criticised for its overconcern with individual employee reactions to their work environments and for its categorisation of employees into "accident-prone" or "machismo" types (Porteous, 1987). There is significant research evidence that macho workers fail to take protective measures against risks because they feel them to be unmanly. They view safety-conscious behaviour as a "sissy"-type activity. Other critics suggest that industrial psychology tends to blame the victim, focusing on individual employee (mis)behaviours rather than on the work environment. Such approaches have often led to an undervaluing of the structural characteristics of the workplace which explain ill health or accidents.

Ergonomics and Occupational Hygiene

Ergonomists and occupational hygienists seek to eliminate risks and improve productivity by modifying the physical environment and conditions within the workplace. Usually employed by managers, these technical experts frequently undertake changes without consultation with either workers or their unions.

Ergonomics focuses on the physical features of the work environment (e.g. workstations, work processes, and machinery), while occupational hygiene is more concerned with the identification, measurement and evaluation of hazards in the workplace, and the development of procedures for their control or elimination. Hazards may include physical, chemical or biological aspects, linked to specific physical illnesses and disease.

A contemporary illustration of the contribution of ergonomics to health and safety is its approach to occupational overuse syndrome (or repetitive strain injury). Ergonomists are concerned to prevent the rising incidence of OOS/RSI by designing workstations to minimise the repetitive strain on workers in selected occupations (e.g. telephonists, word-processing operators). More comfortable chairs, modified keyboards and hourly rest-breaks are usually advocated to reduce the physical and postural strains on such employees.

Occupational hygienists contribute to the reduction of asbestos-caused diseases by identifying high-risk exposure levels and limiting exposure with the provision of protective equipment (e.g. gloves, masks, suits and screens). With other potentially hazardous substances, hygienists have identified threshold limit values (TLV), short-term exposure limits (STEL) and ceiling limits.

Both specialisms tend to focus on individual physical or physiological responses to specified work hazards and, commentators argue, often at the expense of broader, more integrative approaches to the problem of occupational health and safety.

Industrial Sociology

While acknowledging the respective contributions of medical and paramedical strategies to the resolution of health and safety issues, sociologists have criticised their narrow focus on individual and physical factors, and their neglect of the importance of structural elements in the workplace as an explanation of workplace accidents. Sociologists suggest that such aspects as the lack of employee control of their work processes, "production imperatives" and associated reward systems, are viewed as significant contributors to health and safety accidents and disease. The research illustrates that OOS/RSI mainly occurs in semi-skilled occupations (word processing, secretarial and telephonist positions) where it is argued that the employee has little control over their workloads and are often bound to productivity-based bonus systems. Similarly, research studies identify stress as a significant problem in manual as well as managerial positions, possibly due to employees' lack of autonomy or influence over work processes.

Trade Unions

The union movement is less favourably disposed to the sociological perspective, but in general unions emphasise the consideration of multiple perspectives to resolve OHS issues. The trade union movement encourages "multi-discipline, workplace-based research". However, there is little evidence that Irish unions believe that health and safety issues provide an important vehicle through which to implement work reform strategies.

Until the 1970s, many Irish unions showed only limited interest in health and safety issues, preferring to concentrate on negotiations to obtain higher wages and more positive working conditions for their members. "Danger" and "dirt money" agreements were quite common components of industrial relations claims in the 1960s and 1970s, especially in the construction sector and manufacturing industries. Irish unions have in the past been criticised for payment trade-offs in the area of health and safety, rather than active involvement in the prevention of accidents and disease, or the rehabilitation of injured employees.

In part, however, trade union inaction in this area can be explained by a general community and industry ignorance of the causes of, or solutions to, health and safety problems. Management refusal to allow union involvement in risk assessment or workplace design was also a contributing factor.

Briscoe (1995) questions whether occupational health and safety issues fit comfortably within the Irish tradition of industrial relations which emphasises negotiation/bargaining with its associated negotiating ritual where parties adopt opening positions and gradually move towards compromise. He suggests that it is not right to compromise on health and safety issues and advocates that it is wrong if health and safety issues become embroiled in an industrial relations agenda with consequent trade-offs. Basically, health and safety is not a tradable issue.

External factors such as rapid technological change, evidence of union involvement from the Scandinavian countries, the United Kingdom and the United States, combined with the growth of professions concerned with health and safety, have helped to ensure the centrality of health and safety in the concerns of the union movement. Union involvement has had the effect of promoting awareness of the importance of health and safety in all workplace negotiations, forcing employers to address such issues and broadening the scope of health and safety considerations.

The Legal Profession

The growth in health and safety awareness within the workforce has increasingly concerned lawyers and insurance specialists, especially in the settlement of employees' compensation claims. Frequently litigation over health and safety issues ends up in the Irish courts, resulting in compensation to injured employees.

It is arguable that the legal profession has a vested interest in occupational health and safety issues, and there are numerous examples of costly litigation as the result of employer negligence, or their failure to provide healthy and safe workplaces. Legal action has increased significantly since the passing of more comprehensive health and safety legislation in Ireland. Arguments and counter-arguments include reference to medical, ergonomic, occupational hygiene, industrial psychology or sociological perspectives, to help resolve the issue. The courts thus become mediators or arbitrators between the differing perspectives of health and safety "experts", often at significant cost to both employers and employees.

OCCUPATIONAL HEALTH AND SAFETY AND HRM

Health and safety has become increasingly complex, involving a diverse group of specialists, each with different perspectives, interests and objectives. Irish legislation emphasises the importance of health and safety issues to the overall employment relationship. More than any other area of HRM, occupational health and safety requires substantial involvement from employees and, where appropriate, their union representatives, in addition to supervisors, middle and senior management. This is not only legally required, through the system of workplace representation, but simply because health and safety issues pervade all other HRM activities. Job and work design systems involve health and safety considerations; recruitment, training and performance-management programmes encompass health and safety aspects such as employees' physical capabilities and general health status, previous levels of exposure to toxic substances or stress factors. The human resource specialist will usually be involved in health and safety issues at strategic, operational and administrative levels, in consultation with workplace committees, where they exist, unions, managers and the broad range of health and safety experts already discussed in this introduction.

At the strategic level, the human resource specialist will keep abreast of current health and safety issues, legislation and strategies, analysing trends in accident rates and employees' compensation costs, and projecting the impact of the introduction of new technology or new work processes on employee health and safety. In consultation with workplace representatives, unions and managers, human resource managers may modify existing health and safety policies or develop new policy directions.

At the operational level, human resource specialists may chair workplace safety committees, consult with safety representatives or provide advice on procedures that are required to prevent future accidents or injuries. They may also support supervisors and line managers in workplace redesign, provide safety awareness training and safety promotion campaigns, or advise on health and safety consultants to resolve particular issues. Administratively, the human resource department may co-ordinate the collection of statistics on accident rates and work-related diseases, or provide secretarial support to safety committees where they exist.

This handbook is firmly premised on a strategic HRM approach to health and safety. A strategic human resource management approach emphasises the need for individuality, flexibility and adaptability, although one cannot be flexible about whether to implement safety laws already in place. A significant change of approach has taken place with safety laws and regulations in Ireland. The focus has moved from mere compliance with minimum legal requirements to the encouragement of a proactive approach to increased involvement of employees and supervisors, and placing a duty on managers to formulate safety management systems, implement them and monitor their effectiveness.

An HRM approach to health and safety is characterised as follows:

- The need to create a culture in which health and safety are considered important to the organisation. The safety policy statement will contribute to this if it is effectively written, understood and acted upon. The legal requirements must be complied with and risk assessments carried out, as well as the gathering of information about health and safety and the conduct of a cost-benefit analysis. A culture of health and safety awareness requires the use of campaigns and publicity, and the involvement of top management, individuals and teams in its creation and maintenance. This requires regular communications and discussion of health and safety and the contribution that improvements can make to the organisation's overall effectiveness, so that organisational members realise that health and safety are important to the way the organisation operates.

- Commitment from the top to the achievement of progressively higher standards of health and safety as expressed in the safety statement and safety policy. Top management must not only sign the policy documents but also set good examples in terms of health and safety practices, and emphasise that it is an area of importance to current practice and to the future of the organisation by setting up safety systems and monitoring their effectiveness.

- Commitment throughout the organisation, with all parties clear about their own responsibilities for health and safety, the targets they have to meet, and the contribution these make to the organisation's objectives. Safety should be considered an important aspect of performance management, because individuals and teams are encouraged to take responsibility for their own actions and to agree and work towards targets when making improvements.

- Managers must demonstrate, by their example, commitment to the priority of a safer and healthier work environment. They should also find ways to motivate employees to make a contribution to health and safety improvements.

- Policies and procedures should be designed to take account of the priority of a safer and healthier environment. There should also be effective systems to monitor policy and procedural effectiveness.

- Sufficient resources for equipment, training and education should reinforce policies. The provision of effective health and safety costs money, but the cost of not providing such systems will usually be higher.

- The setting of realistic and attainable safety targets for everyone in the organisation.

- Encouragement of all to take responsibility for their own actions and involvement of all in the health and safety management process.

There is evidence to demonstrate that a strategic approach can be effective. Research reveals that organisations with superior health and safety records spend more money on health and safety. In addition to management commitment to safety, it is also crucial to have employee participation. This can be done by empowering employees to take ownership of safety within the organisation (Jones, 1996). It is also essential that managers should establish an atmosphere in which employees feel comfortable reporting unsafe working conditions, so that all potential hazards can be identified. The evidence suggests that managers and employees should form a partnership designed to maximise employee safety and health and acknowledge that a trained safe workforce is the most proactive workforce an employer can have.

THE STATE OF HEALTH AND SAFETY IN IRELAND AT THE BEGINNING OF THE NEW MILLENNIUM

Some General Weaknesses

A number of reports serve to highlight the current state of health and safety in the workplace in Ireland (European Foundation, 1997; Deloitte and Touche, 1997; McAuley Group Report, 1998). These reports highlight six core weaknesses:

- There exists a poor statistical base on which to draw definitive conclusions about the level of accidents and incidents in the Irish workplace. The reports highlight the need to generate statistics so that employers, government and trade unions became more aware of the economic costs of accidents and ill health at work.

- There is a significant lack of investment of resources at State level to enforce health and safety legislation and at company level to implement it. The Health and Safety Authority, in its annual report for 1998, pointed out that the Government investment ratio in safety was IR£5 (€6.35) for every person at work. This contrasts sharply with an annual cost of over IR£30 (€38) per employee in occupational injury claims. The corresponding expenditure for the UK is stg£6 (€10) per employee. There is also a common belief that the Health & Safety Authority is underfunded. This view is reinforced by a confidential and very critical report completed in 2000.

- There is strong evidence of a high rate of under-reporting of accidents by Irish companies. The CSO Labour Force Surveys demonstrate a consistent under-reporting of accidents and ill health caused by work. The surveys reveal that almost 80 per cent of accidents and 95 per cent of cases of ill health were not notified to the National Safety Authority. The level of under-reporting for the farming sector is particularly acute.

- Existing legislation places too much emphasis on physiological aspects of safety at the expense of health and psychological dimensions. There is a solid body of research and opinion that suggests physiological and social dimensions should receive equal attention and are part of a more integrated approach to the management of safety.

- Too little emphasis is currently given to helping organisations manage health and safety in an efficient manner with a minimum of bureaucracy.

- Limited resources are available for research of health and safety issues and there is an absence of dialogue between those responsible for day-to-day safety management and safety researchers. The HSA acknowledges that it is difficult to match the demand for research and information to employers. The poor statistical base also hinders research. This makes it difficult to evaluate the national health and safety system.

State Regulation of Health and Safety

In order to assess the role and contribution of the State to the regulation of safety and health we will focus on the activities of the Health and Safety Authority for the ten-year period 1990-1999, and in particular on its core activities of inspections and the use of enforcement orders.

Inspection Activities

Inspectors carry out the bulk of the State regulatory duties. During inspections, inspectors can offer advice and guidance, provide information and gather research for the Authority's use. **Figure 0.1** presents the total number of inspections undertaken for the years 1990 to 1999 in addition to the percentage change per year.

Figure 0.1: Total Number of Inspections and Percentage Change 1990-1999

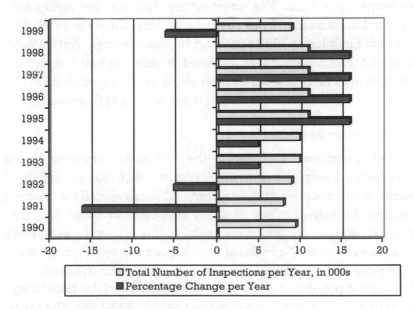

The data reveals a general upward trend in the number of inspections carried out up to 1996, but the last three years have witnessed a decline, most significant between 1998 and 1999. A total of 8,721 inspections were carried out in 1999, compared to 10,747 in 1998. This represents a decrease of almost 19 per cent.

The Health and Safety Authority justifies this decrease in terms of five factors. The primary reasons were the loss of staff from positions due to retirement and promotion and changes in the methodology used for accounting inspections. The combined effect of three other factors — an unanticipated legislative load, a 27 per cent increase in prosecutions initiated and other administrative issues — account for the remainder.

The statistics reveal that 46 per cent of inspections (4,052) in 1999 were conducted in the construction industry. This represents the lowest number of inspections in that sector since 1995. Seventeen per cent of inspections (1,487) were conducted in the manufacturing sector, which has more than double the number in employment compared to the construction sector. This level of inspection represents the lowest number carried out in the manufacturing sector since before 1994. Given the significant risk of injury in the construction sector, it makes sense that there should be more inspections here. The construction and manufacturing sectors in total account for 63 per cent of total inspections in 1999; 37.7 per cent of fatalities in 1999 occurred in these sectors. Agriculture, fishing and forestry, on the other hand, which has had the highest number of total fatalities per annum since 1997, accounted for approximately 7 per cent of the inspections in each of these years.

Total Accidents Reported

The level of accidents reported to the HSA rests ultimately on the involvement of employees themselves, through the reporting of dangerous occurrences and accidents. This is typically a function carried out by management or safety representatives and not employees directly. Accident data enables the Authority to identify the common causes of accidents and implement appropriate solutions to prevent future accidents and dangerous occurrences.

Figure 0.2 presents the number of accidents and the percentage change in the number reported in the period 1993-1999. The statistics point to the success of the Authority in encouraging the reporting of accidents: 99 per cent more were reported in 1999 than in 1993. This trend reveals however that accidents are increasing despite the efforts by the Health and Safety Authority. The most significant increases have occurred in the years 1998 and 1999. Given a base year of 1993, the percentage change is almost 100.

Figure 0.2: Total Number of Accidents Reported and Percentage Change 1993-1999 (measured against 1993 base)

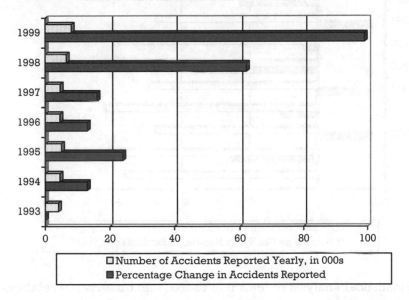

Total Fatalities

Fatalities represent an important indicator when deciding which employment sectors are considered high-risk sectors. One suggests that the efforts of the Authority should be proportionally directed at those sectors that exhibit the highest (or higher) fatality rates. **Figure 0.3** presents the trend for fatalities for the 10 years 1990-2000.

Taking 1990 as a base year, the number of fatalities is 12 per cent higher in 2000 than it was in 1990. The average number of fatalities over the ten-year period from 1990-2000 is 62; however, the years 1995, 1998 and 1999 reported much higher levels of fatality than this average. There is also a higher level of employment in 2000 than was the case in 1990, and it follows that fatalities would be significantly higher as a result of this.

Figure 0.3: Total Number of Fatalities and Percentage Change 1990-2000

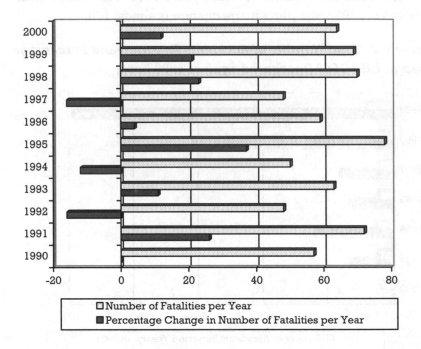

The statistical analysis reveals that there is no observable relationship between fatalities and the number of inspections by the HSA. **Figure 0.4** reveals that it is impossible to discern a trend between these two factors. It is doubtful that any combination of variables could explain such a trend. The fatality data is somewhat limited as it is currently presented. It does not categorise by age, for example. Research suggests that the fatality rate increases significantly with age in the case of falls, collapse, being struck by and against falling objects, etc. The rate of electric shock, however, declines significantly with age.

Figure 0.4: Relationship between the Level of Inspections and the Number of Fatalities

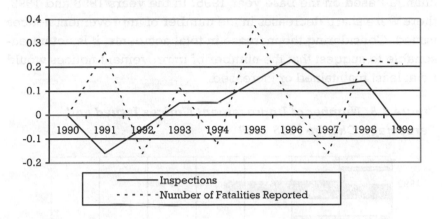

Methods of Enforcement Used by Inspectors

Inspectors possess the power to instruct an employer to prepare and implement an improvement plan that they subsequently approve as satisfactory to eliminate the risks in question. In more serious cases, a Prohibition Notice may be served that prohibits the use of certain equipment or processes. Inspectors also have the power to prosecute a firm (or individual) for breaking health and safety laws.

Improvement Notices

There were fewer improvement notices issued in 1999 than in any of the previous seven years. A total of 873 notices were served in 1999, representing a decrease of 17 per cent on 1998 and less than half the number issued in 1996. This decrease may have been justified if a similar fall in fatality and injury rates occurred, suggesting a general increased awareness of safety issues and improvement in safety management practices. The evidence, however, does not support such a trend. A total of 328 notices was issued to the manufacturing sector, 37.5 per cent of all notices. The construction sector received 141 notices, representing 16 per cent of the total issued. The wholesale and retail sector was the only other sector to receive more than 10 per cent of the total improvement notices issued.

Figure 0.5 presents the number of improvement notices issued by the Health and Safety Authority. It also reveals the percentage change based on the base year 1995. In the years 1998 and 1999, there were sharp decreases in the number of improvement notices issued. Considering the increase in total accidents, it is not unreasonable to suggest that the number of improvement notices would be at least maintained or increased.

Figure 0.5: Number of Improvement Notices Issued and Percentage Change 1995-1999

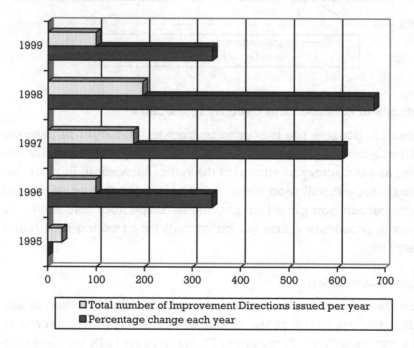

Improvement Directions

Improvement directions are issued to employers where inspectors perceive that a certain *method* or strategy to correct the safety problem is necessary. The direction outlines not only the changes to be made but also the manner in which the changes are to be made. It contrasts with an improvement notice, which only requires certain improvements but does not specify the manner by which these are to be achieved. **Figure 0.6** presents the total number of improvement directions issued for the years 1990-1999.

The number of improvement directions issued over the ten-year period has increased dramatically, but this is primarily because the base-year figure is very low. However, there were no significant changes between 1990 and 1995. The decrease in the number of improvement directions issued from 1998 to 1999 is similar to the trend observed for the issuing of improvement notices.

Figure 0.6: Total Number of Improvement Directions and Percentage Change 1995-1999

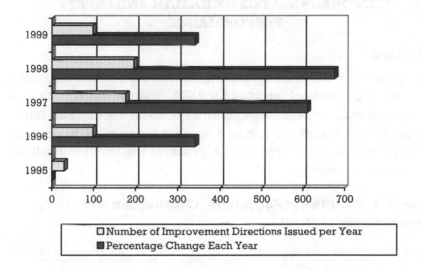

□ Number of Improvement Directions Issued per Year
■ Percentage Change Each Year

Prohibition Notices

A prohibition notice is a signed written notice served on a person who has contravened the safety legislation. An inspector issues a prohibition notice where they are of the view that a serious risk of personal injury exists. The notice is obtained from the High Court and the offender has seven days in which to appeal.

A total of 408 prohibition notices was issued in 1999 compared to 345 in 1998. In 1999 almost 89 per cent of notices were issued to the construction sector. In 1998 the equivalent percentage issued to the construction sector was 84 per cent.

A prohibition order (also called a High Court order) is more serious than a prohibition notice, and the net effect is that the High Court orders that a business cease to operate. Only nine have been issued in a five-year period 1995-1999, all for the construction industry.

The trend is, however, upwards, suggesting that work practices have not improved and that employers have not always implemented the advice and directions of inspectors. It is also likely that inspectors are now enforcing stricter standards thus leading to more prohibition orders being issued. All of the orders issued to date have been to the construction sector.

SECTORAL ANALYSIS OF HEALTH AND SAFETY PERFORMANCE

Fatalities

The agriculture, construction and manufacturing sectors accounted for over 71 per cent of fatalities for 1999. The remaining fatalities are spread over 12 other sectors. Nine of these sectors had fatalities equal to or below two and as a result these sectors do not warrant statistical analysis. **Figure 0.7** presents the trend in fatalities for the three sectors.

Figure 0.7: Fatalities in Agriculture, Construction and Manufacturing 1994-1999

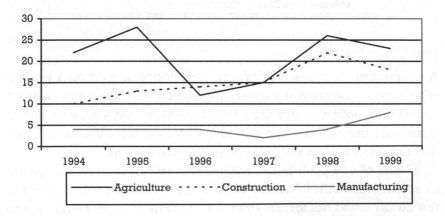

Fatalities in the agriculture sector have remained high for the past number of years. There is no consistent trend, which makes it difficult to establish specific variable causal factors and how they might vary.

The construction sector is the second most important sector for the Authority given the number of fatalities and, therefore, the sector is given considerable attention. The Authority has been unsuccessful in successive years in bringing down the level of fatalities in this sector which contributes 6 per cent of Ireland's GDP.

Manufacturing fatalities in 2000 were 200 per cent more than the equivalent figure in 1994. The year 1999 showed an unprecedented increase in fatalities, which could have been passed off as chance. However, the latest statistics for the year 2000 show that this figure has increased further.

In 1999 33 per cent of all fatalities occurred in the agriculture sector, although this dropped to 12 per cent in 2000. Michael Henry, Chief Inspector of the Health and Safety Authority, argues that "in the past, real reductions in deaths and accidents in the farming sector have often been followed by increases in the numbers of such accidents in subsequent years, so we must not view this year's statistics in isolation" (HSA website). In the construction sector, however, the reverse has occurred and this sector makes an increasingly significant contribution to total fatalities in the workplace. This trend may be attributable to the fact that since the mid-1990s, there has been increasing pressure from the Government to increase the housing supply to curb spiralling housing inflation.

In agriculture the increase in fatalities in 1995 was attributed to the increase in child deaths from three to seven. In an effort to combat this and other fatalities, an "agricultural task force" was set up. It met seven times during 1996 and *considered* the distribution of video and teaching packs on farm safety to national schools. This task force has met every year since, and yet in 1999 the Annual Report states that a sub-committee was continuing to focus on the preparation of the Code of Practice for Children on Farms. Construction fatalities in 2000 were more than 2½ times greater than they were in 1994.

Inspections

Figure 0.8 presents the trend for inspections for the three sectors for the years 1994-1999. The data reveals that the number of inspections has fallen for the agriculture sector. The total number of overall inspections since 1990 has increased. This raises the question as to why the Authority has reduced its level of inspections in this sector. Inspections were reduced significantly in forestry, for example, in 1997 due to the increase in farm accidents. The Authority transferred these resources to agriculture, but this change makes no difference in the overall total even though there was a change within the sector.

Figure 0.8: Inspections in Agriculture, Construction and Manufacturing 1994-1999

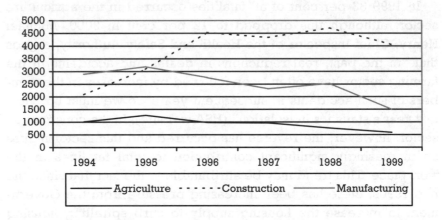

The significant increase in inspections in the construction sector is primarily due to the tremendous growth in this sector during the last decade. The housing market boom brought with it a growth in construction sites and therefore the need for increased inspections. Inspections within the manufacturing sector for 1997 and 1999 fell short of the targets set by the Authority. The statistics also reveal a sharp decline over the years 1994 to 1995. There were 49 per cent fewer inspections carried out in the manufacturing sector in 1999 than in 1994. There was, however, an increase in fatalities as inspection levels declined.

Reported Accidents

Figure 0.9 presents the trend for reported accidents for the three sectors: agriculture, construction and manufacturing.

Figure 0.9: Increase/Decrease for Reported Accidents in Agriculture, Construction and Manufacturing 1995-1999

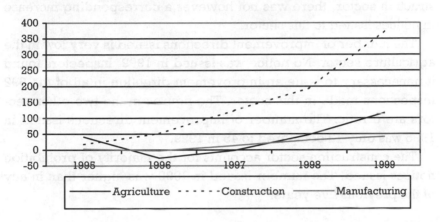

The most significant increase in the level of reported accidents occurred in the construction sector. It was expected that reported accidents would increase dramatically over time. Increased inspections should also have enhanced the awareness of the requirement to report accidents. The statistical evidence reveals that the number of reported accidents in 1997 represents only 26 per cent of that reported in the Labour Force Survey. For the manufacturing sector, there were 42 per cent more accidents reported in 1999 than in the base year (1995). This looks insignificant, given the major increase reported in the construction sector. The Health and Safety Authority welcomed the high level of reporting in its 1999 Annual Report. It claimed that 80 per cent of all accidents were reported in this sector compared to an average of 54 per cent for all sectors.

Enforcement Actions

Table 0.2 presents a summary of the level of enforcement actions for Agriculture, Construction and Manufacturing. The difference between the sectors is significant. Agriculture has the highest fatalities of the three sectors, although the smallest number of notices was issued to this sector. Conversely, manufacturing received the most notices and generally has fewer fatalities than the other two sectors. There were 1,235 notices issued in 1996 compared to only 549 in 1999. This represents a decrease of over 55 per cent. It must be pointed out, however, that 1996 was exceptional in this context. Given the increase in accidents in the construction sector, there was not however a corresponding increase in notices issued to this sector.

The number of improvement directions issued is very low in the agriculture sector. No notice was issued in 1999. Inspectors found it unnecessary to issue an improvement direction in all of the 592 inspections made in this sector. The figures in the two other sectors are erratic. The number of improvement directions issued in 1995 was only 12 compared to 45 in 1999.

The construction sector accounts for the majority of prohibition notices issued. The number issued in 1999 was higher than in any of the previous five years.

Table 0.2: Enforcement Actions Issued by Sector

Improvement Notices Issued					
Year	1995	1996	1997	1998	1999
Agriculture	94	151	61	75	80
Construction	113	352	185	179	141
Manufacturing	647	732	437	449	328
Improvement Directions Issued					
Year	1995	1996	1997	1998	1999
Agriculture	2	6	2	4	0
Construction	1	14	49	50	19
Manufacturing	9	48	58	75	26
Prohibition Notices Issued					
Year	1995	1996	1997	1998	1999
Agriculture	8	15	3	3	1
Construction	86	311	240	289	362
Manufacturing	27	32	30	26	23

The Relationship between Employment, Inspections and Fatalities

We briefly consider the relationship between employment, Inspections and fatalities for the three sectors. **Figure 0.10** presents the trend.

Within the agricultural sector the analysis reveals that inspections for the period 1996 to 1999 are below the 1994 level. This occurred at a time when fatalities actually increased. Employment in this sector continued to decline during this period and this trend is likely to continue. Fatalities are erratic and there does not appear to be any relationship with the level of employment or number of inspections.

Figure 0.10: The Relationship Between Employment Inspections and Fatalities in Agriculture, Construction and Manufacturing 1995-1999

Agriculture

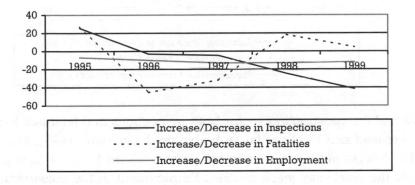

Construction

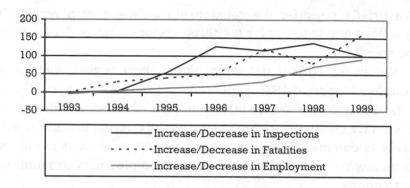

Manufacturing

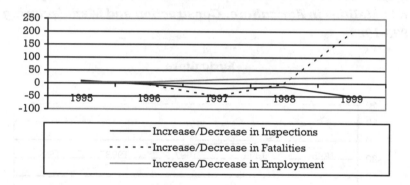

Within the construction sector both inspections and fatalities have increased and have not fallen below the base year (1993). This is the reverse of the situation in agriculture where both are now below the level they were in 1994. Employment in the construction sector increased and so did inspections and the number of fatalities. The reverse was generally true (after 1998 in the case of fatalities) for agriculture. Between 1993 and 1995, fatalities increased faster than the level of inspections and therefore the Authority increased inspections accordingly. Between 1993 and 1996 all three variables — inspections, fatalities and employment — increased. Fatalities declined between 1997 and 1998 at a time when inspections and employment in the sector were on the increase.

Within the manufacturing sector the evidence reveals that, as the percentage of inspections decreased, the number of accidents reported and the percentage of fatalities increased which raises questions as to why the level of inspections was not stepped up.

THE SCOPE AND LAYOUT OF THE HANDBOOK

The handbook focuses on the legal, physiological, psychological and social dimensions of safety, health and welfare and the environment at work. The handbook does not present simple solutions to the problems described in the overview, nor is it to be considered an encyclopaedia covering the corpus of health, safety and environmental law and practice. Instead its focus is upon the key statutory health, safety and environmental requirements that affect Irish business organisations. It also places significant emphasis on the strategies that organisations can use to meet their responsibilities and the human factors that form the foundation of any safety, health and environmental management effort. The overall aim of the handbook is to facilitate the development of positive attitudes and commitment to health, safety and the environment. It seeks to bring about a situation in the Irish workforce where health, safety and environmental issues become intuitive, a routine everyday activity, an integral part of the organisation's culture and the individual's job.

The handbook is structured into five main components. **Part One** deals with the fundamentals of health, safety and environmental law in Ireland and, unlike some traditional handbooks in the area, it addresses safety and health in the wider environment. **Part Two** considers the broad body of research dealing with human factors and ergonomics and identifies some of the issues that should be given consideration in any attempt to manage effectively health and safety dimensions, such as motivation, attitudes, culture, workplace and safety workspace design. Their implications for safety management practice are also considered. **Part Three** focuses on safety management issues. Special attention is given to communication issues, encouraging employee involvement, safety audits and the management of issues such as fire, manual handling, electricity, chemical safety and environmental auditing. **Part Four** focuses on risk management and the specific application of risk concepts to health and safety. Finally, **Part Five** focuses on occupational health, hygiene and the management of stress. It considers contemporary issues within occupational health such as smoking, alcohol and substance abuse, HIV and AIDS.

Throughout each chapter a series of management action checklists is presented, containing safety guidelines and setting out important principles and requirements derived from law and research. These checklists may be of value to safety and environment professionals who wish to influence top management to commit resources to health and safety, to inform line managers of their responsibilities and provide them with benchmarks through which they can verify that they are meeting best practice in terms of health, safety and environmental management. The handbook will also be of considerable value to students of health, safety and the environment and in particular to those with special responsibility for managing such issues in organisations.

PART ONE

THE LEGAL REGULATION OF HEALTH, SAFETY AND THE ENVIRONMENT

Chapter 1

HEALTH AND SAFETY LAW:
THE LEGAL CONTEXT

INTRODUCTION

The legislative and common law positions on health and safety in Ireland are both extremely complex and of direct relevance to the individual manager and safety specialist. Apart from the range of statutory obligations, common law duties are imposed on employers and employees in respect of health and safety. Where, for example, employers do not exercise reasonable care towards employees, who as a result suffer injury, the employers may be found negligent. It should be noted that common law primarily addresses liability arising out of actual illness, injury and/or stress, and therefore is generally not concerned with setting safety standards to be followed by companies. This contrasts with health and safety legislation, which has as its primary role setting out guidelines and principles of safety management that help prevent accidents at work.

This chapter considers the historical development of health and safety law, the attitude of the courts toward the rights of the employee and the duties of the employer. It gives some consideration to the law of tort and the contract of employment. The contract of employment forms the basis for the application of the common law context of employer's duty that will be discussed in **Chapter 2**. The key sources of employment terms are examined, as well as some statutory modifications of the contract implemented by the Terms of Employment (Information) Act, 1994. The chapter concludes with a brief discussion of unfair dismissals and health and safety.

HISTORY OF OCCUPATIONAL HEALTH AND SAFETY LAW

Occupational health and safety law has its origins in the Industrial Revolution. Traditionally the terms "master" and "servant" characterised the relationships between farmers and farm workers and householders and domestic workers. The industrial revolution led to a different working environment, however, where workers frequently operated machinery. This resulted in the terms "master" and "servant" being extended to cover those new working relationships. In time the master/servant relationship came to be treated as a status relationship. In modern times, these terms gave way to "employer" and "employee".

Priestley v. Fowler (1837) was the first personal injury claim in which the nature of the employment relationship was discussed in detail. In summary the facts were as follows: A master butcher employed two servants and had a van for the delivery of meat. One servant loaded the van and the other suffered injury in the course of a journey in the loaded van. At the trial the plaintiff was awarded damages but that decision was reversed on appeal. Lord Abinger concluded:

> To allow this sort of action to prevail would be an encouragement to the servant to omit that diligence and caution which he is in duty bound to exercise on behalf of his master to protect him against the misconduct or negligence of others who serve him . . .

This judgement is generally cited as originating the doctrine of common employment, under which the master was not liable for injuries suffered by a servant as a result of the wrongdoing of another of that master's servants.

The development of employer's duty was therefore restricted by the doctrine of common employment. However, many of its worst features were mitigated by the Employer's Liability Act 1880 in the UK which provided protection for the worker's claim where injury resulted from the negligence of a senior person or one whose orders the workman had to obey.

Three particular phases are evident in the development of health and safety and welfare law in the UK and Ireland, as set out below.

Laissez Faire

The early 19th century was dominated by a strong *laissez faire* economic philosophy. In the context of the employment relationship, it meant that employees should look after themselves and accept the risks associated with the particular type of work undertaken in the course of the employment. This attitude influenced the thinking of the courts, where it was widely held that the law had only a very minor role to play in ensuring safe work conditions. McMahon and Binchy (1990) suggest that:

> ... industry was admittedly dangerous but was clearly regarded as being socially beneficial in the long run; the employee could look after his own interests and, if he chose to accept dangerous employment for an appropriate payment, he should not impose on his employer the obligation to compensate him when things went wrong. The philosophy was given effect through the legal concepts of implied contractual terms, absence of a legal duty of care, contributory negligence, voluntary assumption of risk and the doctrine of "common employment".

In other words, despite the dangers posed to workers, it was considered to be more beneficial to society to allow such dangers to exist. The law was therefore slow to impose legal obligations on employers and regulate the employment relationship.

Industrialisation

Towards the middle of the 19th century, a significant shift in thinking occurred. This was brought about in the main by the growth of the factory system and, more generally, by the growth of the industrial sector in the United Kingdom. There was now a general recognition that workmen needed special protection against dangerous working conditions. The right to recover damages from one's employer at common law slowly emerged as a more humane approach and eventually was reflected in the decisions of judges. Nevertheless, damages remained limited and were not considered a significant sanction by offending employers. Tighter regulations and higher standards of safety were progressively imposed on more and more workplaces, especially mines and quarries. In fact,

claims based on breaches of these standards and statutory obligations became a fruitful source of successful actions against offending employers. The old concepts of absence of any legal duty of
care, voluntary assumption of risk, the doctrine of "common employment", etc. gradually became outdated and were eventually
replaced by more contemporary legislation and legal principles.

Employers' Liability in the 20th Century

The law on the liability of employers to employees evolved in the
20th century to a situation where the employer owes duties arising
out of the existence of the employment relationship. The employer
in general has a common law duty to provide a safe place of work,
competent staff, proper equipment and a safe system of work. In
general, the employer is responsible for the torts of employees,
committed in the performance of their work.

The concept of employer's duty of care is now firmly established in both common law and in statute in Ireland and will be examined in detail in **Chapter 2**.

THE NATURE OF THE LAW OF TORT

An understanding of the law of tort is necessary in order to understand how the concept of duty of care operates. The law of torts,
according to McMahon and Binchy (1990), is a description of those
instances of social conduct that the courts consider should be prohibited and should be penalised. The word "tort" is derived from
the Latin word *tortus*, meaning twisted. In the English language tort
has a purely technical meaning: a legal wrong for which the law
provides a remedy. The law of tort relates to civil wrongs people
carry out, generally against one another, and a plaintiff can seek a
remedy in tort for any civil wrong done.

Many legal academics have attempted to define the law of tort
and there is a lack of agreement on a generic definition. Winfield
and Jolowicz (1990) define it in this way: "tortious liability arises
from the breach of a duty primarily fixed by law; this duty is towards persons generally and its breach is redressible by an action
for unliquidated damages".

This definition, while not exhaustive, helps us to distinguish the
law of tort from other branches of law such as contract or criminal

law. The law of tort is generally concerned with private disputes between individuals and focuses on the provision of compensation to the plaintiff. It must, however, be distinguished from other areas of law and particularly that of contract law. **Table 1.1** provides a set of distinctions between tort and contract law.

Table 1.1: Key Distinctions between Tort and Contract

Tort	Contract
Duties imposed by law.	Duties fixed by parties.
Parties often previously unconnected.	Parties usually connected through pre-contractual negotiations.
Privity of contract irrelevant.	Privity of contract necessary.
Concerned with protecting interests and compensating wrongs.	Concerned with supporting and enforcing promises.
Emphasis on fault in modern law.	Strict liability common.
Rules of remoteness of damage based on foresight of the type of harm.	Rules for remoteness based on proximity.
Aims to restore the plaintiff to pre-accident position.	Aims to treat plaintiff as if contract had been performed.
For limitation, time begins to run from the date the damage occurred.	Time begins to run when breach occurs.

Many of the duties recognised in tort arise by virtue of the law alone and are not fixed by the parties, which is the case with the law of contract. Furthermore, there may never be a contract between the parties in a case where a tort has been committed. This would not, however, be the case with employers' duty of care where a contract will exist, although it may be a verbal or written one or one formed by the conduct of the parties. An appropriate example here would be in a situation where a motorist strikes a pedestrian. Prior to the "tort" there may have been no contact and it is only as a result of the "tort" that contact will be made. This is in direct contrast to the situation with the law of contract, where there is a presumption that the parties have met in order to negotiate the contract itself. These distinctions between tort and contract law are simplistic, but they do provide a general guide to the differences between both branches of the law.

The objectives of tort law are generally categorised thus: appeasement, justice, deterrence and compensation. Thus the remedy in most cases involving a tortious act is an action for damages. The aim here is to compensate a plaintiff for a breach of duty on the part of the defendant. A less explicit aim of tort is to deter others from acting in such a way so as to cause harm to others. Contract law, however, is primarily concerned with enforcing contractual promises and the provision of a remedy for breaches of contract by either party.

The distinction between contract and tort is less clear in practice and very often a plaintiff may be in a position to bring an action against a wrongdoer under either tort or contract. Generally the amount of compensation awarded under tort is considerably higher. A further incentive to the plaintiff to go the tort route is that, for the purposes of limitations of actions, time begins to run in contract when the breach occurs, whereas in tort time does not start to run until the damage occurs.

INITIATING AN ACTION IN NEGLIGENCE

In order for a plaintiff to establish a case of negligence, the plaintiff must prove three issues:

- That a duty of care exists between plaintiff and defendant.

- That a breach of duty has taken place.

- That the plaintiff has suffered damage as a result of the breach.

The plaintiff must show that the defendant caused the damage, and the damage must not be considered to be too remote. When these questions are answered the court must then decide how much damages should be awarded in respect of the damage received by the plaintiff. A number of important concepts underpin these three issues.

Causation

For a plaintiff to be successful in their claim, they must demonstrate that both factual and legal causation were present. Factual causation provides that the defendant cannot be liable unless they have caused the accident. According to McMahon and Binchy (1990), if there is no factual causal link between the defendant's conduct and the plaintiff's injury, then the defendant cannot be liable. If there is, then the defendant may be liable. This is very much a question of fact.

The courts use the "but for" rule in order to ascertain the facts of an action in tort. It has been argued that an act is a cause of an event if the event would not have occurred without (but for) the act in question.

> If the event or effect would have occurred without the act in question then the act cannot be deemed to be a cause (McMahon and Binchy, 1990).

Legal Cause

The purpose of the "but for" rule is "to act as a preliminary filter and to eliminate the irrelevant rather than to allocate legal responsibility" (Winfield and Jolowicz, 1990). It is also necessary to establish whether they are legally relevant to the court's inquiry. Courts make a distinction between "mere conditions" and the "cause" of the event. Mere conditions tend to be inanimate or normal. A cause is more likely to be a voluntary human act or abnormal contingency.

Legal Cause and Remoteness of Damage

Legal cause and remoteness of damage relate to whether the damage of which the plaintiff complains was too remote, that is, a consequence of the defendant's conduct for which they ought not in law be liable. McMahon and Binchy (1990) suggest that the courts will be willing to impose liability only where cause has been proven and the damage is not too remote.

There are situations in which the court will be unwilling to impose liability on the defendant and this is generally where there is a case of *novus actus interviens*. Essentially this pertains to situations where the causal link between the defendant's act and the plaintiff's injuries is said to be broken by an intervening act which is of such a kind that it must be deemed to be the sole or new cause of the plaintiff's injuries. Usually this will be the act of a third party. Where it is proven that the act of a third party and the act of the defendant are the cause of the plaintiff's injuries, both are liable for the full amount of damages, but only one payment is made.

A further complication arises where the defendant claims that the supervening act of the third party is of such a nature as to relieve them of responsibility for the plaintiff's damages, or where the act of the plaintiff supervenes on the wrongful act of the defendant and the acts of both the defendant and the plaintiff contribute to the cause of harm. Then the case is one of contributory negligence. In terms of contributory negligence, the general guideline could be said to be that where an intervening act can have the effect of breaking the chain between the defendant's conduct and the plaintiff, then the decisive question relates to the character of the supervening act or event which will cause it to have the effect of constituting a *novus actus intervien,* relieving the original wrongdoer from responsibility for the harm to the plaintiff.

Measure of Damages

The primary objective of the law of tort is to restore the plaintiff to the position that they occupied before the wrong was committed. Compensation is awarded by the courts in the form of monetary compensation. The issue of the measure of damages will be considered later in this chapter.

THE CONTRACT OF EMPLOYMENT

Formation of the Contract of Employment

A fundamental question when considering the liability of the employer relates to the existence of a contract of service. It is therefore appropriate to give consideration to the contract of employment in the introductory chapter. In general, any person of ordinary contractual capacity is competent to enter an employment contract either as an employer or an employee. This capacity extends even to minors who have limited contractual power under common law. The Infant Relief Act, 1876, for example, recognised this capacity and provides that minors are bound by the contract if it is for their benefit. Children under 14 years of age are forbidden employment and in the case of young persons (persons under the age of 18) their participation is limited by the Protection of Young Persons Act, 1976.

As with all other types of contracts there must be consideration, although the courts will generally not investigate its adequacy. Likewise there must be intent to enter into the contract of employment and its terms must be certain. It is clearly established that the contract must not be tainted with illegality. If such a situation arises the court may sever the illegal proportion of the contract and order performance of the remainder, or alternatively they may come to the conclusion that the contract is totally tainted and therefore cannot be enforced. The most common form of illegality in employment contracts relates to the breach of revenue law.

Different Contracts of Employment

The law makes a general distinction between a contract of service and a contract for service. The former is defined as a contract with an employee whereas the latter is defined as a contract with an independent contractor who is not, in law, an employee and as a consequence much of current Irish employment law does not apply to them. The distinction between both contracts is not always easy to make. There are, however, a number of criteria to distinguish both contracts. **Table 1.2** presents a range of possible distinctions.

We will examine presently how the courts have tried to make this distinction. As a general proposition, however, it can be suggested that the distinction lies not in the outcome of the work performed but in the nature of the obligation.

Table 1.2: General Distinctions between a Contract of Service and a Contract for Service

Contract of Service	Contract for Service
Employer–employee relationship.	Employer–independent contractor relationship.
Usually a continuous relationship.	A once-off relationship to do a specific piece of work.
A duty of care owed to employees under employer's liability.	Duty of care arising from occupier's liability.
Generally liable for the wrongful acts of employees under vicarious liability.	Generally not liable for the wrongful acts of independent contractors.
Protective legislation applies to this form of contract.	Employment legislation does not apply with exception of safety legislation.
Method of payment: wage or salary.	Method of payment: usually a fee.
Tax and PRSI deducted at source.	Contractor responsible for own tax situation.

Under a contract of service there is a general obligation on employees to serve within the scope of their class of work as defined in their contract. Under a contract for service there is an obligation only to do a certain job or series of jobs. The "employee" under a contract for service does not have a general obligation. Yet this distinction is still a very general and abstract one. In practice, the courts have had difficulty distinguishing between both types of contractual arrangement. A variety of tests/criteria have been devised and these will presently be examined. It should, however, be pointed out that the distinctions are not simply of an academic nature. There are some very practical implications, including the following:

- An employee pays income tax under Schedule E, the tax being deducted at source under the PAYE system.

- The rules governing unfair dismissal and redundancy payments apply only to employees and not to independent contractors.

- Provision of a written statement of contractual terms applies only to employees and not to independent contractors. Under the Terms of Employment (Information) Act, (1994) an employer must provide the employee with a written statement of employment terms within two months of the commencement date. An independent contractor does not receive such a statement, although they may receive/agree terms to cover the details of the relationship. These may be orally agreed or they may be in writing.

- Employees owe different and more onerous duties to employers than do independent contractors. These duties include a duty of fidelity, the provision of personal service, the requirement to obey lawful orders and a duty of good faith. An independent contractor does not, for example, have to provide personal service. They can send a deputy in their place.

THE IDENTIFICATION OF THE CONTRACTUAL ARRANGEMENT

The courts have over the years adopted a range of tests to ascertain the relationship between employer and employee. The four most commonly cited tests are: the control test; the organisation (integration) test; the mixed test or economic reality test and the multiple test.

Control Test

Historically the view was taken that the concept of control by the employer over what the employee did, and the manner in which it was done, were the distinguishing characteristics of a contract of employment. The original test was put forward in the case of *Yewers v. Noakes* (1880).

The facts concerned a clerk living in his master's house. It was contended, for tax purposes, that the clerk was a servant acting as caretaker in the house. However, it was held that the clerk was not a servant as he could not be told how to live in the house. The court said: "a servant is a person subject to the command of his master as to the manner in which he shall do his work". Fennell and Lynch (1994) argue that this is the origin of the so-called "command" or "control" test. Under this test, control is the determinative factor as to whether an individual is an employee or not. Initially, the courts applied a strict control test and demanded a high degree of control in the relationship between the worker concerned and the employer before he would be classified as an employee. This, however, has been relaxed somewhat.

In *Performing Rights Society Ltd v. Mitchell and Becker Ltd.* (1924), the court held that the issue was the nature and degree of detailed control. Whether the defendants (the owners of a dance hall) were liable for the breach of copyright by a band engaged to play in the hall centred on the question of whether the band were servants/employees. The court concluded that as the defendants retained total and absolute control over all functions of the band other than their ability to play musical instruments, the contract in question was a contract of service. The contract demonstrated several features appropriate to a contract for service, but the control requirement led the court to designate it a contract of service.

In 1968, Walsh J. stated in the case of *Roche v. Patrick Kelly and Company Limited* (1969) in the Supreme Court:

> ... while many ingredients may be present in the relationships of master and servant, it is undoubtedly true that the principal one, and almost invariably the determining one, is the fact that the master's right to direct the servant not merely as to what is to be done but as to how it is to be done.

The simple fact that a contract may describe a person as an independent contractor is not itself conclusive evidence of the status of the contract. In a High Court decision, *J.E. McDermott, Inspector of Taxes v. Patrick Loy* (1982), Barron J. made the following observation:

> It seems to me that the test really has not changed. When the question is asked who decides what the work is to be and where it is to be done, it seems to me that the purpose is to determine whether the employee is working for himself or for someone else.

A strict application of the control test has, however, diminished over time, largely due to the increasing complexity of the employment relationship. Further, there appears to be a certain judicial dissatisfaction with the use of a single criterion, control, and as a consequence other tests have emerged.

The Organisation (Integration) Test

This is viewed as a more sophisticated test than the control test. It is based upon the premise that an employee is a person whose work is integrated into the business as a whole, whereas independent contractors merely work for the business and perform work that is not fundamental to the business's core activities. In the case of independent contractors there is considered to be no integration since they are essentially working on their own account.

Lord Denning, in the case of *Stevenson, Jordan and Harrison Ltd. v. McDonald and Evans* (1952), first formulated the organisation test. He stated:

> One feature, which seems to run through the instances is that, under a contract of service, a man is employed as part of the business; whereas under a contract for services, his work, although done for the business, is not integrated into it but is only accessory to it.

Although the organisation test did not initially receive much approval, it did signal a recognition that the control test was to a large extent viewed as outdated by the judiciary, and unsuitable in the context of modern employment relationships and the increasing complexity of the modern contract of employment.

The Mixed/Economic Test

Fennell and Lynch (1994) argue that another attempt to formulate an alternative test for the classification of labour services is found in the British case of *Ready Mixed Concrete (SE) Ltd. v. Minister of Pensions and National Insurance* (1968). The contract of employment of a cement lorry driver stated he was "self-employed". The driver purchased his vehicle on hire purchase from a finance company associated with the company he worked for. He had responsibility to paint the vehicle in the company colours, and to insure it. He was also obliged by contract to wear the company's uniform, and drove on company business for the maximum hours permissible each week. Payment was made at a certain rate per mile. He was also obliged to obey all reasonable orders from the company as if he were an employee.

McKenna J. advocated that a contract of service exists where three conditions are met:

1. The employee agrees that in consideration of a wage or other form of remuneration they will provide their own work and skill in the performance of some service for their employer.

2. The employee agrees, expressly or implied, that in the performance of that service they will be subject to the employer's control to a sufficient degree.

3. Other provisions of the contract are consistent with its being a contract of service.

McKenna J. further elaborated that the common law test was not restricted to the power of control over the manner of performing the service, but was wide enough to take account of investment and risk. Fennell and Lynch suggest that he was significantly influenced by an American case, *US v. Silk* (1946), where the test utilised was whether the individual in question was an employee as "a matter of economic reality". Factors, which were considered relevant, included the degree of control, opportunities for profit or loss, investment in facilities, permanency of relation, and skill required in the claimed independent operation. McKenna J. allowed the appeal against the Ministerial decision that the individual was an employee. He took into account issues such as the ownership of assets, the chance of profit and loss being that of the individual, not the company, and his view that the obligation to provide personal service did not exist. On the basis of these factors he concluded that the relationship was more akin to a contract for than a contract of service.

Market Investigations Case

Another contemporary approach to classification and the notion of control is found in the case of *Market Investigations Ltd. v. Minister* for *Social Security* (1968). The "employee" in this case was an interviewer. Market Investigations generally employed interviewers for short periods of time only, had significant latitude in specifying persons to be interviewed and the types of questions which could be asked. These two factors indicated a contract of service. The interviewer had significant discretion in terms of when she worked, and there was no provision for sick pay or holiday pay. The facts of the case also revealed that an interviewer could not be dismissed in the middle of a survey, and the company had little or no control over an interviewer during her actual period of work. They had no way of contacting her and did not know of her whereabouts.

The court decided that the test to be applied was thus: is the person engaged to perform these services performing them as a person in business on their own account, in which case it was a contract for services? On the other hand, if they were working for their employer carrying out the business of the employer, then it is a contract of service. The court took the view that all issues must be considered. It suggested that the factors that are inconsistent with it being a contract of service must be weighed against the issues of control and personal service. It concluded that those other factors did not outweigh the element of control the company exercised or may exercise over interviewers. A contract of service was deemed to exist.

A number of cases have arisen under safety legislation and the issue of the responsibility of the employer to provide a safe place of work, where the question was considered whether an individual is working under a contract of service or not. Some of these are worth considering.

In *Roche v. Patrick Kelly and Co. Ltd.* (1969), the plaintiff was employed to build a barn. Patrick Kelly and Co. Ltd. directed the type of barn, its position, and paid him the sum of £300. The plaintiff, who had to live in the area whilst building the barn, received no expenses. The defendants supervised the plaintiff's work. The plaintiff, after hiring workers and erecting scaffolding, sustained an injury. An important question in the case was whether the employee had a contract of service or not. The Supreme Court held that the determining factor was the element of control. It discounted questions about the type of work to be done or the methods to be utilised. It concluded that Roche was not a servant but a skilled and self-employed person who undertook jobs in his own special field on a lump-sum or fee basis.

In *Lynch v. Palgrave Murphy Ltd.* (1964), the driver of a forklift truck sustained injury. On the question of vicarious liability, Kingsmill Moore J, in the Supreme Court, stated:

> ... the mere power to assign a task and even direct in a general way does not mean that the defendant is liable unless there is power also to control the way in which the act involving negligence was to be done.

The defendant was not vicariously liable for the driver's actions. In this case, the court applied a strict approach to the requisite element of control for a contract to be a contract of service.

The Employment Appeals Tribunal has considered the question of classification of the employment relationship in the context of the Unfair Dismissals Acts 1977-93. The case of *O'Riain v. Independent Newspapers Ltd.* (1978) is significant in this context. The claimant was a cartoonist who began working in 1968. In 1972 O'Riain entered an agreement for the sum of £1,500 p.a. to be paid monthly. This was gradually increased, and in 1977 he was receiving the sum of £3,000. In 1978, Independent Newspapers wished to pay O'Riain £12 per contribution. He did not wish to accept the offer and was informed by letter that his contributions were no longer required. In an unfair dismissal action Independent Newspapers argued that the claim was not within the scope of the Unfair Dismissals Act as he was not an employee. They argued that he was a contributor who supplied cartoons on a basis other than that of a contract of service. In the course of its decision, the Employment Appeals Tribunal (EAT) laid down guidelines to assess whether a person is employed under a contract of service or not. These included the following:

- The element of control as to the time and methods of work.

- The right to hire and fire.

- The issue of whether a person is required to give personal service.

- The element of vicarious liability for the negligence of employees.

- Whether or not the individual had discretion to offer his services to others.

- The method of payment or remuneration.

- The method of payment of income tax and the entitlement to holiday pay.

The EAT cautioned, however, that this was not an exhaustive list, but such factors were important and should be considered when making a decision. The EAT concluded that as there was no real element of control or of personal service in the case before it, the issue of vicarious liability was not relevant and they therefore viewed the plaintiff to be an independent contractor. The fact that he was paid a regular monthly salary, a factor indicating a contract of employment, was not of itself sufficient. Fennell and Lynch (1994) argue correctly that the decision was positive in its efforts to consider a number of factors (not just control) in determining whether the individual is an employee or an independent contractor.

However, the control test still tends to be influential, as illustrated in the case of *O'Friel v. Management of St. Michael's Hospital* (1980). The issue was whether a consultant surgeon was an employee and, if so, whether he came within the provisions of the Unfair Dismissals Act. The Tribunal held that the most significant factor was control. It held that O'Friel was primarily a consultant surgeon, with the hospital having very little control over his activities. The tribunal considered him not to be an employee.

A Multiple Test

More recent Irish case law highlights some significant changes in emphasis, in that control is now merely one of the factors considered, and the limitations of a control test, particularly in the context of highly skilled employees and professional employees, is generally accepted. The decision in *J. E. McDermott, Inspector of Taxes v. Patrick Loy* (1982) illustrates this effectively. The question in this case was whether a representative of an insurance company working on commission was an employee. There was considerable debate about the criteria, with an argument put forward that control was only one of several factors that had to be considered. The *Market Investigations* case was cited to support this point of view. Mr. Justice Barron advocated that the test has not really changed. He believed that the purpose was to determine whether the employee is working for himself or for someone else. Mr. Justice Barron essentially advocated the use of the control test to suit modern employment conditions, and incorporated other criteria similar to those suggested by the EAT.

The case of *Re Sunday Tribune* (1984) is significant because it highlights the limitations of the control test. The issue was whether three journalists employed by the *Sunday Tribune* were employed under a contract of service or a contract for service. The first claimant had been employed as a part-time sub-editor of the newspaper on a shift basis, and was required to attend the company's premises at a specified time. He worked under the guidance and instructions of the chief sub-editor. The second claimant, who was paid a fixed sum weekly for writing the material for a weekly column, was required to attend and participate at the company's editorial conferences, whereas the third claimant furnished regular articles for the company's newspaper. Each had been separately commissioned. Income tax (PAYE) had not been deducted due to an arrangement with the Revenue Commissioners. The three claimants had also worked for other employers while employed by the *Sunday Tribune*.

Ms. Justice Carroll articulated this view:

> The simple test is whether the employer possessed the right not only to control what work the employee was to do but also the manner in which the work was to be done. However the test is no longer of universal application. In the present day when senior staff with professional qualifications are employed the nature of their employment cannot be determined in such a simplistic way.

Justice Carroll concluded that the first claimant's employment satisfied the control test. The second claimant's employment was held to be an integral part of the business of the newspaper. She was employed under a contract of service. The employment of the third claimant, however, was considered not be an integral part of the business of the newspaper because she was under no obligation to contribute on a regular basis. If she did not negotiate, the editor would get articles from some other source. Therefore she was an independent contractor or employed under a contract of service.

Another Irish decision, which highlights the issue, is that of *O'Coindealbhain (Inspector of Taxes) v. Thomas B. Mooney* (1990). The essential issue here was whether the branch manager of an employment office employed by the Minister for Social Welfare was an independent contractor and so assessable for tax purposes under Schedule D. Mr. Justice Blayney (High Court) expressed the opinion that the first test to be considered is the extent and degree of control. He approved of Barron J.'s formulation of the control test in *McDermott v. Loy* and referred to the *Ready Mixed Concrete* case with approval. Blayney concluded that, on the terms of the contract alone, the individual in question was an independent contractor. He placed particular emphasis on the fact that Mooney was not obliged to perform any of the work personally; he was required to provide and furnish the office premises and employ assistants if necessary; remuneration was not described as a wage or salary, but made up of allowances and payments related to the volume of work; the remuneration could vary at the discretion of the employer; and part of the contract required the provision of services by Thomas B. Mooney.

Fennell and Lynch (1994) suggest that this decision creates considerable uncertainty as to the relationships between the control test and other tests that may be utilised by the courts. There is, however, a general recognition of the need to use criteria in conjunction with the control test to identify the modern employment relationship.

Another recent case, which considered the issue of a contract of or for service, is that of *Denny and Sons (Ireland) Ltd. v. Minister for Social Welfare* (1992). In this case a Miss Mahon was recruited by Kerry Foods as a demonstrator at various supermarket outlets. She had worked for the company for a number of years. She worked 27-28 hours per week for 48-50 weeks per year. She received no formal training but had an induction talk and briefing on the products. She supplied only her labour because the company gave her a coat and a demonstration stand. The product used in the demonstration was supplied indirectly by Denny through the supermarket outlet. She had no supervision during work but there was a clause in her contract requiring her to abide by directions and regulations in the supermarket. She received no pay for holidays or illness and was not a member of the company's pension scheme. Claims for payment were submitted on a demonstration invoice, which had to be signed by the manager of the supermarket outlet, and were paid once a fortnight. The invoice also contained a general report and comments of the customers.

Carroll J. delivered her judgement on 18 October 1995, arguing that the issue in this case was whether Sandra Mahon was an employee or an independent contractor. Carroll J. pointed out that she had to consider the facts and the realities of the situation on the ground irrespective of what the actual contract stated or specified. She made reference to a range of tests that can be applied in determining whether a contract of service existed. She concluded that Miss Mahon was subject to the control and direction of Denny and therefore the ingredients of a contract of service existed. Carroll J. appeared to rely on the control criterion even though she made explicit reference to a range of other tests.

This decision contrasts with another case, *Cronin v. Kerry Co-operative* (1990) CC. In this case Judge Moran decided in an appeal from the EAT that Ms. Cronin, who was employed on a similar contract to Ms. Mahon, had a contract for service and there was no jurisdiction to hear an appeal for unfair dismissal.

Table 1.3 presents a summary of the issues to be considered when determining the question of the nature of the contractual relationship between employer and employee.

Table 1.3: Some Issues in Determining the Contractual Relationship

Provision of own services	If it is possible for the engaged person to get someone else to carry out the work contracted for them, it is an employer-independent contractor relationship.
Remuneration	If work is performed for a fee, it cannot be an employer-employee relationship. There must be consideration in the form of a wage or other form of remuneration.
Engagement and Dismissal	Where someone else other than the alleged employer engages a person, this in general indicates that the person who did the hiring employs him or her.
Time of Work	Where the engaged person has considerable discretion in terms of the time taken to carry out the work, the likelihood is that the relationship is employer-independent contractor.
	If the work duration is brief, it is most likely to be interpreted as an employer-independent contractor relationship.
The Workplace	Where the work is done outside of the employer's establishment, the general view is that the relationship is employer-independent contractor.
Provision of Work Equipment	The issue of who pays for and provides the equipment is significant. If the engaged person pays and/or provides it, the relationship is most likely an employer-independent contractor one.

THE PARTIES TO THE CONTRACT OF EMPLOYMENT

There is no exact definition of employee at common law, nor are the various statutes consistent in definitional terms. We have already noted that the term "employee" is distinguished in particular by concept of control by the employer. The Unfair Dismissals Acts, 1977-93 does provide a statutory definition. These acts provide that an employee is an individual who has entered into or works under a contract of employment. The Minimum Notice and Terms of Employment Act, 1973, on the other hand, defines an employee in section (1) so as to exclude the self-employed, whereas self-employed individuals come within the definition of employee for the purposes of the Anti-Discrimination Act, 1979.

There is reasonable clarity with respect to the definition of employer at common law. It derives from the nature of the contract itself and applies only to those who have entered into a contract of employment. In the Irish case of the *Roundabout Ltd. v. Beirne* (1959), this issue was considered. The facts of the case are as follows: in order to surmount the protection provided for a union in relation to picketing, a company made all its non-striking employees directors of the company and therefore it was no longer a matter for the purposes of the Trade Disputes Act, 1906, since contracts of employment no longer existed. There is, however, little attempt to give an explicit definition of employer in contemporary Irish protective legislation.

RIGHTS AND OBLIGATIONS IN THE CONTRACT OF EMPLOYMENT

There are three sources of rights and obligations in the employment relationship in Ireland: the contract itself; the obligation imposed by the constitution and the obligations imposed by statute. The first two will be considered in some detail, however the latter will be considered in the next chapter, specifically as it relates to health and safety legislation.

Rights and Obligations Arising from the Contract

The terms of the contract must, unless contrary to law, be observed by the parties, but there are also certain terms which, while sometimes made explicit, are nonetheless implied into the contracts of employment.

As many contracts of employment still tend to be informal initially, and in any event are not reduced to writing, it follows that there are other sources to guide the parties with regard to the explicit nature of the contract. The first source lies in collective agreements, and also in their more formal consequences, that is to say, employment regulation orders and registered employment agreements. The second source lies in custom and practice, the clarity and weight of which varies from employment to employment, being strongest in traditional employments such as those concerning craft trades. Nevertheless, as Redmond (1984) notes:

> As a direct source of labour law, enforceable in the courts, custom is not a significant source. In certain areas of law, the courts will uphold a custom. However, in such instances the custom must have met the rigorous tests laid down in the past by judicial decisions, i.e. it must be clear and unambiguous; it must reflect a recurring and uninterrupted practice; and it must have been openly practised for a number of years.

Statutory law implies specific obligations into the employment contract, but in their absence and in the absence of express terms the common law considers certain obligations to be implied, and here it is useful to distinguish between the common law duties of employer and the employee.

Common Law Duties of the Employer

The Duty to Provide Remuneration. The employer has a duty, even where it is not explicitly provided for, to pay the employee remuneration. The general rule, however, is that payment is made only for work done. In such circumstances there may be a lay-off without pay, which, if it is not covered by the contract, may be permitted by custom and practice. In circumstances where the employee is temporarily absent from work because of illness, the employer may not normally treat the contract to be at an end, however the employee is only entitled to remuneration for the period of absence if it is provided for in the contract. The right of an employee to information on sickness and sick-pay are among the matters provided for under the Terms of Employment (Information) Act, 1994.

The Duty to Provide Work. The employer does not appear to be under any general duty to provide work for the employee, except where the nature of the employment is such that the employee's reputation or skill depends on their performance as, for example, in the case of an actor or a professional athlete. There is, however, a trend in judicial thinking to extend this principle somewhat and to hold that there is a general duty resting on the employer to maintain the employment relationship.

The Duty to Ensure Safety at Work. The employer has a duty at common law to provide the employee with a safe system of work and in that regard to exercise such care as is reasonable. This issue will be explored in some detail in **Chapter 2**.

The Duty of Respect. The status of an employee has greatly changed in modern times, and this change must be taken into account in what can be implied generally into contracts of employment. The changing nature of the employment relationship has given rise to a significant amount of statutory law, and this in turn has influenced the courts in their understanding of the employment relationship. In the case of the decisions of the Employment Appeals Tribunal, the following implied terms have emerged: the maintenance of trust and confidence by the employer, the provision of support to the employee, the right to be treated with respect by an employer and not to have to endure physical violence or humiliation.

Duties in Respect of Termination. Under common law employers are free, at their discretion, to terminate the employee's contract of employment subject only to such notice as the contract itself specifies. There is now, however, an acceptance in Ireland of the notion that an employee has an interest in their job, which is considered more significant than the contract itself and which, in the view of some, may approach the notion of a property right. This notion is reflected in the development of employment legislation, and in particular in unfair dismissals legislation, which impose on the employer a number of duties that are directed towards protecting the employee's status and the employee's right of continuance in employment.

Common Law Duties of the Employee

The Duty to Obey. The primary duty implied in the case of the employee is to obey the employer's lawful and reasonable instructions. What is reasonable is a matter for determination. Clearly the instruction must be connected with the work that the employee is contracted to do, and in this context the decisions of the Employment Appeals Tribunal are useful. It follows that the employee must not wilfully disrupt the employer's business or their other activities nor may they absent themselves from work without good cause during the time that their contract requires them to be in attendance.

The Duty of Performance. It is the duty of an employee, in return for remuneration, to provide "work and skill". Where an employee is employed because they possess particular competence, it is an implied term that they will perform their duties in a manner which reasonably reflects such competence; that they will be diligent and honest in so doing and that they will exercise care in respect of the employer's property. The employee may be liable to the employer in negligence for any loss or damage that the employer may suffer as a result of their incompetence. Furthermore, employees have a duty to co-operate with their employer. Here may arise the difficult question of the "flexibility clause" or the "mobility clause", which concerns the extent to which an employer may reasonably request an employee, for example, to accept an obligation to work overtime, or to work in a different location, or even on a different machine. The implied term of co-operation must be understood against the background of custom and practice and is particularly significant in the case of craft trades. Even where the contract provides explicitly for flexibility and mobility, the employer's right must be exercised within reasonable limits.

The Duty of Fidelity. This is a difficult and somewhat uncertain concept. There are, however, a number of implied terms of a specific kind that have arisen within the general context of fidelity or good faith.

Spare Time Work. This area is not clearly defined. The general rule is that the employee is free to pursue whatever activities they choose during their non-working time. This must not, however, affect the employee's performance of their work for the employer. On the other hand, an employer cannot argue that simply by working in their spare time an employee is unable to devote all their energy and attention to their job. The employer must be in a position to show that the spare time work actually impacts the work for which the employee was employed. However, the employee may not in such circumstances engage in work that may damage the employer's business, nor, in particular, should they engage in work of a substantively competitive nature.

Confidentiality. Explicit provisions in the contract normally cover this duty. Where it is not, the following term may be implied. The employee has a general duty not to disclose confidential information obtained by them in the course of, and as a result of, their employment. In the absence of an explicit term, however, it may be difficult to prove in practice. The obligation may continue after the employment has been terminated, however the specific duration is again difficult to determine. It is prudent for an employer to make such duties explicit in the contract of employment and to consider the reluctance of the courts to enforce any term that is clearly in restraint of trade.

Inventions by Employees. Under common law, an employee who creates something (an invention) or makes a discovery in the course of employment, or produces material which might be regarded as subject to copyright, is normally, by virtue of an implied term in the employment contract, to be working for their employer and as a result the invention is owned by the employer. This has been modified to some extent by Section (53) of the Patents Act 1964, which provides that, in the event of a dispute, the Controller of Patents and, if necessary, the High Court may determine the matter by, for example, apportioning the benefit of a patent between employer and employee.

Remedies. Remedies for breach of the employment relationship are dealt with in large part by various statutes. Nevertheless, there are a number of common law remedies and principles of law, focusing in particular on the question of the contract's termination.

The Problem of Specific Performance. Traditionally, the courts have refused to decree specific performance of an employment contract either in the case of an employer or of an employee, largely because it appears to be at odds with the nature of an employment contract to do so. Where a constitutional right is infringed, however, the general rule may not apply, and statute law certainly contemplates reinstatement as at least one remedy in the case of unfair dismissals.

Damages. In assessing damages for breach of the employment contract the courts apply the principle of *restitutio in integrum*: the restoration of the person injured by the breach to the position they would have been in if the injury had not occurred. Damages must not be punitive. However, there is some uncertainty in this area. There is a question of how proximate the damage must be, and here it appears that the damage must arise naturally from the breach or it must arise from circumstances contemplated by the parties. There is a further question in relation to the meaning of *restitutio in integrum*, specifically whether it means restoring the *status quo ante* as if the contract had never been entered into, or whether it means putting the injured person in the position they would have been in if the contract had been fully performed. In the case of a fixed-term contract, compensation appears to be based on the loss of employment in respect of the remainder of the contract, subject to the other party's obligation to mitigate their loss. In the case of a contract of indefinite length, which is the type of contract normally encountered, the position is summarised by Lord Denning in *Hill v. Parsons Ltd.* (1972) to the effect that an employee:

... gets damages for the time he would have served if he had given notice, less, of course, anything he has, or ought to have, earned in alternative employment. He does not get damages for the loss of expected benefits to which he had no contractual right.

Rights and Obligations Arising from the Constitution

The Irish Constitution is the basic law in Ireland and provides in Article 40 for certain personal rights relating to the "life, person, good name and property of every citizen". The contract of employment must not infringe any of these rights. In addition to these express rights, the Constitution contains certain implied rights that may be invoked by the employee.

Express Guarantees

The most significant guarantees in the context of the contract of employment that are expressed in the Constitution are: equality before the law, freedom of association, non-discrimination, and the general guarantee of the State "by its laws to respect, and, as far as is practicable, by its laws to defend and vindicate the personal rights of the citizen". These are significant in the context of dismissal law and there is a considerable body of case law in this area.

Implied Guarantees

The right to join a union, that is, freedom of association, is deemed to imply a right not to join and this is of particular significance in disputes concerning a closed shop. In the case of closed shops it is argued that there is an unspecified constitutional right to work, in the sense that a person should not be deprived of their livelihood. While this idea has won general acceptance, it has not formed the *ratio decidendi* in any Irish case. An implied right of considerable importance in the context of discipline and dismissals is fairness in procedures. O'Dalaigh, C.J. pointed out that:

> The Constitution guarantees such fairness and it is the duty of the court to underline that the words of Article (40) Section (3) are not political shibboleths but provide a positive protection for the citizen ...

It is not clear, however, that the implied guarantee of fairness removes the distinction between an employee's rights in such matters and the natural justice to which an office-holder is entitled, although the law appears to have moved in that direction. Finally, it is important to remember that the notion of a contract freely entered into is fundamental to all of the issues discussed in this chapter, and constitutional rights may be waived, it appears, where there is full knowledge and full consent.

Remedies

The Irish Constitution offers little guidance on the remedies to be utilised, where such are required for its implementation. Constitutional remedies in this case are taken to mean remedies available as a matter of constitutional right for the redress of constitutional wrongs. Where a common law remedy is available it should be sought, but where the common law is silent the person wronged is not inhibited necessarily on that account.

Budd J. stated in *Educational Company Ltd. v. Fitzpatrick* (1961) that:

> ... if an established right in law exists, a citizen has the right to assert it and it is the duty of the courts to aid and assist him/her in the assertion of his/her right. The courts will therefore assist and uphold a citizen's constitutional right.

In practice, the remedy usually sought for a breach of constitutional right is a declaration from the court that the right has been infringed; and if a dismissal constitutes the infringement, then the dismissal is void and the contract subsists. A person may also seek an injunction restraining the activity that they regard as unconstitutional. In respect to damages, the Supreme Court stated in *Meskell v. CIE* (1973) "that a person whose constitutional rights have been infringed may sue to enforce or he may sue for damages by reason of infringement" and further "... the plaintiff is entitled to such damages as may upon inquiry be proved to have been sustained by him". However, as mentioned earlier, a court will not normally order specific performance of an employment contract.

TERMS OF EMPLOYMENT (INFORMATION) ACT, 1994

The Terms of Employment (Information) Act, 1994 makes some significant modifications to the form of the employment contract. This Act obliges employers to give details to employees of their conditions of employment within two months of taking up employment. It amends the existing provisions under the Minimum Notice and Terms of Employment Acts, 1973-1991. The Act makes it mandatory to give to all employees, regardless of whether the details were requested, details of the terms and conditions of employment.

Under the Act, an employer is obliged to give new employees a written statement containing the particulars shown in **Figure 1.1** within two months of the commencement of employment. When an existing employee so requests, they must be given a written statement within two months of the request.

An employee who commences employment and subsequently leaves the employment within two months will still be entitled to a written statement of conditions. Furthermore, the Act obliges employers to keep the statement detailing all these conditions for a period of one year after the termination of the employment. Where the employee is required to work outside the State for a period of a month or more, the employer must give the following details in writing to the employee:

- The duration of the employment abroad
- The currency in which they will be paid
- Any other benefits
- The terms and conditions, where appropriate, of their repatriation (at the moment, this information is not obligatory).

If any change is made or occurs in any of the particulars of the statement, the employer is obliged to notify the employee in writing of the nature and the date of the change. Such notification must take place no later than one month after the change takes effect, or where the change results in the employee having to work outside the State for more than one month, the time of the employee's departure.

Figure 1.1: Particulars to be Included in a Written Statement of Conditions of Employment

- The full names of employer and employee.

- The address of the employer in the State and the principal place of business in the State, or registered office.

- The place of work of the employee, or if there is no fixed or main place a statement that the employee is permitted and required to work at various locations.

- The title of the job or nature of the work.

- The date of commencement of the contract.

- If it is a temporary contract, the expected duration, or if for a fixed term, the date on which the contract expires.

- The rate or method of calculation of the employee's remuneration.

- The intervals between payment or remuneration e.g. weekly, monthly.

- Any terms and conditions relating to hours of work, including overtime.

- Any terms and conditions relating to paid leave, other than paid sick leave.

- Any terms and conditions relating to incapacity due to sickness or injury and pensions and pension schemes.

- The period of notice required to be given and received by an employee, either statutory or under the terms of the contract of employment. If this is not readily available, then information on how the notice will be calculated must be provided.

- Details of any collective agreement that directly affects an employee's terms and conditions. If the employer is not a party to the agreement, then particulars should be provided of the bodies or institutions by whom they are made.

If a change occurs as a result of statutory or administrative provisions or collective agreements, there is no requirement for the employer to notify the employee of the change. It does, however, represent good practice to do so, as an employee's ignorance of changes arising from these sources can give rise to unnecessary employee relationship problems.

Making a Complaint under the 1994 Act

A number of options exist in respect of making a complaint under the 1994 Act, as set out below.

The Rights Commissioner

An employee who believes that a breach has occurred may make a complaint to a Rights Commissioner who notifies the employer, hears the evidence and issues a recommendation. A recommendation may take the form of one or more of the following:

- A declaration that the complaint was, or was not, well founded.

- Confirmation of all or any of the particulars contained in the statement given by the employer.

- Alteration or additions to any statement so as to correct an inaccuracy or omission. This altered statement will be deemed to be the statement given by the employer to the employee.

- A requirement that the employer give to the employee a written statement containing the particulars specified by the Commissioner.

- An order directing the employer to pay compensation of an amount not exceeding four weeks' remuneration.

A complaint must be presented to the Rights Commissioner within six months of the termination of the employment. The Rights Commissioner provides the Employment Appeals Tribunal with a copy of the recommendation.

The Employment Appeals Tribunal

A Rights Commissioner's recommendation may be appealed to the Employment Appeals Tribunal within six weeks of the date on which it is communicated to the party. The Employment Appeals Tribunal notifies the other party, rehears the case and makes a written determination. The Tribunal may affirm the recommendation, set it aside or vary it.

If the Rights Commissioner's recommendation is not carried out and is not appealed within the specified time, the employee may bring a complaint to the Tribunal. The Tribunal, without hearing any new evidence, will make a determination affirming the recommendation. Failure to appear before the Tribunal when subpoenaed, or where there is failure to produce documents, constitutes an offence and, on summary conviction, may lead to a fine of up to €1,270 (IR£1,000).

The High Court

The Minister for Enterprise, Trade and Employment (The Minister), or a party to the appeal before the Tribunal, may refer a question or point of law to the High Court where it can be determined conclusively.

The District Court

If an employer fails to carry out a determination of the Tribunal within six weeks of the determination being communicated to the parties, an application may be made to the District Court by the employee concerned, the trade union or by the Minister acting on behalf of the employee. The District Court may, without hearing any new evidence, make an order directing the employer to carry out the determination. If a determination is appealed within the time specified, but the appeal is abandoned, then the specified six week period commences from the date of the abandonment. The District Court can, as appropriate, order an employer to pay interest on compensation outstanding for all or part of the specified period, commencing six weeks after the determination was communicated to the parties, and ending on the day of the order.

Types of Employment Contract

There are many types of employment contract, each reflecting the particular circumstances of the employment concerned. Two common types found in practice in Ireland are fixed-term and specified-purpose contracts, which are regularly used where temporary employment is on offer. The application of the Unfair Dismissals Acts, 1977 - 1993 can be excluded from dismissals resulting from the expiration or expiry of such contracts.

Fixed-Term Contracts

A fixed-term contract is commonly used where the employer and employee know for certain the starting and finishing dates of the contract. Persons employed for a limited period of time are normally employed under fixed-term contracts. The application of the Unfair Dismissals Acts to such contracts may be excluded if the dismissal consisted only of the expiry of the fixed term without it being renewed and the contract is a genuine fixed-term/specific purpose contract. Furthermore, the contract must be in writing, both parties must sign it and it must expressly provide that the Unfair Dismissals Acts will not apply to a dismissal consisting only of the expiry of the term of the contract.

The Employment Appeals Tribunal is strict in its interpretation of the application of this provision. This is illustrated in the case of *Sheehan v. Dublin Tribunal Ltd* (1991). Here the claimant was dismissed when his two-year fixed-term contract came to an end. A clause in his contract dealing with termination stated the following:

> ... on the termination of this contractual arrangement ... you shall have no claim on the company, arising from the termination of the contract ...

It was held that this clause did not specifically provide that the provisions of the Unfair Dismissals Acts, 1977 - 1993 would not apply to a dismissal by reason of the expiry of the two-year period and the claimant's dismissal was therefore found to be unfair.

Seasonal work is often provided by means of a fixed-term contract and sometimes the contract will contain a statement that no work is guaranteed beyond the expiry of the fixed term. There may also be a specific letter of termination at the end of each season. If there is no specific termination at the end of the season, this suggests that the contract is not a temporary contract but one of indeterminate duration with periods of actual employment accumulated over time.

Even where there is a separate contract for each season, and a specific dismissal, the EAT, in dealing with a seasonal worker, will look at the employment history of a claimant. If the employment has been irregular for a number of seasons, and the employee clearly has an expectation of work each season, the EAT will incline towards an interpretation of the contract as one of indeterminate duration. The periods between the seasons will be interpreted as periods of lay-off, and the employee will be deemed to have continued in employment in the meantime, and will be afforded the protection of relevant legislation, which will be implied into the continuing contract of employment.

Specified-Purpose Contracts

These types of contract are often used to cover some specific event where the exact termination date remains unknown at the time of making the contract, e.g. to cover an absentee employee whose return date is unknown or to do a particular once-off job. This type of contract would arise, for instance, in cases where an existing employee is on maternity leave and a replacement is needed for the duration of the leave. It may also arise where a person is taken on for a specific job whose duration cannot be determined at the time the contract is made. Here, as is the case with fixed-term contracts, the application of the Unfair Dismissals Acts may be excluded, subject to the contract being a genuine specified-purpose contract. The situation is illustrated in the case of *Ryan v. CIE* (1986). Mr. Ryan was employed for the specific purpose of relaying track on a particular stretch of the Limerick-Waterford line and was given a contract to that effect. However, the work of relaying could not go on continuously and there would be frequent, and sometimes long, interruptions. CIE knew this at the time of making the contract, and intended that Mr. Ryan could do other work in order to keep him occupied until the track relaying had been completed. This was enough to make the contract something other than a specified-purpose contract, in this case a contract of continuous duration.

Therefore, where a specified-purpose contract is used, the employer should be certain that there is sufficient work related to the specified purpose to keep the temporary employee occupied. If there is not, a fixed-term contract should be considered with the possibility of a renewal for a further fixed term, the terms being related but different in the two contracts, e.g. the initial contract may be for the installation of machinery and the second may be to complete the installation.

DISMISSALS LAW AND HEALTH AND SAFETY

It is beyond the scope of this Handbook to give a detailed treatment of dismissals law. However, the issue of dismissals has significant relevance in the context of health and safety issues. Section 6(4) of the Unfair Dismissals Acts, 1977-93 refers to capacity as the basis to justify a fair dismissal.

An employee's incapacity to do the job for which they were hired can result in dismissal. Attendance problems are a common cause of incapacity, e.g. failure to attend work regularly or persistent lateness. Frequent short-term absences can be justified as reasons for dismissal where:

• The absences occurred over a significant period.

• There was reason to conclude that this pattern would not improve in the foreseeable future.

• Allowing the absences to continue was unacceptable as it established the wrong precedent for other employees.

• Appropriate disciplinary action has been taken — the employee has received warnings of the consequences of failure to improve the attendance record.

Other forms of short-term absence can include a variety of illnesses or regular absences on Fridays or Mondays or after a long weekend. This is not acceptable and, as long as the employer exercises reasonableness and observes due procedures and warnings, dismissal may follow.

A number of cases address the issues of incapacity. In *Farrell v. Rotunda Hospital* (1978), the Employment Appeals Tribunal defined the term "capability" to cover absence from work due to illness. Cases since then clearly illustrate that fitness for work is an important consideration in justifying dismissal. Prolonged absence due to illness and recurrent absences have been considered by the EAT to justify dismissal. In the case of *Reardon v St. Vincent's Hospital (UD74/1979)*: "Incapability may be generally defined as long-term illness". Generally speaking, there is nothing prohibiting an employer dismissing an employee for long-term absenteeism when it can be established that there is no reasonable return to work date.

The law on these matters is now effectively set out in the case of *Bolger v. Showerings (Ireland) Ltd (1990)*. This case identified four requirements that the employer must meet:

1. It was the ill-health that was the reason for his dismissal.

2. That this was substantial reason.

3. That the employee received fair notices that the question of his dismissal for incapacity was being considered.

4. That the employee was afforded the opportunity of being heard.

This case also established that, where there is no dispute between the parties as to the incapacity of the employee, it is not necessary to await medical tests before the decision to dismiss. A note of caution must be added to this last statement, as one obviously has to look at each case on its own merits. However, if the employee has been out from work for an unreasonable length of time and cannot give a return date, dismissal may be reasonable.

A number of practice implications can be derived from the case law. The following are the main ones:

• In the case of absence as a result of alcohol or substance abuse, the employer should in the first instance treat these as if they were an illness. The employer should make every effort to elicit the cause and refer the employee to the appropriate treatment facility in order to combat the dependence. If the absences continue after treatment, or if the employee refuses to seek help, the usual disciplinary procedure should be used. If the problem persists, it may result in dismissal.

• While there is no legal requirement for medical reports/test results affirming the incapacity, it is always wise to have all relevant information available before making a decision to dismiss. Equally, there are no legal definitions of an unacceptable length of absence. If an employer has exercised reasonableness and made the necessary enquiries about possible return to work and comes to the view that no solution is likely, then they may have no real option but to dismiss the employee. If this is the situation, the employer will have to argue the reasonableness of the decision before the Employment Appeals Tribunal. There will always be some uncertainty as to whether an employer is entitled to dismiss.

- Some employees believe that if they are on "sick leave" indefinitely and have submitted the required medical certificates, they cannot be dismissed. This is not the case. Lengthy absences with no foreseeable return to work date can justify a dismissal on grounds of incapacity. Employment contracts or handbooks should allow for examination of the employee by the company doctor in order to examine the employee's fitness for work or otherwise.

- It is well established that, for an employee who is no longer capable of performing their duties, there is no obligation on the employer to provide "light work" or alternative duties (*Guru v. The Office of Public Works (1990) ELR 42*).

- Employers have lost many cases by not complying with reasonable procedures; for example, not asking the employee for a reasonable return date or not sending the employee to a company doctor in order to establish the true medical position and a prognosis for a return date to work.

- If an employer has a sick pay scheme, an employee may not abuse it, for example, by working while on sick leave. Again, it is well established that this may be fair ground for dismissal.

Table 1.4: Examples of EAT Determinations Related to Health and Safety

---

Allergic to Sprays

(Nolan v. Ryan Hotels, UD case 579/98)

Nolan, who worked with Ryan Hotels as a cleaner since 1985, was in the early 1990s diagnosed as suffering from asthma. She was told not to use sprays. She made her supervisors aware of this. Then in 1998, after a manager queried her about an unresolved carpet stain, she was asked to furnish a doctor's letter. She did so and was asked to furnish a further letter setting out a list of the chemicals to which she was allergic.

Her doctor wrote that she should avoid certain substances such as polish, car fresheners, fresh paint, perfumes and cleaning chemicals, which vaporise. However, Ryan Hotels wanted confirmation from her doctor that the chemicals being used in the hotel would not adversely affect her health. On March 10th she was suspended on pay for a week and on March 18th she requested her P45.

Nolan then brought a claim for constructive dismissal. The Tribunal, having commented that it was Ryan's "responsibility to find out more about the allergies before exposing her to risk", noted that it was only at the time of the incident that management became aware of Nolan's allergies. However they dismissed the claim on the grounds that "we cannot find anything wrong with employer's conduct", which they stated was sympathetic and understanding.

Housekeeping and Hygiene Duties

(McCabe v Soletron Ireland, UD case 781/98)

McCabe was employed by Soletron in April 1997 as an operator. The company set up a rota of employees to tidy up litter in the company's grounds and provided gloves and a litter picker for carrying out the task. McCabe refused to take part in the rota, arguing that the task was "unhygienic" and that it was not specified in her employment contract.

The tribunal held that Soletron, in requesting McCabe to carry out the litter tidying function, had "unilaterally changed a condition of the employee's contract". What they should have done was to "have notified her of the intended change and sought her consent". They held therefore that she had been unfairly dismissed and awarded her £643.48 compensation.

Abuse and Intimidation

(Hamill v. J Williams Ltd, UD case 199/99)

Hamill, who claimed that he could not take any more constant abuse and intimidation, resigned from Williams and brought a claim for constructive dismissal. He gave evidence of numerous instances of abuse and recalled an incident where he was criticised for delaying in hospital after a drill bit went through his finger. He said that following this incident the company appointed a safety officer, but they did not provide any protective clothing. Williams did not appear before the Tribunal, which held that Hamill was unfairly dismissed and awarded him IR£1,520 (€1,930).

Working Elsewhere

(Prunty v. Grove Farm, UD 724/98)

Following an accident at work, Prunty was absent on sick leave. Meetings were arranged to discuss his health, but he attended only four out of seven meetings. His employers heard that he was working elsewhere and employed a private investigator, who took pictures of Prunty at work.

Grove Farm dismissed Prunty, who denied he was working elsewhere. He brought a claim for unfair dismissals. The Tribunal, taking account of the private investigator's photos, concluded that Prunty was working elsewhere while on prolonged absence from work, and that his employer had been left with no option but to dismiss him.

Ever Able to Return to Work?

(Ryan v. Securicor Security Services, UD case 733/98)

The question at issue in the Ryan case was whether Ryan would ever be fit to return to work. He was absent following an accident, in which he fell down stairs, as a result of which he instituted a personal injury claim. As required by company/union house agreement, he submitted, on a weekly basis, medical certificates stating that he was unfit for work.

After nine months' absence, the company, whose own doctor was of the opinion that Ryan would never be able to return to work, dismissed him. He claimed that he was unfairly dismissed, as he had submitted medical certificates in accordance with the house agreement and that, when he asked his doctor for a prognosis, the doctor refused, saying that "I'm giving you certs each week". In a majority verdict the Tribunal held that there was no unfair dismissal, as the claimant's ill health was a substantial issue.

Recovery Time

(Keller v Trademet, UD case 142/99)

On 8 May, 1998 Keller suffered a leg injury in an accident at work. Following the accident, he was absent from work and his employer received a solicitor's letter notifying that Keller intended to issue proceedings. On 9 June the employer wrote to Keller seeking medical certificates and a prognosis regarding his return to work. This was not forthcoming and, by the time the claimant was fit to return to work, his position had been filled.

The Tribunal held that the question they had to answer was "whether the period of four months was too short a time to allow for recovery". Notwithstanding the employer's argument that it was necessary to fill the post, they took the view that it was and held that the dismissal was unfair. They ordered that Keller be reinstated.

Dismissed over Pallet Collapse

(Kelly v Fort James, UD 218/99)

Kelly was dismissed following a report by a security guard that he saw Kelly pulling down two pallets containing kitchen towels, so that he could get at two cases of kitchen roll. According to the security guard, who was carrying out a stock control exercise, Kelly pulled down both pallets with his hands, causing both to fall, instead of lifting down the top pallet with his forklift.

At meetings with Kelly and his trade union representatives, Kelly denied the allegations, but at a disciplinary meeting he did not make a statement. The company then decided to dismiss him, on the ground that the action was deliberate and that as it compromised company health and safety policy, it was a dismissible offence.

The Tribunal held that "in the circumstances pertaining to the particular allegation, and the claimant's response to these allegations . . . that the collective effect was a scenario of gross misconduct where the safety of workers, including the claimant, had been compromised wilfully". Accordingly the Tribunal held "the dismissal was fair".

CHAPTER ROUND UP

- Occupational health and safety law has its origins in the industrial revolution. This revolution led the courts to develop the concept of the doctrine of common employment, whereby an employer was not liable for the injuries suffered by employees in the course of employment.

- The doctrine of common employment eventually gave way to the concept of employer's duty of care. The duty of care principle posited that an employer must exercise reasonable care for the health and safety of employers in the course of employment.

- The concept of employer's duty must be understood in the context of the wider law of tort and the contract of employment. The aim of the law of tort is to compensate a plaintiff for a breach of duty on the part of the defendant. Other objectives of tort law include appeasement, justice for the injured party and deterrence.

- The existence of a contract of service is central to the application of the duty of care principle in the employment context. There is considerable debate about what test is appropriate to ascertain the nature of the employment relationship, although the trend is towards consideration of a broad range of characteristics of the specific employment relationship.

- The law on dismissals has relevance to health and safety, specifically where prolonged or recurring absence due to illness or accident is used as a justification to terminate the contract of employment. The case law puts emphasis on the implementation of proper procedures and their application in a fair manner.

- The concept of employers' duty of care is not an absolute but a relative concept. A range of factors determines its application. These include the following: the age of the employee, the level of experience and training, the work context and specifically, the level of risk inherent in the job, the existence of physical disabilities on the part of the employee and the application of relevant international safety standards.

Chapter 2

DUTY OF CARE AND THE ROLE
OF THE COMMON LAW

INTRODUCTION

This chapter considers the role of the common law in the regulation of health and safety law in Ireland. Aside from a range of statutory obligations, there exists a number of common law duties in respect of health and safety at work. In general, where employers do not exercise reasonable care toward employees and where employees suffer injury as a result, the employer may be liable under the duty of care principle. This general statement is subject to a number of qualifications that are considered in detail in this chapter. The chapter considers five important issues:

- The nature of the employer's duty of care and its application.

- The concept of vicarious liability and its relevance to the employee/employer relationship and employer's duty of care.

- The law on occupier's liability and in particular to the Occupiers Liability Act, 1995.

- The common law concepts of damage and loss.

- The defences available to the employer in an employer's liability action.

THE GENERAL NATURE OF THE DUTY OF CARE

It is generally accepted that an employer, under the law of tort, has a specific duty of care, not only to their employees but also to independent contractors. The scope of this duty is considerable, and it is well established that an employer must exercise reasonable care for the safety of employees in the course of their employment.

The duty of care is owed by the employer to those who are employees in the technical sense of that term, those employed under a contract of service. The various range of tests used by the courts to determine the nature of the contractual relationship were considered in **Chapter 1**, but it should be pointed out that the existence of a contractual relationship between the employer and the injured person is not a prerequisite to the existence of a duty of care. A range of cases highlights that quite often a degree of control exists between the employer and injured person, in which case the duty of care principle is relevant to determine the question of liability.

The scope of the duty of care has been analysed in detail in Irish case law. It is possible to make a number of important general statements about the scope of the duty at this stage:

- The employer's duty to an employee does not extend to every aspect of the employee's existence. The activities of the employee considered relevant are those performed in the course of the employment and include activities that are normally and reasonably incidental to that employment.

- The duty owed by the employer is a personal one. This means that an employer who must or who chooses to entrust to another the performance of the duty of care that is owed to the employee remains responsible for the performance in like manner as if the employer had in fact performed it. So, for example, if a system of work devised for an employer by a third party is not reasonably safe, or if equipment manufactured by a third party is defective due to negligence in its manufacture, with the result that an employee is injured, the employer is liable, for they are considered to have failed in their personal duty to ensure that reasonable care is exercised for the employee's safety.

- The employer's duty is owed to employees as individuals and not as a class. This has legal significance. It basically means that, in determining what reasonable care is required in the circumstances, the personal characteristics of the individual employee in question will be considered. The courts have considered such issues as age, experience, physical and mental capacities of the employee, etc. These attributes may operate to increase or diminish the risk of damage sustained and impact on the standard of care required of the employer.

- The employer may owe a duty of care with respect to the protection of the employee's property against wrongful interference by third parties.

- Since the law considers an independent contractor to be "their own boss", the employer does not generally owe an independent contractor a duty of care of the same scope as that which is owed to an employee. The following appears to be the general position:

  ◊ The employer owes no duty as to the manner in which an independent contractor or the staff of an independent contractor carries out work, except where the employer interferes by giving directions and those negligent directions result in injury.

  ◊ The employer may be liable where the work involves unusual dangers and the employer has not provided a warning of the dangers to the unsuspecting contractor.

  ◊ If the employer provides equipment or help, there is a duty of care to ensure that the equipment is safe.

  ◊ Where an employer engages a number of contractors on the same project, a duty of care in negligence is owed as the head contractor.

  ◊ Where the employer remains the occupier of the premises where work is to be carried out, the employer may be liable as an occupier in respect of injuries resulting from the static conditions of the premises.

The duty of care principle will now be considered in terms of its individual sub-duties.

THE LEGAL BASIS OF THE DUTY OF CARE PRINCIPLE

The case of *Donoghue v. Stevenson* (1932) had major implications in terms of a number of issues pertaining to the development of employer's duty of care principle at common law. The basic facts of this case are as follows: The plaintiff brought an action against the manufacturers of ginger beer that was purchased for her by a friend from a local café. On pouring the beer into a glass, she noticed what appeared to be the remains of a decomposed snail floating out of the neck of the bottle into her glass. The plaintiff suffered gastro-enteritis and nervous shock as a result of drinking some of the beer and witnessing the decomposed snail. The case proceeded to the House of Lords on the basis that an action existed for the tort of "negligence", even though there was no contract between the plaintiff and the manufacturer of the ginger beer. The basis of the case was that the manufacturer of the beer owed a "duty of care" to the customer to ensure that there was no harmful substance in their product, and that in this case they breached their duty and the plaintiff suffered an injury as a result.

The House of Lords found in favour of the plaintiff. Four important issues emerged from the case:

- Negligence was recognised for the first time as a separate tort in its own right.

- An action for negligence exists irrespective of whether a contract exists.

- An action for negligence will succeed where the plaintiff can prove that a duty of care is owed by the defendant to the plaintiff and that this duty has been breached resulting in damage which is not too remote.

- In order to establish the existence of a duty of care the "neighbour principle", which is based on the notion of reasonable foresight, will be applied.

The *Donoghue v. Stevenson* case emphasised the notion of "proximity", which was defined in that case as:

> "... acts or omissions which any moral code would censure
> cannot in a practical world be treated so as to give a right to
> every person injured by them to demand relief".

The trial judge went further to formulate the "neighbour principle"
so as to limit the scope of further actions. It is only when this principle applies that a duty of care can be established and the basis of
an action in negligence is in place. The principle can be defined as
follows:

> You must take reasonable care to avoid acts of omissions
> which you can reasonably foresee would be likely to injure
> your neighbour.

Who then in law is my neighbour? This was stated to be:

> ... persons so closely and directly affected by my act that I
> ought reasonably to have them in contemplation as being so
> affected when directing my mind to the acts or omissions
> which are called into question.

This principle had the effect of broadening the tort of negligence
into many spheres of life, but primarily the case developed the
notion of "duty of care".

The courts have observed that a person is entitled to be as negligent as they please towards the whole world if they owe no duty
to them. The ingredients of what a "duty of care" consisted of were
considered by Lord Wilberforce in the case of *Anns v. London Borough of Merton* (1977). This case reiterated the principle laid down
in *Donoghue v. Stevenson* and outlined what became known as the
two-step test. Lord Wilberforce commented:

> Once there was sufficient proximity between the parties and
> the damage could be foreseen, then there exists a *prima fa-
> cie* duty of care on behalf of the defendant, unless there is a
> specific reason to exclude responsibility.

This comment points to the need for (a) proximity and (b) foresee-
ability, in order to prove that a duty of care exists.

This two-step test received much support in England until the
case of *Peabody Donation Fund (Governors) v. Sir Lindsay Parkerson*

and Co. (1985) where Lord Keith observed that the test was too definitive and did not take into account whether the imposition of a duty of care on a defendant is just and reasonable. In *Yeun Kun-Yeu v. A.G. for Hong Kong* (1987), the judicial committee pointed out that "the two stage test . . . is not . . . in all circumstances a suitable guide to the existence of a duty of care". Thus, in England it appears that a three-step test now exists, specifically, that the damage was reasonably foreseeable, there was sufficient proximity and it must be just and equitable. However, doubts have been cast on this view as a result of *Murphy v. Brentwood* (1990). In this case, Lord Keith recommended an "incremental" approach by reference to decided authorities. It is now generally accepted that, in the UK at least, the *Murphy* case ended the possibility of adapting the two-step test.

The Irish courts, however, have generally followed the two-step test and this has been observed in a number of cases including *Purtill v. Athlone UDC* (1968), *McNamara v. ESB* (1975) and *Ward v. McMaster and Louth County Council* (1985).

THE STANDARD OF CARE

The notion of a reasonable standard of care is based on the premise that individuals must conform to a certain standard of behaviour in any given situation. The standard is expressed in terms of the hypothetical or "reasonable" man. The purpose of this standard is to ensure objectivity. It is not sufficient for a person to do their best, as this may not be to the standard of the "reasonable" person. Conversely, a standard of perfection is not required either. It is not a question of how one acts but how one, being a reasonable person, ought to act. Case law suggests that there are a number of modifying factors that the court uses when considering what is reasonable behaviour. These include the basic knowledge and physical capabilities of the injured party.

If courts were to impose a single criterion for assessing a "standard of care" without taking into account the individual's personal circumstances, it might lead to significant injustices. Where the courts draw the line in relation to these modifying factors is unclear, but it is prudent to state that the standard which is reasonable is that standard of care given the individual's particular circumstances.

Employers' liability gradually developed as a legal principle, but it is now settled in law that an employer has a duty towards an employee to take reasonable care for their safety in all the circumstances of a given employment situation. Nevertheless, an injured employee, in seeking compensation for an injury at work, must state how and why the employer was in breach of their duty of care. It is not sufficient simply to suggest that the employer was negligent.

The legal duty owed to employees is a personal one, which may vary in relation to the person employed — a greater case for young, inexperienced, feeble-minded or physically disabled employees is required.

In his judgement in the Supreme Court decision in *Rodney v. The Rev. Fr. Philip Connolly PP* (December, 1986), Mr. Justice McCarthy said that liability should be tested in all cases by asking the simple question, "Was there a failure to take reasonable care?".

Broadly speaking, the legal position is that an employer will be liable to compensate an employee for any injury that takes place in the course of employment, if the injury or damage is the result of lack of care on the employer's part. This lack of care is referred to as negligence. In order to establish that the employer was negligent, the employee must do more than show simply that an injury was sustained at work.

This apparently self-evident principle had to be set out in the High Court case of *Johnson v. Gresham Hotel Limited* (November, 1986). In that case, the plaintiff, Mrs Johnson, was injured when she slipped at the top of a small flight of stairs in the kitchen area. She claimed that the cause of her slip and fall was that the floor at the top of the stairs was slippery. Stated simply, her case was that she would not have fallen if the floor had not been slippery. She could give no evidence to support that contention — indeed, there was substantial evidence to the contrary. Her claim failed. In the course of his judgement, Mr Justice Lynch gave a clear and helpful outline of the legal position as he saw it: "The duty of the defendants as employers is to take reasonable care for the safety of their employees in all circumstances of the case".

The employers are not insurers of the safety of the employees, that is to say, just because an accident happens to an employee does not mean that the employers are automatically liable to pay damages to the employee. As Henchy J. says in *Bradley v. CIE*:

> The law does not require an employer to ensure in all circumstances the safety of his workmen. He will have discharged his duty of care if he does what a reasonable and prudent employer would have done in the circumstances. The onus is on the injured worker to show that the employer was at fault in some way or other if the worker is to recover damages from the employer.

Mr. Justice Lynch then went on to consider the plaintiff's argument that there were precautions that should have been taken by the employer to prevent such accidents. He rejected this argument. He quoted with approval from the judgement of Mr. Justice Kingmill Moore in *Christie v. Odeon (Ireland) Limited* (1957):

> It is of little avail to show, after an accident has happened, that such and such a precaution might in the circumstances have avoided the particular accident. The matter must be considered as it would have appeared to a reasonable and prudent man before the accident. Such a man would take into account the probability of an accident, its probable seriousness should it occur, the practicability of measures to avoid it.
>
> An employer is not an insurer, and to make accidents impossible would often be to make work impossible. In the opinion of the Court there was no evidence of any failure on the part of the employer to take any precaution which a reasonable and prudent man would think it was folly to omit, nor was there evidence of any failure to exercise all reasonable care in providing a proper system of working.

A good example of what it is not reasonable to expect of an employer is provided by the case of *Bradley v. CIE* (1976). In that case, the claimant was a signalman whose duties included servicing lamps on certain signals at the top of vertical signposts. He reached the lamp by climbing the half-inch round steel ramps of an almost vertical steel ladder, which was attached to each signal post. Whilst descending the ladder his right foot slipped on a ramp, he fell to the ground and was injured.

Evidence was given that Mr. Bradley's fall would have been prevented, if an elliptical steel cage had been attached to the ladder so that he could go up and down in the cage. He claimed damages and the High Court jury found CIE had been negligent in failing to provide a safe place at work. He was awarded damages.

On appeal to the Supreme Court, it was held that the suggested steel cage had not been shown either to have been one which was commonly used by other railway operators, or one a reasonably prudent employer would think was obviously necessary for the protection of his employees. CIE's appeal was upheld.

An employer is not obliged to warn an employee of obvious risks, where the employee should have been aware of them himself. However, if an employer has created an unnecessary risk, it might not be sufficient to forewarn the employee of the danger and they may be liable if the employee is injured.

An employer may escape liability if the injury that occurred was beyond the bounds of reasonable foresight, and was the result of a combination of unlikely contingencies. Specific factors considered in assessing whether conduct is negligent include the probability of an accident occurring, the gravity of the threatened accident, the social utility of the defendant's actions and the total cost of eliminating risk.

Contractual Issues and the Existence of a Duty of Care

A complicated matter relates to the impact of the contractual relationship between the parties involved in a negligence action. This issue is considered in *McCann and Cummins v. Brinks Allied Ltd* (1997).

The plaintiffs were security men employed by Brinks and had sued both defendants in negligence in respect of injuries sustained when they were set upon by raiders while delivering cash to a branch of the Ulster Bank. Due to the layout of the particular bank branch, the nearest point which the security van could get to the bank door was 42 feet away and because there was an intervening car on the day of the raid the plaintiffs were obliged to park the security van some 47 feet from the bank door. The armed raid occurred while traversing that distance.

There had been three previous robbery incidents at the bank branch, and Brinks' personnel were involved on two of those occasions. The bank had in fact been requested by Brinks to provide a better and simpler access to the bank premises and had also been advised by an inspector in the Garda Síochana to provide better access.

The High Court, in awarding damages to the plaintiff, held that there was a failure on the part of Brinks to provide the plaintiffs with a safe system of work and to take all proper and reasonable precautions for their safety. No liability was imposed on the bank.

Brinks appealed to the Supreme Court and sought an indemnity or contribution in relation to the damages on the grounds that the bank should have been held to have been a concurrent wrongdoer. The issue to be decided was whether, in the particular circumstances of the case, the bank owed a duty of care to Brinks' employees.

The Supreme Court referred to the terms of the standard commercial agreement that existed between Brinks and the bank. The agreement did not contain a clause providing that Brinks would agree to assume the risk of any damage or injury to its employees. Brinks had, however, expressly "reserved to itself the absolute discretion as to the means, route and procedure to be followed in respect of the storage, guarding and transportation" of the cash. O'Flaherty J. stated that it was "clear that the bank, by engaging Brinks, were also avoiding a risk of injury or damage to their own employees to which they might otherwise be exposed if they had the task of transporting the cash". Brinks, his Lordship noted, had presumably exacted an appropriate commercial price. Given that the bank had engaged Brinks to carry out a hazardous activity, and one for which they would be responsible for the safety of their own staff, it would be wrong to infer that the relationship between the parties was such as to hold the bank as being in a position of owing a duty of care to the Brinks' employees.

The court held that the legal solution to the problem posed is to say that the parties reached an agreement that the risk should lie with Brinks to make sure that the cash was delivered safely and that was the extent of the bank's interest. In this case the contract between Brinks and the bank was a circumstance that prevented any duty of care arising from the part of the bank vis-à-vis the Brinks' employees. The appeal was dismissed.

ELEMENTS OF THE EMPLOYER'S DUTY OF CARE

The duty of care principle has already been defined in general terms. In the leading Supreme Court case of *Dalton v. Frendo* (1977), it was defined thus: "the duty of an employer towards a servant is to take reasonable care for the servant's safety in all circumstances of the case". However, it does not follow that the employer is an insurer of the employee's safety in all circumstances.

The courts have not laid down one unitary duty of care, which is owed by the employer to the employee, to be applied without regard to the employee's individual circumstances. The duty can be modified as a result of a number of factors including the individual's age, knowledge and experience. In general terms, there is no obligation on employers to warn employees of obvious risk. However, where an employer fails to remove an "unnecessary risk" which is created by the employer, the employer may be liable where injuries occur. Reasonable care, however, is all that is required of an employer who is not expected to foresee every risk that may possibly cause injury within the workplace. In the case of omissions, the same principles apply, in that the defendant may be found guilty of negligence as a result of omissions.

The duty of care is nowadays generally considered to fall into four sub-categories: to exercise reasonable care with regard to (a) the provision of a safe place of work, (b) the provision of proper equipment, (c) the provision of competent staff and (d) the provision of a safe system of work. It should be pointed out, however, that these do not represent four separate duties but one, namely, to take reasonable care for the employee's safety in the course of employment.

Safe Place of Work

An employer owes a duty to take reasonable care to ensure that the premises where employees are required to work are reasonably safe for the purpose of such work and the means of access/egress are likewise safe. This duty of care is a continuing one, which is personal to the employer and cannot be discharged by entrusting its performance to a competent independent contractor. It extends to safeguarding the employee not only against hazards arising from the static conditions of the premises, but also from dangers arising from activities and processes carried out on the premises. Case law illustrates that the scope of this duty includes questions of access and egress, systems of inspection and maintenance, dangerous floors, stairs and ladders, fencing, the demarcation of hazardous areas, protection from harmful processes, etc.

The employer owes a duty of care with regard to the safety of the premises of third parties on which they require their employees to work. This dimension of the duty is illustrated in *Dunne v. Honeywell Control Systems Ltd. and Virginia Milk Products Ltd (1991)*. The first defendant employed the plaintiff as a service technician. He was injured in a fall when descending a ladder, after repairing equipment at the second defendant's premises. The ladder was found to be dangerous for a variety of reasons, including the fact that it posed a problem for a worker to carry a tool case up and down.

The first defendant, although having no control over the second defendant's premises, was found to have been in breach of duty, as no warning was given to the plaintiff of the risk of carrying the tool case on the ladder. Barron J. held that the duty in respect of the provision of a safe place of work included an obligation to inspect places where an employee would be sent.

Courts are reluctant to impose a high standard in respect of premises not owned by employers, but which employees are required to visit. This is demonstrated in *Mulcare v. Southern Health Board* (1988). The plaintiff worked for the defendant, providing home help to elderly patients. She injured her ankle on an uneven floor in a patient's house and alleged negligence on the defendant's part in failing to examine the house in advance. She had previously visited the house on a number of occasions over a seven-year period without injury.

The claim was rejected on the grounds that the house was not sufficiently unsafe as to require the defendant to take action for the plaintiff's protection. The case raises an issue as to the balance between the social utility in providing the home help service and the risk to employees; it also raises a public policy issue on interference with property rights. The only practical measures open to the defendant would be either to insist that the patient carry out repairs or to withdraw service.

It should be pointed out, however, that the scope of the duty may vary in that it will depend on the circumstances. Cases that illustrate this sub-duty are presented in **Figure 2.1**.

Figure 2.1: Safe Place of Work Cases

In **Bradley v. CIE (1976)**, Mr. Bradley was a lineman. He was coming down the ladder of a signal pole, carrying a lamp, which he had just replaced on the pole. He fell from the pole and sustained a severe back injury. The expert engineer who gave evidence for Mr. Bradley said that the accident could have been prevented if there had been a safety cage around the signal pole. CIE pointed out that it had over 1,000 signal poles on the rail system, that other rail companies did not have safety cages on signal poles and that there had not been an accident on any of their poles for over ten years prior to this accident. The Supreme Court found that CIE had taken reasonable precautions in relation to signal poles. Bradley received no compensation; this decision may now be considered as less than good law.

McCarthy v. Southern Health Board (1995), McCarthy was employed by the Southern Health Board and was walking along a concrete footpath, which formed part of the roadway leading to a hospital building controlled by the defendant. McCarthy slipped and fell and sustained injuries. The incident occurred on a winter morning after a cold night and at the spot where McCarthy slipped, some water had accumulated and had frozen into an icy patch. The plaintiff had not noticed this prior to her fall. She claimed that the defendant was in breach of its duty of care to her as an employer and/or occupier. The High Court held that the duty of the defendant was to take reasonable care for the safety of people having lawful recourse to the hospital premises. The most careful employer/occupier could never ensure that there would not be an occasional accumulation of water in such weather conditions. The case was dismissed.

In *Dunne v. Dublin Cargo Handling Ltd.* (1996), the plaintiff was employed as a docker. On emerging from the hold of a ship, he was crushed by a crane operated by his employers. The crane was equipped with red flashing lights, which the plaintiff heard when he emerged from the hold, but, despite hearing this warning, he was injured. The judge struck out the claim. The defendants were not in breach of any duty owed to the plaintiff by failing to have a signals-person to alert the crane driver to passers-by. The defendants had a perfectly good system of work that was operating properly. Costs were awarded to the defendant, but stayed in the event of an appeal.

In *O'Donnell v. Glesson and Woods* (1996), the plaintiff, aged almost 60 at the time of the accident, was retained by the second defendant to do a short period of work involving the roofing of barns at the premises of the first named defendant. The plaintiff fell through a portion of the roof. He sustained fractured ribs and a partial collapse of the left lung. He spent two months in hospital and underwent a tracheotomy followed by a thoracotomy. Both procedures left considerable scarring. The plaintiff lost over three stone in weight during his hospital stay. Two and a half years after the accident, the plaintiff suffered a disabling stroke. The plaintiff had made a good recovery in the period prior to the stroke. On the ordinary principles of causation and probability, it would be unwarranted to attribute the sequel of the stroke to the accident. Generally damages were assessed on the basis of the accident alone. The judge awarded IR£40,000 (€50,789) for pain and suffering to date, allowing for the injuries, some limited provision for loss of earning and loss of social life and a further IR£15,000 (€19,046) for the ongoing repercussions that would have applied if he had not suffered a stroke, together with costs.

In *Dunne v. Lawter Products Ltd* (1997), the plaintiff's injuries arose out of an explosion in the defendant's factory. He suffered second-degree burns, which had healed but left his skin very sensitive and pale as a result of a loss of pigmentation. He also suffered a recurrence of a psoriasis complaint. The plaintiff also developed a phobia in relation to the factory. He was out of work for 18 months and was only able to return to work after psychiatric help. He suffered continual anxiety in relation to attending for work at the factory. The judge recognised that the plaintiff had been involved in a horrific accident and had been lucky to escape without worse injuries. He was quite satisfied that the phobia he experienced in relation to the factory was genuine. Although the plaintiff was likely to continue working for the foreseeable future, the judge recognised the possibility that he might not be able to cope and took this into account in awarding general damages. He awarded IR£27,500 (€34,917) to date and £32,500 (€41,266) into the future, and IR£21,000 (€26,664) special damages and costs.

In *Boyle v. Marathon Petroleum (Ireland) Ltd* (1995), the plaintiff was the employee of the defendant and worked on an offshore platform owned by the defendant. While working on the first floor of the platform, he was required to stoop, as the headroom was never more than four feet, ten inches. These cramped conditions were due to the presence of a mid-floor, which had been installed for safety reasons. Because the plaintiff was required to stoop, he was unable to see where he was going, and as a result, he injured himself by banging his head.

It was common sense that the platform was unsafe in that it would not be permissible to have such hazards and cramped conditions in a conventional factory. The plaintiff did not claim that the defendant was negligent, but that it was in breach of its statutory duty pursuant to s. 10(5) of the Safety, Health and Welfare (Offshore Installations) Act 1987. The High Court found that since the mid-floor was in constant use, and the lower floor was used much less frequently, the defendant had done all that was reasonably practicable, and dismissed the plaintiff's claim.

On appeal to the Supreme Court, the plaintiff submitted that it was not open to the trial judge to make such a finding since no evidence had been offered by the defendant as to the thought processes by which it had reached the decision to install the middle floor. The Supreme Court held, in dismissing the plaintiff's appeal, that the onus of proof rested on the defendant to show that it did what was reasonably practicable. That duty was more extensive than the common law duty of employers to exercise reasonable care in respect of their employees, and that since the statutory duty applied to "every workplace" on the installation, the defendant was entitled to balance the greater risk, which had been removed by the installation of the mid-floor, against the lower risk that had resulted in injury to the plaintiff.

In *Barclay v. An Post and Martin Murray* **(1998),** the plaintiff, a postman, was delivering post to an area of townhouses and apartments that were fitted with low letter-boxes at the bottom of each door, not more than a few inches off the ground. The plaintiff alleged that when he bent down to reach the low letter-box at a premises owned by the second named defendant, he suffered a sudden and agonising attack of pain in his lower back. The plaintiff was diagnosed with acute lower back strain, with possible lumbar disc damage. He was treated with analgesics, anti-inflammatory drugs and rest; he was fit to return to work in or about the end of August or the beginning of September 1993. On 21 October 1993 the plaintiff was employed on overtime to deliver post to a new development of 350 houses, again which had low letter boxes. The plaintiff suffered a recurrence of his back problems; a CT scan subsequently showed disc protrusion at two levels.

The court held that on balance the first named defendant had taken reasonable care to deal with the hazard of low letter-boxes in so far as it lay within its power. By 1976, it had succeeded in having proper height and other specifications for letter-boxes included in the Irish Standard, and in most recent times it had made sustained and genuine efforts to improve the situation both in urban and rural areas. In addition, it had provided a training course for its employees in manual handling, which warned of the hazards of bending and twisting. The first named defendant's duty of care toward the plaintiff included a duty to ensure that, in the short term after his illness, he did not take up duties that would put undue and extraordinary strain on his back and the delivery that the plaintiff undertook on 21 October 1993 was such a duty. In the circumstances, the defendant had not properly discharged the employer's reasonable duty of care in the case of the plaintiff's second injury and as such the first named defendant was liable for that injury.

Sources: Irish Law Times Report and Raymond Byrne, Senior Management Briefing, NIFAST Ltd.

Safe Plant and Equipment

An employer owes a duty of care in negligence to take reasonable care to ensure that employees are provided with suitable equipment to enable them to perform their work safely, and further, the employer owes a continuing duty to exercise reasonable care to ensure that the equipment is properly maintained. Like the previous sub-duty, it is a personal duty and cannot be delegated. The courts have given particular emphasis to this aspect of the employer's duty. Case law illustrates that the courts have held that where the employer fails to provide the necessary equipment and the employee, despite express prohibitions, proceeds with the job and sustains injury, the negligence of the employer in failing to provide such equipment will not be rendered too remote by the employee's negligence. Proper instructions are also important; it is not sufficient that the employer simply informs the employee that safety equipment is available. Rather, the employer must take reasonable steps, up to and including disciplinary action, to ensure that employees use such equipment. The courts have pointed out that the employer's duty under this heading covers the following issues:

- All equipment supplied must be safe. Such equipment must not short-circuit, explode, disintegrate, etc. (*Deegan v. Langan*, 1966).

- The employer must provide equipment that is essential for the safety of the employee (*Kennedy v. Hughes Dairy Ltd*. 1989).

- Equipment that is initially suitable may become dangerous due to inadequate maintenance. Thus, the employer's duty extends to taking *reasonable* measures to repair or replace deficient equipment. In *Burke v. John Paul & Co Ltd* (1967), the employer was found to be negligent where a blunt blade on cutting equipment caused the plaintiff to suffer a hernia, due to the exertion of additional force. *Barry v. Nitrigin Eireann Teo* (1983) stemmed from the fact that the effectiveness of the earmuffs, supplied to the plaintiff, deteriorated due to a deficiency in the spring mechanism that kept them in place. This neglect led to the failure to remedy the deficiency; the initial selection of the earmuffs need not necessarily have been negligent, as the deficiency may not have been discoverable.

- The case of *Heeney v. Dublin Corporation (1991)* involved the failure to provide breathing apparatus to fire-fighters. The defendant had begun introducing the equipment some eight years prior to the incident in question and its provision to the particu-

lar branch of the fire brigade had been authorised two years before the incident. Thus the failure to provide the equipment was
held to be negligent. The obligation here is not confined specifically to safety equipment, but extends to all equipment that prevents a foreseeable and avoidable hazard.

In considering cases involving suitable equipment, it is important to
remember that technology is rapidly advancing. What might be
suitable some years ago may now not be considered so. Furthermore, where an employer provides equipment that is designed to
safeguard employees, the employee must then be seen to use it.
There is a similar obligation under the Safety, Health and Welfare at
Work Act (1989), which is discussed in detail in **Chapter 3**. Failure
to use or to wear safety equipment could render employees liable
for contributory negligence.

There is a considerable body of case law on this issue. Cases
which illustrate the scope of this duty are presented in **Figure 2.2**.

Figure 2.2: Safe Plant and Equipment Cases

In ***Kennedy v. East Cork Foods Ltd.*** **(1973)**, Mr. Kennedy was adjusting a hopper that had come out of position. When performing
this check, his left hand made contact with blades in the dicing
machine underneath and he lost two fingers. The dicing machine
originally had a guard on it to prevent contact with its blades,
however this had been replaced with a removable guard. The Supreme Court held that the company had not complied with Section
(23) of the Factories Act 1955, in respect of the guarding of dangerous parts of machinery. Mr. Kennedy was awarded damages
which, in today's terms, would be over €100,000.

In ***Minister for Industry and Commerce v. Skerries Shirt Co. Ltd.***
(1959), the Minister had prosecuted the company under the Factories Act, 1955 for an accident on one of the company's steam shirt
pressing machines. The machine was operated by two people,
one of whom placed a shirt on it for pressing, while the other operated the dual buttons to put the machine in motion. The supervisor of this machine noticed that some threads seemed to be attached to the top-plate that came down on to the shirts for pressing. Without telling either of the two operators, she leaned across
the press to remove the threads. The person operating the buttons

could not see her and she pressed the operating buttons. The supervisor's hand was caught under the top-plate and it was later amputated because of the injuries to it. The High Court held that the supervisor's actions could not have been foreseen and, as a result, the company had exercised reasonable care. The case was therefore dismissed.

In *O'Meara v. O'Brien & Braun Medical Limited* (2000), the accident happened when a nurse, who had been trained to use an autoclave machine that sterilises medical instruments and had, the judge commented, "achieved expertise through frequent use", was about to open the machine. Steam emanated and caused severe burns to 19 per cent of her body area. As a consequence, she had to have skin grafts and plastic surgery. While she had, the judge noted, borne her misfortune with "very little complaint" and is likely to have a full functional recovery, she is going to suffer permanent "cosmetic disability". The injured nurse sued both the hospital where she was employed and the manufacturers of the machine. The judge held that the machine was supplied and maintained by the manufacturer, who "cannot but have been aware that frequent use was the very reason for having it". It had been acquired by the hospital so that the operating theatre could cope with a high volume of eye operations without substantial gaps between operations for sterilising the instruments.

Having expressed himself as being satisfied that the nurse had operated the machine in accordance with the manufacturer's instructions and that the hospital had not failed in its training obligations, the judge held that the manufacturers were responsible for the accident. He commended the company for the openness of its accident investigation procedure and for not looking at matters from a "legal perspective". However, he held, quoting their own findings, that as the technical data supplied with the machine did warn of the dangers of frequent use — that, on completion of a cycle, the machine should be allowed to cool for 20 minutes — the manufacturers were "responsible for the dangers which caused the accident". Assessing damages, the judge awarded the injured nurse IR£2,976 (€3,78) for special damages (out of pocket expenses), IR£75,000 (€95,230) for general damages (pain and suffering) to date and IR£25,000 (€31,743) for future general damages, making a total award of IR£102,976 (€130,752).

In ***Armstrong v William J Divan and Sons and Westpark Motor Company* (2000),** an accident happened when Mr. Armstrong, who was a helper on a delivery truck, was checking the truck. As he stepped onto the side crash bars on the passenger side behind the rear wheel, they collapsed under him, causing him to fall to the ground. He sued both his employer and the garage, which had recently repaired the truck. His employer told the court that, as far as it was concerned, the case was one for assessment of damages only, and that it did not accept responsibility for the defect in the repairs to the truck that caused the deliveryman's injuries. The employer argued that the accident happened because the garage to which it had sent the truck to repair the side crash bars, which had become loose and defective, had not done the job properly.

The employer contended that, by sending the truck to be repaired by the garage, which had satisfactorily carried out repairs on its fleet in the past, it had taken all reasonable care to ensure its employee's safety. The garage, however, disputed that it had been asked to repair the particular sidebar that collapsed. However, the President of the High Court, Mr. Justice Morris, held that the garage had been requested to carry out the particular repair and, having heard engineering evidence, he held that the repair had been carried out defectively. On the issue of compensation, Mr. Justice Morris awarded the injured deliveryman a total of IR£117,160 (€148,762) damages, made up of IR£40,000 (€50,789) for past general damages (pain and suffering), IR£60,000 (€76,184) for future general damages and IR£17,160 (€21,788) for loss of earnings. Then, holding that the deliveryman's employer was entitled to rely on the reputation of the garage that carried out the repairs — a garage described by the judge as reputable main dealers — he ordered that the garage should pay the compensation awarded.

Sources: Irish Law Times Report and Raymond Byrne, Senior Management Briefing, NIFAST Ltd.

Competent Staff

An employer owes a duty to exercise reasonable care in the employment of staff to ensure that they are reasonably competent to perform their work, so that in the course of their duties they will not expose other employees to unnecessary risk of injury. This aspect of the duty is important in the context of vicarious liability. For an injured employee's claim to succeed, the employee must demonstrate that the employer was negligent in initially employing an incompetent individual, or in maintaining in employment an employee who was initially competent or that the employee's present incompetence ought to have been known to the employer and appropriate action taken. It has been pointed out that this duty places a particular onus on employers:

- To clarify the personal qualities and skills required to do the particular job.

- To ensure that there is a systematic recruitment and selection procedure in operation.

- To provide the necessary training to do the job and provide special remedial training where necessary.

- To hire competent staff, including subordinates and supervisors.

For a number of reasons, fewer claims seem to be brought under the headings of incompetent staff than under the other three subduties. Three cases that were litigated involved some form of practical joke being played by one member of staff on another. Two cases that illustrate the application of this duty are presented in **Figure 2.3**.

Figure 2.3: Competent Staff Cases

In **Hough v. Irish Base Metals Ltd.** (1967), Mr. Hough was injured when jumping away from a gas fire that had been placed near him by another employee in the repair shop where they worked. It emerged during the case that such activities had started happening only shortly before the accident. The employees considered the "lark" to be a "bit of fun" and it had not been reported previous to management, who would have had difficulty in detecting it because it would usually be over in an instant. The Supreme Court held that the company had met the standard of supervision required. Therefore, no compensation was awarded in this case.

In **Barrett v. Anglo Irish Beef Producers Ltd.** (1989), Barrett was employed as a fork-lift driver. He was injured when the truck fell over. He had just taken over from another employee who was inexperienced in the operation of the truck and who parked it on a dangerous slope. One of the forks had either been allowed to move inwards or to be wrongly positioned.

The High Court imposed liability on the basis that the company had permitted the inexperienced co-worker to use the truck and park it in a dangerous place. The Court reduced damages by 25 per cent because Barrett had attempted to continue the process of tipping the load when he could have lowered it and moved the truck to a safer position as well as checking the forks.

Sources: Irish Law Times Report and Raymond Byrne, Senior Management Briefing, NIFAST Ltd.

Safe Systems of Work

The concept of a safe system of work includes all activities that are normally and reasonably incidental to the nature of work. It covers work methods procedures and management practices. The standard of care is no higher than that to be expected of an ordinary prudent employer, therefore employers will have met the requirements of the law if they can demonstrate that their system of production is in accordance with the accepted good practices of the particular trade.

An employer is generally not legally responsible simply because the accident happened to the employee during the course of the employment. In the case of *Dalton v. Frendo* (1977), the Irish Supreme Court considered a claim brought by Dalton, a builder and carpenter, who was employed in 1975 under a contract of service to put some cords into windows, erect a toilet and build a timber partition as well as cutting or lopping trees that were growing in Frendo's garden. Dalton arrived at Frendo's home with an electric saw for the purpose of cutting trees. In order to carry out the work, Dalton requested a loan of Frendo's ladder. This was a step-ladder made of tubular steel. Dalton took the ladder and placed it near a row of trees that he intended cutting. He placed it in such a way that two of the legs were on the flower-bed and the other two were on the lawn. Dalton continued lopping the branches for about an hour when the ladder swayed to one side because two of the legs had sunk into the ground. He lost his balance with the result that the saw made contact with his hand and he was injured. The judge held:

What is reasonable care for the safety of a workman must be measured by such risks and hazards as are known or ought to be known by those in control or those which can reasonably be identified. This must be considered in the circumstances of each case having regard to the nature of the work involved, the place where it takes place, and the age, experience and skill of the workman. But the employer is not an insurer.

The court found that Dalton should have positioned the ladder with greater care, given that he was working with a potentially dangerous piece of equipment. The employer could not reasonably be held responsible for the accident. The court therefore found against Dalton.

The duty to take reasonable care and to provide a reasonably safe system of work is not well understood. It is generally accepted that it essentially means forethought on the part of the employer of the hazards that may reasonably be anticipated in carrying out any particular job and an action, to the extent that reasonable care requires, to eliminate the hazard. In practical terms it means the organisation of the workforce, the workplace and equipment, giving necessary instructions, warnings and supervision so as to secure the safety of employees.

The Supreme Court decision in *McSweeney v. J.S. McCarthy* (2000) has set out the issues to be considered when assessing whether a system of work is safe. The court was hearing an appeal against the dismissal in the High Court of a claim by a painter that he was injured when he fell from a ladder that he was climbing. The painter, who worked for a firm of painting contractors, had been painting pipes in a factory. Ducts obscured the pipes and, in order to gain access, the painter had to move his ladder and place it against ducting that was in front of the pipes. The top of the duct was 12 feet, two and a half inches from the floor. To gain access, the painter would have to climb onto and over the duct, having first mounted the ladder. The painter placed the ladder against the ducting and, having looked for, but not found, the foreman (the only colleague working on the premises with him), whom he was going to ask to hold the ladder, he started to climb. The ladder was unsecured both at the top and the bottom. When he reached the top of the ladder and was in the process of getting onto the duct, the ladder slipped and the painter fell to the ground and sustained injuries.

The High Court judge held that the painter, as an experienced worker, was to blame for the accident and dismissed his claim. In considering the painter's appeal, the Supreme Court noted that both parties accepted that the ladder constituted an unsafe means of access to the place where the work was to be done. Somebody should have been at the foot of the ladder holding it while the painter climbed it. The Court also noted that the foreman had given the painter no instructions on securing the ladder.

Having held that it is the employer's common law duty to provide "a reasonably safe system of work", Mr. Justice Murray, who delivered the Court's judgement, said that "there are many factors which come into play" in assessing whether a system of work is reasonably safe or not. He argued that "a safe system of work is not susceptible to a single all-embracing definition". He defined a system as "a set of procedures according to which something is to be done". The organisation of the procedures "involves foresight and forethought on the part of the employer".

As it is the employer "who assigns the work", the employer must have addressed in advance the foreseeable risks inherent in the work to be done. If the work is highly complex or dangerous, the employer may be under a duty to establish an elaborate system, which is strictly supervised and enforced. In other circumstances, "a mere warning or specific instruction may suffice". Turning his attention to the suggestion that an experienced and competent employee would be fully aware of the dangers of the task, Mr. Justice Murray said that, while experience and competence is a relevant factor, the employer cannot use it as an excuse for ignoring the duty to ensure there is a safe system of work. Nor can the employer leave it up to an experienced worker to devise a safe system or to decide whether there should be such a system.

Commenting on the employee's duty to co-operate, Mr. Justice Murray said "co-operation is a mutual matter" and could "include a refusal by an employee to apply a system of work",but, as there was no system, that did not apply in this case. He also held that the employer was in breach of its duty to have a person holding the ladder.

The Supreme Court overturned the High Court judge's decision. The Court held that the painter's employer failed to provide a safe system for work. The foreman failed to:

- Consider how the work should be carried out and the difficulties that might arise, which would expose the painter to the risk of injury.

- Give the painter instructions on securing the ladder.

- Tell the painter where to contact him if he needed him to hold the ladder.

The Court suggested that one means of addressing the problem would have been for the foreman to tell the painter to postpone the work until he had located the foreman to hold the ladder. However, while the court held that the employer was responsible for the accident, they held that the painter contributed by ascending the ladder, knowing it was not secured and that no one was holding it. "As an experienced workman", he "was not taking reasonable care for his own safety", the judge said. The Court held that accordingly he was in breach both of common law of care and of the duty of self-care imposed by the Factories Act, 1955 (s125(7)). The injuries suffered by the painter were, Mr Justice Murray concluded, caused partly by his employer's negligence and partly his own lack of care. The Court apportioned liability for the accident on the basis that the employer was 60 per cent and the painter 40 per cent responsible.

Figure 2.4: Safe Systems of Work Cases

Dunleavy v. Glen Abbey Ltd. (1992). Approximately half of Mr. Dunleavy's duties involved carrying and lifting loads in the company's factory premises. He was lifting a 35 kg carton with another person, when the other person let go. Mr. Dunleavy was jolted by the weight and sustained a back injury. It emerged that Dunleavy had not been trained in manual handling procedures. The judge found that the company was in breach of the Manual Handling Regulations (1972) (since replaced by the General Application Regulations (1993)). The judge awarded IR£15,000 (€19,046) compensation, because the injury was not severe.

In *Brady v. Beckmann Instruments Inc.* (1986), Mr. Brady contracted dermatitis while working for the company. The company argued that it had put in place an effective local exhaust ventilation system. It regularly monitored exposure levels to the substance that gave rise to the dermatitis and its records revealed that the level of exposure was 20 times less than the acceptable US exposure level, or Threshold Limit Value (TLV), for this substance. Evidence was presented that there was no known previous case of dermatitis where there was such a low level of exposure. In the circumstances, the Supreme Court decided that the company had taken reasonable precautions and no compensation was awarded.

In *Kenefick v. J.A. Wood Ltd.* (1975), Kenefick was employed by the defendant company as a storeman. In the course of his work, he saw that a toolbox left on the ground was obstructing access to a storeroom. Bending down and attempting to lift the toolbox, he felt a jerk on his back and suffered an injury. He claimed that the defendant was in the breach of its duty of care and also in breach of statutory duty under the Factories Act (1955) and the Manual Labour Maximum Weights and Transport Regulations Act (1972), in failing to provide instruction and training in safe methods of lifting weights. The High Court held that, while the plaintiff's work did not involve much lifting of heavy weights, it was nonetheless reasonably apparent that he would be required to lift heavy objects from time to time. The defendant was in breach of its duty of care to the plaintiff and in breach of its statutory duty. The defendant was found to be 85 per cent liable.

In *Walsh v. Securicor Ireland Ltd* (1989), Walsh was employed as a driver with a security firm and was ambushed by armed robbers and injured. He had travelled the same route between 10 a.m. and 10.20 a.m. every Thursday, delivering large amounts of cash. He had done this for at least seven years. The High Court found the defendant liable on the basis that it was not very sensible to use the same route at the same time for so many years. The Court considered the view that it was necessary to adhere rigidly to particular times and noted that the defendants appeared not to have ever considered the issue of changing it.

In *McDermid v. Nash Dredging & Reclamation Co.* (1991), the plaintiff was untying ropes connecting a tug boat to a dredger. The system of work required the captain of the tug to wait until the plaintiff knocked twice on the wheelhouse door before starting off (in order to ensure that the plaintiff was clear of the ropes). The plaintiff was seriously inured when the captain took off without waiting for the knocks, resulting in the plaintiff being dragged into the sea as the ropes tangled around his legs. The failure to implement a suitable designed system of work constituted a breach of the employers' duty of care for the plaintiff's safety.

In *O'Donnell v Minister for Defence* (1992), the plaintiff, a private in the army, was taking part in a "shooting plates" competition, which involved both shooting and running. In the course of competing, he fell and sustained serious injuries to his mouth and a less serious injury to his shoulder. It was claimed on behalf of the plaintiff that the starting system was faulty in that he was left unsure of what to do and that his attention was diverted from watching where he was running, hence causing him to fall. However, in examination, the plaintiff claimed that the cause was the uneven terrain. The judge dismissed the claim. The method of starting the competition by blowing a whistle was acceptable and no one claimed that they could not hear the whistle. In addition, the plaintiff had specifically stated that there was something wrong with the ground that had caused him to stumble. However, the Finner camp, in Bundoran, Co. Donegal, in which the competition took place, had been used by the army for this purpose for generations. The ground was uneven, but requiring the battalion to conduct its competition there did not amount to negligence. He awarded costs to the defendant.

In *Murphy v. Slane Meat Packaging Co.* (1996), the plaintiff cut himself across the forearm in the course of his work as a boner. He spent eight days in hospital and underwent three months of physiotherapy. He complained of loss of power, grip and pain in cold weather. There was a suggestion that the plaintiff did not go back to work because he was told that he would not be welcome if he brought an action against his employers, but the judge rejected this. The judge also criticised the fact that the surgeon who had treated the plaintiff originally was not called to give evidence and that the plaintiff's expert witnesses did not discuss the plaintiff's injuries with that surgeon.

Liability was admitted. With regard to the extent of the injuries, the judge accepted the evidence of the defendant's medical experts, that the nerves in the plaintiff's arm were not affected, which suggested that the injury was not particularly deep. The judge did not accept that grip would be affected nor that cold weather should cause pain. General damages of IR£7,000 (€8,888) were awarded to take into account the period of hospitalisation and the period he was out of work on the basis that he should have been fit to work by Easter 1993. Special damages, including lost wages to April 1993, amounted to IR£4,050 (€5,142) reduced by IR£800 (€1,015) for social welfare, resulting in a total award of IR£10,250 (€13,014) damages, together with costs.

In *Lennon v. Midland Health Board* (2000), the plaintiff was employed in a hospital laundry. Initially she was assigned to light duties but later was transferred to heavier work, taking over a task formerly performed by a male. She was assigned to working on large washing machines. This involved loading heavy laundry, which when washed could weigh up to three times more than its dry weight, removing the washed load from the machines, placing it on a trolley and bringing it to drying machines which had to be loaded. The woman complained that, because of the repetitive nature of the work, she suffered a serious back injury.

She commenced work in the laundry in June 1984 and resigned in September 1987. She first complained about suffering back pain in October 1986 and was certified by her GP as being unfit for work. She returned to work but was unable for the work and was again off work with a doctor's certificate. Her doctor referred her to a specialist, who reported that he "could find nothing seriously wrong". She went back to work but refused to do heavy work because she did not feel up to it and she resigned. Subsequently she went to England and worked in what the judge described as "a sedentary job". In 1992 her English GP referred her to a specialist, who found "an internal disc disruption". Following this she had two operations, but still she claimed continued to suffer back pain. In 1993 she commenced proceedings against her former employer, claiming that the work she had to do was too heavy for a female and that she got "virtually no training". A consultant engineer gave evidence that the work was too hard for a female employee.

Defending the claim, the employer presented evidence that employees were trained by being put to work with the person who was about to leave the job. This way employees could, it was argued, familiarise themselves with the workings of the particular machine. Dismissing the claim, the judge held that the injury was caused by the repetitive nature of the work but that, in the circumstances, the training provided was adequate and accordingly the employee's back injury was not attributable to any negligence on the employer's part.

In *Heeney v. Dublin Corporation* (1991), Heeney (deceased) had been employed as a station officer with a fire brigade. He died in October 1985 after inhaling gases while fighting a fire in a building without breathing apparatus. It was established in evidence that the Fire Authority had in 1977 started to provide crews with breathing apparatus and to organise courses for the training of firemen. By 1984 all permanent fire brigade employees had been issued with breathing apparatus but the fire brigade in question had not received the apparatus or any training. The deceased employee had made enquiries about when these issues would be dealt with. The High Court held that the Fire Authority ought to have provided breathing apparatus for its full-time crews before it had done so and the brigade should not have been allowed to go into buildings without breathing apparatus in cases where the station officer would have required their use. The absence of proper instruction was also wrong.

Sources: Irish Law Times Report and Raymond Byrne, Senior Management Briefing, NIFAST Ltd.

Employers' Liability and Stress

Although the courts have long recognised an employer's liability for physical injury suffered by employees as a result of the employer's negligence, the issue of whether employers were liable for mental injury arising from continuous exposure to stressful circumstances in the workplace was heretofore a grey area. However, there is evidence that in recent years the courts and the legislature have begun to come to grips with the notion that an employer can be liable for mental injury caused as a result of stress at work.

The question being asked by many in the legal profession is whether employers are liable in situations where employees suffer psychiatric harm as a result of their work situation. Given the recency of the issue, it is perhaps best to consider the issues at stake with reference to a number of landmark cases that give an insight into the thinking of the courts today.

In the leading British case of *Walker v. Northumberland County Council* (1992), the judges' view of the issue was as follows:

> Whereas the law on the extent of this duty had developed
> almost exclusively in cases involving physical injury to the
> employee as distinct from injury to his mental health, there
> is no logical reason why risk of psychiatric damage should
> be excluded from the scope of the employers' duty of care.

This suggests that the courts are willing to accept that employers do owe a duty to their employees to protect them from both physical and psychiatric harm.

In this case the plaintiff worked for the defendants as an Area Social Services Officer, with considerable responsibilities, in the highly populated area of Blyth Valley. The area had an exploding population with a very high incidence of child abuse, which was the area of responsibility of the plaintiff. He had complained to his superiors over a number of years of the lack of resources available to carry out the job, but this proved unsuccessful. Mr. Walker suffered a nervous breakdown in November 1986 and was off work until March 1987. After returning to work, he again took leave as a result of a more serious breakdown in September of the same year. The Council dismissed Mr Walker on the grounds of permanent ill health. Mr. Walker sued the Council for breach of its duty of care and while the Council admitted that it owed a duty to provide him with a safe system of work and to protect him from reasonably foreseeable risks, it rejected the claim that it was reasonably foreseeable that his work would expose him to a risk of mental injury. The High Court found in favour of the plaintiff and stated that the defendant was in breach of its duty in relation to the second breakdown. The Court pointed out that employers owe a duty to employees not to cause them psychiatric damage by the volume or character of the work that they are required to perform. They saw no logical reason why risk of injury to the employee's mental health should fall outside the scope of the concept of an employer's duty of care.

A number of other cases have followed the thinking of the *Walker* case. The case of *Petch v. Customs and Excise Commission* (1993) further reinforced this individual approach, although in this case the plaintiff was unsuccessful as the Court found that it was not reasonably foreseeable that the plaintiff would suffer a mental breakdown, because all along he had shown himself to be able to cope with the workload and had been enthusiastic to take on more work.

In the Australian case of *Gillespie v. Commonwealth of Australia* (1991), the judge, referring to an employer's liability for work-induced psychiatric injury, pointed out:

> Foreseeability for present purposes is to be considered only in so far as the degree of remoteness of harm sustained by the plaintiff set the perimeters of the steps that a reasonable person in the position of the defendant would have taken to reduce the risk to the extent that any unnecessary risk was eliminated. In practical terms, this means that the plaintiff must show that the defendant unreasonably failed to take such steps as would reduce the risk to what was a reasonable, that is, a sociably acceptable level. It may be that this takes the court into an area of value judgement for which the inscrutability of a jury verdict may provide a more appropriate means of expression.

Commentators argue that the approach of the Irish courts to psychiatric injury caused by stress in the workplace is unclear. However, in applying the duty of care test as set down in *Ward v. McMaster & Louth County Council* (1985), there is no reason why the Irish courts could not and would not follow the approach of their UK brethren. There is evidence that the Irish courts have applied the identical principle in cases concerning employers' liability for physical injury and indeed have limited the duty in exactly the same way. Furthermore, in *Eithne Curran v. Cadbury Ireland Limited* (1999), Judge McMahon, referring to the *Walker* decision, stated that there was no reason to suspect that our courts would not follow this line of authority if it came before them. Similarly, in the case of *Saehan Media Ireland Limited v. A Worker* (1999), the Labour Court stated that "work-related stress is recognised as a health and safety issue and employers have an obligation to deal with instances of its occurrence which are brought to their attention".

An important issue in the context of stress relates to the term of the employee's contract. The issue at stake in the *Walker* case was whether the implied term of his contract, which was that the Hospital Authority would take reasonable care for his health and safety, took precedence over the express term of his contract that stated that he must work a minimum of 40 hours per week and be available for a further 48 hours of overtime, which he claimed was having a detrimental effect on his mental health. An objective legal view would be that the implied terms could not override the express terms of the contract, yet the appeal trial judges disagreed on this point of law, and were of the opinion that each employee had different stamina levels and, where the employer knew or ought to have known that, by requiring an employee to work the hours he did, they exposed him to the risk of injury, then they should not have required him to work those hours. The case was eventually settled out of court but highlights the issue of the subjectivity of the area and also the conflict between implied and express contractual terms in such cases.

The "eggshell" rule is pertinent here because it points out that victims must be taken as employers find them, even though the extent of the injuries was not foreseeable. In other words, if the employer is aware that an employee is susceptible to mental ill health, they cannot avoid liability on the basis that the extent of their injuries was not reasonably foreseeable. It should be noted, however, that the employer must be aware of the particular susceptibility and, if this is not the case, no liability arises. In the case of Mr. Walker, the defence successfully argued this by pointing out that social workers in his position are generally not susceptible to breakdown and, therefore, the Council could not have foreseen the initial breakdown and thus was not liable.

In the aforementioned *Curran v. Cadbury Ireland Limited* (1999), referring to section 2 of the Safety, Health and Welfare at Work Act, 1989, which defines personal injury as including "any disease or any impairment of a person's physical or mental condition", Judge McMahon made it clear that an employer is under the obligation to avoid both physical and mental injury in the workplace. In the case in question, an employee in a chocolate factory restarted a machine, which had been stopped, without notification. After realising that there was a fitter in the machine at the time, the worker thought she had killed the fitter or at least caused him serious injury.

Mrs. Curran's evidence was that, when she arrived at the scene where the fitter was, she was "blinded with panic". Judge McMahon held that the employer was in breach of the duty of care it owed to its employees, that it was reasonably foreseeable that the breach could cause to the employee a great shock which could easily result in a psychiatric illness, and that psychiatric illness was in fact caused.

The judgement in the *McGrath v. The Garda Commissioner* (1998) case is interesting in that it suggests that claims for stress may now be successful if the employer's negligence is established and the employee contests that anxiety was caused by that negligence. Mr. McGrath, a garda, had been suspended following failure to account for monies received. He had challenged the various attempts made to hold internal disciplinary investigations, and having succeeded, he then disputed the validity of his suspension. Mr. McGrath made four claims in total, including a claim for damages for personal injuries and for the loss of standing in the community arising from his suspension. Judge Morris referred to the established negligence of the defendant and their failure to carry out their appropriate duties with reasonable care. Mr. McGrath was awarded IR£40,000 (€50,789) in compensation for the stress, anxiety and general disruption to his enjoyment of life. Most importantly, no reference was made in judgement as to whether the stress and anxiety was reasonably foreseeable either generally or in relation to Mr. McGrath. Furthermore, no reference was made to medical evidence or any medical or psychiatric illness.

Nervous Shock

The cases of *Alcock v. Chief Constable of South Yorks* (1991) and *McHugh v. Minister for Defence and the Attorney General* (1999) provide the most recent guidelines in relation to cases involving nervous shock. The judgement of the House of Lords in the Alcock case highlights a number of issues in relation to duties owed to individuals. A duty will only arise (in addition to psychiatric harm being foreseeable) where the plaintiff is a rescuer, where he feared for his own life, witnessed a trauma, arrived on the scene shortly afterwards and has proximate relationship with the victim, or was a "conduit pipe", which means that they were put in the position of believing that they had been, or were about to be, the cause of another's death or injury as the result of the defendant's negligence and suffered shock-induced illness as a result. Bystanders are generally excluded and damages can only be recouped where a recognised psychiatric illness is diagnosed. Finally, where shock causes physical injury damages are recoverable.

This ruling seeks to categorise those people who are entitled to recover damages; however, in reality, it is very difficult to distinguish between mere bystanders and witnesses to a traumatic event. It also poses problems in the sense that an individual who may not have been a rescuer or have feared for their own safety, but were exposed to traumatic events, will as a result of this ruling be unable to seek damages (*Robertson and Rough v. Forth Road Bridge Joint Board* (1995)).

The Supreme Court held in the *Kelly v. Hennessy (1995)* case that, in order to recover damages for nervous shock, it must be established that (a) the claimant actually suffered a recognisable psychiatric illness; (b) the illness was shock-induced; (c) the nervous shock was caused by an act or omission on the part of the defendant; (d) the shock sustained by a claimant must be by reason of actual or apprehended physical injury to the claimant or a person other than the claimant; (e) the plaintiff was owed a duty of care by the defendant not to cause him or her a reasonably foreseeable injury in the form of nervous shock as opposed to personal injury in general.

In 1993, the High Court had awarded Mrs. Kelly IR£35,000 (€44,440) for nervous shock to date, and IR£40,000 (€50,789) for the future as a result of her husband and one of her daughters suffering permanent brain damage after being involved in a car crash caused by the negligence of Mr. Hennessy. Mrs. Kelly was not involved in the crash but was informed of it when telephoned by a family relative. Appealing this decision in 1995, Mr. Hennessy contended that, while he accepted that Mrs. Kelly was suffering from post-traumatic stress disorder, it was not a psychiatric illness of the kind that gave rise to damages for nervous shock. It was also contended that the post traumatic stress disorder had been caused by the strain placed on Mrs. Kelly of caring for her family rather than the shock attributable to the accident, and that he did not owe a duty of care to her.

The Supreme Court dismissed this appeal on all grounds, finding that Mrs. Kelly suffered immediate nervous shock after the incident, which was aggravated upon visiting her family in hospital immediately after the accident. While Mrs. Kelly was not a participant in the accident, she was injured as a consequence of the event, and as such, was a secondary victim.

The facts of the *McHugh v. Minister for Defence and the Attorney General* (1999) case are interesting. The point about McHugh is that he did not sue for the PTSD he suffered as a result of a number of incidents. He sued because he alleged that the army had been negligent in failing to recognise and treat the symptoms of PTSD that he was suffering from. As a result, instead of recovering from the condition, it became chronic.

During November 1992, McHugh was exposed to a life-threatening incident that involved the unexpected and negligent discharge of a gun by a sergeant who had been standing beside him. He suffered a severe immediate reaction and was very distressed. Early in January 1993, he came upon a jeep that appeared to have been blown up and to have bodies around it. Later, in February, he was part of a team that had to perform hazardous duties and who were exposed to the sight of mutilated and chopped-up corpses.

McHugh was deeply affected by these incidents. His condition was noticed by his fellow soldiers and NCOs and was brought to the attention of the platoon commander. When McHugh returned home in April 1993, he saw a commandant but was not referred for medical treatment. Only when he told his sergeant, late in 1993, that he was going to leave the army was he referred for treatment. The army psychiatrist he attended diagnosed that he was suffering from PTSD.

Rejecting a defence claim that McHugh should have identified his condition, Mr. Justice Budd, who had heard evidence that he army had been aware of PTSD problems since 1990, held that they had failed in their duty to take reasonable care to ensure the safety and health of their employees. He awarded McHugh IR£218,900 (€277,945), including sums of IR£65,000 (€82,532) for pain and suffering to date, IR£40,000 (€50,789) for future pain and suffering and IR£67,593 (€85,825) for loss of past earnings and pension losses.

The rules as set out in this judgement and in other Irish cases would indicate that, to pursue a claim for PTSD, a person must ei-

ther themselves be the victim of the injury, which should have resulted from a traumatic event, or they should have close ties of
love and affection with the injured person. They should have witnessed the incident that caused the injury, or come across the injured person and/or incident very shortly after it occurred.

Claims for Personal Injury and Time Limits

The Statutes of Limitations (1957-1991) provide that a claim for
personal injury as a result of negligence, nuisance or breach of
duty must be brought within three years from the date of cause of
action occurring or the date of knowledge, if later, of the person
injured. Personal injuries include any disease and any impairment
of a person's physical or mental condition. For minors (people under 18 years of age) the claim may be brought up to three years
after their 18th birthday — up to their 21st birthday.

Occasionally a person may contract a disease that is slow to
manifest itself, or a comparatively trivial incident may lead after
many years to epilepsy or some cancerous condition. For example, in cases of pneumoconiosis and asbestosis, substantial injury
to the lungs may be in existence for years before it is actually discovered.

The Statute of Limitations (Amendment) Act, 1991 entitles a
person to make a claim up to three years following the diagnosis of
a condition in the circumstance above. The "date of knowledge"
(Section 2 of the Statute of Limitations (Amendment) Act, 1991) refers to the date on which the individual first had knowledge of the
following facts:

- That the individual actually had been injured.

- That the injury in question was significant.

- That the injury was attributable in whole or in part to the act or
  omission which is alleged to constitute negligence, nuisance or
  breach of duty.

- The identity of the defendant(s).

- If it is alleged that the act or omission was by another person,
  the identity of that person and the facts supporting the bringing
  of an action against that person.

The "knowledge" includes what the injured person should know from facts that are observable or ascertainable to that person with medical or other expert advice. A person has to take all reasonable steps to obtain that knowledge.

In cases where a claim is statute-barred, there is nothing prohibiting the person bringing their claim because the argument of time limits is a defence to a claim. There is the possibility that the defence may not be allowed.

If a person dies within the three-year limitation period, such proceedings for alleged injury must be brought within three years from date of death, or from the date that the personal representative became aware of the facts of the case, whichever is the later.

VICARIOUS LIABILITY AND THE EMPLOYEE/EMPLOYER RELATIONSHIP

A generally accepted principle of the application of the law of tort is that the person who commits a wrong is liable for its consequences. However, there may be others who are jointly and severally liable. This notion is called the principle of "vicarious liability". Vicarious liability, in essence, means that an employer may be liable for the wrongs committed by employees during the course of their employment. The word "vicarious" derives from the same Latin word as *vicar*. Employers cannot do all the work that needs to be done so they use the services of employees; the employer acts vicariously through the employee. Part of the reasoning for such a principle in law arises from the fact that, in the case of an employee injuring someone while at work, in many instances suing the employee is not worthwhile; the employer usually possesses the greater resources and insurance or both.

As a general rule, employers are vicariously liable for anything done by their employees during the course of the employer's business. Therefore, if an employee causes injury to a third party, that party may take action in respect of injury directed against the employer. This is a very broad rule, so the courts have put some restrictions on it.

Employers will be liable to third parties with whom they usually have had no direct contact, in situations where they cannot be said to have any personal blame, merely because they have employed someone who committed a tort. This means that the injured party can seek redress from the employer in the form of compensation even if they cannot identify the individual, or if the individual has fled the jurisdiction.

Some of the more important principles that the courts have developed in respect of vicarious liability are now considered.

Control

Reference has already been made to the control test in **Chapter 1**. The essence of the test is to establish whether the employer has control over both "what" and "how" aspects of the employee's performance. Where the employer does have control in respect of what the employee does and the methods utilised, the employer may be held vicariously liable for the acts of employees in their employment. In most instances, the employer will be liable for the torts committed by employees in the course of employment.

The use of the control test does have limitations and an effective example of this may be seen where employees are on loan to another employer or where the employee is so skilled that it would be impossible for the employer to exercise control over how the work is performed.

Generally, where an employee is on loan, the initial employer is considered the vicariously liable one (*Mersey Docks and Harbour Board v. Coggins and Griffiths* (1947)). The original employer bears the burden of proving that responsibility for the torts of the employee has shifted to the second employer.

In respect of highly skilled employees, the employer may be held to be vicariously liable for the wrongs of the employee even though they are not in control of how the employee carries out the work. Where the employee who carries out the work is a professional or is a trained person who has worked for many years to gain particular skills that the employer probably does not possess, it is very difficult to prove that the employer actually has "control". What became known as the "hospital cases" clearly demonstrates the difficulties in relation to those employees who are so highly skilled that it would be impossible for their employer, i.e. the health boards, to have control over what and how work was carried out.

The case of *O'Donovan v. Cork Co. Council* (1967) involved an action against a surgeon and an anaesthetist who were employed by the County Council. The plaintiff claimed negligence and although the Council denied negligence it did not contest that it could be held vicariously liable for the actions of the medical staff.

The Existence of a Contract of Service

In order for an employer to be vicariously liable for the wrongful acts of employees, a contract of service must exist. As already outlined in **Chapter 1**, there are two types of contract of employment: a contract of service and a contract for service. For the purpose of vicarious liability, the employer is only liable for the acts of those employees who have a contract of service. There are, however, certain circumstances where an employer may be liable for the wrongdoing of independent contractors. The employer may be liable for the acts of independent contractors where the employer:

- Failed to meet a statutory safety and health obligation.

- Was negligent in the selection of an independent contractor.

- Where the act in question is a highly dangerous one such as electrical work or demolishing a building.

- The act was subject to strict liability imposed by the law.

The law takes the view that, in these cases, ultimate responsibility cannot be delegated to an independent contractor.

The Scope of the Employment

The wrongful act must be committed within the scope of employment. This could mean, for example, that the employer would not be liable for the wrongful acts of employees who work from nine to five, five days a week, if the wrongdoing is committed at the weekends.

Generally, if an employee acts outside the scope of their employment the employer will not be vicariously liable. In *Duff v. Orr* (1941), a butcher and meat salesman was required to escort his employer on delivery rounds. While on the rounds on one particular day, the employee took the van and injured the plaintiff. The court held that this activity was outside the scope of his employment and therefore the defendant could not be held vicariously liable. Furthermore, if an employee goes on a "frolic" of their own unconnected with the employment, their employer will not be liable. In the case of *O'Connell v. Bateman* (1932), an employee borrowed his employer's lorry after work to visit his parents and subsequently was involved in an accident. The court held that this was a "frolic" of the employee and therefore the employer could not be held vicariously liable. The word "frolic" has been defined as "an activity which is totally unrelated to what you were employed to do".

Employers who forbid certain types of behaviour, the result of which is an injury to a third party, do not automatically exonerate themselves from liability (*Strong v. McAuley, McIlroy and Co. Ltd.* (1929)). There is, however, some case law to suggest that where forbidden behaviour by an employee results in injury to a third party, the courts may view the activity as outside the scope of employment and therefore liability could not rest with the employer; it is only one of the many factors that may be taken into account by the courts. Finally, employers are not generally liable for the criminal acts of their employees.

The concept of vicarious liability presents major problems for employers. The substance of the doctrine is that, if an employee, whilst acting in the course of employment, negligently injures another employee or an employee of an outside contractor working on a site, or even a member of the public, the employer will be liable for the personal negligence. Vicarious liability is the basis on which most claims for personal injury causing accidents are successful. **Figure 2.5** presents examples of cases on vicarious liability.

Figure 2.5: Vicarious Liability Cases

Kennedy v. Taltech Engineering Co. Ltd (1989). Kennedy suffered injury as a result of a light-hearted prank that occurred on the factory floor at the end of the shift. Kennedy, a teenager, was a machine operator and, as he was leaving the factory floor, he put on his jacket which had a large crisp bag protruding from the pocket. He was called over by the supervisor, who was talking to another employee who was holding a large metal plate with sharp edges. The supervisor took the bag from the pocket and, by way of reflex action, Kennedy grabbed the bag and hit his hand against the metal plate. The High Court held that the supervisor's negligence led to the accident and imposed liability on the employer.

Reilly v. Ryan **(1991).** Reilly had gone to the defendant's city-centre public house to talk to the manager. He was standing close to the bar when a man wearing a balaclava came in with a knife in his hand and instructed the manager to give him £40 from the till. The manager grabbed Reilly and used him as a shield. The intruder stabbed Reilly in the right arm. However, the judge (Blayney J.) held that the plaintiff's action should fail. This finding, however, has been severely criticised.

COMMON LAW DAMAGES FOR ACCIDENTS AT WORK

A plaintiff who takes an action in tort may look for monetary compensation (damages), an injunction or both to prevent further repetition of the wrongful act committed by the defendant. Damages, however, is the most common tortious remedy. The assessment of damages involves a prediction of what would have happened if the accident had not occurred in the first instance. The objective of the award of damages is to put the plaintiff in the position they would have been in if the accident had never happened. This is a difficult objective to achieve in the majority of cases.

There are five categories of damages that may be awarded by the courts:

- **Nominal damages** are awarded if the action is proved but the plaintiff has suffered no loss. The plaintiff will receive a very small sum of money just to demonstrate that the plaintiff won.

- *Restitutio in Integrum* and **Compensation**: The purpose here is to compensate the plaintiff for any loss that has been suffered. The aim is to put the plaintiff back in the position they were in before the tort was committed. However, this approach can be limited where, for example, an employee has lost a limb, because it is impossible to put that individual back in the position they were in before the tort took place.

- **Contemptuous damages** are usually awarded in libel actions in which the plaintiff has technically proven the case but the court wishes to express its disapproval that the action was brought to court in the first instance. The award will generally penalise the plaintiff because it will not include the plaintiff's costs.

- **Aggravated damages** or **exemplary damages**: These damages are awarded if the court wishes to express disapproval of the defendant's actions as a result of which the plaintiff has suffered more than would normally be expected in a given situation. The intention of the court is to punish the wrongdoer by giving an additional award on top of the award of compensatory damages. The aim is to deter others who might be tempted to act in the same way as the defendant.

- **Special and General Damages**: Special damages are generally quantifiable pecuniary losses up to the date of the trial. They are assessed separately from other awards since they can be pleaded. The exact amount to be claimed is known at the time of the trial. These damages are a matter of record.

    Future losses are called "general damages", which covers all losses that are not capable of exact quantification, and can be divided into two categories: pecuniary and non-pecuniary. The court must come to an exact sum, which is the present value of the future loss, and the courts use the multiplicand and multiplier formulae to establish this.

    The multiplicand is defined as the sum that represents the plaintiff's annual lost earnings at the date of the trial. This is a question of fact. The multiplier is a notional figure, which represents a number of years by which the multiplicand must be multiplied in order to calculate the future losses. This figure is of course very arbitrary and based on comparable cases.

By their nature, general damages are concerned with mental anguish. They are non-physical and therefore not readily amenable to calculation.

THE ASSESSMENT OF LOSS

Pecuniary Losses

There is little difficulty in assessing the amount of lost earnings up to the time of the trial. It is, however, more difficult to assess the future loss of earnings that an employee may suffer as a result of an accident at work. A number of factors must be taken into account when seeking to assess the value of the future loss of earnings of an employee. An in-depth discussion of these is beyond the scope of this publication. However, we will briefly consider the main factors.

Physical Condition of the Plaintiff

Because of the particular injury sustained by the employee, it may be impossible or dangerous for them to be employed in certain occupations and the courts must factor this in when seeking to establish the loss of earning capacity of the employee.

Age of the Plaintiff

This raises the issue of whether the employee's working life, as a result of injuries, has been cut short and, if so, can they be compensated for the "lost years". The opinion of the courts is that an employee is entitled to claim for years in their working lifetime that have been lost as a result of the injuries sustained by them.

The Labour Market

The state of the labour market will also be taken into consideration when assessing future loss of earnings. Union officials and others who may have knowledge of the particular area of work in which the employee was active may be used to give evidence in relation to employment in that particular sector of the workforce.

Other Possibilities Affecting Earning Capacity

Where there is an issue of the possibility or probability of some disability or illness arising or developing in the future, this will affect the amount of damages to be awarded.

Non-pecuniary Losses

Non-pecuniary losses include pain and suffering and loss of life expectancy as a result of workplace injuries.

Pain and Suffering

The employee will be compensated for pain and suffering, both directly related to the tort that they have suffered from and also for present and future suffering that may be endured. Because pain and suffering are subjective in nature, the courts have considerable difficulty in deciding what amount should be awarded and, to this end, the case of *Sinnott v. Quinnsworth Ltd.* (1984) introduced the IR£150,000 (€190,460) rough tariff. The facts of the case concern a young man who was involved in a motorcycle accident and became quadriplegic as a result of his injuries. The reasoning behind the award was that, while the plaintiff's injuries were horrific in terms of lifestyle change, the pain and suffering endured may have been considerably greater in other circumstances. This ruling does not say that IR£150,000 is the ceiling or floor of compensation that can be awarded, but rather a yardstick for future cases.

In a High Court judgement in the case of *Connolly v. Bus Éireann and others* (1996), Mr. Justice Barr stated that it was over 11 years since the Sinnott cap was fixed and he took the view that the appropriate amount was now IR£200,000 (€253,947).

The Loss of Life Expectancy

The existence of the right not to have one's life span reduced by the tortious act of another was first recognised in England in 1935. In Ireland the issue is how much the individual, who is still alive, should be compensated in respect of a reduction in their life expectancy as a result of a tortious act of another. Although limited Irish case law exists to provide an indication of the sums involved, the courts are prepared to award for loss of life expectancy, but such awards are generally moderate in nature.

GENERAL APPROACH TO DAMAGES IN IRELAND

Until 1998, juries decided the award of damages in personal injuries cases. Jury trials were then abolished, primarily due to their unpredictability and the impact of high awards on insurance premiums. Claims under £5,000 are dealt with by the District Court, although very few cases come under this limit. The majority of cases fall within the range £5,000 to £30,000 and are heard by the Circuit Court. The High Court hears appeals from the Circuit Court and is the court of first instance where damages claims exceed £30,000. **Table 2.1** presents an analysis of the ratios of general damages to special damages for different levels of compensation.

Table 2.1: Proportion of General to Special Damages by Award Size

Total Award Value Range IR£	Number of Cases	Avg. Special Damages IR£	Avg. General Damages IR£	Ratio of General to Special Damages
0-20k	50	1,609	10,893	6.8 to 1
>20k-40k	53	4,373	24,016	5.5 to 1
>40k-60k	29	8,196	38,966	4.8 to 1
>60k-100k	15	18,631	55,227	3.0 to 1
>100k-150k	10	52,052	70,100	1.4 to 1
>150k-200k	9	74,348	100,611	1.4 to 1
>200k	4	110,209	125,125	1.1 to 1

Source: DTTI 1995, Doyle Court Reports

The data suggests that there is an inverse relationship between the size of special damages and the amount of general damages. The trend suggests that the judiciary is likely to compensate for low levels of special damages by awarding higher levels of general damages. In case of relatively less serious injuries, general damages are almost seven times that of special damages.

The Deloitte and Touche Report on Insurance Costs in Ireland (1996) calculated general damages for a range of different injuries. Typical examples include the following:

- For leg injuries, most general damage awards are in the range IR£10,000 (€12,700) to IR£35,000 (€44,440).

- For back injuries, most general damage awards are in the range IR£10,000 (€12,700) to IR£35,000 (€44,440).

- For neck injuries, most general damage awards are around IR£20,000 (€25,400).

The Deloitte and Touche report suggests four factors it believes have contributed to the rise in the cost of personal injury claims in Ireland:

- Special damages now include a provision for past and future medical expenses.

- General damages awards are a multiple of special damage awards. The upward growth in special damages awards has lead to a similar upward growth in general damage awards.

- Legal costs have increased with the rising value of compensation for special and general damages. High legal costs are related to the very considerable settlement period for large personal injury claims in Ireland.

- The number and type of specialist expert witnesses have increased in the last five years. They have contributed to an increase in the fees component of total settlement costs.

In general, the pronouncements of the Supreme Court suggest that, even in very serious cases of personal injury, the court must adopt a realistic approach to awarding compensation for general damages. It is clear that the amount awarded should not incorporate punitive damages and that compensation for general damages must be fair and reasonable and have regard to the general level of incomes in society.

DEFENCES AVAILABLE TO THE EMPLOYER

The two types of defence available to a defendant, namely, contributory negligence and voluntary assumption of risk, will be examined in this section. Although both have been substantially modified as a result of the introduction of the Civil Liability Act 1961, a brief insight is provided into the workings of both forms of defence, and how these doctrines have been modified by the 1961 Act.

Employer Position

The insurance company's solicitor and counsel will act on the employer's behalf and handle all court documentation. However, it is important that an employer requests that all court pleadings be conducted as speedily as possible, the reason being that if damages are awarded, or if the case is settled, such monies will be computed on the basis of loss. Thus the shorter the time, the less loss will be incurred. Loss will comprise not only lost earnings but account will also be taken of the physical condition of the employee, the state of the labour market, non-pecuniary loss, e.g. payment for suffering, loss of amenities, loss of life expectation, etc. Employers should ensure that they are fully informed of all documents that are exchanged between the parties.

Settlement

Cases are often settled out of court. Unfortunately, if the case is settled long before the hearing is due, the employer may have little or no input. Of course, if matters are settled at the door of the court, the employer will be there as a witness, so he can have some input. However, he is still in the unfortunate position that the insurance company is in control, so to speak.

Costs are also a major item in any of these cases as there are legal costs and witness costs. Both sides will have retained solicitors, one senior counsel and possibly one junior counsel and, no doubt, expert witnesses, including medical consultants, engineers and actuaries.

Contributory Negligence

Contributory negligence can be defined as a lack of care for one's own safety. Its effect in an employer's liability action is to reduce the amount of compensation the court will award to an individual in the event of an injury. This is the most common form of defence used by employers. While the aim is not to completely exonerate defendants from their liability, it has the effect of distributing proportionately the level of fault and therefore it can diminish the amount of damages awarded.

Initially, as the law of employer's liability developed, there was a strict application of this defence. The view prevailed that a defendant needed to show some fault on behalf of the plaintiff, which in turn resulted in freedom from liability for the employer and would exonerate the employer from paying any compensation.

This strict application of the doctrine of "contributory negligence" became diluted as a result of the Civil Liability Act, 1961. The Act abolished the use of contributory negligence as an absolute defence by employers. Section 34(1) addresses the issue of apportionment of damages in respect of the doctrine of contributory negligence; this apportionment is based on the degrees of fault of the parties concerned. An employee's failure to exercise reasonable care for their own safety will not amount to contributory negligence in respect of damage, unless that damage results from the particular risk to which the employee's conduct has exposed them (*Moore v. Nolan* (1960)).

The purpose of this rule is to ensure that the employee's lack of care for their own well-being can be shown to have been directly related to the injuries suffered as a result of the employer's negligence. If this is not the case, and the plaintiff's careless actions can be shown not to have influenced the injury that in fact occurred, then there is no basis for contributory negligence.

An employer will have to produce evidence that an employee contributed to his accident, otherwise this argument will not be accepted by the court.

The courts are aware that the employer sets standards of care and that the employee may be obliged to accept a less than adequate level of safety. For example, in *Stewart v. Killeen Paper Mills Ltd* (1959), IR436, an employer customarily failed to keep in its correct place a protective guard on a dangerous machine in a paper mill and thus caused the employee operating the machine to take a chance in grabbing at paper and injuring himself. He was not found to have contributed to his accident. Kingsmill Moore J. stated that "where it can be shown that a regular practice exists unchecked, it is difficult to show contributory negligence by a workman who follows such practice". Other matters, such as the employee's failure to wear protective clothing or to comply with the safety requirements, would imply contributory action on the employee's part.

An employee cannot be held guilty of contributory negligence if he simply does the job he is instructed to do. In such circumstances, where the employer makes it quite clear that the job has to be done, it is not incumbent on the employee to make further protests about safety.

Once again, the youthfulness and possible inexperience of an employee will be considered in determining whether there was any contributory negligence in a given case. Youth and inexperience must be recognised by the employer when assigning a task to an employee.

In *Stakelum v. Bank of Ireland* (1999), the plaintiff was, and at the date of hearing of the case still was, employed by the bank as the porter in a branch in a country town. Among the porter's duties were maintaining the gardens at the rear of the bank and changing external light bulbs. For the purpose of performing these tasks, the porter purchased a ladder with monies provided by the bank. On occasion he was asked to pick apples and he used the ladder for that purpose. The accident that gave rise to the claim happened when he was using the ladder to pick apples. He placed the ladder close to the apple tree and climbed. As he did so, the ladder buckled and gave way under him. He fell to the ground and injured his right arm.

The porter gave evidence that, before he used the ladder he had not noticed anything wrong it, but that, after the fall, he found that the caps on the feet were missing and that the feet themselves were bent.

Engineering evidence was given that though the ladder complied with British Standards, it was classified as a class three ladder suitable only for domestic use. According to the engineer, it was not suitable for use outdoors because it was too narrow, too light and its feet were too small. Evidence was also given that there were safety instructions on the ladder. The porter told the court he had not read the instructions. The absence of the caps was significant because, if they had been on the ladder when the porter climbed it, they would have, as the judge put it, "inhibited" its sinking into the ground, which was, the judge held, the cause of the accident.

Considering liability, the judge held that the porter had contributed to the cause of the accident by his failure to read the safety instructions and because he had failed to notice the defects in the ladder. However, he said he could not "exonerate" the bank, as the obligation to take care required them to ensure that equipment used was free from defects and suitable for the purpose for which it was being used. The bank should, he said, have carried out a risk assessment before allowing the porter to use it and it should have drawn his attention to the safety instructions. As it took neither of these precautions, it was equally to blame for the accident. Having assessed damages at IR£18,500 (€23,490), the judge awarded the injured porter half the sum, IR£9,250 (€11,745).

Volenti non fit Injuria (Voluntary Assumption of Risk)

In its infancy the defence of *volenti non fit injuria*, or voluntary assumption of risk, held little regard for the rights of the employee. The basis of this doctrine is that the employee consented to the dangerous act and therefore cannot complain when it transpires. In practice, it may have meant that, where an employee was aware of the likelihood of injury as a result of the negligent act of an employer, but nevertheless was subjected to this physical risk and injury transpired, the employee was not be in a position to seek redress.

The Civil Liability Act (1961) under Section 34(1) modified this outdated and strict approach. In *O'Hanlon v. ESB* (1969) the trial judge pointed out that:

> . . . what used to be called the defence of *volenti non fit injuria* . . . can now be properly described as . . . the defence that the plaintiff, before the act complained of, agreed to waive his/her legal rights in respect of it.

Although the defence of *volenti no fit injuria* in its traditional sense has disappeared, liability can be waived where the defendant can show that by contract they were not liable, or where before the act the plaintiff agreed to waive their rights.

Although no real difficulties arise in relation to "contracts" and the effect of exempting the defendant from liability, difficulties do arise in relation to what constitutes "agreement". Section 34(1)(b) points out that agreement necessitates "some sort of intercourse or communication between the defendant and the plaintiff"; however, where this is one-sided or of a non-verbal nature, difficulties arise.

In *McComiskey v. McDermott* (1974), the issue of non-verbal or one-sided communication was considered. The defendant was the driver of a car who had a sign in the window stating that passengers travel at their own risk. The High Court held that such a sign did not bind the passenger as it did not specifically indicate that it had emanated from the driver, that he intended it to bind the plaintiff or that the plaintiff had accepted its implications.

To date the defence of "contributory negligence" is the most commonly used by defendants in cases of negligence. The Civil Liability Act, 1961 has put both the doctrines of *volenti non fit injuria* and "contributory negligence" on a modern footing and they therefore no longer have the calamitous effect they once had on an employee's case.

CHAPTER ROUND-UP

- The courts have interpreted the employer's duty of care principle in terms of four sub-duties: safe place of work, safe systems of work, competent staff and safe plant and equipment. The courts also emphasise that the duty is a personal one, owed to employees as individuals and not as a class. Furthermore, the duty does not extend to all aspects of the employee's existence, but only to those performed in the course of employment. In general, an employer does not owe a duty of care to independent contractors.

- The duty of the employer is to act in a responsible manner in terms of the safety and health measures taken. What constitutes "reasonable" will depend on the nature of the industry, the existence of international standards regulating the industry and the knowledge and physical capabilities of the employee.

- The legal concept of vicarious liability is closely related to the employer's duty of care principle. The concept of vicarious liability states that the employer may be liable for the wrongs committed by employees during the course of employment. The question of whether this liability arises depends on whether there is the requisite control inherent in the relationship, the nature of the contractual relationship itself and whether the act was committed within the scope of the employment relationship.

- The types of damages awarded in Ireland to injured employees include nominal damages, and special and general damages. Special damages are generally quantifiable recurring losses up to the date of the trial. General damages cover future losses and by their nature are less capable of exact quantification. The courts use a multiplicand and a multiplier to establish the quantum of general damages.

- In Ireland, the level of court awards suggests that there is an inverse relationship between the size of special damages and the amount of general damages. The courts are likely to compensate for low levels of special damages by awarding higher general damages. In general, the courts try to adopt a realistic approach so that compensation for general damages must be fair and reasonable.

- Two primary defences are available to the employer: contributory negligence and voluntary assumption of risk. Contributory negligence is essentially a lack of care on the part of an employee for their own safety. Its effect is to reduce the amount of compensation the court will award to an injured employee. Voluntary assumption of risk is essentially a partial defence and there are difficult issues relating to agreeing to contract away rights.

Chapter 3

STATUTORY REGULATION OF HEALTH, SAFETY AND WELFARE: CORE REGULATION

INTRODUCTION

This chapter sets out the primary legislation governing health, safety and welfare in Ireland, and discusses in detail the Safety, Health and Welfare at Work Act,1989. It also explains the rules governing claims for personal injury caused by breach of statutory duty. In general, where a statutory provision will support an action for breach of statutory duty, the employee frequently claims both common law negligence and breach of statutory duty. The chapter is structured as follows:

- It describes the nature of statutory duty.

- It provides a detailed account of the Safety, Health and Welfare at Work Act, 1989.

- It considers in detail the provisions of the Safety, Health and Welfare at Work (General Application) Regulations 1993 that build on the principles of health and safety set out in the Safety, Health and Welfare at Work Act, 1989.

THE NATURE OF STATUTORY DUTY

There are two broad categories of statutory duty:

- Duties created by the Oireachtas primarily for enforcement in the criminal courts. The Acts that create these duties are properly a part of public rather than private law.

- Duties created by the Oireachtas to provide remedies for the victims of personal injury at work. Their purpose is to regulate private rights and they are in effect statutory modifications of common law liability.

Actions founded on statutory duties have a number of important features in common:

*   The duty relied upon was created by the Oireachtas, not by the courts. Defining the duty is therefore an exercise in statutory interpretation.

*   The duty, though originally created by the Oireachtas, will have to be interpreted by judges. Such interpretations create precedents that are binding in any further consideration of the issue and of persuasive authority in the interpretation of like statutes.

*   Liability is not necessarily liability for negligent conduct. The Oireachtas rarely chooses negligence as the sole criterion of liability. Liability is often strict in nature.

THE MINES AND QUARRIES ACT, 1965

The Mines and Quarries Act, 1965 regulates the health, safety and welfare of employees in both mines and quarries. The Safety, Health and Welfare at Work Act, 1989 has repealed a number of provisions of the Act. The majority of the requirements of the Act are not absolute but are qualified by the criterion of "practicability", which is outlined in section 137 of the Act. This limitation of practicability does not, however, provide a very effective or universal defence. The Act imposes specific duties on the "manager" of the particular mine or quarry and also on other officials. This however does not discharge the mine or quarry "owner" from liability for damages as a result of actions of employees in the course of their employment.

Definition of Mines, Quarries and Owners

A mine is defined as:

> ... an excavation or system of excavations made for the purpose of, or in connection with, the getting, wholly or substantially by means of involving the employment of persons

below ground, of minerals (where in their natural state or in solution or suspension) or products of minerals (Sec 3 (1) of the Act).

A quarry is defined as:

... an excavation or system of excavations made for the purpose of, or in connection with, the getting of minerals or products of minerals, being neither a mine nor merely a well or borehole or a well and borehole combined (Section 2).

The difference is that a mine includes persons who are employed underground and the process of excavation is wholly or at least substantially carried out by these people.

The "owner" in the context of the Act means the person for the time being entitled to work a mine or a quarry. Where a contractor is working on behalf of the owner, then the contractor is deemed to be the owner.

Owners of mines or quarries have particular duties imposed on them by the Act. The owner has a general duty imposed on them to ensure that the premises is well laid out, planned, managed, and worked in accordance with the Act and its regulations. Written instructions must be given to all employees that outline their responsibilities, and these are to be sent to the Inspector of that mine or quarry.

The Mines and Quarries Act, 1965 specifies that a manager must be employed who essentially takes the task of management away from the hands of the owner. In the case of a mine, this manager must be "qualified" as outlined by the Mines (Manager and Officials) Regulations Act, 1970. The owner may be the manager provided he has the necessary qualifications. This provision only applies where 14 or more people are employed underground.

The manager is given the task of managing and controlling the mine, although under the instruction of the owner. The manager has certain rights if the instructions given by the owner interfere with the manager's statutory duties. The manager is charged with the duty of ensuring that all other employees and non-employees execute their obligations. He must also appoint persons to carry out inspections of the premises and to be in charge of, or to supervise or conduct, operations.

Principal Duties Relating to Mines

Part Three of the Mines and Quarries Act, 1965 imposes duties in relation to the following areas: shafts and entrances, roads, winding and rope haulage apparatus and conveyors, ventilation, lighting and lamps, electricity and electrical apparatus, blasting materials and devices, fire precautions, dust precautions, precautions against external dangers to workings, duties of officials and workmen in cases of danger, machinery and apparatus, buildings, structures and access thereat, training and discipline, first aid, lifting excessive weight and other general welfare provisions. Sections 32 to 35 impose duties relating to the means of ingress and egress to mines via shafts and entrances and their safety.

Specific provisions are detailed below.

Entrances and Shafts in Mines

Section 32 stipulates that every mine must have at least two shafts or outlets, to which people must have communication and, furthermore, the shafts should afford separate means of ingress and egress. It must also ensure that where ten or more people are employed, should one of the shafts becomes blocked, the other will allow access to the surface.

Protection from Falling Down Shafts

Every mine must have an enclosure barrier at the surface of the pit that ensures that nobody will accidentally fall down the shaft. This barrier must be properly maintained.

Roads in Mines

The Mines and Quarries Act, 1965 provides that any road in a mine (made after 1970) must be made so that there are not any sudden changes in its direction, height, width and gradient, unless the particular circumstance of the mine would make such roads inadvisable for reasons of safety. Movement of vehicles along the roads of mines is also legislated for. The Act points out that vehicles or other loads are not permitted to travel on roads in mines if they or their loads rub off the roof, sides or anything supporting the roof or sides. The Act provides that the manager of the mine must specify the maximum loads that can be carried in vehicles on any length of road in a mine and also their maximum speed. Safety of foot passengers is also provided in that only authorised persons are allowed move along the road and only when vehicles are specifically stopped so as to let the individual pass.

Support in Mines

Sections 49 to 55 contain provisions dealing with support in mines. There is a duty to ensure that all the roads, roofs and sides are secure. This is the responsibility of the mine manager. There also must always be sufficient material for support at the place where a person who may require it is working. If the support is not in place, no work may take place. If an employee wishes to withdraw from the roof or sides of a mine, he must do this by a method or device by which he is in a place of safety.

Ventilation

The manager must ensure that effective ventilation is always in operation so as to dilute gases that are inflammable or to render them harmless and to provide air containing sufficient oxygen.

Where ventilation is not operational or is interrupted, it is the duty of the manager to ensure access is denied to that area of the mine affected until proper ventilation has been restored. The Mines (General) Regulations Act, 1975 highlights other areas such as measurement of air passing through the mine, functioning of fans for ventilation and precautions that must be taken with respect to fans below ground.

Lighting

Under Section 62 the manager has a duty to ensure that suitable and sufficient lighting both above and below ground is available where employees work or pass through. Furthermore, the use of electricity and electrical apparatus is dealt with under Section 65 (1), which makes provision for the generation, storage, transformation and use of electricity at mines, and the use, construction, installation, examination, repair, maintenance, alteration, adjustment and testing of electrical apparatus and electrical cables at mines. If an inspector is of the opinion that the use of electricity underground may increase the risk of an explosion or accident, he may restrict the use of such electrical may restrict the use of such electrical apparatus. Under Section 68 of the Act, provision for the prevention, detection and combating of outbreaks of fires in mines is provided for. The efficient conduct of rescue operations is also provided for under this section.

Section 87 provides that suitable and sufficient sanitary conditions must be provided to those working in the mine. If both sexes are present, separate conveniences must be supplied. These conveniences must be properly maintained and kept clean. Sections 61 and 62 impose a duty to provide changing, messing and washing facilities. Under Section 89 the manager must provide and maintain an adequate supply of water to be positioned at convenient points.

Duties Relating to Quarries

Part Four of the Mines and Quarries Act, 1965 provides for the health, safety and welfare of persons employed in quarries and these duties are added to by the requirements of the Quarries (General) Regulations, 1974, the Quarries (Electricity) Regulations, 1972 and the Quarries (Explosives) Regulations, 1971.

The quarry manager is given the task of discharging many of the duties specifically ensuring that quarry operations are carried out in such a manner so as to avoid falls both inside or outside the quarry. They must also ensure a safe means of access to the quarry unless it is not practicable to do so.

The quarry manager must also ensure that where vehicles running on rails are being used, devices are installed so that accidents to a person as a result of the vehicle running out of control are prevented. Section 82 requires that all buildings and structures at the quarry be kept in a safe condition and a safe means of access to any place or building at the quarry where people work be provided for and maintained (Section 83).

Fire precaution is also legislated for and there is a duty to ensure that, where there is a risk of an outbreak of fire in any area of the quarry, people working in that area will be prevented from doing so unless steps are taken so as to ensure that two or more means of egress are provided from the room or area where the risk lies so as to avoid an individual becoming trapped.

THE SAFETY, HEALTH AND WELFARE AT
WORK ACT, 1989

The origins of the Safety, Health and Welfare at Work Act, 1989 can be traced to the recommendations of the Barrington Commission that reported in 1983. This was a most comprehensive report and highlighted many weaknesses in Ireland's system of occupational health and safety in the workplace. Some of the weaknesses highlighted are worth considering because they serve to remind us of the considerable task that had to be undertaken by the then new national authority and the social partners if the situation were to improve. The key weaknesses identified were as follows:

- A general absence of a systematic, comprehensive and rational approach to occupational health and safety. This manifested itself in a heavy reliance on the law as a mechanism of regulation, with no attempt being made to specify the objectives of such legislation. There was a lack of clear priorities and it resulted in the promotion of a safety management philosophy that was reactive rather than proactive in nature.

- The system was too narrow in focus, concentrating almost exclusively on factories, mines, quarries, construction and shops. The definition of a factory specified in the 1955 Factories Act, and amended by the Safety in Industry Act, 1980, gave rise to problems of interpretation, with the result that many workplaces escaped the provisions of the legislation. The legislation at that time served to propagate many misconceptions about health and safety as a management responsibility. Particular misconceptions included the following: confusion about who was responsible for safety in the organisation, the many and varied roles of the State, the almost exclusive emphasis on physical hazards and the absence of mechanisms to review and appraise the system at the level of the workplace.

- Many of the provisions introduced by the Safety in Industry Act, 1980 did not work effectively in practice. The general system of safety committees did not function to the desired level. In particular, the legal provisions on their composition and duties were perceived to be inflexible; consequently they were not set up in many small organisations; they were perceived as talking shops with little action and, more importantly, it was argued that they were an organisational phenomenon that did not affect any other area of industry.

- The safety statement, which the Safety in Industry Act, 1980 viewed as a key mechanism for policy formulation and the encouragement of management accountability, was largely unsuccessful. The evidence suggested that many statements were written to comply with the Act, and there was a failure of the legislation to recognise that the statement did not operate unless there was commitment, financial resources and a range of support systems in operation to implement aspects of the statement. The direction of the safety statement contents was confused. There was too much emphasis on means and not enough on ends. The legislation required a description of the safety arrangements, yet there was no mention of the objectives or the means of assessing the achievement of those objectives. There appeared to be a fear on the part of some organisations to commit themselves to paper in case it might be interpreted as an admission of liability in future litigation by injured employees.

The pre-1989 legislation did not specify strongly or in a sufficiently clear manner the responsibilities of employers, employees and other parties. It was not possible to extract a set of general underlying principles that could be applied to all sectors and there was much emphasis on a punitive rather than a preventative philosophy.

General Features of the 1989 Act

The 1989 Act is a comprehensive piece of legislation covering 61 provisions, organised into nine sections and five schedules. The main sections are as follows:

Part I (Sections 1–5) deals with the general issues such as definitions, e.g. employee, self-employed person, etc.

Part II (Sections 6–13) represents the core of the Act in that it covers major issues. In particular, it sets out a number of general duties. These duties fall into the following categories:

- Duties of the employer in relation to their employees.

- Duties of the employer and the self-employed as regards others who may be affected by work activity.

- Duties of persons in control of the place of work.

- Duties of employees.

- Duties of designers, manufacturers and importers of articles and substances.

These duties are, in the main, statutory enactments of the common law duties discussed in **Chapter 2**. The 1989 Act provides a basis for issuing of codes of practice and regulations on all of the general duties.

Part III (Section 15–20) provided for the establishment of a National Authority for Occupational Safety and Health and the appointment of advisory committees by the Authority.

Part IV (Sections 27–31) and the Second, Third and Fourth Schedules deal with the need to review the existing health and safety legislation and replace it over a period of time with new regulations and/or codes of practice. The Fourth Schedule lists a wide range of issues on which regulations may be made. The Act also points out that codes of practice will be admissible in evidence in court.

Part V (Sections 34–41) gives the Minister power to appoint other bodies by regulation to enforce health and safety law. The Authority and other agencies can appoint inspectors and it is envisaged that they will play an important role in safety management. The wide range of powers and enforcement possibilities given to inspectors under the Act is designed to facilitate this. The Act gives the Authority the power to obtain a High Court order restricting or prohibiting the use of a place of work in cases where there is a risk of serious injury.

Part VI (Sections 42–45) contains provisions relating to obtaining information as well as restrictions on the disclosure of information. These are aimed at protecting the interests of all the relevant parties.

Part VII (Sections 46–47) provides the Authority with the power to conduct investigations or to direct inquiries in the case of particular accidents, diseases or occurrences.

Part VIII (Sections 48–53) deals with the power of the new Authority to take court proceedings. The Authority or relevant enforcing agency can prosecute offenders under the Act. The Act lays down a general penalty of up to IR£1,500 (€1,904) for a summary fine or IR15,000 (€19,040) for a conviction on indictment. The Act specifies that, in the case of unauthorised disclosure of information or activities carried on contrary to the terms of a licence from the authority, the above-mentioned fines or a prison sentence of up to two years on indictment can apply.

Part IX (Sections 54–61) deals with a range of miscellaneous matters. Two of the most significant provisions are: industrial premises will for the purposes of fire safety be brought within the Fire Services Act, 1981 and it is now possible to bring particular work activities under the control of a licensing arrangement.

Duties of Employers

There is a duty imposed on employers to ensure the health, safety and welfare at work of all employees. These duties can be categorised as follows:

Buildings

- The design, provision and maintenance of a safe place of work. Issues include: Is it sufficient given the demands of the work? Are there systems and procedures in place to maintain the place of work? How are they implemented?

- To ensure safe means of access to and egress from the place of work.

Equipment/Procedures

- Provision and maintenance of machinery that does not have any safety risks inherent in it.

- To ensure safety with regard to articles or substances in use.

- To ensure that the organisation has adequate and up to date emergency procedures.

- To ensure safe systems of work.

- The provision and maintenance of suitable protective equipment when there are hazards that cannot be controlled or eliminated.

Facilities

- The provision and maintenance of welfare facilities; this may include counselling facilities, medical examination and employee assistance programmes to deal with the effects of drug abuse, severe injury or bereavement counselling.

- The provision of information, instruction, training and supervision; this could include information on the safety record of the organisation, specific instruction on the use of machinery, training programmes to develop safety awareness and the effective supervision of staff to ensure compliance with safety and procedures.

Services

- The use of specialist services to provide for the health, safety and welfare of the workforce. This might include the provision of eyesight and/or skin specialists and sound engineers.

Section 7(1) imposes a duty on the employer to take reasonable steps to ensure that persons not employed, but who may be affected by the activities of the employer, are not exposed to risks to their health and safety. This provision has specific application to members of the public and visitors. Section 8 imposes obligations on the employer *vis-à-vis* contractors. The Act specifies that the employer must take appropriate steps in relation to the place of work, access to and egress from the place of work and any article or substance in the place of work as it relates to contractors. Byrne (1994) suggests that, at a minimum, the employer must ensure that contractors work only in a separate bonded area to minimise interaction with others. He also recommends that equipment should not be made available to contractors and that the contractor's insurance policy should be read carefully.

Employers are required to consult their employees and to take account of their views and representations. Employees are also required to promote and co-operate in developing measures to ensure health and safety. **Table 3.1** presents a summary of duties on employers.

Table 3.1: Summary of Duties Imposed on Employers under 1989 Act

S6.2a	Provide a properly designed and maintained place of work such that it is safe and without risk to health.
S6.2b	Provide a properly designed and maintained means of egress from and access to the place of work.
S6.2c	Provide a properly designed and maintained plant and machinery such that it is safe and without risk to health.
S6.2d	Provide a properly planned, organised, performed and maintained system of work such that it is safe and without risk to health.
S6.2e	Provide such information, instruction, training and supervision as is necessary for ensuring the safety and health of employees.
S6.2f	Provide suitable protective equipment where it is not possible to eliminate or reduce a risk to a safe level as appropriate for ensuring the safety and health of employees.
S6.2g	Provide and revise adequate plans to be followed in emergencies.
S6.2h	Ensure the safety and health of persons working with an article or substance.
S6.2i	Provide and maintain facilities to ensure the welfare of employees.
S6.2j	Obtain the services of a competent person for the purpose of ensuring the safety and health of employees.

Duties of Employees

Section 9 imposes general duties on employees at work as follows:

- To take reasonable care for their own safety and that of any other person who may be affected.

- To co-operate so that all relevant provisions are complied with within the workplace.

- To use, in a safe manner, all equipment provided.

- To report any problems of which they become aware that might have an effect on health, safety and welfare.

- To wear protective clothing provided by the employer.

Furthermore, under Section 9(2), it is provided that no person shall intentionally or recklessly interfere with or misuse an appliance, protective clothing, convenience, equipment or other means or thing provided in pursuance of any of the relevant statutory provisions or otherwise for securing the health, safety or welfare of persons arising out of work activities.

Duties of Manufacturers and Suppliers

Section 10 of the Act places specific obligations on any person who designs, manufactures, imports or supplies any article for use at work. These are specifically to:

- Ensure that any article be designed, constructed, tested and executed so that it will not cause injury or present a risk to health to any worker who uses it.

- Take appropriate steps that users are given adequate information about the uses of the particular component, article etc. so that it will not be a risk to safety or health.

- Provide revised information based on any tests or new information which comes to light.

- Carry out appropriate research for the purposes of discovering how to eliminate risks to health and safety which arise from the design.

- Ensure, in the case of substances, that they are safe and without risk to health, and that appropriate tests are carried out on the substance and that appropriate information is provided on the substance's properties.

Duties of Designers and Builders

Section 11 of the Act imposes a duty on designers and builders to ensure that reasonable steps are taken to effect a place of work that is safe and without risk of health.

In general, the duties set out in Sections 6-11 are imposed on the employer who may find himself liable to prosecution for failing to meet them. However, because of the duties imposed on the employee (Section 9), an employee may likewise be liable to prosecution by the Health and Safety Authority. It is not possible for the company to take out insurance to cover the possibility of a criminal prosecution.

Implementation of the Legislation

Irish health and safety law is based on the notion "so far as is reasonably practicable". This phase has been subject to legal interpretation both in the UK and Ireland.

In the case of *Edwards v. National Coal Board* (1949), Asquith LJ stated:

> "Reasonably practicable" is a narrower term than "physically possible", and seem to me to imply that a computation must be made by the owner in which the quantum of risk is placed on one scale and the sacrifice involved in the measures necessary for averting the risk (whether in money, time or trouble) is placed in the other, and that, if it be shown that there is a gross disproportion between them — the risk being insignificant in relation to the sacrifice — the defendants discharge the onus on them.

This formulation of the term provides some form of defence of the employer. It suggests that, even where a precaution is technically possible, an employer may not need to take preventative steps if the risk is low and the cost of reducing it is disproportionately high.

The formal and ultimate legal test of compliance with this duty has always been for a judge to decide whether or not the efforts made in a particular case were "reasonably practicable". From this it can be seen that the target of the new legislation, instead of the previous highly prescriptive approach that told employers exactly what to do, is for employers to put in a management effort proportional to the harm that could arise from the work. What is "reasonably practicable" at any time will vary. New technology or a growing awareness about a hazard, such as asbestos, will change what is considered acceptable. This means that other guidance and information put out by trade associations or published in human resources magazines and similar publications are also relevant to managing safety. At any time "reasonably practicable" means the acceptable good practice relevant to the type of work. In determining what is reasonably practicable in a particular situation, a court will balance the extent of the risk involved against the cost of prevention of that risk. A very high risk that is cheap to prevent can be contrasted with a very low risk that is comparatively expensive to prevent.

In the case of *Boyle v. Marathon Petroleum Ireland Limited* (1999), the Supreme Court reviewed the meaning of the term "reasonably practicable". While the subject matter of the case application was S.10(5) of the Safety, Health and Welfare (Offshore Installations) Act, 1987, the Supreme Court's view on the test of "reasonably practicable" has broader application. O'Flaherty J. affirmed the view of the High Court that the onus of proof was on the defendant to show that what he did was reasonably practicable and O'Flaherty J. then reviewed the standard of reasonable practicability in the following terms:

> I am . . . of the opinion that this duty is more extensive than the common law duty which devolves on employers to exercise reasonable care in various aspects as regards their employees. It is an obligation to take all practicable steps. That seems to me to involve more than that they should respond; that they, as employers, did all that was reasonably to be expected of them in a particular situation. An employer might sometimes be able to say that what he did by way of exercising reasonable care was done in the 'agony of

the moment', for example, but that might not be enough to discharge his statutory duty under the section in question.

Reasonable practicability is therefore a different legal concept from that of negligence. The burden imposed by what is "reasonably practicable" is set at a higher standard than that imposed by the general principle of negligence. For reasonable practicability, there must be a gross disproportion. In financial terms, this means that the money required to be spent would have to be very significant before it would not be "reasonably practicable" to take the precautions. Nevertheless, what could be construed as "reasonably practicable" for a multinational corporation might not necessarily pertain for a small corner shop. This is a matter for each individual employer. However, as pursuant of s.50 of the Safety, Health and Welfare at Work Act, 1989, in any prosecution for an offence consisting of a failure to do something, so far as it was practicable or "reasonably practicable", it is for the accused to prove that it was not practicable or was not "reasonably practicable" to do more than was in fact done to satisfy this duty or requirement.

THE MANAGEMENT OF HEALTH AND SAFETY

The Safety Statement

One of the key elements of the Safety, Health and Welfare at Work Act, 1989 is the requirement in Section 12 for organisations to formulate a safety statement. The Section obliges employers and the self-employed to prepare a written safety statement that specifies the manner in which the health, safety and welfare of all employees is going to be managed.

The statement must be based on a professionally conducted identification of the hazards and an assessment of the risks to health and safety on the premises to which the safety statement relates. The statement has a number of key components, which are as follows:

Statement of General Policy

The safety statement should begin with a declaration, signed at the top management level on behalf of the employer who has ultimate responsibility for health and safety, of the employer's commitment to securing a workplace that is as safe and as healthy as possible. Because the safety statement must be relevant at all times to the health and safety of the employees, it must be revised accordingly as circumstances dictate.

It should also indicate how the contents will be brought to the attention of the safety representative, the employees and other people in the workplace who might be affected by its contents.

Identification of Hazards

A hazard is anything that can potentially cause harm. The first step in safeguarding health and safety is to identify hazards. Each employer is required to examine the place of work systematically and identify existing hazards. The statement should refer to any relevant legislation or standards dealing with the hazard.

Assessment of Risk

If there is a hazard present, the next step is to determine the likelihood of its happening and the consequences of its happening. There are always difficulties in assessing risks, and best practice in any activity should always be used as a yardstick. Some risks such as exposure to chemicals or noise may require physical measurements to be taken.

The services of a competent person should be obtained to assess the risks, if the employer is unable to do so. If changes (such as new plant, new working practices or new materials) occur in the workplace, there must be a new assessment of the risks and the safety statement must be updated accordingly. The revision must be brought to the attention of everyone affected by the change and in particular the safety representative.

Arrangements

Once a hazard is identified and the risk is assessed, the necessary arrangements must be made to protect health and safety; control measures and safeguards must be put into effect. Because conditions in the workplace vary considerably, a solution that is appropriate for one workplace may not be adequate for another. Best practice is to remove the hazard. If this is not possible, other means of reducing the risk must be used.

Organisation

The safety statement must specify how the arrangements for safeguarding health, safety and welfare will be carried out. The following must be covered:

- **Resources**. The safety statement must provide details of the resources committed by the employer in terms of time, people and finance to secure the health, safety and welfare of employees.

- **Co-operation Required by Employees**. There is a duty on employees to take care of their own safety while at work. Co-operation is also required in the case of using suitable protective equipment or clothing provided by the employer. The co-operation required from the employee to implement the statement must be clearly outlined and cannot be couched in vague generalities. Where disciplinary implications for failure to comply with the safety requirements arise, they should be specified. An employee is also required to report either to the supervisor or employer any defects in plant, equipment, place or system of work that might endanger health and safety and the system of doing so should be indicated.

- **Responsibility**. The safety statement must include the name of the person at senior management level who is responsible for the overall implementation of the statement. It must also allocate responsibility for each arrangement identified as being necessary to secure effective health and safety in the organisation.

- **Consultation and Information**. In addition, the safety statement will specify arrangements for consultation with employees and safety representatives on health and safety matters. It is also specified that employees must be provided with details of information that they are entitled to and where that information is stored. Furthermore, training in health and safety for employees and management must be outlined.

Employees' Rights under the 1989 Act

In addition to imposing duties on employees, the 1989 Act confers specific rights on employees. Employees have the right to make representations to and to consult their safety representative on matters of health, safety and welfare in the place of work. This is a general right. Byrne (1994) argues that all employees can exercise the right to be their own safety representative. The Act does, however, include a reference to a safety representative who may be elected by employees to represent them in consultations with the employer.

Whereas the Safety in Industry Act, 1980 put the emphasis on committees, the 1989 Act promotes the election of a "safety representative" by employees. Section 13 sets out the requirements in relation to safety representatives.

Appointment and Overall Function

The employees at a place of work are entitled to select and appoint one of their number to act as a safety representative. A safety representative may consult with and make representations to the employer on health, safety and welfare matters relating to the employees in the place of work. The employer is obliged to consider these representations and act on them if necessary. The purpose of these consultations is to prevent accidents and ill health, to highlight safety problems in the workplace and to identify means of overcoming them.

Investigations

A safety representative may investigate accidents and dangerous occurrences in the place of work to find out the causes and to help identify any remedial or preventive measures necessary. A safety representative must not interfere with anything at the scene of the incident nor obstruct any people with statutory obligations from doing anything required of them under occupational health and safety legislation.

Consulting with Inspectors

A safety representative is entitled to consult a health and safety inspector either orally or in writing about any aspect of health, safety and welfare at work and may receive advice and information from the inspector in relation to such matters.

Carrying out Inspections

A safety representative may undertake inspections in the place of work to identify hazards and risks to health and safety. The employer must, however, be notified before such an inspection can take place. The frequency of inspection must be agreed with the employer and no employer may unreasonably withhold agreement.

There is no fixed duration for which an inspection should take place and this will generally be a function of the size and type of operation being inspected. Different types of inspection include safety tours, safety sampling (sampling of particularly dangerous activities) and safety surveys.

Under section 13 (8) of the 1989 Act, the safety representative is entitled to time off, having regard to all the circumstances, without any effect on remuneration, so as to obtain the knowledge required to discharge their function. Safety representatives are entitled to time off to carry out their function as a safety representative and should not be at any disadvantage in relation to their employment as a result of fulfilling their duties.

Enforcement of the Legislation

The 1989 Act, established the Health and Safety Authority (HSA). The Authority's main functions are set out as follows:

- To make adequate arrangements for the enforcement of all health, safety and welfare legislation.

- To review the effectiveness of existing legislation.

- To encourage good safety management practices and behaviour in the workforce.

- To provide advice and information when requested.

- To issue licences for specified activities.

- To issue approved codes of practice (ACoPs) that specify technical standards and act as a form of guidance on the legislation. These codes are admissible in court in the case of criminal prosecutions.

The Authority also manages a team of inspectors who have been given additional enforcement powers under Sections 35 to 37. The specific instruments that the inspector has available are considered later in this Chapter.

Figure 3.1 presents a list of specific powers of inspectors when doing a factory visit, although, in addition to these, the Authority may apply under Section 39 of the Act to the High Court for a prohibition order in relation to certain activities. Such an order can be obtained on an *ex parte* basis. Prosecutions can be initiated by the authority by way of summary trial in the District Court. The maximum fine is £1,500. It is also possible to bring a prosecution by way of indictment to be heard by judge and jury in the Circuit Criminal Court or the Central Criminal Court. There is no limit to the fine that can be imposed. Imprisonment is also an option but only where there was a failure to obey a prohibition notice, an unlawful disclosure of information obtained under the 1989 Act and/or breaking of the terms of a licence issued under the 1989 Act.

Prosecutions under the 1989 Act

Prosecutions for breaches of health and safety law are governed by the 1989 Act. Any person responsible for a breach of health and safety law can be prosecuted. Companies are the most common defendants in criminal prosecutions, but individuals, including the directors, officers or servants of companies, can also be prosecuted. Indeed, the latter, being human entities as distinct from legal ones could, in sufficiently serious cases, be imprisoned, whereas a company can only be fined. Prosecutions can arise as a result of failure to comply with a Notice issued by an Inspector, or as a result of an unsafe practice or other technical breach of the many health and safety statutes. It is unusual for the HSA to prosecute immediately where a breach is detected following a routine inspection because, more often than not, a Notice will achieve the desired remedial effect. However, where the breach is detected following an accident, particularly a fatal accident, a prosecution may well follow without the use of Notices.

Figure 3.1: Specific Powers of Safety Inspectors

- To enter premises at reasonable times or any time where there is a danger.

- To use the services of a police officer if they feel that they will be obstructed.

- To carry out an investigation or inspection.

- To take any equipment or material required for any purpose.

- To take photographs, measurements and recordings as necessary.

- To take copies of and inspect relevant documents.

- To take samples of articles or substances found on the premises, or to sample the atmosphere in the vicinity of the premises.

- To have any article or substance dismantled or subjected to any process or test.

- To take possession of any article or substance that is necessary to facilitate an examination, to prevent tampering or to make available as evidence in proceedings.

- To require a person to make statements and provide information.

- To require parts of the premises to be left undisturbed as long as is deemed necessary.

- To require assistance as necessary.

- Any other power which is necessary.

All offences created by health and safety legislation are summary offences. A summary offence is one that can be tried by a judge sitting alone without a jury. Such prosecutions will take place in the District Court. There is no possibility of imprisonment following a conviction for a summary offence and fines cannot exceed £1,500 per individual offence although several offences may be prosecuted together with individual fines attaching to each. The court also has the power to award costs against an unsuccessful defendant. Generally, the HSA will institute summary prosecutions. An accused person convicted in the District Court has the right to appeal their conviction and/or their sentence to the Circuit Criminal Court where the case will be fully retried before a Circuit Court judge sitting without a jury. A summary prosecution must be initiated within one year from the date of commission of the alleged offence.

Some offences created by health and safety legislation can be tried either as summary offences or as indictable offences. An indictable offence is one that must be tried by jury if the accused person so insists. Prosecutions on indictment can only be taken by the Director of Public Prosecutions on the basis of a file sent to his office by the HSA or other agency.

Where the accused insists on trial by jury, the case must be heard by the Circuit Criminal Court, before a jury. However an indictable offence can still be disposed of as if it were a summary offence (i.e. it can be disposed of by the District Court without a jury) where the following conditions are met:

- The accused waives their right to trial by jury.

- The Director of Public Prosecutions consents to summary disposal.

- The District Judge accepts that the case is fit to be tried summarily. Indictable offences usually carry a higher penalty.

Indictable health and safety offences heard in the Circuit Criminal Court generally carry an unlimited fine and/or imprisonment for a term not exceeding two years. However, where an indictable offence is tried summarily in the District Court, the fine is limited to IR£1,500 (€1,904) per offence and the accused cannot be imprisoned (the penalties are the same as with summary offences).

A person convicted of an indictable offence can appeal to the Circuit Criminal Court as with summary offences above, if the case has been tried summarily. The appeal takes the form of a full rehearing. Where the case has been heard in the Circuit Criminal Court, the defendant has the right of appeal to the Criminal Appeals Division of the Supreme Court against conviction and/or sentence. The appeal, however, is not a full re-hearing and is based on transcripts of the evidence of the original proceedings in the

Circuit Criminal Court. Examples of offences from the Safety, Health and Welfare at Work Act, 1989 that can be tried on indictment are breaches of Sections 6, 7 and 12. There is no time limit on prosecutions on indictment.

For a general summary of the Irish court system, see **Figure 3.2**.

Figure 3.2: The Irish Court System

Criminal Courts	Civil Courts
District Court — judge only: • Summary prosecution. • Indictable offences tried summarily. • Indictable offences sent forward for trial or sentence.	District Court — judge only: • Claims not exceeding IR£5,000.
Circuit Criminal Court: • Indictable offences tried by jury. • Appeals from the District Court (full re-hearing – judge only).	Circuit Court — judge only: • Claims exceeding £30,000.
Special Criminal Court: • (Central Criminal Court (High Court)). • Not relevant to health and safety law.	High Court — judge only: • Claims exceeding IR£30,000. • Appeals from Circuit Court (full re-hearing). • Constitutional cases. • Cases referred from civil or criminal District Courts. • Orders closing down workplaces.
Supreme Court: • Appeals from Circuit Court (and Special and Central Criminal Courts). • Three judges.	Supreme Court — 3 or 5 judges: • Appeals from High Court. • Cases referred from Circuit Criminal and Civil Courts. • Constitutionality of a proposed law.

Part VII of the 1989 Act invests the HSA with the power to direct any of its staff or any other competent person (as defined in the Act) to investigate the circumstances surrounding any accident, disease, occurrence, situation or any other matters. Failure to comply with specified provisions of the Act or regulations made under S.28 is a criminal offence. The particular penalties are specified in S.49 of the Act. These include fines and terms of imprisonment. The maximum fine on summary conviction is IR£1,500 (€1,904). For conviction on indictment, the fine is imposed at the discretion of the court.

Under S.39(1) of the (1989) Act, the HSA may apply *ex parte* to the High Court for an order when it "considers that the risk to the safety and health of persons is so serious that the use of the place of work or part thereof should be restricted or should be immediately prohibited until specified measures have been taken to reduce the risk to a reasonable level". Since 1996 nine such orders have been issued by the High Court.

The *Roseberry Construction Company Ltd. v. McIntyre, Drennan and Hillis (2001)* case resulted in a landmark ruling under the Act. Two men were killed following an accident at a construction site, when a trench they had been working in collapsed on top of them. Investigations by the HSA and the Garda Síochána found there to be an "utter disregard" for health and safety on site, according to Judge Groarke. There was a compulsory obligation on the company to provide side-supports for trenches more than 1.25 metres deep. The trench in which the two men were working was 3.1 to 3.3 metres deep and had no supports in place.

Evidence that the equipment for providing the supports was on the site and that the subcontractor in charge of the trench had been informed twice of the need for supports, but appeared to be too busy to carry out his safety obligations, resulted in a record fine. In his judgement, Judge Groarke fined Roseberry Construction IR£200,000 (€253,947) for breaches of health and safety regulations and fined its director, Mr. McIntyre, IR£40,000 (€50,789). The subcontractor, Mr. Drennan, was fined IR£7,000 (€8,888) for breaches of health and safety legislation, while the driver of the digger that had been excavating the trench, Mr. Willis, was fined IR£1,000 (€1,270) on one count of failing to comply with the Act.

Another case that involved a criminal prosecution is *National Authority for Occupational Safety and Health v. Southern Health Board* (District Court 1999-2000). The substantive issue in this case concerned an employer who did not deal adequately with the risk of violence to its employees. The Southern Health Board pleaded guilty to breaches of sections 6 and 12 of the 1989 Act. The case originally arose as a result of the investigation of two incidents of violence against staff at Cork University Hospital. The Judge adjourned the case as a result of representations that specific preventative measures were implemented.

The first case involving the prosecution of individual directors and managers in Ireland was *National Authority for Occupational Safety and Health v. Noel Frisby Construction Ltd and Noel Frisby* (1998). The HSA inspector had found numerous contraventions of the Safety, Health and Welfare at Work (Construction) Regulations 1995 at a building site in Ardkeen Village, Waterford. When charged with breaches of section 6 of the Safety Health and Welfare at Work Act (1989) and section of the Safety, Health and Welfare at Work (Construction) Regulations 1995 (duties of contractors), both the company and Mr. Frisby pleaded guilty to the charges. The company was fined a total of IR£1,600 (€2,031) and Mr. Frisby was fined IR£400 (€508) under section 48(19) of the 1989 Act.

Figure 3.3 presents a summary of the proposed changes to the 1989 Act, which are due to become law towards the end of 2002.

Figure 3.3: Safety, Health and Welfare Act, 1989: Summary of Proposed Amendments

---

Section 9: General Duties of Employees

Where competence requirements necessitate an assessment of an employee's ability to perform work safely and without risk to others, then the employee should be under a duty to attend training and face enforcement action if he/she refuses to do so.

This may have an effect on disciplinary procedures where employees disobey orders and the employee can say he/she is within their rights until enforcement procedures are taken and concluded.

Section 11: General Duties of Persons Who Design or Construct Places of Work

Section 11 currently provides that those who design and construct places of work shall design and construct them so that they are, in so far as is reasonably practicable, safe and without risk to health. It is proposed that this requirement should extend to the maintenance of buildings during subsequent use.

Those who build or construct buildings will most likely find this proposal unreasonable, since normally the responsibility of the maintenance of a building is transferred to the client on completion.

Section 12: Safety Statement

A number of amendments are proposed:

1. As well as specifying how safety will be secured at work, employers will be required to specify how safety will be managed.

2. To take account of the judgement in the *Mullen v. Vernal Investments* case, when Mr Justice Barron held that an employer was not liable for an accident because it did not occur at the place of work, it is proposed that the words "at work" be substituted for "place of work".

3. Persons with responsibility for safety may be identified by name.

4. Instead of the provision that certain companies (effectively plcs) report on safety in their annual report, all employers will be required to carry out an annual review of their safety statement.

It is thought that employers should publish the review of their annual safety statement so that the information is available to all employees.

Section 13: Consultation and Safety Representatives

It is proposed that the section be amended to:

1. Give statutory recognition to safety committees, while not making them mandatory.

2. Make it clear that there may be more than one safety representative in a workplace.

3. Allow that safety representatives should be periodically entitled to time off for training and retraining.

Section 35: Improvement Directions and Plans

Within one month of the receipt of an Improvement Plan from an employer, an inspector should respond, indicating whether he/she is satisfied that the plan is adequate and, if the inspector is not satisfied, he/she may direct that the plan be revised and resubmitted within a specified time limit set out in the direction.

Section 36: Improvement Notices

Two amendments are proposed:

1. That a party on whom a notice has been served should have the right, where the party feels it has rectified the matters specified, to apply in writing to an inspector to review the situation and withdraw the notice.

2. That an inspector can seek confirmation from the notice party that the notice has been complied with.

Section 37: Prohibition Notice

As with an improvement notice, it is proposed that where a notice party believes they have complied with the notice, they can request an inspector to withdraw the notice and an inspector can request confirmation from the notice party that the notice has been complied with. The time period for appeals to the District Court against a notice would be increased from seven to 14 days.

Sections 42-45: Obtaining and Disclosing Information

The HSA is satisfied that it has the power to obtain information from individuals. In order to assist in framing policy, it is proposed that the Authority be given power to require organisations to provide information to the Authority.

The Authority would like to receive more information on the causes of accidents, types of injury from the Insurance Industry. Even though the Authority currently receives information, there is a feeling that it needs to be in more detail than previously.

There are also amendments proposed for functions of the Authority (section 16), advisory committees (section 17), review of legislation (section 27), power to make regulations (section 28), special reports and enquiries (section 46), powers to direct enquiries (section 47) and the position of HSA inspectors as witnesses at inquests (section 56). These amendments will affect the working of the Authority rather than the Safety Health and Welfare practices.

Offences

The most significant proposal for a new offence covers cases where, despite the existence of a serious, imminent and unavoidable danger to the safety, health and welfare of an employee, the employee is instructed to work, with the result that he/she suffers serious injury or death. Other proposals are that it shall an offence not to release employees for training and for employees to fail to attend training. Breaches of the new duties proposed will also be offences. These proposals all fall under section 48 of the Act.

Penalties

The Authority has recommended that penalties will include increased fines and the categorisation of offences. It is proposed that section 49 be divided into three categories of penalties, reflecting the gravity of the various offences.

Category One Offences

These offences would be triable in the District Court, under summary jurisdiction, with a maximum fine of €3,174 (IR£2,500) per offence. Included in this category are failures to have a safety statement; to specify the manner in which safety shall be secured (and in light of the recommendations, presumably managed); relating to hazard identification; to specify safety arrangements; to list names (to include job titles as a possible alternative); to comply with an inspector's direction; of the self-employed to prepare a safety statement; to consult employees and to inform safety representatives of an inspector's arrival at a place of work.

Offences of not releasing employees to attend training or the employee refusing to attend training and a safety representative's right to information are including under this category. It also takes account of obstructing an inspector and preventing a person answering an inspector's questions.

Category Two Offences
These offences may be tried summarily in the District Court or on indictment in the Circuit Court. If the accused is convicted , they may be fined to a maximum of €3,174 (IR£2,500). If the trial and conviction are on indictment, the fine can be for €31,740 (IR£25,000). Under the current terms of the Act, there is no limit on the fines that the Circuit Court can impose. To date the highest fine imposed has been €19,046 (IR£15,000). The Circuit Court's maximum in civil cases will be €101,579 (IR£80,000) from 1 January, compared to a previous limit of €38,092 (IR£30,000). Among the offences are breaches of the duty of care on employers, the self-employed, employees and other persons concerned with places at work and also designers/manufacturers/suppliers/importers as regards articles and substances at work. Other offences include making false statements, false entries in documents, forging documents, pretending to be an inspector, failure to comply with a court order and breach of conditions of a licence issued by the Authority.

Category Three Offences
These could be tried in the District Court or by indictment in the Circuit Court. A conviction would carry a fine, up to a maximum of €3,174 (IR£2,500) in the District Court and a maximum of €127,000 (IR£100,000) in the Circuit Court. There is also the possibility of a jail sentence of up to two years. The new offence of instructing an employee to work where there is imminent and serious danger will be classified as a Category Three offence, as will carrying on work in contravention of a prohibition notice.

On-the-Spot Fines
On–the-spot fines will apply where there is clearly a breach of statutory duty and where no injury is involved. Offences such as failure to have a safety statement and failure to report an accident are examples of an offences that could warrant an on-the-spot fine.

Defining Competence
There will be an attempt to define what "competent person" means. It is expected to be defined as: "a competent person shall be deemed to be one who, in respect of the task they are required to perform,

possess the necessary skills, relevant experience and/or qualifications considered necessary and appropriate to the nature of the work to be undertaken".

Consolidation

Section 6

Section 6 sets out the general duties of employers to ensure, in so far as is reasonably practicable, the safety, health and welfare of employees. General Application Regulations concerning the general duties of employers' (R5); protective and preventative services (R8); emergency duties (R9) information (R11); training (R13) and health surveillance (R15) will be incorporated into section 6.

Section 8

It is proposed that the duties under this section and section 6 that require employers and the self-employed sharing a workplace to co-operate be written into section 8.

Section 9

Duties on the correct use of machinery and use of PPE and its proper return to storage apply under section 9.

Section 12

The HSA recommends that section 12 be changed and have sections 8 and 11 incorporated into it. This would mean that section 12 would cover the designation of employees for protective and preventative services and risk assessment.

SAFETY, HEALTH AND WELFARE AT WORK (GENERAL APPLICATION) REGULATIONS, 1993

The 1993 Regulations must be viewed in the context of the Safety, Health and Welfare at Work Act, 1989 which places general duties on employers and employees as well as duties on employers to prepare a safety statement and to put in place a mechanism for consultation on health and safety issues. The Regulations make explicit what is already implicit in the 1989 Act. There is nothing novel or radical in the Regulations in that they are based on well-proven safety management measures and principles. They are best viewed as a framework for compliance and effective safety management because they define what needs to be done in some detail and articulate a range of fundamental issues such as consultation, training, information, manual handling and personal protective equipment which should be implemented by organisations.

Enforcement of the Regulations

The HSA's strategy for enforcement of these Regulations is similar to that for the 1989 Act. Enforcement is not viewed in isolation but takes place in the context of the objectives of the 1989 Act and the role and function of the HSA inspection. The Inspectorate of the Health and Safety Authority is the direct instrument of intervention and its primary function is to ensure compliance with the provisions of the 1989 Act and all associated regulations.

Inspection practice generally concentrates on assessing the effectiveness of the organisation's management of health and safety. The quality of safety statements is generally examined by focusing on how particular elements are implemented in the organisational setting. The inspector normally checks whether the issues raised in the Regulations are addressed and in place within the specific organisation. The overall purpose is to determine whether the information in the statement is adequate and whether it reflects the actual working conditions and practices in the organisation. Inspectors generally use a sampling approach to achieve this objective.

The HSA can prosecute through the courts if it is of the view that the law is not being followed. This course of action is generally considered slow, uncertain and expensive in terms of the use of inspectors' time. The 1989 Act and the 1993 Regulations enable the inspector to take executive action with court backing in three major ways. In essence, the strategy is gradual enforcement — a flexible incremental response to non-compliance by an organisation. The options available are as follows.

Improvement Direction and Plan

Where the inspector is of the opinion that activities involve or are likely to involve risk to the health and safety of persons, they may serve an Improvement Direction in writing on the person in control requesting the submission to them, within a specified time period for their approval, of an improvement plan setting out the proposed remedial action. If they are not satisfied with the plan, they may direct that it be revised.

Improvement Notice

Where an inspector is of the opinion that an employer is contravening any of the relevant statutory provisions, they may serve an Improvement Notice in writing on that employer. This notice will specify the provisions in question; give the reasons for their opinion; where applicable, state that the employer has failed to submit or implement an improvement plan and direct the employer to remedy the contravention.

An employer who is aggrieved by an improvement notice has a period of 14 days in which to appeal to a Justice of the District Court. The notice does not take effect for at least 14 days.

Prohibition Notice

Where the inspector is of the opinion that activities involve or are likely to involve a risk of serious personal injury to persons at any place of work, they may serve a Prohibition Notice on the person in control or the employer. The prohibition notice will state that the inspector is of a particular opinion, and will specify the matters which give or are likely to give rise to question, will specify whether there are contraventions of statutory provisions and prohibit the carrying on of the activities covered in the notice. An employer aggrieved by a prohibition notice may, within a period of seven days, appeal the case, but this will not delay the implementation of the prohibition notice.

When a prohibition notice is ignored, the inspector may apply for an order from the High Court to prohibit the continuance of the activities in question. The inspector has the power to revoke a prohibition notice.

The general practice suggests that inspectors are conscious that many employers are overwhelmed by the volume of Regulations and they allow a reasonable amount of time for the employer to become familiar with and implement them. However, where there are risks of serious injury that contravene the Regulations, the enforcement procedures will be utilised immediately. The core of modern inspection practice is generally the assessment of the workplace formulation of the safety statement and its effective implementation. This is usually effected through the implementation of a sampling approach.

Accident Reporting Requirements

The requirements of Regulations 58–63 of the Safety Health and Welfare at Work (General Application) Regulations, 1993 replace the accident reporting requirements of the Safety in Industry Acts, 1955 and 1980 and the Mines and Quarries Act, 1965. The requirement to report occupational accidents is extended to all places of work, to employees and the self-employed and to persons training for employment, as well as to persons not at work who may be injured as a result of work activities. The requirement to report an expanded list of dangerous occurrences as specified in Schedule XII has been extended to all workplaces except those covered by the Mines and Quarries Act, 1965, where the existing provisions continue to apply. The Regulations require that organisations keep records of all accidents.

The Regulations require that, when certain specified events occur, the responsible person must report the event in writing, in the approved form, to the HSA and must keep a record of it. In the event of death or of a dangerous occurrence, the responsible person must first notify the HSA by the quickest practicable means. The specified instances are as follows:

• The death of any person irrespective of whether they are at work as a result of an accident arising out of or in connection with work.

• The death of any employer or self-employed person that occurs some time after a reportable injury, but not more than one year afterwards.

• An accident to any employee or self-employed person that disables them from carrying out their normal work for more than three consecutive calendar days.

• Injury requiring medical treatment to a person not at work as a result of work activity.

- One of the list of dangerous occurrences specified in Schedule XII of the Regulations.

The responsible person may, depending on the circumstances, be the employer of an injured person, a self-employed person, someone in control of a premises where work is carried out, someone who provides training for employment or the next of kin of a self-employed person.

Separate forms have been approved for accidents and dangerous occurrences, with a supplementary form for other accidents. In all cases, the forms must be sent to the HSA.

Display Screen Equipment

Part VII of the 1993 Regulations set out provisions on "display screen equipment", which is defined as "any alphanumeric or graphic display screen, regardless of the display process involved". This definition incorporates other technologies apart from CRT, including liquid crystal display. This Regulation defines an "employee" as an individual who habitually uses display screen equipment as a significant part of their normal work. The identification of such individuals will take place during assessment and through employee consultation. A "workstation" is defined as including the screen and keyboard that comprises the interface between the operator and the screen. It also includes accessories such as diskette drive, telephone, modem, printer, document-holder, work-chair and work-desk. A number of exceptions from the requirements of the Regulations are as follows:

- Drivers' cabs or control cabs for vehicles or machinery
- Computer systems on board a means of transport
- Computer systems mainly intended for public use
- Portable display screen equipment not in prolonged use at a workstation
- Calculators, cash registers and any equipment having a small data or measurement display required for direct use of the equipment

- Typewriters of the kind commonly known as "typewritten" with windows.

The Regulations specify the employer's duties and compliance requirements in the Tenth and Eleventh Schedules.

There is an obligation on the employer to carry out a risk assessment of workstations to evaluate health and safety conditions. These health and safety conditions particularly apply to risks to eyesight, physical problems (muscle, bone and tendons), and mental stress problems. Where appropriate, the employer can analyse the workstation and take appropriate measures to remedy any risks found. The employer must ensure that employees have periodic breaks away from display screen duties. The employer must inform their employees about the measures they have taken with regard to risk reduction and breaks away from display screen work. Employers must also provide appropriate training for employees in the use of workstations before the start of such duties, and whenever any significant change takes place. The employer must "make available" eye and eyesight tests for employees.

Display Screens

The display screen must have clear characters, a stable image, adjustable brightness and contrast, and should be free of uncomfortable glares and reflections.

Keyboard

The keyboard must have a matt surface, an ergonomic arrangement of the keys and key symbols must be legible. The Eleventh Schedule specifies that the keyboard must be separate from the screen, and tiltable.

Environment

There must be sufficient space for the user to change position and vary their movements. In the Eleventh Schedule this requirement is considerably extended to the addition of requirements for a workspace that must provide adequate surface, an adjustable document-holder, adequate space for users to find a comfortable position, and a work-chair that must be stable and comfortable, have its height and back adjustable and the addition of a foot rest.

Employee/Computer Interface

The employer must ensure that software is suitable for the task, and it should be easy to use. Systems should provide feedback to employees on their performance and should display information at a pace, and in a format that is suitable to employees. The principles of software ergonomics should also be applied. We consider these in Chapter Seven.

Information and Training

There is a duty on employers to provide information and training to employees in relation to the measures that they have taken to comply with the Regulations. They must provide training to employees before they commence work with VDUs and also where the workstation has been substantially modified.

Lighting

In terms of lighting, this must be properly balanced and be free from glare and reflections. All radiation should be reduced to negligible levels. The Eleventh Schedule specifies that blinds must be provided to attenuate daylight, noise must be reduced to a minimum, equipment must not produce excess heat and an adequate level of humidity should be established and maintained. The Eleventh Schedule goes on to specify that software should be suitable for the task, "user friendly" and that there should be no quantitative or qualitative checking facility unless this has been agreed with the employees or their representatives. Systems should provide feedback to individual employees on their performance.

Eyes

There is a duty on employers to "make available" to every employee who requires it an eye test and eyesight test. An eye test is defined as an examination of the eye itself using an ophthalmoscope. This examination is normally carried out by doctors or optometrists. An eyesight test on the other hand is a test of a person's visual ability. This includes the ability to focus at various distances and to keep the two eyes co-ordinated. Small difficulties with visual ability may be what give rise to the need for glasses at various stages. In choosing whether to have an eye or an eyesight test, the employees may choose either or both. These tests must be made available before starting VDU-type work, at regular intervals thereafter or where an employee experiences visual difficulties that may be due to display screen work.

Optometrists and trained doctors may decide that the employee needs glasses for display screen work (for work at the 50 cm to 70 cm distance). These glasses must be paid for by the employer, but not glasses for any other purpose such as reading or distance vision. Where an optometrist or trained doctor detects any more complex problem, the employee must be referred to a specialist ophthalmologist at the employer's expense. **Figure 3.4** lists issues to be covered in VDU eyesight tests.

Figure 3.4: VDU Sight Tests: Issues to be Covered

- Ability to read N6 print at between 30 cm and 60 cm.

- Either monocular vision or good binocular vision. In the latter case, heterophoria should be well compensated, with prisms if necessary. Diplopia is not admissible.

- No obvious central (+/- 20 degrees) visual field defects in the dominant eye.

- Normal near point of convergence and accommodation for the user's age, clear ocular media. Absence of ocular disease.

- Normal colour vision is required only if the VDU work is unusually colour-dependent.

- Measurement and assessment of refractive error.

The Regulations on Carcinogens

The Regulations on carcinogens apply to all places of work where certain classes of carcinogenic substances, preparations or processes are used. A carcinogen is defined as anything that causes cancer and it can refer to a specific chemical substance or a particular job or industrial process with which there is seen to be an associated risk of cancer.

The classes of carcinogens coming within the scope of the Regulations are those substances classified as category 1 (known human carcinogens) or category 2 (suspect human carcinogens) under Directive 671548/EEC on the classification, packaging and labelling of dangerous substances. These substances also have the risk phrase, "R45 may cause cancer", applied to them.

Preparations, defined as mixtures of two or more substances that contain more than 0.9 per cent of a substance classified as a category 1 or 2 carcinogen in Annex 1 of Directive 67/548/EEC, must also be labelled as carcinogenic with "R45 may cause cancer", under the rules of Directive 88/379/EEC (S.I. 393 of 1992). Premises using such preparations will also fall within the scope of the Regulations.

The processes or types of work listed in the First Schedule of the Regulations come within the scope of the Regulations.

This Code of Regulations puts in place, for the time, specific legislation that obliges the user of carcinogens to carry out risk assessments, control the use of carcinogens, reduce the worker's exposure to carcinogens and to make health surveillance available to exposed workers.

Risk Assessment

This involves the identification of the carcinogens in use in the workplace, and assessment of their potential to harm the exposed worker. This potential is dependent on the physio-chemical properties of the carcinogens, the quantities used, the processes in which they are used and their potential to exist in the working environment. Most of this information should be available from safety data sheets.

Risk Reduction

Once the risk from a carcinogen has been identified, control measures must be implemented in order to reduce it and, where possible, to eliminate it.

Monitoring

Monitoring involves the quantification of the concentration of the carcinogen in the atmosphere to which the worker is exposed and also the concentration level with the threshold limit value for the carcinogen.

Information and Consultation

Workers exposed to carcinogens should be given the following information: the name of the carcinogens in use, their potential to cause cancer, the results of the risk assessments, the results of the monitoring programme and the personal protective equipment available.

The Regulations furthermore specify that consultation should take place between the employer and their employees on issues such as the evaluation of safety measures, the assessment of risks, limiting exposure, and training and record-keeping.

Health and Surveillance

The employer is obliged to make health surveillance arrangements available to employees that are appropriate to the risks involved. These arrangements should include the maintenance of records of the names of the workers exposed to carcinogens, name of the carcinogens, level of exposure, results of risk assessment and individual medical examinations.

The Regulations on First Aid

Part IX of the General Applications Regulations, 1993 specify the requirements for first aid. First aid is categorised into two areas: life saving and injury minimisation, and first aid in cases of minor injury. Employers have a duty to provide first aid equipment at each place of work. Where necessary, employers must also provide an occupational first aider.

First Aid Equipment

The Regulations stipulate that employers must provide first aid equipment that is adequate and appropriate, given the particular circumstances, so that first aid can be given where required. **Table 3.2** outlines the contents of different-sized first aid kits. While not hard and fast with respect to the types of dressings to be used, no ointments, tablets or pills should be kept in the first aid boxes. The only exception to this general rule is where specific antidotes have to be kept because of a particular risk prevailing within the organisation.

First Aid Rooms

Regulation 87 stipulates that certain places of work must be provided with a first aid room. This Regulation applies to new places of work established since 1993 and does not have a retrospective application, unless that place has undergone structural changes such as an extension or conversion after 1993. The first aid room must be provided where the size, type and scale of activity dictate, and/or where the level of accidents requires such a room.

Table 3.2: Contents of First Aid Box

Materials	First Aid Box Contents		
	1-5 Persons	6-25 Persons	26-50 Persons
Adhesive plasters	12	20	40
Sterile eye pads	—	2	4
Triangular bandages	2	6	6
Safety pins	2	6	6
Medium dressings	—	6	8
Large dressings	1	2	4
Extra large dressings	—	3	4
Individually wrapped wipes	8	8	10
Paramedic shears	1	1	1
Pairs of latex gloves	1	2	2
Sterile eye wash	1	2	2

The HSA provides guidelines on the types of premises that are required to provide first aid rooms. The HSA emphasises that, where the premises present a high risk from hazards, a first aid room must be provided with adequate staff and equipment. It must be kept fully stocked, cleaned and ready for use at all times. A first aider must always be available, and the room should never be used for any other purpose than the provision of first aid services. It must be spacious (with room to manoeuvre) and positioned near points of access/egress. The entrance to the room must be wide enough to accommodate an ambulance trolley, wheelchair or stretcher and must be effectively ventilated, heated and lit with provisions made for covering the floor, which must also be easy to clean. Waiting facilities and adequate signs must be in place so as to identify the room, while a further notice of the names where the first aiders can be contacted/located must be desplayed. The room must also have a means of communication, preferably a telephone.

Occupational First Aiders

The Regulations define an occupational first aider as a person who is the holder of a Certificate in First Aid issued in the last three years. An occupational first-aider who has done their basic three-day course will require a course of at least one day's duration if they renew their certificate every three years. The Certificate in First Aid must be issued by an occupational first aid instructor. Occupational first aid instructors must be recognised as such by an "approved" person. These bodies include organisations such as the Civil Defence, Irish Red Cross Society, NIFAST Ltd., Order of Malta Ambulance Corps, St. John's Ambulance Brigade and the National Ambulance Training School. Regulation 56 requires that every employer must ensure that an adequate number of first aiders are provided, given the number and type of hazards present in the particular workplace.

Particular places of work may also require specialised training for occupational first aiders. These include meat factories, woodworking factories, factories prone to accidents (more than one a week), hospitals, factories where the risk of poisoning by toxic substances exist, where there is a risk of burns and in underground mines. Other factors that must be considered include the distance between the place of work and medical services.

Regulations on Place of Work

Part III of the Regulations, together with Schedules II and IV, extend to most places of work many of the requirements that already existed under the Factories Act, 1955 and the Offices Premises Act, 1958. A number of places of work are not covered. These include: means of transport used outside the undertaking, construction sites, extractive industries, fishing boats and fields, woods and land forming part of an agricultural or forestry undertaking but situated away from the undertaking's buildings. Working out in the fields or in the forest is not covered by the Regulations; however, workshops and buildings attached to these industries are covered.

Stability and Solidity

There is a basic requirement for all places of work to be of sound construction and free from defects. The Regulations state that buildings that house places of work shall have a structure and solidity appropriate to the nature of their use.

Cleaning of Equipment

The Regulations state that any equipment and devices for use at work in a place of work or for prevention or elimination of hazards must be regularly cleaned to an adequate level of hygiene, and must be monitored and maintained to ensure that faults are rectified as soon as possible.

Ventilation of Enclosed Workplace

Five requirements are specified in the Regulations in respect of ventilation. These include the following:

- Steps must be taken to ensure that there is sufficient fresh air in the place of work, having regard to the working methods used and the physical demands placed on the employees.

- Where a forced ventilation system is used, it has to be maintained in working order.

- Any deposit or dirt likely to create an immediate danger to the health of employees by polluting the atmosphere shall be removed without delay.

- Any breakdown in a forced ventilation system should be indicated by a control system where this is necessary for the employees' health.

- If air conditioning or mechanical ventilation installations are used, they should operate in such a way that employees are not exposed to draughts that cause discomfort.

Room Temperature

The 1993 Regulations specify that, during working hours, the temperature in rooms containing workstations should be adequate for human beings, having regard to the working methods used and the physical demands placed on the employees. The temperature in rest areas, rooms for duty staff, sanitary facilities, canteens and first aid rooms must be appropriate to the particular purpose of that work area. Windows, skylights and glass partitions should allow excessive effects of sunlight to be avoided in places of work, having regard to the nature of the work and of the place of work. The issue of appropriate temperatures is dealt with in **Chapter 8**.

Doors and Gates

The Regulations require that doors and gates installed in places of work should be suitable for the number of persons employed and the nature of work carried out.

Movement of Pedestrians and Vehicles

Traffic routes should be organised in such a way that vehicular traffic and pedestrians can move throughout the place of work in a safe manner. The passageways should be wide enough and the surface suitable for the safe movement of the largest vehicle liable to use them. Allowance should also be made for the size and design of vehicles coming into the premises from outside. This only applies to new places of work.

All routes to emergency exits and the exit itself must be kept clear at all times, while danger areas must also be clearly indicated. Where employees operate in an area where a danger exists as a result of the possibility of objects or employees falling, the area must be equipped with devices that prohibit unauthorised entry. Furthermore, where employees are authorised to enter a dangerous area, they must be sufficiently protected.

Loading Bays and Ramps

Loading bays should have at least one exit point and, depending on their length, an exit point at each end may be required.

Room Dimensions

Workrooms should have sufficient surface area, height and air space to allow employees to perform their work without risk to their safety, health or well-being.

Outdoor Places of Work

This section extends certain requirements to outdoor places of work; it applies to places of work away from the main place of work.

Sanitary Equipment

This section sets out general requirements for the provision of toilet, washing and cloakroom facilities at places of work.

Windows and Skylights

It should be possible for employers to open, close, adjust or secure windows, skylights and ventilators in a safe manner.

Excavators and Travelators

This places an obligation on the employer to have in place emergency stop devices, etc.

Rest Rooms and Rest Areas

Rest rooms or rest areas for existing places of work and rest rooms for new places of work should be provided to help safeguard employee's health and to promote safety in an undertaking.

Pregnant Women and Nursing Mothers

Pregnant women and nursing mothers should be able to lie down to rest in appropriate conditions.

Employees with Disabilities

Places of work must be arranged to take account of employees with disabilities. Due to the variety of design options in facilitating access and safety for people with disabilities, and the wide range of disabilities and their varying degrees of effect, specialist advice should be sought from the National Rehabilitation Board.

Regulations on Work Equipment

Regulation 19 places a duty on employers to ensure that work equipment is suitable for the work to be carried out and is properly adapted for such purpose. In selecting work equipment, employees must take account of the specific working conditions and hazards in the workplace and any additional hazards posed by the use of work equipment. There is a requirement that an employee should not be required to use any excessively heavy piece of work equipment or to use 220-volt hand tools in damp or confined situations where low-voltage equipment could be used instead.

Where it is not possible to ensure that work equipment can be used by employees without risk to their health and safety, appropriate measures have to be taken to minimise exposure to risk. Work equipment must always be used for operations and under conditions for which it is appropriate.

There is a duty on employers to ensure that employees have at their disposal adequate information and, where appropriate, written instructions on the work equipment they are using. This should specify the conditions of use of work equipment, foreseeable abnormal situations and the conclusions to be drawn from experience, where appropriate, in using such work equipment. Specific requirements in this regard include the following:

- **Controls:** Work-equipment control devices that affect safety must be clearly visible and identifiable and appropriately marked where necessary. The controls used in the normal running of the equipment should not be placed where anybody using them might be exposed to a hazard, and they should be designed or positioned so as to prevent, as far as possible, accidental operation.

- **Controls for Starting Work Equipment:** It must be possible to start work equipment only by a deliberate action on a control provided for that purpose. This does not apply to restarting or a change in operating conditions as a result of a normal operating cycle or an automatic device.

- **Controls for Stopping Work Equipment:** There is a requirement that all work equipment must be fitted with a control to stop it completely and in a safe manner. The equipment's stop control must have priority over the start control. Where appropriate, and depending on the hazards, work equipment must be fitted with an emergency stop device. It should be easily reached and activated and easy to locate.

- **General Hazards:** Work equipment presenting hazards due to emissions of gas, vapour, liquid or dust must be fitted with appropriate containment or extraction devices (or both) near the source of the hazard. The Regulations specify that the most economical way to do this is to prevent such contaminants entering the air of the workroom by designing or fitting extraction devices as near as possible to the source of the hazard. Work equipment that presents hazards due to overturning or objects falling from it should be fitted with appropriate safety devices.

  Where there is a risk of physical contact with moving parts of work equipment that could lead to accidents, those parts must be provided with guards or devices to prevent access to danger zones or to halt movement of dangerous parts before the danger zones are reached. Access to dangerous parts of work equipment must be prevented or the movement of the dangerous parts stopped before any part of a person can reach it. Guards and protection devices must be of robust construction, not give rise to additional hazards, and easily removed or rendered inoperative.

  Work equipment parts that are a risk at high or low temperature must be protected to avoid the risk of employees coming into contact with these parts. Preventative measures may be designed into the equipment as well as organisational measures such as training and warning signs.

- **Warnings and Markings:** Work equipment must bear warnings and marking so as to ensure the health and safety of employees. Warning devices on work equipment must be unambiguous and easily perceived and understood.

Regulations on Personal Protective Equipment

The fundamental principle underpinning Part V of the 1993 Regulations is the notion that personal protective equipment should be used only as a last resort. Personal protective equipment (PPE) is defined as "all equipment designed to be worn or held by an employee for protection against one or more hazards likely to endanger the employee's health and safety at work, and any additional clothing, equipment or accessory designed to meet this objective". The Regulations specify that PPE does not include:

- Ordinary working clothes and uniforms not specifically designed to protect the health and safety of an employee.

- Personal protective equipment for the purpose of road transport.

- Sports equipment.

- Self-defence or deterrent equipment.

- Portable devices for detecting and signalling risks and nuisances.

The definition of "personal protective equipment" is considered broad enough to cover both clothing and equipment necessary for the employee to wear or hold to protect themselves against one or more risks to their health and safety while at work. It includes protective helmets, earphones and earmuffs, safety goggles and face shields, dust filters, protective gloves and garments, protective boots and shoes, barrier creams, life jackets, safety hazards and fluorescent clothing including armbands. These apply to all places of work.

Provision of PPE

There is a duty on every employer, where there is a risk to the health, safety and welfare of their employees, to avoid or limit such risks primarily by technical and organisational measures. If such measures are not adequate, personal protective equipment must be used to combat the unavoidable residual hazards.

The Regulations specify that no charge should be made to an employee for the provision of personal protective equipment where it is necessary to protect their health, safety and welfare when performing work. However, where the employee requests and the employer permits the use of the personal protective equipment outside the workplace, the employer may request a contribution towards the cost of the personal protective equipment. This cost must be equivalent to the additional wear and tear on the PPE.

The Regulations do not, however, address the issue of whether the employer has a duty to ensure that all PPE provided is worn. Byrne (1994), however, suggests that the duties imposed in relation to the selection and suitability of PPE would appear to indicate that they have a similar responsibility in relation to the wearing of PPE. Byrne (1994) also highlights that the common law duty of care must be borne in mind by employers in this context. English and Irish courts have emphasised the need for employers to follow through from the provision of PPE and make reasonable efforts to ensure that PPE is worn. The 1989 Act requires employees to wear PPE, but this does not mean that failure to do so on an employee's part will act as a defence for an employer. They are required to show what steps were taken to ensure that the PPE was worn, and that where none were taken, the effect will only be to reduce the level of compensation paid out by the employer.

Conditions and Compatibility

Regulation 23 states that the employer must determine the conditions of use of PPE, in particular the period for which PPE is worn, on the basis of: the seriousness of the risk, the frequency of the exposure to the risk, the characteristics of the workstation of each employee and the adequacy of the PPE.

Under Regulation 22, systematic analysis must be carried out before any PPE is chosen. Where more than one piece of PPE must be worn simultaneously, there is a duty on the employer to ensure that they are compatible and do not render either ineffective.

Employees also have duties imposed on them by the Regulations in respect of PPE. Once they have been provided with PPE, and given the necessary level of training and instruction, they must make full and proper use of PPE, use the PPE in accordance with the instructions given under Regulation 2b and take all reasonable steps to ensure that PPE is returned to storage after use.

Choosing PPE

Protective equipment may be used only if it is in perfect condition and fully capable of affording the protection expected of it. The selection of the personal protective equipment must also take account of the physical effort required in its use, the duration of use, the requirements for visibility, mobility and discomfort to the wearer and the proper wearing and fitting of the equipment. It is essential that the employee using the personal protective equipment should be consulted and involved in its selection.

Activities Requiring PPE

When faced with deciding which activities require the use of PPE, employers can take account of the Guide List of Activities contained in the Sixth Schedule of the Regulations. Regulation 21(3) states that they must take account of this list. It is not, however, exhaustive.

Assessment of Risks

The Regulations require employers to make an assessment to determine whether the personal protective equipment chosen is suitable for the risks involved. The level of the risk must be known so that the performance required of the personal protective equipment can be estimated and the level of protection realistically achieved.

Maintenance of PPE

The employer has a duty not only to provide, but also to maintain the personal protective equipment in good working order at all times, by any necessary cleaning, storage, repair or replacement. Personal protective equipment should be thoroughly examined by competent and properly trained staff in accordance with the suppliers' and manufacturers' instructions to ensure that it is in good working order before being used by the wearer.

Suitability of PPE

Regulation 21(2) states that an employer must ensure that PPE:

- Is appropriate for the risks involved, without causing increased risks.

- Takes account of existing conditions at the place of work.

- Takes account of ergonomic requirements and employees' state of health.

- Fits the wearer correctly after any necessary adjustments.

These activities must be carried out before the PPE is chosen. It is important that the employer ensures that the PPE is appropriate for the risks involved without causing increased risks. Byrne (1994) suggests that if the PPE selected is not "appropriate for the risks involved", it may not provide the level of protection required. Byrne goes further and adds that more damage may be caused, since the wearer may be under the impression that they are being protected when in fact they are not. Where there is a chronic hazard, the problem becomes particularly acute because measurements may have to be carried out before the equipment can be selected properly. Finally, all PPE bought and supplied must comply with national standards per Reg. 21(4).

Information, Training and Instruction

The employer has specific requirements under Regulation 26 to provide appropriate information, instruction and training to employees to enable them to make proper and effective use of any personal protective equipment provided, and to protect them against the health and safety hazards of the workplace. The training should include both the theoretical and practical elements required for efficient use of the personal protective equipment. Practical elements would include demonstrations in the wearing of PPE. They should also be made aware of the types of risks against which PPE protects.

Regulations on Electricity

These Regulations require precautions to be taken against the risk of death or personal injury from electricity in work activities and apply in all places of work. The Regulations replace the Factories (Electricity) Regulations, 1972 and the Factories (Electricity) (Amendment) Regulations, 1979. The 1993 Regulations are more concerned with general electrical safety requirements than with detailed specifications. It is envisaged that they will be supplemented or backed up by codes of practice issued or approved from time to time under Section 30 of the 1989 Act. The Regulations apply to all electrical equipment and installations in the workplace and to all work activities that have a bearing on electrical safety.

Regulation 34 states that the Regulations apply to "the generation, transformation, regulating, rectification, storage, transmission, distribution, provision, measurement or use of electrical energy in every place of work". This is a very comprehensive approach to the regulation of electricity use in industry. The Regulations apply in all places of work, except mines and quarries. Electrical equipment and installations used exclusively for testing and research purposes and medical electrical equipment are exempt from the requirements of the Regulations, but adequate precautions must be taken to prevent danger in all cases.

Hazardous Environments

Regulation 37 states that where electrical equipment is exposed to a hazardous environment, it should be constructed and installed in such a way as to ensure that individuals are protected from the dangers outlined in Regulation 36. Hazardous environments (as outlined by the Regulation) include: the possibility of mechanical damage; the effect of weather, natural hazards, temperature on pressure; the effects of wet, dirty, dusty, or corrosive conditions; and any flammable or explosive substance or atmosphere.

Duties of Employers

As a result of these duties, employers must put in place and regularly review appropriate procedures for the use of electricity. Employers must comply with these Regulations and any other relevant codes of practice. Employers must also ensure that the use of electricity in their particular workplace complies with industry standards such as BS 5345, which is concerned with electrical equipment for use in potentially explosive atmospheres.

Identification and Marking

Regulation 38 points out the need to identify and mark equipment so as to prevent dangers occurring. Regulation 39 states that live parts that may cause danger must be covered by insulating materials or have suitable other precautions taken for them. Finally, Regulation 40 states that, where any conductive part may become live, earthing and automatic disconnecting of the supply so as to prevent danger must be put in place.

Suitability and Condition of Electrical Equipment

Electrical equipment must be constructed, installed, maintained, protected and used so as to prevent danger. Danger is defined in the Regulations as:

> ... risk of death or personal injury or danger to health from electrical shock, electric burn, electrical explosion or explosion caused by the use of electricity or from mechanical movement of electrically driven equipment.

There is a requirement that it should be appropriate to the environmental conditions to which it is exposed and should be suitably identified and marked.

Protection against Electric Shock

Protection against direct contact should be provided either by insulation, or other precautions should be taken. Protection against indirect contact should be achieved either by earthing and automatic disconnection of supply or by other suitable means (see Regulations 39 and 40).

Portable Equipment

Portable equipment supplied at a voltage above 125 volts should be protected by a residual current devoid (RCD) with a tripping current not exceeding 30 milliamps.

On building sites or in wet areas, portable equipment (unless its rating exceeds 2 KVA) must be supplied at reduced low voltage (not exceeding 125 volts) and portable hand lamps are restricted to 25 volts (see Regulation 41).

Finally, where a transformer is used to supply electricity to portable equipment at a voltage not exceeding 125 volts, or a portable handlamp at a voltage not exceeding 25 volts AC, it must be of the double-wound type and the centre point of the biver or secondary winding must be earthed.

Overcurrent Protection

Protection must be provided against the effects of excessive currents due either to faults or overloads. This is usually achieved by fuses or circuit breakers (see Regulation 43). Under Regulation 42, every electrical joint and connection must be of adequate construction as regards conduction, insulation, mechanical strength and protection to prevent the danger referred to in Regulation 36.

Safety in Work Activities

Danger arising from working at or near electrical equipment must be prevented. The Regulations envisage that this can be achieved by the provision of suitable switching and isolation facilities; precautions against electrical equipment already dead becoming live; safe work procedures and practices; and the provision of adequate working space, access and egress and adequate lighting where work is being carried out in an area in which electrical equipment could pose danger (Regulation 47).

Competence in Electrical Work

Adequate knowledge of electricity, experience and understanding of electrical work, and an ability to recognise potential hazards are required before engaging in electrical work. Where electrical work is carried out that might give rise to dangers specified in the Regulations, the individual working in such a situation must have adequate technical knowledge and experience so as to prevent such danger or else be under close supervision. The Regulations do not specify the qualifications required. Where outside contractors are utilised, electrical work must comply with the National Rules for Electrical Installations.

Live Work

Regulation 46 (2) states that live work (where equipment is connected to a source of electricity supply or is in normal use) cannot take place unless: it is unreasonable for the equipment to be dead; it is reasonable for the person in question to be at work on the live equipment; and suitable precautions, including the provision of protective equipment, are taken to prevent the danger referred to in Regulation 36.

Testing and Inspection

All new electrical installation must be inspected and tested by a competent person after completion and a certificate of test completed. Inspectors may require similar inspection, test and certification of existing electrical installations.

Regulations on Manual Handling

In almost all sectors of industry the manual handling of loads (i.e. transporting or supporting a load by hand or bodily force, including lifting, putting down, pushing, pulling, carrying or moving) will be undertaken.

In May 1990 the EU adopted a Directive on manual handling that, in general, requires employers to avoid the need for manual handling where there is a risk of injury or, where this is not possible, to assess their manual handling operations and take appropriate steps to avoid or reduce that risk.

Manual handling is defined by the Regulations as any manual transporting or supporting of a load by one or more employees and includes: lifting, putting down, pushing, pulling, carrying or moving a load that involves a risk to employees. There are three components to Part Six of the Regulations that deal with manual handling: (a) the duty to avoid manual handling, (b) the duty to reduce risk where manual handling is unavoidable, and (c) the duty to provide training and information to employees.

Avoidance of Manual Handling

Risks from the manual handling of loads are best avoided by the elimination of such operations. In situations where this is impracticable, manual handling should be minimised as far as is reasonably possible. Regulation 28 (a) provides that employers should consider all systems of work in their place of work involving manual handling of loads and, where appropriate, redesign tasks to avoid the need to move loads manually and to fully utilise mechanical handling devices, for example, lift trucks, pallet trucks, trolleys, conveyors, chutes and scissors lifts.

Where necessary, additional mechanical handling devices should be introduced to avoid or reduce manual handling operations.

Assessment

Where the employer cannot avoid the hazardous manual handling of loads, there is an obligation to make an assessment of such operations likely to be carried out in the workplace. The assessment should identify where improvements or other measures are necessary to reduce the risk of injury from manual handling. Four specific factors must be considered.

- **The task**: Are there any tasks that involve foreseeable risks? For example, unsatisfactory body movements or posture; excessive lifting or lowering distances, for example from floor level to above waist height; excessive pushing or pulling distances, or situations where the load is required to be held or manipulated at a distance from the trunk.

- **The load**: Are there any loads unsuitable for manual handling, for example, too heavy, bulky, slippery, wet, sharp, unknown offset centres of gravity, unstable or contents likely to shift?

- **The working environment**: Are there any areas of the workplace unsuitable for manual handling operations, for example constricted work areas, narrow aisles, areas of extreme temperature (hot or cold), over-steep slopes or changes in floor level?

- **The individual person's capability**: Are there any employees unsuitable for manual handing operations, for example, pregnant workers, people with known medical conditions?

Where the assessment process identifies manual handling of loads where there is a risk of injury, appropriate measures should be implemented to reduce those risks as far as is reasonably practicable.

Information and Training
The 1993 Regulations specify that where it is reasonably practicable to do so, employers should give employees precise information about the weight of a load and, where the centre of gravity is not centrally positioned, the location of the heaviest side of the load, perhaps by ensuring that the weight and/or the heaviest side is clearly marked on the load itself. Where this is not done, employers should give employees a general indication of the weights and centres of gravity of the range of loads to be handled sufficient to make employees aware of the potential risks.

There is also a duty on employers to ensure that employees clearly understand how a manual handling operation is designed to safeguard their health and safety. Training activities should complement a safe system of work and not be a substitute for it. A training programme should provide a clear understanding of:

- How potentially hazardous loads may be recognised.

- How to deal with unfamiliar loads.

- The proper use of handling aids.

- The proper use of personal protective equipment.

- Features of the working environment that contribute to safety.

- The importance of good housekeeping.

- Factors affecting individual capability.

- Good handling techniques.

SAFETY, HEALTH AND WELFARE AT WORK (GENERAL APPLICATION) (AMENDMENT) REGULATIONS, 2001

In May 2001, acting under powers conferred by the Safety, Health and Welfare at Work Act 1989, the Government introduced the following amendments to the Safety, Health and Welfare at Work (General Application) Regulations, 1993.

Regulations on Work Equipment

Regulation 19(e – m) requires that employers provide their employees with adequate information and comprehensible written instructions, where appropriate, on any work equipment. Such information must relate to the conditions of use of the equipment, any foreseeable abnormal situations that may arise, and, where applicable, the conclusions to be drawn from the experience of using such equipment.

Employers are obliged to make employees aware of the safety and health risks relevant to them, of work equipment present in the workplace, and any changes affecting them in relation to work equipment situated in their immediate work area, even if they do not use the equipment.

If the safety of work equipment depends on the installation conditions, there is a requirement that inspections are carried out before and after the equipment is put into service. Inspections must also be carried out by a competent person on work equipment that is exposed to potentially deteriorating conditions. Such inspections must be carried out periodically, or where exceptional circumstances arise that are liable to make the equipment unsafe. The results of these inspections must be recorded and kept for five years from the date of inspection for assessment by inspectors of the National Authority for Occupational Safety and Health. In the event of such work equipment being used in another place of work, it must be accompanied by evidence of the last inspection carried out.

Regulations 21-27 outline the safety measures to be taken with mobile work equipment. Specifically, mobile work equipment with ride-on employees must be fitted and designed so as to reduce the risks for employees during the journey. Potential risks include trapping by wheels or tracks; seizure of the drive unit; the rolling over of the equipment; and risk of the employee being crushed between parts of the equipment and the ground.

Health and safety regulations relating to self-propelled work equipment are covered in Regulations 28-33. Any self-propelled equipment that could, in motion, give rise to potential risks must have facilities for preventing unauthorised start-up. Stopping and braking equipment must be in place, with auxiliary devices installed where the driver's direct field of vision is inadequate to ensure safety. Self-propelled work equipment used at night must be equipped with appropriate lighting so that the work may be carried out. Only those employees who have been appropriately trained may drive self-propelled work equipment. Employers also have a duty to implement measures to prevent employees on foot coming within the area of operation of any self-propelled work equipment. If the work can only be done properly with employees on foot in the area, appropriate measures must be taken to prevent them from being injured by the equipment.

Regulations on the lifting of loads

Regulations 34-49 cover the lifting of loads by work equipment. The strength and stability of permanently installed equipment must be assured and displayed by means of clear markings as to the safe working load for each configuration of the machinery. Any accessories used in lifting loads must clearly identify the characteristics essential for safe use. Such accessories must be stored in a way that ensures they will not be damaged. The installation of this equipment must minimise the risk of the load striking employees, drifting dangerously or falling freely, and being released unintentionally. Where equipment is used for lifting or moving employees, precautions must be taken to prevent the risk of the unit falling or the user falling from said unit. Persons may only be lifted by means of equipment and accessories specifically provided for this purpose.The control position must be manned at all times while lifting employees and a reliable means of communication must exist.

Employees must not be present under suspended loads, unless required for the effective operation of the work and loads must not be moved above unprotected workplaces usually occupied by employees. Where the operator of such equipment cannot observe the full path of a load either directly or by auxiliary means, a competent person must be in communication with the operator to guide him or her and organisational measures taken to prevent collisions of the load that could endanger employees.

Employers must ensure that all lifting operations are properly planned, appropriately supervised and carried out with the safety of the employees in mind. Measures should also be implemented to avoid the resultant risks of control being lost over the lifting of a non-guided load in the event of a complete or partial power failure. Suspended loads should not be left without surveillance unless access to the danger zone is prevented and the load has been safely suspended and is safely held.

Open-air use of work equipment for non-guided loads must be discontinued where meteorological conditions jeopardise the safe use of the equipment and expose employees to potential risks.

CHAPTER ROUND-UP

- Legislation on health and safety imposes a wide set of legal duties on employers. These duties are generally strict in nature and are subject to the rules of statutory interpretation. Such interpretations by their nature create precedents that may be binding in any further consideration of issue.

- The Mines and Quarries Act, 1965 regulates the health, safety and welfare of employees working in mines and quarries. The majority of its provisions are qualified by the criterion of practicability. The Act imposes a set of duties relating to entrances, protection from falling down shafts, roads in mines, and support, ventilation and lighting.

- The Safety, Health and Welfare at Work Act, 1989 represents the most comprehensive set of provisions on safety management. It is a framework Act imposing a range of duties on employers, employees and designers. The key feature of the Act relates to its formulation of the safety statement as a primary means of managing safety within the organisation. The Act makes provision for safety representation by employees and includes detailed provisions relating to the powers of safety inspectors.

- The Safety, Health and Welfare at Work (General Application) Regulations, 1993 and 2001 give effect to many of the principles of safety set out in the 1989 Act. The regulations make explicit rules and regulations on key safety issues such as manual handling, personal protective equipment, consultation, the work environment, first aid, training and electricity. The regulations are clearly based on effective safety management measures.

Chapter 4

STATUTORY REGULATION OF SAFETY, HEALTH AND WELFARE: OTHER LEGISLATION

INTRODUCTION

This chapter considers other important pieces of primary and delegated legislation in the area of health and safety. A significant amount of delegated legislation is now formulated in the form of regulations or administrative actions. This legislation is significantly driven by legislative developments within the European Union (EU). This chapter will first consider the influence of the EU on health and safety legislation and then discuss how these directives have been implemented in Ireland.

This chapter first considers the role of the EU in formulating health and safety legislation. It then discusses specific pieces of legislation dealing with occupier's liability, fire services, dangerous substances, maternity, smoking in the workplace, working time and safety in construction.

THE ROLE OF THE EU IN OCCUPATIONAL SAFETY, HEALTH AND WELFARE

The main focus of EU health and safety legislation in recent years has been on the Framework Directive and its subsidiary directives, which are generally referred to as the daughter Directives. The principal reason why these Directives have been the subject of so much attention is that many of them impact on health and safety across the entire range of workplace activity.

While the focus of attention has previously been on Directives, the EU has been very active in enacting or proposing legislation to control the use, preparation, marketing and labelling of chemicals, and other substances that might be dangerous.

Three EU institutions make legislation. They are:

- **The European Commission**. This is the body that proposes legislation. A Commissioner who wishes to propose legislation must obtain the support of a majority of colleagues in the Commission. There are 20 members of the Commission. The Commission is divided into Directorates. The Directorate concerned with Social Policy is DG V, which is responsible for health and safety issues.

- **The Council of Ministers**. This is the body that must approve legislation. Health and safety legislation is the concern of the Social Affairs Council. A government Minister from each member state sits on the Council. Working on the Council is a Committee of Permanent Representatives. Working Groups do the detailed work. The Social Questions Working Group considers all health and safety proposals.

- **The European Parliament**. The Parliament debates proposed Directives. It may suggest amendments to Directives. Most health and safety legislation proposals would be debated twice in Parliament. However, the Council of Ministers may, if it is in unanimous agreement, overrule amendments.

Social policy legislation must be proposed under the auspices of Article 118 of the Treaty of Rome as modified by Article 118A or by a tripartite consultative process involving the Union of Industry and Employer Confederations in Europe (UNICE) and the European Trade Union Conference (ETUC), under which the Commission consults with these bodies to seek agreement for what might best be called an idea. If the idea finds support, it becomes a proposal and may then be adopted as a Directive.

In general, the Commission proposes, the Council of Ministers approves and the Parliament debates. In practice, it is a long-drawn-out, complex process. In general, the European way is to negotiate, to bring people along and to get as much agreement as possible. While the European Court of Justice does not feature in the legislation-creating process, it may have a role to play if it is asked to decide whether a legislative proposal is properly proposed.

The Dangerous Agents/Substances Directives have been implemented. Ireland's record on implementing the Social Policy, Health and Safety Directives is generally considered reasonable. The Danes have the best implementation record. Among those with poorer records are Greece, Spain, Portugal, Italy and, surprisingly, Belgium and Germany.

The question of the late and/or partial implementation of EU directives has been considered in a number of cases. European law in general indicates that once a deadline for a directive passes, the principles found in the directive are legally enforceable. In the case of *Francooch v. Italian Republic* (1991), the European Court of Justice found that the State would be liable if individuals suffer damages as a result of infringements of community law. It identified three conditions for the application of this rule:

- The directive must involve the granting of rights to private individuals.

- The contents of these rights must be identified by reference to the provisions of the Directive.

- There must be a causal link between the breach of the member state's obligations and the damage suffered by the individual concerned.

How a claim for compensation is to be processed is a matter for each individual state.

On the question of partial implementation, the situation is less clear. It appears that where there is doubt the courts will look back to the Directive to clarify the situation.

THE REGULATION OF FIRE: THE FIRE SERVICES ACT, 1981

A range of statutory provisions regulates fire in Ireland. The Fire Services Act, 1981 updates the organisation of the fire service at national level and imposes general statutory duties on persons who have control over certain premises as well as people in those premises. Sections 16–19 deal with the organisation of fire services at a national level. The specific provisions are as follows:

- Each local authority is designated as a fire authority under the Act.

- There is an obligation placed on the fire authority to make appropriate provision for the prompt extinguishing of fires in buildings, to establish and maintain fire brigades and to ensure adequate provision for the reception of and response to calls.

- There is an obligation to train fire personnel in effective fire-fighting.

- The Act enables the Fire Services Council to carry out an advisory role, prepare codes of practice, standards or regulations relating to fire.

The remainder of the Fire Services Act, 1981 deals with fire fighting and safety within premises. There is a set of general obligations placed on persons who control premises to ensure effective fire-safety arrangements. The Act specifies that the following premises are covered:

- Those used for the provision of sleeping accommodation.

- Institutions that provide treatment or care.

- Premises used for purposes of entertainment, recreation or instruction, or for use as a club, society or association.

- Premises used for the purpose of teaching, training or research.

- Premises used for any purpose where there is access to the premises by members of the public, irrespective of whether they pay.

Section 55 of the Safety, Health & Welfare at Work Act, 1989 includes a factory as one such premises. The duty placed on the person having control of the premises is to take all reasonable steps to guard against fire and to take all reasonable steps to ensure that persons on the premises are safe in the event of a fire. There is also a duty imposed on such persons to conduct themselves in such a manner that they are not exposed to fire as a result of an act or omission of theirs.

The Fire Safety in Places of Assembly (Ease of Escape) Regulations, 1985 specify certain details to which the person in control has to adhere in places of assembly, to ensure that persons can use escape routes safely in the event of a fire. **Figure 4.1** presents a checklist of fire precautions that should be taken to observe the provisions of the Fire Services Act (1981).

Figure 4.1: Fire and Fire Precautions: A Checklist

- Have we acted in accordance with S 18 of the Fire Services Act to (a) take reasonable measures to guard against the outbreak of fire? and (b) to ensure the safety of persons on the premises if fire breaks out, in so far as is reasonably practicable?
- Is our building potentially dangerous (S 19 Fire Services Act) because of the absence of adequate:
  ◊ fire extinguishers/fire fighting appliances?
  ◊ means of escape?
  ◊ automatic detection?
  ◊ emergency lighting?
  ◊ fire procedure notices?
  ◊ power supply and/or lighting systems?
  ◊ heating or ventilation systems?
- Is there anything of an inflammable nature in or on the building, including construction materials and furniture or fittings that makes the building dangerous (S 19 Fire Services Act)?
- Has a fire safety notice under S 19 Fire Services Act been served on us, and have we:
  ◊ complied with it?
  ◊ appealed it?
- Have we taken account of fire in our emergency plan (S 6.2(g) Safety, Health & Welfare at Work Act, 1989)?
- Do we have adequate means of access and egress (S 6.2(b) Safety, Health & Welfare at Work Act, 1989)?
- Does our emergency plan (SI 44/93 Reg 9) take account of fire and:
  ◊ note fire services to contact?
  ◊ provide information for and training of staff?
  ◊ ensure fire fighting equipment is available?
  ◊ provide for orderly evacuation of premises?
- If we build a new building, alter or extend or change the use of our existing building, we need to obtain a fire safety certificate (Building Control Regulations (1991 S 8).
  ◊ have we done any of these things?

◊ have we obtained a fire safety certificate?

◊ are we planning to do any of these things?

- Have we got in place a fire detection system that complies with IS 3218:1989?

- Have we checked our fire extinguishers?

- Building demolition — have measures been put in place to ensure people are not at risk from fire (S1 138/95 Construction Regulations, Reg 9)?

- Do the provisions for fire fighting and rescue of the Mines and Quarries Act (S 69) and Regulations S1 226/72) apply to any of our workplaces?

- If so, do our arrangements comply with requirements?

- Can the organisation produce a fire certificate upon request?

- Who is responsible for fire precautions in the organisation?

- Is the fire log up to date?

- Has a fire drill taken place in the last 12 months?

- Do employees know what to do if they discover a fire or hear the fire alarm?

- Are fire marshals and deputies formally trained?

- Does the induction procedure include a thorough fire briefing outlining all fire exits and assembly points?

- Do daily inspection arrangements include a check to ensure that all fire routes and exits are clear of any obstruction?

- When we conduct a fire drill, do all occupants leave the building apart from nominated key staff required to remain to attend to essential duties?

- Does our evacuation plan include arrangements to hold a post-evacuation wrap-up meeting and a communication to staff on the success or otherwise of the drill?

- Whenever changes in layout are made, is the effect upon existing exit signs, extinguishers, audibility of alarms and so on, taken into account at the planning stage?

- Do the plans attached to our fire certificate reflect the present layout?

- Does everyone have two routes of escape in case of a fire?

- Are the routes to escape clearly visible?

Sections 19–20 provide that a fire authority can serve a fire notice where it is of the belief that a building is potentially dangerous. A potentially dangerous building is defined as one, which would, in event of a fire occurring in it, constitute a serious danger to life. **Figure 4.2** presents some of the factors that may lead a building to be considered potentially dangerous.

Figure 4.2: Potentially Dangerous Building Criteria

- A large number of people visit the building.
- The flammable nature of the materials used in the building or of the furniture and fittings in the building.
- The absence of proper means of egress from the building.
- The absence of adequate fire equipment, emergency lighting or means of escape.
- The absence of adequate steps in the procedures to be followed in the event of fire.
- The nature of the material stored in the building.
- The possibility that a fire would spread quickly.
- The system of power supply or lighting is defective.
- The heating or ventilation is defective or presents a fire hazard.
- Any other justifiable reason.

CODE OF PRACTICE ON FIRE

The Department of the Environment has issued a code relating to fire. The code itself does not absolve the company of its responsibility to comply with any separate measures, which a Fire Authority may specify.

Section 1 — Management Duties

This section outlines the main responsibilities of management in relation to fire safety. It stresses the importance of undertaking an appropriate fire safety programme, and the need to appoint a responsible person to take charge of it. The various duties are described in general and are outlined, as appropriate, in more detail in later sections.

Section 2 — Fire Prevention

Day-to-day fire prevention measures are a key element in the fire safety management of premises. The Code recommends a number of appropriate precautions, including the establishment of good housekeeping practices, periodic inspections, the identification and elimination of potential fire hazards both inside and outside the premises and the application of safety rules.

Section 3 — Staff Training

The safety of users of places of assembly will be enhanced if staff know what to do both before and during an outbreak of fire or other emergency. This can be achieved by ensuring that all staff (including temporary and part-time personnel) receive appropriate instruction and training.

Section 4 — Fire and Evacuation Drills for Management and Staff

Management and staff should undertake these drills so that they will be familiar with what should be done in the event of a fire occurring. The section outlines a range of procedures that should be followed in the event of a fire or other emergency.

Section 5 — Informing the Public

It is extremely important that, in a place of assembly, members of the public be fully aware of the fire safety precautions in the premises. This can be achieved by the display of notices regarding the action to be taken in the event of a fire or an alarm being given and also by announcements before the commencement of entertainment, etc. and at regular intervals at which the public are present.

Section 6 — Escape Routes

The Fire Safety in Places of Assembly (Ease of Escape) Regulations, 1985 provide that certain fire safety precautions related to escape routes and exit doors should be taken by every person having control over a place of assembly and that a person in a place of assembly shall not prevent or obstruct the person in control from complying with the Regulations. The Regulations are repeated in this Code as ease of escape is an integral part of the process of fire safety in places of assembly. Additional management guidance is given as to precautions necessary to ensure the effectiveness of escape routes.

Section 8 — Assisting the Fire Brigade

This section details measures that should be taken to assist the fire brigade when it is responding to a fire or other emergency call.

Section 9 — Record Keeping

It is essential that a record be kept of the actions taken to implement and oversee the fire safety programme. This section outlines the information that should be recorded.

THE OCCUPIERS' LIABILITY ACT, 1995

The Occupiers' Liability Act, 1995 was enacted to increase the protection for occupiers of land against claims by trespassers and recreational users. It was hoped that it would create a climate where occupiers are not deterred from making their land available for recreational users because they are fearful of being sued for personal injuries.

The Act was heavily influenced by the Law Reform Commission's Report on occupiers' liability. Some of its key recommendations were as follows: to divide entrants into two separate classes (visitors and trespassers), to ensure a common duty of care existed towards all visitors, a duty not to injure trespassers or recreational users intentionally, to have no special exemption for child members who are recreational users or trespassers and that occupiers should be able to extend or restrict their liability by means of agreement or notice.

In order to be classified as a recreational user, the person in question must not pay in any way for the privilege of entry. Parking fees are the exception to this rule. The Act refers to the imposition only of a reasonable charge.

A trespasser is defined in S.1(1) as an entrant other than a recreational user or visitor. Section 4(1) provides that an occupier owes recreational users or trespassers on premises a restricted duty not to impose injury or cause injury to be imposed on them. Further, they owe them a duty not to injure their property intentionally and not to act with reckless disregard for them or their property unless, and in so far as, the occupier has extended their duty in accordance with S.5. In this case, negligence principles do not apply and the duty of the occupier is set at a lower level. The section adopts the approach that trespassers and recreational users should largely be able to take care of themselves. Therefore, occupiers will not be liable except where they intentionally behave with reckless disregard for the presence of an entrant.

In determining whether or not an occupier has acted with reckless disregard, regard shall be had to all the circumstances of the case including the following factors (S.4(2) of OLA):

1. Whether the occupier knew of or had reasonable grounds for believing that a danger existed on the premises.

2. Whether the occupier knew or had reasonable ground for believing that the person and, in the case of damage, property of the person, was or was likely to be on the premises.

3. Whether the occupier knew or had reasonable grounds for believing that the person or the property of the person was in, or was likely to be in, the vicinity of the place where the damage existed.

4. Whether the danger was one against which, in all the circumstances, the occupier might reasonably be expected to provide protection for the person and property of the person.

5. The burden on the occupier of eliminating the danger, or of protecting the person and the property of the person from the danger, taking into account the difficulty, expense or impracticability, having regard to the character of the premises and the degree of the danger of so doing.

6. The character of the premises, including the desirability of maintaining the tradition of open access to premises of such a character for such an activity.

7. The conduct of the person, and the care which they may reasonably be expected to take for their own safety while on the premises, having regard to the extent of their knowledge thereof.

8. The nature of any warning given by the occupier or another person of the danger.

9. Whether or not the person was on the premises in the company of another person, and if so, the extent of the control the latter person might reasonably be expected to exercise over the other's activities.

The Act defines a "visitor" as person whose presence on the premises is lawful. The term covers those invited onto a premises by the occupier as well as those permitted by the occupier to be there. It also embraces, as of right, those authorised under statute to enter premises for some official purpose.

The status of visitor is conferred by virtue of the purpose of the visit. Therefore, a shop customer who steals goods would be engaged in an activity inconsistent with the purpose for which he or she is on the premises, namely to look at or buy goods. By engaging in the act of theft, the status of visitor is lost.

Section 4(3) of the Act provides that an occupier shall not be liable for a breach of the duty imposed by S.4(1)(b) where a person, who enters a premises, or while present thereon, commits an offence, save where the court determines otherwise in the interests of justice.

Section 3 establishes the duty of care that is owed by occupiers of premises to visitors. The duty is in effect the "common duty of care". Consequently, there is an obligation on the occupier to take reasonable care to ensure that the visitor does not suffer personal injury or damage to his or her property as a result of any danger existing on the premises. The effect of this provision is to apply general negligence principles to this area of law. Consequently, before any liability may be imposed, there must be a breach of the duty that an occupier owes to a visitor and the damage suffered by the visitor must be caused by that breach. The duty owed will depend on the facts of each particular case and what is reasonable in all the circumstances.

Section 3 makes particular provision for the care of children accompanied by an adult. It is reasonable for an occupier of premises to assume that a child visitor, in the company of an adult visitor, would be supervised and controlled to some degree. However, it is most unlikely that this section will operate to significantly relieve an occupier of a duty of care towards a child. Historically the judicial approach in all courts towards child plaintiffs has been sympathetic, and particularly so where the child has suffered serious injury. In *Meaney v. South Dublin County Council* (1995), the High Court held that there was both an onus on a person in control of a child to avoid foreseeable risk and an onus on the plaintiff to prove that the occupier owed the child entrant a duty and that duty was breached. A similar approach is likely to be adopted in cases arising under the OLA.

The Act introduces a new category of entrant called a recreational user. Recreational users are defined as those persons who, without payment of any charge, enter onto premises to engage in a recreational activity carried on in the open air. Such recreational users may include people who engage in hill walking, hunting or swimming, as well as a team sport such as football. The recreational user classification similarly applies to those who visit sites or buildings of historical, national or scientific significance. Where an occupier permits a recreational activity to be engaged in, it will not automatically result in the elevation of an entrant to the visitor status.

Modification of Duty by Occupier

Under Section 5, an "occupier" may modify the level of duty owed to entrants. This is possible where the occupier, in the form of a notice or agreement, takes on a higher duty towards entrants than is required by the Act. The occupier has the power to reduce the level of duty owed to entrants, by use of notices or by agreement, provided that the occupier takes reasonable steps in bringing the notice or agreement to the attention of the entrant and acts reasonably in doing so. However, the basic duty owed to trespassers and recreational users is the minimum duty, which the occupier can impose on other types of entrants. Warnings that are sufficient to enable a visitor, having regard to the warning, to avoid injury or damage may also absolve an occupier from liability.

Section 6 provides that an entrant who is not a party to a contract cannot have their rights taken away by that contract. In other words, an occupier who has a contract with an independent contractor to allow certain persons onto the premises for the purposes of carrying out work cannot incorporate into that contract agreed with the independent contractor any clause that diminishes the occupier's duty to those persons to that which is owed to a trespasser. An occupier may not be liable under Section 7 of the Act, provided he has taken reasonable care in engaging an independent contractor, for any injury or damage caused to an entrant as a result of the independent contractor's negligence.

Defences

The Act does not affect the general defences of self-defence, the defence of others and the defence of property. In *Ross vs. Curtis* (1989), the High Court held that reasonable force may be used to repel a thief, where the occupier feared that he was in imminent danger. The contributory negligence provisions of the Civil Liability Act, 1961 still apply, and therefore entrants who contribute to their own injury as a result of failing to take reasonable care for their own safety will be faced with a reduction in the damages awarded for injuries sustained where liability is proven in an action against the occupier.

Other Provisions

Section 8 specifies three additional provisions:

* **Self-defence, the defence of others or the defence of property.** The existing law that an occupier is permitted to use reasonable and proportionate force to defend his property is retained.

* **Any liability imposed on an occupier as a member of a particular class of persons.** Section 8(b) provides for the retention of the common law duty of care that an employer owes to an employee. For example, employers owe a specific duty to their employees to provide them with a safe place of work, safe system of work, competent staff and proper equipment. This section also preserves the wide range of employers' duties towards employees enshrined in the health and safety legislation.

* **Ultra-hazardous activities.** Section 8(c) reinforces the protection that employees had previously where ultra-hazardous activities are concerned. Where such ultra-hazardous activities

are involved, the occupier may not delegate his obligations to, for example, an independent contractor.

Figure 4.3: Recent Cases on Occupier's Liability

In *Geraghty v. Glynns Hotels Ltd* (1997), the plaintiff suffered a fractured ankle from a fall on a wet and slippery floor. Her ankle was in plaster of Paris for some time and she had to undergo physiotherapy. She had made an almost full recovery. She suffered intermittent pain, particularly in bad weather, and occasional swelling. She had difficulty walking long distances. The doctors did not anticipate arthritis. Her injuries had been complicated by prior congenital hip difficulties but this could not be attributed to the accident. The judge awarded IR£10,000 (€12,700) general damages for pain and suffering to date and IR£5,000 (€6,348) for pain and suffering in the future. In addition he awarded IR£1,124 (€1,427) special damages and a certificate for senior counsel. An order for costs had previously been made.

In *Corrigan v. Meagher and Others* (1997), the plaintiff, who was aged 16 at the time of the accident, trained twice weekly in the martial art of Tae Kwon-Do at the local school hall of the Presentation Convent in Cashel. During a training session, the plaintiff was performing Tae Kwon-Do in his bare feet on the floorboards, as was usual, when he lost his footing. He sustained a dislocation to his left patella. The injury was painful and did not heal well due to a pre-existing condition of which he was unaware. The school hall had a wooden floor, about 30-40 years old, with soft wooden boards. Nails protruded on occasion and were hammered down, but there was no evidence that nails played a part in the incident. The plaintiff claimed that the floor had become slippery and dangerous either through perspiration or through waxing and that the room was hot and clammy. There was some conflict of evidence as to when the accident occurred and as to how many people were present.

The judge dismissed the claim. He held that a person who provides premises or who acts as an instructor in respect of sporting activities does not guarantee that there will be no injuries. A person who takes part in a sport must accept the inherent risks and must bear the consequences, unless, on the balance of probabilities, the injury was caused by the negligence of some other party. The judge held that the hall had been used for PE for many years and for Tae Kwon-do for a number of years and that it was well maintained and suitable for the purpose and that there was sufficient ventilation. There was no allegation that the instructor mis-instructed the plaintiff or asked him to do something of which he was incapable. The defendants sought costs against the plaintiff who was now of age. The instructor had paid insurance premiums to the Irish Amateur Martial Arts Association but that body had issued him a fraudulent certificate. Accordingly, he was uninsured and was personally liable in the action. Nevertheless, the judge refused to make a costs order.

Liability of Landlords as Occupiers

Because of the way in which the term occupier is defined in the 1995 Act, it is envisaged that a landlord may, despite having let premises, find himself liable to tenants. The existing case law provides some justification for this view. In *Clancy v. Dublin Corporation* (1988), the Supreme Court ruled that a visitor to the premises might recover damages for injuries received after falling down a stairs. The stairs had a defective rail installed by the landlord. There was evidence that the accident might have occurred due to the visitor's drunkenness. If, however, the tenant or the stranger creates the danger, then the landlord will not be liable.

THE MATERNITY PROTECTION OF EMPLOYEES ACT, 1994

With the introduction of the Maternity Protection of Employees Act, 1994, many of the protections and entitlements afforded to employees under existing legislation have either been altered, or new entitlements and protections have been added. The purpose of the 1994 Act is to provide protection for all pregnant employees, employees who have recently given birth and those that are breast-feeding. The service qualification, which is associated with many pieces of employment legislation in Ireland, does not apply here. All female employees who have notified their employers of their pregnancy are covered. Employees who are employed under a fixed-term contract are covered by the Act so long as the pregnancy arises before the expiration of that fixed term.

The length of maternity and adoptive leave has been increased with effect from 8 March 2001. The Maternity Protection Act, 1994 (Extension of Periods of Leave) Order 2001 and the Adoptive Leave Act, 1995 (Extension of Periods of Leave) Order 2001 provide that maternity leave is extended by four weeks to 18 weeks and it also provides for a further four weeks of unpaid leave. The employee is entitled to take a total of eight weeks of unpaid leave. In the case of adoptive leave, the employee is entitled to 14 weeks leave with Adoptive Benefit from the Department of Social Community and Family Affairs and/or pay from the employer where this is specified in the contract of employment. The same arrangements apply in respect of Maternity Benefit and maternity pay from the employer.

Pregnant workers are entitled to take time off from work, without loss of pay, to attend antenatal and post-natal care medical appointments. The entitlement in respect of post-natal appointments applies during the first 14 weeks immediately after the birth. The employee is obliged to give the employer two weeks written notice on each occasion when time off is required to attend appointments, except in the case of the first appointment where they may be obliged to produce an appointment card.

Where health and safety risks are identified and it is not technically or objectively feasible to move an employee to other suitable work, employees will be entitled to health and safety leave.

Leave on Grounds of Health and Safety

Under the Safety, Health and Welfare at Work Act, 1989, it is a requirement to have a risk assessment carried out in respect of employees who are pregnant, who have recently given birth and employees who are breast-feeding. If a risk is identified by such an assessment, the employer is then obliged either to remove the risk or, where that is not possible, move the employee to more suitable work. If it is not possible to move the employee to "suitable other work" given the practicalities of the situation, then the employee is entitled to safety leave and the employer is obliged to make a payment to the employee for the first three weeks of that leave.

The employer will be obliged to pay the employee only once in respect of one period encompassing the pregnancy, its consequent confinement, the following 14-week period of having recently given birth and the attendant period of breast-feeding, if any, up to six months' duration. Furthermore, the leave in the first three weeks can be for a number of shorter periods and need not necessarily be one continuous period. A certificate stating the reason, as well as the commencement and finish dates of the leave, must be given to the employer. If the employee is on a fixed-term contract and the leave coincides with the end of the contract, the leave will end. Finally, where the conditions that gave rise to the leave no longer apply, the leave will end, or where the leave runs up to the date that the maternity leave is due to commence. There is an obligation on the employee to notify the employer when they are no longer vulnerable to the risk that gave rise to the leave in the first place.

Protective Leave

Where an employee is on maternity leave, health and safety leave or where a father is entitled to leave as a result of the death of the mother and during natal care absences, the employee is deemed to be in the employment of the employer. Therefore, all employment rights that would include annual leave, increments and seniority are preserved as if the employee was not absent from work at all. Public holiday entitlements were also maintained during maternity leave and leave where a father is entitled to it (death of mother) although employees absent on health and safety leave do not retain such entitlements. Even where additional leave is concerned, the employee's employment relationship with the employer continues to exist although the absences do not count as reckonable service, and in turn affect rights that employees obtain based on reckonable service.

Return to Work after Health and Safety Leave

Under Section 20 if, while the employee is on leave, the employer does find work which is suitable, or where they are able to remove the risk that gave rise to the leave in the first place, the employer must notify the employee immediately in writing and the leave will cease.

If an employee who was breast-feeding was granted leave and ceases to breast-feed, she should notify her employer who will take all reasonable steps to grant the employee the position she held prior to the commencement of the leave. If a pregnant employee who was granted leave becomes aware that her circumstances have changed so that she is no longer vulnerable to the risk that gave rise to the leave in the first place, she should notify the employer. Again, her employer must take all reasonable steps to grant the employee the position she held prior to the commencement of the leave. In all of the cases relating to Section 20, the leave will cease seven days after the employee has received notification, or as soon as the employee resumes work, whichever is the earlier.

Protection from Dismissal or Suspension

An employee who is absent from work on protective leave or natal-care absence is protected against an employer seeking to terminate their employment, suspend the employee from employment or giving notice of termination of the employment that would expire subsequent to the absence. An employee who is dismissed solely or mainly as a result of exercising their legal right under the Act has been dismissed unfairly (Unfair Dismissals Acts, 1977-1993). If the employee is dismissed as a result of her pregnancy, as a result of giving birth or from breast-feeding, that dismissal is deemed to be unfair.

Where an employee's contract is terminated under the Redundancy Payments Act, 1967–1984, the Unfair Dismissals Act, 1977-1993 or the Minimum Notice and Terms of Employment Act, 1973, the date of the termination of the contract shall be from the expected date of return to work as notified to the employer.

Any disputes, so long as they do not pertain to a dismissal or a health and safety risk, can be referred by either party to a Rights Commissioner within six months of the commencement of the dispute. On receipt of a decision, the parties have leave to appeal to the Employment Appeals Tribunal within four weeks. **Figure 4.4** presents a number of questions that should be considered by organisations in respect of the maternity legislation.

THE PARENTAL LEAVE ACT, 1998

The Parental Leave Act, 1998 sets out two forms of leave that may be taken by employees. The Act applies to "employees", which is given a broad meaning to include all those who work under a contract of service or of apprenticeship or under which a person agrees to do or perform work personally. It includes office-holders working for the State and the Garda or the Defence Forces, Local Government Officers, Officers of Health Boards and Vocational Education Committees.

Figure 4.4: Compliance with the Maternity Legislation: Some Questions

- In our safety statement, have we identified pregnancy/maternity associated hazards, assessed risks and put controls in place?

- If an employee informs us she is pregnant/breast-feeding, have we carried out a health and safety assessment?

- Have we informed the employee or her representative of assessment results?

- The assessment indicates a risk. We must see whether we can: (a) remove the risk; (b) protect against it; (c) if neither of the above can be done, adjust the working conditions or hours or both.

- If we cannot remove or protect against the risk or change conditions/hours, have we offered suitable alternative work.

- If no suitable alternative work can be offered, have we offered health and safety leave.

- Has employee on health and safety leave requested a health and safety leave certificate?

- Have we given it?

- Does it state: leave granted, commencement date, expected leave period?

- Have we given employee details of her earnings so that she may lodge same with the Department of Social Welfare in order to claim health and safety leave benefit?

- While on health and safety leave, the employee must be paid by us for the first 21 days. Have we paid her at the rate of her normal weekly wage?

- The circumstances at work have changed, making health and safety leave unnecessary. We must notify employee without delay. Have we done so?

- Have we taken action to inform employees or their representatives of the measures taken concerning their health and safety during pregnancy/maternity?

Some of the more specific provisions of the Act are as follows:

- The right to parental leave is given to natural and adoptive parents. An adoptive parent is one in respect of whom an adoption order has been made and continues in force (Section 6(9)). The leave must be taken before a child reaches the age of five. But, for the adoptive parents of a child born on or after 3 December 1993 and adopted between then and 2 June 1996, and who was aged between 3 and 8 at the time of adoption, the leave must be taken within two years of the adoption order and can be taken at any time up to 31 December 2001.

- The right applies to both parents of a child but there can be no transfer of one parent's right to another. Each is entitled to it but may not exchange it (Section 6(7)).

- In order to be entitled, the employee must have completed one year's continuous employment before any period of parental leave begins (Section 6(4). An exception is made for people who have at least three months' service by the latest day on which they could commence a period of parental leave but the period of the leave is restricted to one week for each month of continuous employment at the time of the commencement of the leave. Parental leave is 14 weeks in total. The period may be taken all at once (Section 7(1)(a)). If not, agreement between the employee and the employer or their respective representatives is required so that the employee may take the leave in periods of days or even hours. The precise calculation of the shorter periods is left for agreement, but in default a statutory provision is made (Section 7(2)(a)(ii)).

- For parents with more than one eligible child, the maximum of 14 weeks may not be exceeded in any one year. An exception to this is made for children of a multiple birth. Any longer period in respect of children (not multiple births) requires the consent of the employer (Section 7(3)).

- An employee must give two notices. By Section 8(1) not later than six weeks before the commencement of the leave, the employee must give notice of their proposal to take leave. This must specify the date it starts, its duration, "the manner in which it is proposed to be taken" and it must be signed. Once given, it can be revoked provided a "confirmation notice" has not been given. A confirmation notice (Section 9(1)) must be given at least four weeks before the commencement of the parental leave, again specifying the date of the commencement, the duration and the manner of the leave and it must be signed. In other words, this must confirm the earlier notice. An employee who does not comply with the notice requirement may still have parental leave counted but this requires the agreement of the employer who has a discretion to grant it (Section 8(4).

- Once a confirmation document has been given, the employer and employee may agree to postpone leave or part of it, or to curtail it or vary it in any manner in which they agree. The confirmation document must be amended accordingly. Curtailed parental leave can be taken at any other time as agreed.

- The employer may object. Under Section 11(2) an employer receiving a notice of parental leave might take the view that it would have "a substantial and adverse effect on the operation of his or her business", etc. The reasons for this must be:

  ◊ seasonal variations in the volume of work.

  ◊ the unavailability of a person to carry out the duties of the employee seeking parental leave.

  ◊ the nature of their duties.

  ◊ the number of employees in employment.

  ◊ the number of employees whose periods of parental leave coincide with the relevant employee's.

- In these circumstances, the employer may give notice to the employee not later than four weeks before the intended commencement of the leave postponing the leave to such time not later than six months after the intended commencement date, as may be agreed upon by the employer and the employee. Any notice given under Section 11 by the employer must first be preceded by consultation, and the grounds for the postponement must be set out in the employer's statement given under Section 11. Parental leave may not be postponed more than once unless the ground is seasonal variation in the volume of work. In this case, it may be postponed twice.

- Once both parties have signed a confirmation document, postponement is not possible. If, during the period of postponement, the child attains the age of five (or an adopted child the age of eight), the right continues and is extended accordingly.

It is specifically provided by Section 12 that there should be no "abuse" of this provision. The entitlement is subject to the condition that it must be used to take care of the child concerned. An employer who has reasonable grounds for believing that it is not being used for this purpose may give notice terminating the leave. The notice must contain a statement of the grounds for this belief. A notice such as this requires the employee to return on the specified date. When an employee who gives a Section 8 notice to an employer who believes that they are not entitled to parental leave, the employer may refuse to grant it.

The Parental Leave European Communities Regulations 2000 extend the entitlements of parental leave to certain parents of children born a specified period outside the date range of the principal Act. The 2000 Regulations provide the following extended entitlements:

- Natural (and adoptive) parents of children born between 3 December 1993 and 2 June 1996.

- This extension entitles parents to 14 weeks parental leave in respect of each child born or adopted within those dates.

- Parents must avail of the new entitlements not later than 31 December 2001.

Force Majeure Leave

Force majeure Leave is provided for in Section 13 of the Parental Leave Act, 1998, and the Parental Leave (Notice of *Force Majeure* Leave) Regulations, S.I. No. 454/98.

This section of the Act entitles an employee to paid time off where, for urgent family reasons owing to the injury or illness of an immediate family member, the immediate presence of the employee is required. Under these circumstances, the employee is entitled to paid leave of up to three days in any 12 consecutive months, or five days in any 36 consecutive months. Part days shall be regarded as full days for the purposes of the maximum number of days one can take (IBEC, 1999). Although the injury or illness of the appropriate persons justifies the taking of *force majeure* leave, interestingly, the death of one of these persons is not stated to be sufficient grounds for taking the leave (*Irish Law Times*, 1999).

Employers' concerns with this new entitlement are that it will be treated as an automatic entitlement to additional paid sick leave. It is for this reason that IBEC have encouraged their members to call the entitlement Emergency Leave or Emergency Family Leave (IR Databank, May 1999). A study on Parental Leave for SIPTU of 28 union branches indicated that the leave was more commonly known as "emergency leave". From an employee's perspective, the stipulation that part days are regarded as full days is disappointing. The nature of an emergency suggests that an employee will be contacted initially at their employment, consequently their first day's leave entitlement may only represent a fraction of their working day, e.g. one hour.

Scope

The immediate family members covered by the Act include:

- A child/adoptive child of the employee.
- A spouse or person with whom an employee is living as husband and wife.
- A person to whom the employee is in *loco parentis*.
- A brother or sister of the employee.
- A parent or grandparent of the employee.

In the author's opinion, the scope of the Act is clearly defined. However, one case has gone before a Rights Commissioner in this regard. This claimant argued, unsuccessfully, that his mother-in-law came under the scope of the Act (this case is considered in more detail below).

Service Requirement/Protection of Employment Rights

There is no service requirement for an employee to take *force majeure* leave. This is to be welcomed, as there is an increasing number of part-time and short-time workers emerging in Ireland. During an absence on *force majeure* leave an employee is regarded as being in the employment of the employer, and retains all of their employment rights. *Force majeure* leave cannot be treated as part of any other leave (e.g. sick leave, adoptive leave, maternity leave, annual leave, or parental leave) to which the employee is entitled (IBEC, 1999). This is in keeping with the definition of parental leave as described above.

Notice

By definition, prior notice does not arise in the case of *force majeure* leave. The nature of Emergency Leave means that the urgent family reasons due to injury or illness of an immediate family member cannot be forecast or predicted in advance (IR Databank, May 1999). For an injury to qualify, therefore, it must be of a substantial nature and an employee's presence must be indispensable. Illness is not defined or qualified in the legislation, but equally it must be of a nature that requires the immediate and indispensable presence of the employee.

By not defining illness, the legislation has failed to provide both employers and employees with any direction or guidelines. The need for an employee's presence to be indispensable is also ambiguous. As will be seen in later sections, the poor wording of this section of the legislation has led to disagreements having to be ruled on by a third party.

An employee who has availed of the entitlement must, as soon as is reasonably practicable thereafter, give written notice to their employer stating that they have taken such leave and the date on which it was taken. The employee must also include a statement of the facts entitling them to the leave (IBEC, 1999). This part of the legislation can become problematic if employees are unwilling to give full details of their circumstances, possibly due to the upsetting nature of their absence. In one case that came before a Rights Commissioner (PL 37/99/JH), the Commissioner was unimpressed when it became evident that the employer was not aware of the full facts.

The Statutory Regulations referred to above prescribe a formal Notice to Employer of *force majeure* leave to be completed by an employee immediately following their having availed of the entitlement. The regulations permit employers to tailor this Notice to their own requirements provided that it contains the essential information and declaration prescribed.

The statutory form of notice, which must be submitted, does not, in itself, absolve the employee of the obligation to inform the company of their absence as soon as possible in accordance with the normal company rules. It must be borne in mind, however, that the type of circumstances which might reasonably justify the taking of *force majeure* leave might also be expected to militate against the strict adherence to normal company policy in this regard (IBEC,1999).

Evidence

The legislation does not require an employee to furnish their employer with any independent evidence in support of them having taken *force majeure* leave. Equally, however, that does not in any way preclude an employer from seeking appropriate independent evidence from an employee who has taken *force majeure* leave to show that it was not inappropriately taken or, more seriously, was taken by the employee under false pretences (IBEC, 1999). A point to note, however, is that there are no provisions in the legislation equivalent to those relating to parental leave for dealing with a situation where an employer believes that an employee is abusing *force majeure* (*Irish Law Times*, 1999).

Reference of Disputes to Rights Commissioner

The employer or employee may refer a dispute in relation to entitlement under the Act to a Rights Commissioner. Disputes concerning the dismissal of an employee are dealt with under the provisions of the Unfair Dismissals Acts, 1997 and 1993. A reference to the Rights Commissioner concerning a dispute in respect of Parental/*Force Majeure* leave under the Act must be made in writing within six months of the occurrence of the dispute (IBEC, 1999). This provision in the Parental Leave Act, 1998, regarding the resolution of disputes does not apply to members of the Defence Forces.

Appeal from Decision of Rights Commissioner/Redress

Either party may appeal a decision of the Rights Commissioner to the Employment Appeals Tribunal by giving written notice to the Tribunal within four weeks of the date on which the Rights Commissioner's decision is given. To date the number of cases referred to the EAT is quite low due to the relatively short time that the Act has been in force. The Rights Commissioner and the Employment Appeals Tribunal may order redress, as they consider appropriate, comprising either or both of the following:

• The granting of parental leave

• The payment by the employer of compensation not exceeding 20 weeks' remuneration. Employers have been critical of the extent of remuneration available, especially considering the ambiguity surrounding some aspects of the legislation.

Enforcement by the Circuit Court

If a person fails or refuses to comply with a decision of the Rights Commissioner or a determination of the Tribunal, the other party, or the Minister for Justice, Equality and Law Reform, may apply to the Circuit Court for an order directing compliance (IBEC, 1999). The proper Circuit for such proceedings is the county in which the employer (not the employee) ordinarily resides or carries on any business, profession or occupation (*Irish Law Times*, 1999). Either party to proceedings in the Employment Appeals Tribunal may appeal a determination to the High Court on a point of law only.

Protection against Dismissal

An employee is protected against dismissal if they exercise, or propose to exercise, their rights to Parental/*Force Majeure* leave. Protection is also available if an employee is not permitted to return to work following a period of Parental/*Force Majeure* leave.

In *Carey v. Employment Appeals Tribunal*, the High Court overturned the RC's and EAT'S decisions on a case involving the docking of a day's pay when a mother missed work to look after her daughter. Ms Justice Carroll overturned the tribunal's finding and directed that Ms. Ann Carey's employer, Penn Racquet Sports of Mullingar pay a day's pay under *force majeure* provisions of the PLA 98. The mother involved was concerned that a rash on the child's body might have been a serious illness. Following a visit to her GP, Ms. Carey was assured that the rash was not serious. The judgement by Justice Carroll took account of the mother's inability to diagnose the seriousness of the illness and the fact that Ms. Carey was a lone parent coping with this crisis on her own. Justice Carroll pointed to the "overly restrictive" view of the RC and the EAT in this case, and deduced that it was reasonable for Ms. Carey to take the view that her immediate presence with her daughter was indispensable. As Ms. Carey lived some distance away from her workplace, it was not possible for her to return to work on the day in question. This case, and the extent to which Ms. Carey was willing to pursue the issue, points to the emotive nature of these type of disputes, with Ms. Carey quoted as saying that "she has forgotten about the day's pay — but she was very hurt at the time" (IT, JAN 13, 01, web). Justice Carroll stipulated that S13 provisions should not be "interpreted based on an *ex post facto* analysis as to whether the illness or injury was sufficiently urgent to warrant the leave" (ELR, March 2001, p1). The ruling in this case is important in that it is the first determination to overturn both the RC and the EAT decision and points to the claimant's interpretation of the problem at the time of the crisis as an issue to be considered in future decisions.

Table 4.1 provides a summary of the most controversial aspects of the Parental Leave Act in respect of *force majeure* leave.

Table 4.1: Summary of Recent Rights Commissioner Decisions on Force Majeure Provisions of Parental Leave Act, 1998

Cases	Date	Gender of Employee	Outcome	Reason Given by Rights Commissioner
C Meehan v Wyeth Medicia	12/04/00	Female	Not Granted	Claim did not fall into the category of FM for the 2nd and 3rd day of illness
D Quinn v APW Enclosures Systems	16/04/99	Male	Not Granted	Mr Quinn's presence at home on the day in question was not "indispensable"
M Quinn v APW Enclosures Systems	16/04/99	Male	Not Granted	Mr Quinn's presence at home on the day in question was not "indispensable"
V Mason v R Hudson, H&K Dublin Ltd	12/04/99	Male	Granted, 1 Day	The interpretation of "immediate" in this dispute is the period of time commencing at the cessation of work on one day and finishing at the cessation of work the following (consecutive day)
G McKiernan v Boxmore Plastics	16/09/99	Male	Granted, 1 day	If circumstances are such that an employee must, by necessity, be physically present for the purposes of providing support or comfort for a relative on a short term, urgent basis this meets the requirements of the purpose of the Parental Leave Act in respect of FM
T Fitzpatrick v Boxmore Plastics	16/09/99	Female	Granted, 1 day	Ditto

Cases	Date	Gender of Employee	Outcome	Reason Given by Eights Commissioner
D Crowe v Boxmore Plastics	16/09/99	Female	Granted, 1 day	Ditto (3 cases ruled on together)
M Conroy v Cappagh Orthopaedic Hospital	12/10/99	Male	Granted, 3 days	In the absence of any objective rules regarding the use of the word "indispensable", one can only apply a "reasonable subjective test" to the present circumstances
S Hanaway v Securicor Ireland Ltd	18/05/99	Male	Granted, 1 day	His presence was absolutely essential and necessary thus falling within the meaning and intention of the Act
A Carey v Penn Racquet Sports	07/09/99	Female	Not Granted	The symptom proved to be indicative only of a minor ailment
M Dutton v E Hudson, H&K Dublin	12/04/99	Male	Not Granted	Mr Dutton's knowledge of the appointment well in advance precluded him from benefit under the Act
S Kearns v Eastern Health Board	17/01/00	Male	Not Granted	The illness from which the child suffered did not make the presence of the appellant indispensable

Cases	Date	Gender of Employee	Outcome	Reason Given by Rights Commissioner
M Gill v Fruit of Loom	15/02/00	Female	Granted, 2 days; 1 day not given	1st day personally caring for the child, 2nd day letter from hospital supports her claim, however on the third day given that there is an early finishing time she should have made other arrangements
A Doherty v Fruit of Loom	15/02/00	Male	Granted, 1 day; 1 day not given	Statements from his GP and subsequently by Letterkenny General Hospital entitled him to 1 day. There is no evidence that he attempted to make alternative arrangements for the other day. It was not absolutely necessary that he be the parent to continue to stay
D&M Quinn v APW Enclosures	21/10/99	Male	Granted, 1 day;, 1 day not given	His presence was indispensable the first day because his family was ill and there was a possibility of meningitis
D Munnelly v Warners (Eire) Teoranta	20/01/00	Male	Not Granted	He failed to show that his presence at the hospital was indispensable
AN Other v Company X	01/11/99	Male	Not Granted	The claimant's immediate presence with his daughter was not indispensable
AN Other v Company Y	01/11/99	Male	Not Granted	The Act does not confer any entitlement on an employee arising from the illness of a mother-in-law

Cases	Date	Gender of Employee	Outcome	Reason Given by Rights Commissioner
P Connors v Waterford Stanley	28/10/99	Male	Not Granted	The worker's claim was rejected based on the doctor's determination that his presence was not needed for tonsillitis
SIPTU & Mallinckrodt Medical	31/05/99	Female	Not Granted	Consecutive days can qualify but the qualifications of "urgent", "immediate" and "indispensable" must apply on each day
SIPTU and Gallagher Dublin	06/08/99	Female	Granted, 2 days; 1 day not given	Granted for the second also but not the third, stated the illness of a small child is obviously of importance to a single parent
SIPTU and Mallinckrodt Medical	09/03/00	Female	Not Granted	The claimant on Sunday foresaw the problem that could arise on Tuesday, and had an opportunity to make arrangements for same
Kearns v Eve Holdings	08/03/00	Male	Not Granted	The illness from which the child suffered did not make the presence of the claimant indispensable once the child was returned home
O'Halloran v Tillotson Ltd	29/03/00	Female	Not Granted	The claimant had failed to show that her immediate presence was indispensable
McGaley v Liebherr Container Cranes Ltd	27/03/00	Male	Not Granted	The claimant had failed to show that his immediate presence was indispensable

CARER'S LEAVE ACT 2001

The Carer's Leave Act 2001 provides for the temporary absence from employment of employees for the purpose of providing full-time care and attention to a person requiring it. In particular, the Act is designed to protect the employment rights of the employee during the period of absence. The Act applies to all employees who have one year of continuous service and there is a prohibition on the employer denying the employee the right to take the leave.

Entitlement to Carer's Leave

The Act sets out a number of requirements in respect of an employee's right to take Carer's Leave. These key requirements are:

- The employee must be employed for a continuous period of 12 months.

- The relevant person or persons in need of care must be in need of care on a full-time basis.

- The employee must provide the employer with a written decision from a Deciding Officer who is an officer of the Department of Social Community and Family Affairs. The leave cannot be taken until this decision is received by the employer.

- The employee may be required to prove that he/she will be providing full-time care and attention to the relevant person.

- An employee will not be entitled to take Carer's Leave where another employee is absent from employment during the same period and is caring for the relevant person.

- The employee is generally limited in undertaking any paid employment during the period of the leave.

- The employee is entitled to a period of Carer's Leave for one relevant person at any one time.

The Extent of the Leave

Where an employee meets the requirements, he/she will be entitled to take leave for a period not exceeding 65 weeks. It may be taken as one continuous block of 65 weeks or in a number of periods, the duration of which do not exceed 65 weeks. The Act allows the employer to refuse, on reasonable grounds, a request by an employee for a period of leave of less than 13 weeks duration. The employee is entitled to be informed of the grounds for refusal in writing. Where an employee takes a number of periods within the 65 weeks, there must be an interval of six weeks where it applies to the same person. Where it applies to another relevant person, the interval must be six months.

The employee must provide the employer with a minimum of six weeks notice of his/her intention to commence Carer's Leave. If exceptional or emergency circumstances exist, this notice period may be waived and the employee may take the leave as is reasonably practicable. The employee must inform the employee of the proposed start date, the manner in which it is to be taken, the duration of the leave, and include a copy of the Deciding Officer's decision or a copy of the application to the Deciding Officer. Prior to confirmation by the Deciding Officer, the employee may withdraw an application in writing. The employer and employee must sign a confirmation document not less than two weeks before the proposed commencement date of the Carer's Leave.

Protection of Employment Rights

The Act states that an employee taking a period of Carer's Leave is considered to be still working. Continuity of employment is not broken and the right and obligations relating to employment are not impacted. The only rights that are not proceeded are those related to the right of remuneration, superannuation, benefits and contributions. An employee's right to annual leave and public holidays is maintained only during the first 13 weeks from the commencement date.

The Act makes it clear that an employee's absence from work during a period of Carer's Leave will not be considered to be part of any other leave to which the employee is entitled. This includes sick, annual, adoptive, maternity, parental or *force majeure* leave. A period of probation or apprenticeship may be suspended during a period of Carer's Leave, where the employer decides that it would not to be consistent with the leave.

The Act prohibits the employer from penalising an employee for taking or proposing to exercise his/her rights to take Carer's Leave. An employer is prohibited from dismissal, unfair treatment or an unfavourable change in the employee's conditions of employment.

During the period of leave, the employee may undertake limited self-employment in the employee's home, undertake employment outside the home for up to 10 hours per week and/or attend an educational or training course or undertake voluntary or community work for up to 10 hours per week. The employee must give not less than four weeks notice of his/her intention to return to work. The basis of the return to work must be the same as existed prior to the employee taking the leave. Where such an arrangement is not possible, suitable alternative employment must be provided and continuity of service must be provided.

Dealing with Disputes and Redress

Disputes under the Act may be referred to a Rights Commissioner. The dispute may relate to an employer's interpretation of the Act, an employer's penalisation of the employee or an employee's dispute over his/her entitlements under the Act.

A Deciding Officer will deal with disputes concerning:

- An employer's opinion as to whether the relevant person is in need of full-time care and attention.

- An employer's opinion that the employee does not satisfy the qualifying conditions.

- An employer's opinion that the employee has undertaken, or is proposing to undertake, employment/self employment that is prohibited under the Act.

The employee may refer a dispute in writing to a Rights Commissioner within six months of the date of the alleged contravention of the Act. The Rights Commissioner will issue a written decision. This decision may be appealed by either party to the Employment Appeals Tribunal within four weeks of the date of the decision. The Rights Commissioner or the Tribunal may provide two forms of redress:

- Affirm the entitlement of the employee to Carer's Leave of such length and time as so specified.

- An award of compensation of up to 26 weeks' remuneration to the employee, payable by the employer.

The Tribunal may refer a question of law to the High Court for determination. A party to a dispute may also appeal a Tribunal determination to the High Court on a point of law.

THE ORGANISATION OF WORKING TIME ACT, 1997

Legislation Repealed by the Act

The 1997 Act, in providing for the transposition of the Directive, other than Articles 8, 9, 10, 11, 12 and 13 which will be implemented under the Safety, Health and Welfare at Work Act, 1989, where they are not already in force under the Act, repeals and replaces eight major pieces of legislation or parts thereof.

These are: the Conditions of Employment Act, 1936 and 1944; Night Work (Bakeries) Act, 1936; Night Work (Bakeries) (Amendment) Act, 1981; Shops (Conditions of Employment) Act, 1938; Shops (Conditions of Employment) (Amendment) Act, 1942; Holidays (Employees) Act, 1973; and Section 4 of the Worker Protection (Regular Part-Time Employees) Act, 1991, dealing with working time.

They are now replaced by a single Act that sets down the same basic standards for all workers (except those exempt or excluded). Although these Acts provided very important protection for the workers concerned, large sections of the workforce did not have any protection in relation to their working hours. Also, new patterns of working-time such as zero-hours contracts were not covered by these Acts.

Non-application of Act or Provisions Thereof (Section 3)

In accordance with Article 1(3) and Article 17(1) of the Directive, members of the Garda Síochána and the Defence Forces are not covered by any of the provisions of the Act. Also, Part 11 of the Act dealing with minimum rest periods and maximum hours do not apply to persons engaged in sea fishing or other work at sea or to the activities of a doctor in training. There are further exclusions for persons who are employed by relatives and who are members of that relative's household, provided the place of employment is a private dwelling house. A person who determines their own working time, whether or not the provision for the making of such determination by that person is made by his or her contract of employment, is also excluded.

In relation to the exemption of persons who determine their own working time, this exclusion is intended to cover only limited categories of employees such as managing executives, senior employees who control staff or financial affairs of an organisation or company and technical or professional staff who by the nature of their work decide on and control their own working time and rest periods.

The Minister for Enterprise and Employment retains a power to make regulations under the Act to exclude other categories of employees from the scope to the legislation. Such regulations have been issued exempting certain transport employees (Organisation of Working Time (Exemption of Transport Activities) Regulations (1998) (SI No. 20 of (1998)) from the rest break, daily and weekly rest periods, maximum weekly working hours and night work provisions of the Act. Regulations have also been issued exempting employees in the prison service, fire fighters and the airport police fire service (Organisation of Working Time (Exemption of Civil Protection Services) Regulations (1998) (SI No. 52 of (1998)).

Exemptions (Section 4)

This section exempts, from the daily and weekly rest provisions, an employee each time he/she changes shift and an employee whose work involves periods of work spread out over the day. Subsection (3) allows the Minister, while ensuring that compensatory rest is provided, to exempt specified sectors set out in Article 17(2) of the Directive from the provisions of the Act regarding daily and weekly rest, rest intervals at work, night working and information on working hours.

It is important to note that these are not blanket exemptions for these sectors but are confined to employees engaged in certain activities in these sectors where, by reason of the nature of the work, the employee is directly involved in ensuring continuity of service or production or where there is a significant seasonal element to the work (Meenan, 1999).

One set of Regulations has so far been issued: Organisation of Working Time (General Exemptions) Regulations (1998) (SI No. 21 of 1998). These provide that persons employed in certain activities are exempt from the daily and weekly rest, rest intervals at work and night working provisions of the Act. The Code of Practice issued by the Labour Relations Commission (Organisation of Working Time (Code of Practice on Compensatory Rest Periods and Related Matters) (Declaration) Order, 1998 (SI No. 44 of 1998) provides guidance on what constitutes equivalent compensatory rest.

These exemptions do not permit derogation from the 48-hour weekly limit but do have the effect of extending the general reference period for averaging from four months to six months for those employees engaged in the activities covered by the exemptions.

Daily and Weekly Rest Periods (Sections 11 and 13)

Sections 11 of the Act implements Article 3 of the Directive and sets out the minimum daily rest period. This section adheres to the original text of the Directive, even though the second sentence of Article 5 was annulled by the Court of Justice, in subsection (5), that, unless an employee is obliged by their contract of employment to work on a Sunday, one of the rest periods must include a Sunday.

The Act permits flexibility with regard to both daily and weekly rest periods and work breaks. These include situations where the work is spread out over the day and at shift changes (Section 4). In addition, in an emergency or other exceptional circumstances, there is flexibility in relation to the night work and information on working time provisions (Section 5). In other instances, flexibility can be provided by way of a collective agreement that has been approved by the Labour Court. However, compensatory rest arrangements or other means of protection must be provided in these instances (ICTU, 1998).

Sunday Working (Section 14)

Although Sunday working was not addressed in the Directive, it was incorporated into the Act on the basis that Sunday work has a significant impact on the quality of life of workers as well as being important to the efficient operation of the enterprise.

This section of the Act provides that an employee required to work on a Sunday is entitled to a premium payment for the work, which may consist of a payment or time off in lieu or a combination of both. Although the level of compensation is not specified in the Act it does specify that the Sunday premium is to be set by reference to the going industry rate, which will be determined by the Labour Court by looking at collective agreements already in force for comparable workers.

A Code of Practice on Sunday working in the retail trade was made on 19 November (1998) (SI No. 444 of 1998) in relation to the Sunday work supplemental provisions. In the preparation of the Code, which was designed to assist employers, employees and their representatives in observing the (1997) Act in relation to Sunday work, submissions were sought from IBEC, ICTU, MANDATE, and SIPTU .

Rest Breaks and Intervals at Work (Section 12)

This section implements Article 4 of the Directive and provides for an entitlement by employees to a rest break while at work of 15 minutes in a period of 4.5 hours work and 30 minutes in a period of 6 hours work. Subsection (4) provides that breaks at the end of the working day do not satisfy these requirements. This section was amended at Committee Stage in the Dáil to provide that the 30-minute minimum period might be extended to one hour for certain categories of workers. It would appear that this was done to preserve the existing rights of shop workers (under the Shops (Conditions of Employment) Act (1938) to a one-hour lunch break. Consequently the Organisation of Working Time (Breaks at Work for Shop Employees) Regulations (1998) (SI No. 57 of 1998) restore the one-hour break entitlement of shop workers.

Weekly Working Hours (Section 15)

This section implements Article 6 of the Directive and provides that an employer shall not allow an employee to work for more than 48 hours in a week. The reference period, which should only take into account time spent carrying out the activities of work, is:

1. Two months for employees who are night workers (section 16 of the Act).

2. Four months for most employees.

3. Six months for certain activities and employment, such as agriculture, tourism, or the postal services.

4. Up to 12 months for employees covered by a collective agreement approved by the Labour Court (Section 24 of the Act).

The 48-hour week came into effect generally on 1 March 1998 but the transitional provisions contained in the Fifth Schedule provide for a phased introduction by 1 March 2000, whereby employees will be permitted to work up to 60 hours in the first year and up to 55 hours in the second. To avail of these provisions, the procedures set out in the Fifth Schedule must be observed — primarily that an agreement has been reached between the parties that has been approved by the Labour Court. The Labour Court, in considering whether to grant such approval, will have due regard to issues of health and safety .

Nightly Working Hours (Section 16)

This section implements Article 8 of the Directive and provides definitions of "night time", "night work", "night worker" and "special category night worker". In accordance with Article 8, this section provides that where a night worker is not a special category night worker, the employer must ensure that the employee does not work more than an average of eight hours per night or 48 hours per week averaged over a two-month reference period. A collective agreement (approved by the Labour Court) may extend the period over which the night working is averaged.

Provision of Information in Relation to Working Time (Section 17)

This section provides that an employee is entitled to be notified in advance of the hours that the employer will require the employee to work. If starting or finishing times are not specified in a contract of employment, the employee must get 24 hours notice of the times unless they are well known or fixed. The employer can of course, call people in at short notice to deal with emergencies or unforeseeable events.

Zero-Hours Working Practices (Section 18)

This provision was not required by the Directive but was included following representations from ICTU and relevant unions (ICTU, 1998). It applies to what are known as "zero-hour contracts", which refer to arrangements where an employee is either asked to be available for work without the guarantee of work, or where an employee is informed that there will be work available on a specified day or days. This section provides that, in the event of an employer failing to require an employee to work at least 25 per cent of the time that the employee is required to be available to work for the employer, the employee will be entitled to payment for 25 per cent of the contract hours or 15 hours whichever is the lesser.

Holidays (Sections 19–23)

Sections 19, 20, 21, 22 and 23, which relate to holiday provisions, apply to all employees (except the Gardaí and Defence Forces) working under a contract of employment. These sections, which constitute Part 111 of the Act, as well as transposing the provisions of the Directive, repeal and update the Holiday (Employees) Act, 1973 and Section 4 of the Worker Protection (Regular Part-Time Employees) Act, 1991 and introduce new protections.

Section 19 implements Article 7 of the Directive and sets out a statutory minimum for annual leave as four weeks in a leave year, to be introduced on a phased basis until 1999 (IBEC, 1998b). The first Schedule of the Act sets out the transitional provisions in relation to annual leave entitlements. It should be noted that there is now no qualifying period for annual leave. All employees regardless of status or service quality are entitled to paid annual leave based on the hours that they work (Department of Enterprise, Trade and Employment, 1997).

Section 19 also sets out the three mechanisms for earning entitlement to annual leave. These mechanisms allow for the increase in holiday entitlement from three weeks to four weeks, or from 6 per cent to 8 per cent of time worked for part-time employees.

Section 20 sets out the criteria which apply to the times at which annual leave should be granted and to the arrangements whereby an employee will be paid for their leave. It stipulates that, although an employer determines the times at which annual leave may be taken, the employer must take into account both the opportunities for rest and recreation available to the employee and the need for the employee "to reconcile work and any family responsibilities". In addition the employer must give the employee or his/her trade union one month's notice before the annual leave is due to commence (IBEC, 1998b). Regulations have also been issued (Organisation of Working Time (Determination of Pay for Holidays) Regulations (1997) (SI No. 475 of 1997)) clarifying the arrangements for calculating pay for holidays.

Section 21 sets out the criteria that apply to public holiday entitlements and Section 22 provides that the mechanism to be used for calculating the rate of pay for a public holiday shall be set out in Regulations, in this case the Organisation of Working Time (Determination of Pay for Holidays) Regulations (1997) (SI No. 475 of 1997). There are, at present, nine public holidays as set out in the Second Schedule.

Section 23 relates to "Compensation on cessation of employment" and provides that an employee is entitled to the payment of any holidays or public holiday compensation owing at the time of cessation of employment.

Collective Agreements (Section 24)

This section empowers the Labour Court to approve "collective agreements" that have been concluded to vary the basic terms of the Act concerning working time. The Court must, however, be satisfied before approving the agreement that it accords with the Directive and that it is valid and voluntary and that the health and safety of the individual is safeguarded. According to Cassells

(1998), this section of legislation introduced an innovative approach to the implementation of the legal rights of workers and represents a major departure from the traditional approach to the implementation of such rights and introduces a new element into industrial relations practices and procedures in Ireland.

Refusal by an employee to co-operate with employer in breaching Act (Section 26).

This section provides that an employer shall not penalise an employee who refuses to co-operate with an employer in breaching the Act.

Complaints Procedures (Sections 27–31)

The Act sets down a detailed complaints procedure for dealing with complaints about entitlements under the Act. Complaints should be submitted in writing to a Rights Commissioner within six months of the alleged contravention of the Act (this period can be extended to 12 months in exceptional circumstances). Either party may appeal the Rights Commissioner's decision to the Labour Court within six weeks of the decision. A Labour Court determination may be appealed to the High Court on a point of law. Failure to implement a Rights Commissioner's recommendation can result in a determination of the Labour Court, which may then be enforced through the Circuit Court.

Prohibition on Double Employment (Section 33)

This section states that there is a prohibition on double employment. However, it is allowed as long as the total hours worked do not exceed the maximum allowed under the Act.

Records (Section 25)

This section requires an employer to keep records of details of the hours of work and of holidays for its employees for the previous three years to show compliance with the Act. The Minister may prosecute an employer for infringements of the Act and on conviction, an employer may be held liable for a fine not exceeding IR£1,500 (€1,904) (Connaughton, M.G., 1998).

IMPLEMENTATION AND INTERPRETATION
OF THE 1997 ACT

Grey areas exist with regard to many of the provisions contained in the Act. For example, in the cases of *John Sisk & Sons Ltd v. Mr Joe Adams* (DWT 2799); *Pierce Contracting Ltd v. Mr William Helsin* (DWT 2899); *Scafform Ltd v. Mr Andrew McGuinness* (DWT 2999) and *Zoe Developments Ltd v. Mr Damien Reville* (DWT 3099), which related to the holiday pay of workers at their weekly rate, the workers in each case held that travelling time, which is payable to employees in the construction industry, is a regular allowance that does not vary in relation to the work done and is part of their normal weekly rate of pay within the meaning of Article 3(2) of the Organisation of Working Time (Determination of Pay for Holidays) Regulations (1997) (SI No. 475 of 1997). The employer in each case held that the relevant payment is in respect of expenses incurred by employees in consequence of their employment and is not reckonable for holiday pay. The Rights Commissioner concluded in her decision (WT25/99GF) that the payment was an allowance. However, the Labour Court subsequently found that the workers' complaint was not well-founded and it set aside the Decision of the Rights Commissioner.

According to their own estimate, Rights Commissioners were expecting approximately 200 cases a year; however, in 1998, there were 395 cases and this increased to 526 in 1999 (Labour Relations Commission, 2000). The role of the Labour Court under the Act is to determine appeals of Rights Commissioners' decisions under the Act and to determine complaints that Rights Commissioners' decisions, under the Act, have not been implemented.

The government's decision not to avail of the individual opt-out clause in Article 18(1)(b) of the Directive, whereby employees could volunteer to work more than the maximum 48 hours a week is very controversial. According to IBEC (1996):

> ... key flexibilities at the complete discretion of the Irish Government which would assist in minimising competitive damage apparently may not be utilised. In the context of current pressures in the marketplace, this position is incomprehensible and unacceptable.

To alleviate concerns, the Organisation of Working Time Bill was amended at Committee Stage in the Dáil to allow for the 48-hour week to be phased in over the first two years of the Act, i.e. from 1 March 1998, if contained in a collective or non-collective agreement/notice. However, there is no provision for the Labour Court to approve any non-collective agreement/notice covering a period after 29 February 2000. According to IBEC, this approach is "entirely inappropriate and in many cases unworkable" and suggests a bias against unorganised employments.

If employees do not consent, through their unions, to the transitional opt-out, then employers will be obliged to put the necessary measures in place to ensure full compliance with the legislation. On the other hand, in cases where employers have sought to comply with the legislation and implement a 48-hour week, employees have sought compensation for loss of earnings. For example, Roadstone/CRH was served with strike notice when it sought to introduce the 48-hour week. The employees sought a future earnings guarantee to compensate for loss of earnings but the company refused arguing that it was simply implementing the law. The matter was referred to the Labour Court, which ruled in the Company's favour .

A recent European Court decision has further defined what is working time. The Court held that:

1. Time spent on call must be regarded in its entirety as working time and where appropriate overtime, if the doctors are required to be at the health centre. If they are merely required to be contactable, only the time linked to the actual provision of primary health care must be regarded as working time.

2. Work performed while on call constitutes shift work.

3. Doctors in primary health care teams who are regularly on call at night may not be regarded as night workers by virtue of the provisions of the Working Time Directive alone.

Two questions that arise and may have to be clarified in the future are:

1. Is a worker working from the time he/she receives a call back to work or is the worker only working from the time he/she commences actual work?

2. When, for example, does working time commence for a worker leaving home on a Sunday evening to attend a Monday morning work conference/training session, where the obligation on the worker is to be there at commencement time and a worker who lives nearer the venue could travel in the morning?

Rest Breaks

Many companies have been forced to change their work practices as a result of the limits on daily and weekly rest breaks. For example, in the case of *Coastal Line Container Terminal Limited v. SIPTU* (DWT 499), which is the only case to-date to have been referred to the High Court under the Act, the substance of the complaint was that the employee crane drivers were not provided with compensatory rest under paragraph 4 of the Working Time (General Exemptions) Regulations (1998) (SI No. 21 of 1998). The employer maintained that such employees were excluded as they fell within the scope of the Organisation of Working Time (Exemption of Transport Activities) Regulations (1998) (SI No. 20 of 1998). The Court determined, on 16 December 1999, that the employees were dock workers and involved in the provision of services at harbour as contained in paragraph 3 (d)(ii) of the General Exemption Regulations (SI No. 21 of 1998) and therefore not covered by the exemptions, and accordingly the employer should ensure that each of the crane drivers had available a rest period and break so as to comply with the provisions of the Working Time (General Exemptions) Regulations (1998) (SI No. 21 of 1998) (Department of Enterprise, Trade and Employment, 2000). This determination upheld the earlier decisions by the Rights Commissioner and the Labour Court.

In the case of *Bord na Móna v. SIPTU* (DWT 1199), the dispute concerned 24 general operatives employed on a four-cycle, 12-hour shift pattern. The Union sought to have the workers provided with rest periods in accordance with Section 12 of the Act. This would involve the workers taking rest breaks away from their work stations during their shifts. The factory operates 24 hours per day, seven days per week. The company believed that, under the Act, this situation was covered under the General Exemptions Regulations (SI No. 21 of 1998). The Court determined that the workers were directly involved in ensuring continuity of service and production and therefore the company was covered under the Statutory Instrument SI/21/98. However, the Court also determined that discussions should take place between the parties as to how breaks could be implemented to comply with Section 6(1) of the Act, which allows the employer to vary the terms of Section 12 of the Act, as long as compensatory rest is provided.

Zero Hours Contracts

Many employers feel that obligations under this section of the Act with regard to payments to employees will incur high costs to their business. For example, in the case of *Ocean Manpower Ltd v. Marine, Port and General Workers' Union* (DWT 198), which was the first appeal made under the Act, the Union sought, on behalf of the worker concerned, entitlement to benefit from the zero-hour provision. The company rejected the claim on the grounds that the worker's casual status precluded any entitlement under the Act. The Court found that the agreement between the Union and the company clearly required employees to remain available for work during defined periods. Employees were also required to report to the company's premises at a specified time for the purpose of being allocated work. While the company may not have rigidly enforced these obligations, they were part of the agreement and a requirement in the employees' contracts of employment and that in these circumstances the Court was satisfied that Section 18 of the Act applied.

Record-keeping

The obligation on employers to keep records to show they are in compliance with the Act inevitably puts cost pressure on the employer. While the legislators claim that there is no need to introduce "surveillance"-type record keeping, employers are required to keep time-keeping and attendance records for three years. These records must encompass all hours worked by every employee, including managers, supervisors and operational staff. Although some organisations have introduced costly swipe card systems, others are introducing manual recording systems, which place particular emphasis on the hours worked above normal contracted hours.

The monitoring of this information is also causing problems. The definition of working time means that rest periods and breaks — whether or not they are paid — are excluded from the calculation of working time for the purpose of averaging working hours. The requirement to exclude annual leave, maternity leave, parental leave, adoptive leave and sick leave means that each employee will have an individual period. To add to the confusion, public holidays are added in as flat days.

Holidays

Part III of the Act, which relates to holidays, is perhaps the most controversial of all sections. Of the cases brought before the Labour Court under the Act, 90 per cent relate to this section (Labour Court, 2000). Such cases concern disputed arrangements for leave, disputes over the actual amounts of leave and also alleged non-payment of leave. For example, the case of *O'Connor Mohan & Company Solicitors v. A Worker* (DWT 1398) concerned a worker who claimed that she was entitled to a further three days' holiday payments under the terms of the Organisation of Working Time Act, 1997. The company rejected the claim on the basis that the worker had received her full entitlements. The claimant by her own admission had taken 15 days annual leave and also received Christmas Eve as a day of annual leave. This gave her 16 days annual leave, which was in accordance with her entitlement under the Act for the leave year April 1997 to April 1998. Therefore, there was no legal entitlement to any compensation for outstanding leave. At the hearing, management clearly indicated that the claimant's conditions of employment entitled her to 15 days annual leave and five extra days at Christmas, as well as Christmas Eve. The Court believed that the total entitlement received by the claimant for the year was 16 days. As this case was brought under the Organisation of Working Time Act, 1997, the Court has no jurisdiction to recommend the terms of the Act's provision.

In the case of *Dargle Cabs v. A Worker* (DWT 1198), a worker claimed that the company had not paid holiday and overtime money due to him. The company rejected the worker's claims stating that the worker received all benefits due to him while in the employment of the company. The company appealed the Rights Commissioner's Recommendation (WT88/89) that the worker receive compensation for three weeks wages in full and final settlement of all his claims. The Court found that the Rights Commissioner erred in her calculations to the claimant's advantage and found that the claimant should be paid compensation in the amount of IR£500 (€635) in full settlement of his claims under the Act.

In the case of *North Western Health Board v. SIPTU* (LRC 16142), nine staff brought a case against the hospital in which they worked. The employees concerned worked a week on/week off roster — 11.5 hours per day for seven days. For public holidays on which they worked, they received 11.5 x 2 plus a day (eight hours) off in lieu. For public holidays on which they did not work, they were paid as usual as well as receiving a day off. The union was seeking an allowance of 11.5 hours rather than 8 hours for each public holiday, whether the employees worked or not. According to the Board, the implementation of the Organisation of Working Time (Determination of Pay for Holidays) Regulation, 1997 was applicable to all staff throughout the health service. The provision of one-fifth of the standard working week was clearly stated as being the entitlement of workers and it was not possible for the Board to enhance that entitlement. The Court found in favour of the Board as it was expected to conform with the provisions of the Organisation of Working Time Act, 1997, with regard to public holiday entitlements for those who are required to work on public holidays.

Double Employment

In addition to monitoring the time employees work while they are at work, employers have also been made responsible for ensuring employees do not exceed the maximum hours — even if working for a second employer. The Act has put the onus on employers to find out whether a person is working elsewhere and if so, to total all the hours worked. According to IBEC (1998), some responsibility for disclosing details of other employment should be placed at the employee's door.

Sunday Premium

The growing demand for services at evenings, weekends and the extension of Sunday trading has meant that Sunday may now be one of the busiest days for some companies. As such, the payment of a Sunday premium to employees is putting additional cost pressures on employers and, in particular, on those who operate smaller businesses. For example, in the case of *Gerard Griffin New Express v. Mr Davin McHugh* (DWT 2499), the employer was instructed to pay its employees compensation for working a Sunday.

THE EMPLOYMENT EQUALITY ACT, 1998

The Employment Equality Act, 1998 contains provisions regarding disability and harassment that have significant implications for health and safety.

General and Sexual Harassment

The Act provides for the first statutory definition of sexual harassment. The definition of sexual harassment of A by B is:

- Any act of physical intimacy by B towards A, other than an act which no reasonable person could consider to be sexually offensive, humiliating or intimidating to A.

- Any express request by B for sexual favours from A.

- Any other act or conduct (including, without prejudice to the generality, spoken words, gestures or the production, display or circulation of written words, pictures or other material) that a reasonable person would consider to be sexually offensive, humiliating or intimidating to A.

In relation to sexual harassment, the Act now provides that if, at a place where A is employed or otherwise in the course of A's employment, B sexually harasses A and either:

- A and B are both employed at that place or by the same employer, or

- B is A's employer, or

- B is a client, customer or other business contact of A's employer, and the circumstances of the harassment are such that A's employer ought reasonably to have taken steps to prevent it,

then, for the purposes of the Act, the sexual harassment constitutes discrimination by A's employer, on the gender ground, in relation to A's conditions of employment. As such, the employer is responsible for any sexual harassment in the above situations.

The Act also prohibits general harassment in the workplace. General harassment occurs where B harasses A in relation to A's characteristics. Again A's employer is responsible for such harassment where:

- A and B are both employed in the same place or by the same employer,

- B is A's employer, or

- B is a client, customer or other business contact of A's employer and the circumstances of the harassment are such that A's employer ought reasonably to have taken steps to prevent it.

Any act or conduct (including, without prejudice to the generality, spoken words, gestures or the production, display or circulation of written words, pictures or other material) constitutes harassment of A by B if the action or other conduct is unwelcome to A and could reasonably be regarded, in relation to the relevant characteristic of A, as offensive, humiliating or intimidating to A.

An employer may have a defence to a charge of general harassment, if they can show that they took such steps as were reasonably practicable to prevent B from harassing A.

If discrimination occurs, the employer may be liable to the employee/potential employee for the act of discrimination, if the employer committed the act or the employer's employees or customers committed it. If an employee/potential employee believes they have been the victim of a discriminatory act, they may lodge a complaint with the Director of Equality Investigations. This is a new post created by the Act. The Director has the power to conduct an investigation or may refer the complaint to a mediation officer.

If the Director of Equality Investigations finds that a person has been discriminated against, the Director may — in disability, harassment or sexual harassment cases — order compensation of up to two years' pay, or a maximum of €12,700 (IR£10,000) if the claimant is not an employee, and also order equal treatment in a manner that is relevant in the particular case.

Disability

The disability provisions of the 1998 Act reflect, though they do not mirror, the provisions of the UK Disability Discrimination Act (1995). It is suggested by a number of commentators that the Irish legislation defines disability "solely in medical terms". The UK Act excludes certain conditions, such as addiction to alcohol, drugs or nicotine, whereas the Irish legislation does not.

Based on the definition of disability in the 1998 Act, it is important to consider disability in very broad terms. Commonly, when people think of a person being disabled, they think in terms of a person whose movements are confined because of obvious physical infirmity. But the definition in the legislation is much broader. Partial hearing loss, partial loss of sight and a weak heart may all be disabilities. Dyslexia could be deemed to be a disability, depending on the interpretation applied to section 2(f).

In the context of health and safety, its function is to ensure that the employer adopts an approach that removes the potential for a disabled person to be discriminated against or harmed, which applies also to the disability provisions of the 1998 Act.

This has provoked discussion and debate in Ireland. The original Employment Equality Bill was declared unconstitutional because it required employers in some circumstances to provide special facilities for disabled employees. The Supreme Court held that the Bill's provisions could impose an undue cost and constitute an unjust attack on employers' property rights.

The Act provides (section 16(3)(b)) that "an employer shall do all that is reasonable to accommodate the needs of a person who has a disability by providing special treatment or facilities". However, because of the Supreme Court decision, an employer does not have to go to any great expense — the term used is "other than nominal cost" — to comply with the requirement.

Table 4.2: Definitions of Disability, Harassment and Sexual Harassment

---

"Disability" means:

- the total or partial absence of a person's bodily or mental functions, including the absence of a part of a person's body,

- the presence in the body of organisms causing, or likely to cause, chronic disease or illness,

- the malfunction, malformation or disfigurement of a part of a person's body,

- a condition or a malfunction which results in a person's thought processes, perceptions of reality, emotions or judgement or which results in disturbed behaviour, and shall be taken to include a disability which exists at present, or which has previously existed but no longer exists, or which may exist in the future or which is imputed to a person.

Harassment (section 32) (summary of section)

The Act seeks to protect employees/potential employees against discrimination on nine grounds: gender (which relates to sexual harassment), marital status, family status, sexual orientation, religious belief, age, disability, race or membership of the travelling community. A person may be harassed by conduct which is unwelcome and offensive, or intimidating, on one of these grounds and may be in the form of words, gestures, and the production and display of written words, pictures and/or other materials. The harassment may be caused by the employer, a co-worker or a customer/client. The harassment must occur in the workplace or in the course of employment.

Sexual harassment (section 23) (summary of section)

Sexual harassment is defined as acts of physical intimacy, requests for sexual favours, or conduct including spoken words or gestures or the production, display or circulation of written words, pictures or other materials. Such actions amount to sexual harassment if it is reasonable for the recipient employee to regard them as offensive or humiliating and if they are unwelcome.

Vicarious Liability

The 1998 Act puts on a statutory footing what was formerly the practice of imposing vicarious liability on the employer.

Section 15 of the 1998 Act deals with vicarious liability and provides that:

- Anything done by a person in the course of their employment shall, be treated for the purpose of this Act as done also by that person's employer, whether or not it was done with the employer's knowledge or approval.

- Anything done by a person as agent for another person with the authority (whether express or implied and whether precedent or subsequent) of that other person all be treated for the purposes of this Act as done also by that other person.

In proceedings brought under this Act against an employer in respect of an act alleged to have been done by an employee of the employer, it shall be a defence for the employer to prove that the employer took such steps as were reasonably practicable to prevent the employee:

- From doing that act.

- From doing, in the course of their employment, acts of that description.

This section provides employers with a defence so that vicarious liability is not automatically imposed. The defence is to show that the employer took such steps "as were reasonably practicable" to prevent the harassment. The precise scope of the defence has yet to be established through the development of case law on the subject.

Figure 4.5: Recent Cases on Harassment and Bullying

Sullivan v. Southern Health Board (1997)

This case, which was brought by a consultant in Mallow Hospital, arose from the Health Authority's failure to engage another permanent consultant, which led to an increased workload for Dr. Sullivan. The Supreme Court confirmed the High Court's determination that Dr. Sullivan was entitled to damages for "the stress and anxiety caused to him in both his professional and domestic life by the persistent failure of the Board to remedy his legitimate complaints". The question of the level of damages was remitted to the High Court.

Leeson v. Glaxo Welcome (1999)

This case arose in the context of a claim for constructive dismissal. The Employment Appeals Tribunal awarded IR£22,500 (€28,569) for unfair dismissal on foot of a claim by a secretary that the Managing Director of the company (to whom she reported) had routinely bullied her to the point where she had felt that she had no alternative but to leave the job. The decision of the Employment Appeals Tribunal was reversed by the Circuit Court on appeal. The Circuit Court was of the view that the Managing Director had legitimate complaints about the employee's work and that it was entirely appropriate in the context of their close working relationship that he would offer criticism with a view to bringing about future improvements.

Wyse v. St Margaret's Country Club (1999)

In this recent case a cleaner who claimed to have been "bullied out of her employment" and to have been "insulted" and "verbally abused" by the chef in the country club was awarded IR£1,000 (€1,270) for constructive dismissal. In assessing the level of the award, the Employment Appeals Tribunal indicated that it was taking account of her "hasty action on the morning in question".

Kerwin v. Aughinish Alumina (2000)

The plaintiff in this case, an acting supervisor, endured intimidation at the factory along with other supervisors. Mr. Kerwin agreed with the factory's management that he would resign from his position, bring an unfair dismissal claim and be subsequently reappointed. Mr. Kerwin was taken back after the unfair dismissal case, but as a welder rather than a supervisor. The High Court awarded IR£50,000 (€63,500) for stress and associated health problems in light of this breach of agreement.

Allen v Independent Newspapers Ltd (2001)

In this case, Ms. Allen, a former crime correspondent for the *Sunday Independent*, had numerous restrictions imposed upon her job, where previously she had been allowed considerable freedom in pursuing crime stories. She also claimed that she had been bullied by colleagues resulting in a deterioration of the general atmosphere in the workplace and that conflicts with her immediate supervisors remained unresolved. Ms. Allen's supervisors, including her editor and personnel manager, were aware that she had complained about these working conditions in writing, but presumed that her grievances had been resolved. Ms. Allen resigned from Independent Newspapers before any formal investigation was initiated.

The Employment Appeals Tribunal held that Ms. Allen had been constructively dismissed and was entitled to IR£70,000 (€88,881) compensation on the grounds that Independent Newspapers had failed to deal with her legitimate claims of bullying through any formal or informal process.

A v Shropshire County Council (2000)

The plaintiff in this UK case suffered a nervous breakdown, following the introduction of a new disciplinary code of conduct for students by a new head teacher. Many of the teaching staff, including the plaintiff, did not agree with the new disciplinary code, culminating in a worsening of the general teaching environment in the school. It emerged that, even though the plaintiff showed signs of deteriorating health over a long period of time, no help was made available to him during this time. The case was settled out of court for stg£300,000 (€486,000).

TOBACCO (HEALTH PROMOTION AND PROTECTION) REGULATIONS, 1995

Prior to the introduction of the tobacco regulations, a company's decision to prohibit smoking was usually as a result of a concern for safety and hygiene. This may be the case, for example, where inflammable substances are used on the factory floor. The Tobacco (Health Promotion and Protection) Regulations, 1995 have expanded the scope of the restrictions already in place. As a result, smoking has now been prohibited or restricted in a range of primary public facilities.

Smoking is prohibited in:

- **Public Offices**: In the circulation space and in the offices to which the public has access and in buildings owned or occupied by the state or semi-state bodies.

- **Schools and Third Level**: In any part (including school yard) of a primary or secondary school, except where specific facilities are provided for staff to smoke. In the buildings of third level colleges, smoking is allowed in canteens, licensed premises and private offices.

- **Food Preparation Areas**: In the kitchens in hotels, restaurants, cafes, snack bars and licensed premises. In the retail, storage and food preparation areas of supermarkets and grocery store.

- **Bus and Railway Stations**: In the waiting rooms in bus and railway stations.

- **Sports Centres**: In the indoor spectator and games areas of sports centres.

- **Cinemas, Theatres, Concert Halls**: In the auditorium of a cinema, a theatre or a hall, which is purpose-built for the holding of concerts.

- **Art Galleries, Museums and Libraries**: In art galleries and museums which belong to the state and public libraries.

- **Trains, DART, Buses**: In all trains owned or operated by Iarnód Éireann, smoking is allowed in the bar area in self-contained areas designated for smoking. In the DART and buses owned or operated by Bus Éireann and Bus Átha Cliath.

- **Health Premises**: Smoking is prohibited in designated places within health premises, hospitals, nursing homes, maternity homes, centres for the mentally handicapped, centres for the physically handicapped and psychiatric hospitals.

- **Restaurants and Canteens**: Smoking is prohibited in designated places within restaurants, canteens, cafes, snack bars and dining cars of trains.

The issue of the development of smoking policies to meet this set of regulations is considered in **Part Five** of this Handbook.

CONSTRUCTION SITES: THE SAFETY, HEALTH AND WEL-
FARE AT WORK (CONSTRUCTION) REGULATIONS, 2001

The Safety, Health and Welfare at Work (Construction) Regulations, 2001 introduce significant changes to the 1995 Regulations
and, effective from 1 January 2002, repeal their provisions. These
Regulations are wide-ranging in scope and apply to building projects, civil engineering projects, and maintenance activities connected with existing buildings. They specify requirements concerning the regulatory design and management of health and
safety for construction sites and they set out detailed operational
regulations for construction work. The Regulations, in general, impose duties on contractors who are mainly employed in construction work.

The Nature of Construction Work

Regulation 2 defines construction work as including any project
that involves work on structure. This may include its construction,
alteration, conversion, filling out, renovation, repair or upkeep.
The definition set out in the Regulations also includes both maintenance and cleaning operations. The Regulations define construction work by making reference to key stages of a project including
the preparation of a structure such as site clearance, evacuation,
investigation, etc., the lagging or insulating of foundations, the assembly of prefabricated elements to form a structure, the disas-
sembly of prefabricated elements, the removal of a structure or
part of one and the installation, commissioning, repair, removal of
services which are normally fixed within a structure. The term
"structure" is broadly defined to include buildings, docks, tunnels,
bridges, waterworks, pipelines, etc. It is sufficiently broad to
cover all civil engineering works as well as activities that may be
termed building work. Drilling, mining and quarrying activities
are excluded from the definition of construction work.

Design Stage and Construction Stage

The Regulations make an important distinction between the design
and construction stages of a construction project. The design stage
is defined as the period of time during which the design of a project is prepared. It does not include the design of temporary works

by a contractor to facilitate the construction. The term "design" is defined to mean the preparation of drawings, specifications, etc. or any component of a project.

The construction stage is defined as the time starting when preparation of the construction site begins, starting with the design of temporary works and ending when construction is completed.

Health and Safety Plan and Safety File

The Regulations place a considerable degree of emphasis on the preparation of a health and safety plan and the preparation of a safety file where more than one contractor is engaged on a construction project. The Regulations do not give a precise definition of a health and safety plan, but it is clear that it is somewhat similar to a safety statement. Therefore, in preparing such a plan, specific risk assessment must be undertaken together with the specification of organisational measures to effectively implement safety policies.

The plan will have effect for the duration of the project, after which it becomes redundant. The Regulations indicate that a safety and health plan is required where the construction work will last longer than 30 working days or the volume of work will exceed 500 person days or where work on the site involves particular risks. The Second Schedule gives examples of such risks and they may include situations where workers are at risk from chemical or biological substances, where they are at risk of burial under earthfalls or where they may fall from a height or where the work involves working near high-voltage power lines, etc. The Regulations specify that the project supervisor for the design stage must prepare, on a preliminary basis, a health and safety plan. This must, however, become a full plan for the construction stage. Where the work does not require a plan, there is still a requirement under the Safety, Health and Welfare at Work Act, 1989 to prepare a safety statement.

The obligation to prepare a safety file exists where the project involves the use of more than one contractor. This file must contain relevant health and safety information, which has to be considered in subsequent construction work, following completion of the project. This may relate to pipe work or electrical work. Unlike the safety plan, the safety file may have a long shelf-life and it must be available for inspection by individuals who need it in order to comply with statutory duties imposed by other safety, health and welfare regulations.

Duties on Parties to the Construction Project

The Regulations place duties on a number of parties to a construction site. These include the client, the project supervisor at both design and construction stages, construction employees and other individuals.

The Client

Regulation 2 defines the client as any person engaged in trade or business or other undertaking who commissions or procures the carrying out of a project for the purposes of such trade, business or undertaking. The definition includes human beings, companies, local authorities and government departments. The 2001 Regulations specifically exclude people building private houses or having extensions built. The Regulations impose three mandatory duties on the client:

- To appoint a project supervisor for the design stage of every project.

- To appoint a project supervisor for the construction stage of every project.

- To keep available any safety file for inspection by any person who needs information in the file in order to comply with statutory duties.

The project supervisor is perceived as an agent of the client.

The Project Supervisor at Design Stage

The Regulations specify that the project supervisor must be a competent person. The project supervisor for the design stage must actively take account of any health and safety plan and/or safety file during the design of a project and where they may be estimating the period of time required to complete the project.

There is also a duty to co-ordinate the activities of other individuals engaged in design work related to the project.

The project supervisor at the design stage must prepare a preliminary health and safety plan that provides a general description of the project, its duration, other work activities taking place on the site and a specification of work which will involve particular risks to the health and safety of employees. The Regulations specify that the project supervisor for the design stage may appoint a competent person to act as a health and safety co-ordinator for the design stage and must pass on relevant information to the project supervisor for the construction stage, that needs to be included in the safety file.

Designers

Regulation 5 sets out duties that are imposed on any person who is employed in work activities related to the design of a project other than the project supervisor. There is a lack of clarity with respect to the term "designer". However, the important issue relates to the functions that are assigned to that person. There is a duty on the designer to take account of the principle of prevention contained in the Safety, Health and Welfare at Work (General Application) Regulations, 1993 and relevant health and safety plans and files. There is also a duty to co-operate with project supervisors in the design and construction stage and to provide them promptly with information on safety risks that designers are aware of and to take into account any directions received from project supervisors for the design and construction stages.

Project Supervisor at Construction Stage

A wide range of management and design duties is imposed on the project supervisor for the construction stage. The primary duties are:

*   There is a duty to give advance written notice to the HSA in relation to work scheduled to last for more than 30 days or exceed 500 person days in volume. This notice must include details of the address of the construction site, description of the project and other important information on start dates, duration and number of people who will work on the site.

- Develop a health and safety plan for the site, make adjustments to the plan where required and specify measures to deal with risky work activities.

- Prepare a safety file, make adjustments to the file and, on completion, deliver the safety file to the client.

- Co-ordinate day-to-day activities as they relate to the implementation of the 1995 Regulations, organise co-operation between contractors and ensure the implementation of Regulation 6 of the General Application Regulations, 1993.

Contractors

The Regulations define a contractor as an employer whose employees carry out or undertake construction work or any person who carries out construction work for a fixed or other sum and who supplies material and labour or who simply supplies labour alone. There is a duty on the contractor to apply the principles of prevention set out in the General Application Regulations, 1993 in a consistent manner. He is also obliged to:

- Keep the construction site in good order and in a good state of cleanliness.

- Specify the conditions under which materials can be handled.

- Locate workstations taking into account access, areas of passage, and movement of equipment.

- Determine the layout of storage areas, particularly dangerous materials or substances.

- Ensure co-operation between employees and self-employed persons.

- Co-operate with the project supervisor for the construction stage to enable the supervisor to comply with statutory provisions.

- Take into account, in a prompt manner, any directions of the project supervisor for the construction stage.

- Provide relevant information, including a copy of the safety statement under the 1989 Act, and provide information to the HSA on any accident or dangerous occurrence which the contractor would be obliged to under the 1993 General Regulations.

- Appoint safety officers where more than 20 persons are under the direct control of the contractor.

All other persons at work on a construction project have an obligation to comply with the 1995 Regulations, report any defects they discover in plant and equipment that might endanger safety, health and welfare and make proper use of safety helmets, harnesses and other personal protective equipment provided for their health and safety.

The 2001 Regulations make some significant new additions to the 1995 Regulations in a number of key areas. In particular, a significant new focus of the 2001 Regulations is the strong emphasis given to training. A number of mandatory requirements are now imposed on employers and employees in respect of training. These are presented in **Figure 4.6**.

Figure 4.6: Mandatory Training Requirements on Employers and Employees

---

By January 1ˢᵗ 2002:
All new construction workers will have to have received FÁS Safe Pass safety awareness training and possess a FÁS Safe Pass registration card, before they can work on-site.

All basic scaffolders will have to be in possession of a FÁS Construction Skills Scheme Certification card, certifying they have received relevant training.

By May 1ˢᵗ 2002:
All workers on all new sites will be required to have received FÁS Safe Pass safety awareness training and to hold a Safe Pass card before they can work on site.

By July 1ˢᵗ 2002:
The requirement to possess a FÁS Construction Skills Certification Scheme card will be extended to advanced scaffolders, tower crane operations, slinging/signalling, and telescopic handler operations.

By June 1ˢᵗ 2003:
All construction workers will have to have received FÁS Safe Pass

---

safety awareness training and possess a Safe Pass card before they can work on-site.

Certain trades workers will be required to be in possession of a FÁS Construction Skills Certification Scheme card, certifying that they received the training relevant to their trade. These include scaffolding, lower crane operation, slinging/signalling, tractor/bulldozer operation, mobile crane operation and telescope handler operations.

Where more than 20 people are employed on a site, a site safety representative must be elected or appointed. The PSCS has a duty to co-ordinate the arrangements for the selection of the site safety representatives.

The Tenth Schedule outlines a set of procedural requirements in respect of the selection of site safety representatives. These are in summary:

- If, after work commences on a site, workers select their own safety representative, he/she shall be recognised as such by the project supervisor construction stage (PSCS).

- The views of all workers on the site must be considered if, before work commences on a site, a safety representative has been selected by the employees of any contractor, and it is proposed to confirm that person as site safety representative.

- If there is no safety representative and the number of workers on site normally exceeds 20, the PSCS must invite all site workers to elect a safety representative.

- If they are unwilling to do so and request the PSCS stage to organise a selection process, the PSCS must do so.

- If a safety representative is not selected, the PSCS must invite site workers or their representatives to nominate someone willing to take on the role and, if more than one person is put forward, the PSCS must determine which candidate has the most support.

- If all of these attempts to elect a site safety representative fail, the PSCS must nominate a provisional site safety representative.

- If subsequently site workers (in a process involving 50 per cent or more of the workers) elect a safety representative, that person must be recognised as site safety representative.

The regulations mandate that all contractors and persons under their control are required to employ only those who hold a FÁS Safe Pass and FÁS Construction Skills Certification Register cards.

There is a requirement that, when such individuals are employed, they give written confirmation to the project supervisor construction stage (PSCS)that they possess the relevant certification.

The regulations impose a duty on the PSCS to ensure that all of these arrangements are in place.

Safety Consultation

Major changes are now in force in respect of the rights of the site safety representatives. There is a requirement that the PSCS must inform all persons working on-site who the site safety representative is and keep available for inspection details of that person and the selection process by which they were chosen.

The 2001 Regulations confirm for site safety representatives a number of important rights. They are in many respects similar to those given to the more conventional safety representatives found under the 1989 Act. Four sets of specific provisions should be noted here:

- Site safety representatives are entitled to:
  ◇ receive information from the PSCS regarding health and safety.
  ◇ make representations to the PSCS and/or to any contractor.
  ◇ investigate accidents and dangerous occurrences.
  ◇ make representations to and receive information from inspectors.
  ◇ carry out inspections (must give notice and get agreement, which cannot be unreasonably withheld) and to investigate potential hazards and complaints for workers.
  ◇ accompany an inspector on a site inspection (unless the inspection is for the purpose of investigating an accident).

- Site safety representatives are entitled to time off work, without loss of remuneration:
  ◇ to enable them to acquire the knowledge to act as a safety representative.
  ◇ to discharge the function of site safety representative.

- Site safety representatives shall not be placed at a disadvantage in relation to their employment, as a result of discharging their duties.

- The PSCS must make reasonable efforts to inform the site safety representative if an inspector enters a site to carry out an inspection.

Appointment of a Safety Officer

Regulation 10 sets out the requirement that contractors are obliged to appoint a safety officer in either of two situations:

- The contractor has normally under his/her direct control 20 or more persons on any site at any one time, or

- The contractor has more than 30 persons engaged in construction work at any one time

It is also specified that, where an appointment of a safety officer is made, that officer must be qualified in terms of experience training and have sufficient expertise to advise on statutory requirements, to ensure general supervision of safety and to promote safe work conduct. This is an important regulation because it refers to persons under the direct control of the contractor and therefore includes not just employees but all those whose work the contractor controls.

Welfare Requirements

The regulations mandate that the PSCS is responsible for coordinating welfare facilities such as washing, eating, sanitary facilities, etc. The regulations are quite specific on a number of key welfare issues, including a provision that wash basins are to be provided according to a specific scale: six with the addition of one for every unit of 20 persons at work when the numbers of persons exceeds 100, any fraction of a unit of 20 persons being treated as a full unit. A further requirement is that, where practical, all sanitary conveniences shall discharge into a main sewer.

Figure 4.7 presents a set of guidelines when appointing a contractor.

Figure 4.7: Appointing a Contractor: Client Action Checklist

- Is there a section on health and safety in the standard qualification and/or tendering specification of the organisation?

- Does this include questions relating to accident records, enforcement orders and does it require tenderers to submit a copy of their safety policy?

- Who evaluates the health and safety responses?

- To what extent does the health and safety evaluation influence contractor selection?

- Is there a meeting of short-listed tenderers at which health and safety issues are covered?

- Does the organisation publish a contractors' handbook setting out the organisation's rules and requirements?

- Does the organisation have a policy regarding the lending of tools to contractors?

- Are safety officers and maintenance staff involved:

  ◊ in contractor selection?

  ◊ in the preliminary meeting with the successful contractor?

  ◊ during the tenure of the contract?

  ◊ at the handover induction/testing/commissioning?

- Does the organisation require that the contractor communicate all accidents, dangerous occurrences and near misses that occur on the premises?

- Check the contractor's safety record.

- Check with HSA to see if the contractor has been prosecuted/convicted/served with a prohibition notice.

- Check the contractor's insurance record (get the contractor's written permission to authorise insurers to release information).

- Check the contractor's investment in H&S training and education.

- Seek the contractor's safety statement.

- Is the contractor familiar with similar projects and the client's industry/sector?

- Can the contractor ensure that subcontractors are aware of safety?

- Check how the contractor will integrate their safety arrangements with yours?

- What safety supervision arrangements will the contractor have in place?

- Seek and check safety references.

NON-FATAL OFFENCES AGAINST THE PERSON ACT, 1997

This Act defines "serious harm" as "any injury that creates a substantial risk of death or which causes serious disfigurement or substantial loss or impairment of the mobility of the body as a whole or of the function of any particular bodily organ or member". Any person found guilty of causing serious harm either intentionally or recklessly will be guilty of an offence and will be liable on indictment to a fine or life imprisonment or both.

Harassment is a criminal offence under section 10 of the Act. It makes it an offence for any person to harass another person by "persistently following, watching, pestering ... or communicating with him or her". Harassment occurs where the perpetrator seriously interferes with the other person's peace and privacy or causes alarm, distress or harm to the other, and that a reasonable person would realise that this would be the result.

For an individual charged under section 10 on a summons in the District Court, there is a maximum fine of £1,500 and or 12 months imprisonment. On indictment, there is the possibility of an unlimited fine and/or 7 years imprisonment.

Under section 13, a person who intentionally or recklessly partakes in behaviour that creates a substantial risk of death or serious harm to another will be guilty of an offence. Such an offence carries the same penalties as those for harassment.

Section 24 of the Act abolishes the law that provides teachers with immunity from criminal liability in respect of physical chastisement of pupils.

Section 25 relates to the evidential value of certain certificates in proceedings alleging the cause of harm or serious harm to a person. Such a certificate claiming to be signed by a registered medical practitioner and pertaining to an examination of that person is evidence of any fact thereby certified, unless the contrary is proved. The certificate does not require proof of any signature or that any such signature is that of such practitioner.

NOISE REGULATION: THE NOISE REGULATIONS, 1990

The Noise Regulations, 1990 cover all workplaces except people working in air, sea and transport business. Employers are required to ensure that noise levels in the workplace are assessed and measured periodically so as to pinpoint employees who are exposed to noise levels of 85dB(a) or over. This periodic assessment must be based on a full day's exposure, and the results must be kept for three years. If, as a result of such an assessment, the noise level is identified as being greater than 90dB(a), the employer is obliged to give reasons for the noise levels and implement a programme of measures. The programme would have the objective of reducing the level of noise, where practicable, to which the employees are exposed.

Employees who are exposed to 90dB(a) or over are obliged under the regulations to wear hearing protection. Furthermore, if a particular area in the workplace has noise levels exceeding 90dB(a), the employer is obliged to mark off the area, restrict access and post signs stating that: the noise level is likely to exceed 90dB(a); ear protectors are available; and ear protectors must be worn.

A medical practitioner must be made available to employees who are exposed to levels 85dB(a) on a daily basis, to carry out hearing checks. The results of these checks must be kept for 15 years. Employees are not, under the regulation, forced to take such tests, all that is required is that the service be made available to them. However, once the initial test has been taken, a second test must be made available at further intervals, the frequency of such tests depending on the level of noise to which the employee is exposed on a daily basis.

Information and Training

In workplaces where noise levels exceed 85dB(a), employees must receive information and training from the employer in relation to:

- Potential risks to their hearing arising from noise exposure.

- Measures taken by the employer to comply with the 1990 Regulations.

- Obligations to comply with protective and preventive measures.

- Wearing of ear protection and the role of checks on hearing.

One of the most interesting test cases in relation to hearing loss as a result of the employee's work environment is that of *Barry v. Nitrigin Éireann Teo and Irish Fertiliser Industries plc* (1983). The case poses important questions such as whether exposure to noise causes deafness, whether hearing protection reduces employees' exposure to noise levels and the obligations of the employer to provide protection against noise levels at work.

The defendants employed the plaintiff since 1979. In 1985, a medical examination revealed that he suffered from bilateral deafness due to noise exposure. Proceedings for damages were instituted on the grounds that the deafness had been caused by breach of the employer's statutory duties to him under the Factories (Noise) Regulations, 1975 and a breach of the employer's common law duty of care to him.

The defendants cited as being the originating cause of his deafness Barry's hobby, pigeon shooting, and his previous employment, working for an agricultural contractor. They did, however, admit that the noise level in the workplace contributed to the deafness.

The judge rejected the claim that his hobby was the cause of his deafness, but did accept that his previous employment had contributed somewhat. The judge pointed out in his decision that the primary cause of the deafness was Barry's exposure to noise while in employment with the defendant. He highlighted a number of areas where the defendant had failed, when seeking to protect employees from exposure to noise. Their failures related to:

- The ear protection which had been provided had worn down over time and had not been replaced.

- Safety glasses that were provided for safety purposes reduced the effectiveness of the ear muffs.

- When having to communicate by radio, the plaintiff had to remove the ear protection while still in the noise atmosphere.

The employer was also found to be in breach of their common law duty of care to the plaintiff as the system of work was defective. The plaintiff was awarded IR£50,000 (€63,500) in compensation as a result of the loss of hearing. The failure by the employers in this case to protect employees from excessive noise levels would also be regarded as failure to comply with the requirements of the 1990 Regulations.

A recent study carried out for the Health and Safety Commission (HSC) in the UK (1996) by the Institute for Employment Studies calculated that it costs stg£35 (€56) per employee to comply with noise protection regulations. The cost of conducting the first noise assessment varies from between stg£300 (€486) for smaller companies (5-24 employees) to stg£1,500 (€2,430) for larger establishments (300+ employees). The costs of subsequent assessments varied between stg£200 (€324) and stg£1,200 (€1,944). The cost of providing PPE averaged stg£860 (€1,393) per employee. Training costs averaged stg£5.60 (€9) per employee. Setting up an Ear Protection Zone costs around stg£100 (€162) per employee and stg£75 (€121) a year to maintain.

Figure 4.8 presents a set of guidelines for organisations related to noise management.

Figure 4.8: Issues Concerning Noise at Work

- Do warning signs identify noisy areas?

- Does everyone in a noisy area need to work there?

- Are employees aware of the dangers of noise and knowledge-able on the use of ear protectors?

- Does the ear protection provided give adequate protection?

- Has the manufacturer's information about noise levels been checked by actual measurements?

- Will changes in work methods or machine wear affect noise levels?

- Are loose panels or unbalanced rotating parts contributing to noise and vibration?

- Would better maintenance or a slower running speed reduce noise levels?

- Has everything been done to reduce noise exposure?

CHAPTER ROUND-UP

- There exists a wide range of ancillary legislation that contains provisions related to health and safety at work. Most of this legislation has its origins in EU directives. The EU has been very active in recent years in enacting or proposing directives on a wide range of health and safety issues. These directives are then implemented by member states. If the directive is not implemented within the time scale specified in the directive, the general rule appears to be that the principles found in the directive are largely enforceable.

- The Fire Services Act, 1981 provides for the organisation of fire services at national level but has specific relevance to employers because of the duties it imposes on persons in control of premises. There is an obligation imposed on the controllers of premises to ensure effective fire safety arrangements. The person in control must take all reasonable steps to ensure that persons on the premises conduct themselves in such a manner that they are not exposed to fire as a result of acts or omissions.

- The Occupier's Liability Act, 1995 has significantly modified the common law and, most significantly, it classifies entrants into visitors, recreational users and trespassers. The Act imposes a different duty on occupiers in respect of each class of entrant. An occupier for the purpose of the Act is defined as the person exercising such control over the state of the premises that it is reasonable to impose on that person a duty towards an entrant in respect of a particular danger existing on those premises.

- The Maternity Protection of Employees Act, 1994 provides protection for all pregnant employees, employees who have recently given birth and those who are breast-feeding. The Act provides that pregnant employees are entitled to take time off without loss of pay, to attend ante-natal and post-natal care medical appointments. The employee will also be entitled to take leave on grounds of health and safety where it is not possible to remove the risk or provide her with suitable alternative work. The employer is obliged to make a payment to the employer for the first three weeks of that leave.

- The Organisation of Working Time Act, 1997 sets out statutory rights for employees in respect of rest, maximum working time and holidays. These new rights apply either by law or through legally binding collective agreements. These agreements may vary the times at which rest is taken or the average period over which weekly working time calculated. The new maximum average working week is 48 hours. Averaging may be balanced over a four, six or 12-month period depending on the circumstances.

- The Safety, Health and Welfare at Work (Construction) Regulations, 2001 are wide-ranging in scope and apply to building projects, civil engineering projects, and maintenance activities connected with existing buildings. The Regulations make an important distinction between the design and construction phases of a construction project and place a considerable degree of emphasis on the preparation of a health and safety plan and the preparation of a safety file where more than one contractor is engaged on a construction site. The safety plan is similar to that of a safety statement.

- The Noise Regulations, 1990 require employees to ensure that noise levels in the workplace are assessed and measured periodically. Where limits are above those specified in the legislation, steps must be taken to rectify the situation. A medical practitioner must be made available on a daily basis to employees who are exposed to such levels to carry out hearing checks.

- The Parental Leave Act 1998 and the Carer's Leave Act 2001 provide two forms of leave for general welfare reasons. The Parental Leave Act entitles an employee who is the natural or adoptive parent of a child to leave from their employment for a period of 14 working weeks to take care of the child. The 1998 Act also provides that an employee is entitled to leave with pay for urgent family reasons owing to an injury or illness of a member of family. The Carer's Leave Act 2001 provides for the temporary absence from employment of employees for the purpose of the provision of full-time care and attention to a person requiring it.

Chapter 5

INSURANCE AND HEALTH AND SAFETY AT WORK

INTRODUCTION

This chapter considers the subject matter of insurance and more specifically its role in the context of health and safety in organisations. It is important for the safety practitioner and the student of health and safety to understand the main principles of insurance. The chapter will first of all consider the nature of the insurance contract and some of the more important principles of insurance. It will then focus on the nature of employer's liability and public liability insurance and their relevance to the health and safety specialist. The chapter will also set out guidelines in respect of both types of insurance and concludes with a short section on self-insurance.

WHAT IS AN INSURANCE CONTRACT?

The Insurance Act, 1936 is of little assistance in defining insurance or an insurance contract. It does provide a definition for various types of insurance business, but this does not help in deciding what an insurance contract is. It is necessary to discover the nature of such a contract because various rules of law relate to insurance contracts, such as the rules requiring utmost good faith and insurable interest and, in order to know whether these rules apply to a particular contract, it is also important to know whether the contract is one dealing with insurance. In view of this, it is important to be able to establish the nature of an insurance contract.

In general, a contract of insurance is any contract whereby one party assumes the risk of an uncertain event, which is not within his control, happening at a future time, in which event the other party has an interest, and under which contract the first party is bound to pay money or provide its equivalent if the uncertain event occurs.

This definition points to a number of important elements:

- Firstly, there must be a binding contract between the two parties and the ordinary laws of contract apply to establish whether such a contract exists. Thus the contract should bind the insurer to meet its obligations to make payment when a specified event occurs. The right to receive payment must be evident. According to the English case of *Medical Defence Union v. Department of Trade* (1979), a right to be considered for a discretionary benefit following a loss is insufficient. In this case, the MDU was a company whose members were medical practitioners and its business consisted of conducting legal proceedings on behalf of members and indemnifying them in respect of awards and costs. The members did not have a right to these benefits; merely the right to request that they be given assistance should a third party claim arise against them following an accident relating to their practice as medical practitioners. As the members did not have a right to assistance, it was held that the MDU was not carrying on insurance business.

- Secondly, the event insured against must be uncertain; it must not be something that is bound to occur. If the event is bound to occur, the insurer and insured will be trading cash. The insurer will be a holder of cash pending the occurrence of the event and then, on the occurrence of the event, will pay out the amount concerned less expenses.

- Once a contract is found to be one of insurance, there must be insurable interest in its subject matter.

  ◊ It is necessary that the insurer should, on the happening of the uncertain event, provide money or money's worth to the insured. It is not necessary that only money be provided.

It is therefore difficult to define an insurance contract, but it is possible to suggest that it consists of an arrangement whereby one party, the insurer, in return for a consideration, the premium, undertakes to pay the other party, the insured, a sum of money or its equivalent in kind upon the happening of an uncertain event.

COMMENCING AN INSURANCE CONTRACT

The normal rules concerning the commencement of a contract apply to insurance contracts. Clarke (1993) highlights that there must be offer, acceptance, consideration and intention to contract. A contract comes into existence once an offer has been accepted. These requirements will now be considered in relation to insurance.

The Proposal Form

For most types of insurance, an applicant is required to complete a proposal form before the insurer will consider accepting the risk being presented. In the case of large risks, a proposal form may not be required but certain information will be requested in order for the insurer to consider whether to accept the risk.

The proposal form contains a series of questions, designed to assist underwriters in calculating the premium they would like to charge or to decide whether they wish to accept the proposal at all. The questions relate to personal details of applicants, as well as their past insurance history. If the insurance is to cover property, details of the physical nature of the risk will be required. If the proposal is in respect of life cover, details of the applicants' health and their medical history will be requested. On completion of the proposal form, the document is forwarded to the insurers who consider the risk and decide whether they are prepared to accept it and, if so, at what rate. The proposal form is normally an offer made by the proposer to the insurer, which the underwriter can accept or reject. The offer is made on the basis that the proposer is prepared to deal with the insurer on their normal terms and conditions. If the underwriter accepts the risk on normal terms, a contract comes into existence. If the underwriter wishes to impose additional terms, this is a counter-offer that the proposer can accept or reject. Once the essential terms of the contract relating to premium, nature of the risk, subject matter of insurance, and duration of cover have been agreed, a contract comes into existence and a policy may be issued.

Some contracts issue so-called acceptance letters, which state that a contract does not come into existence until the first premium is paid. This is in fact a counter-offer, which is open to acceptance or rejection by the insured. Once the premium has been paid, the contract comes into existence. In *Canning v. Farquhar* (1886), the proposer completed an application form for insurance and this was accepted by the insurer subject to payment of the premium. Before payment was made, the proposer fell over a cliff and was severely injured. The proposer's agent forwarded a cheque to the insurer and informed them of the accident. The insurer refused to accept the premium. Shortly thereafter the proposer died and a claim was submitted to the insurers on the basis that, in forwarding the acceptance letter, the insurer had accepted the insurances. The Court of Appeal held that the company was not liable. The majority considered that the insurer had offered insurance on the basis that the insured's good health would continue between the time that the acceptance letter was sent and the receipt of the premium. This warranty was breached when the proposed suffered an injury and the submission by the broker of the premium together with details of the injury was really a new proposal.

In effect, the requirement that the premium must be paid is a counter-offer open to acceptance or rejection by the insured and, once the premium was paid, the contract would come into existence. It could be argued that the requirement for payment is a condition precedent. The contract exists but does not come into effect until the premium is paid. There is a duty to disclose all material facts right up to the time that the policy comes into force. If the policy does not come into force until the premium is paid then the duty of disclosure continues until this point.

Sometimes no proposal form is completed but cover is granted verbally. In this case, the underwriters normally obtain as much information as they need and then decide whether they are going to accept the risk. It is possible the underwriters might agree to accept the risk at a premium to be negotiated between them and the insured. In this case, cover is effected as soon as the parties have agreed the essential aspects of the contract. The relevant terms are:

• The definition of the risk covered.

- The duration of the insurance cover.

- The amount and mode of payment of the premiums.

The exact time that the contract of insurance actually comes into force will have to be judged by the surrounding circumstances. In all cases, the rule relating to offer and acceptance will have to be applied.

Unfortunately, the courts have failed on a number of occasions to consider the question of when a contract comes into force. In the unreported Irish case of *Harmer v. Century Insurance Co.* (1983), the plaintiff proposed for a health insurance policy on 8 June 1979. A proposal form was completed and forwarded to the insurers. On the bottom of the form was a note "The Office must be notified of any changes in the health and circumstances of the life to be insured prior to the assumption of risk". The form was acknowledged and the proposer was required to undergo a medical examination. On 24 July 1979 the plaintiff received a letter from the company, which stated that:

> Risk will be assumed only when you have fulfilled the requirements set out on the attached slip provided there has been no change in the information given in connection with this proposal. Therefore please complete and return the slip without delay, but if there has been any change in the health or other circumstances which could affect the risk, we must be informed of it.

The statement constituted an offer made by the company subject to the completion of the slip attached to the form and to there being no change in health. This could be accepted or rejected by the insured. This slip stated that the proposer accepted the terms set out in the letter dated 24/07/79 and that a signed direct debit mandate/other remittance was enclosed. The policy was then issued and, in this document, it was stated that the policy was not in force until the first premium had been paid. The effective date of the policy was said to be 17/08/79 and the date risk assumed 31/08/79. The premium was paid by the insured on 31/08/79.

On 9/08/79 the plaintiff attended the doctor's surgery complaining of chest pains and a cold. The doctor considered this to be a minor illness and put the patient on antibiotics. Five days later, he returned to the doctor still complaining of the aforementioned symptoms. His condition began to deteriorate in September 1979. His condition worsened and he had to undergo further treatment for a year, until he was finally cured in September 1980.

On making a claim against his health policy, the insurers refused to meet the claim on the basis that they had not been informed of a material fact. The argument being that the cold was material to a prudent underwriter when considering the risk. The court held that this was not the case and that the number of visits to a doctor was not material. It would seem that the offer made by the company in July was subject to "no change in the information given" and "no change in health". These provisions had been breached and therefore the terms of the offer had not been complied with and there was no contract.

Despite this argument, most common law courts have dealt with a case of this nature in the manner argued; that is, whether there was a breach of a material fact. Despite this, the judge seems to have left the matter open for argument on the basis of the existence of a contract.

Another point to consider is that, if the letter of acceptance is considered to be an offer open to acceptance by the proposer, then either party could withdraw before the offer was accepted. This does not appear to be the case as the insurer is not, generally speaking, entitled to withdraw his acceptance letter.

Utmost Good Faith

When a proposal form is completed, this is made the basis of the contract. Consequently, any misrepresentation made on this form will go to the root of the contract and allows the underwriter to consider the policy void from inception. Even in the case where a proposal form is not completed, the proposer must inform the insurer of all material facts pertaining to the risk. A contract of insurance is one of utmost good faith.

This means that the insured must reveal all material facts pertaining to the risk he requires to be insured. The issue then is: what constitutes material fact? There are many decisions in which its meaning was discussed. In most cases, the definition in the UK Marine Assurance Act 1906 has been held to be applicable. This states:

> Every circumstance is material which would influence the judgement of a prudent insurer in fixing the premium, or determining whether he will take the risk.

In other words, the test is one of the prudent underwriter. The question to be asked is whether a prudent underwriter would consider the fact to be material in deciding the premium to be charged or whether they wished to underwrite the risk. This definition was approved in the Irish case of *Chariot Inns v. Assicurazioni Generali* (1981). Despite the acceptance of this definition, the judge went further and applied an extended definition that had been quoted in *Marene v. Greater Pacific Insurance* (1976), where the test was stated to be:

> ... a fact is material if it would have reasonably affected the mind of a prudent insurer in determining whether he will accept the insurance, and if so, at what premium and on what condition?

Thus an element of reasonableness was brought into the definition.

The issue of definition was also discussed in an unreported judgement heard in the Irish Supreme Court in 1986: *Aro Road and Land Vehicles Ltd. v. Insurance Corporation of Ireland Ltd*. In this case, a director of the insured company had been convicted of ten counts of receiving stolen motor parts about 20 years before the circumstances leading to this action. He had contracted with CIE and applied for insurance for his goods being transported by them. During the course of the negotiations, no proposal form was completed and no enquiry made or information proffered concerning the previous conviction. During the course of the transit, the goods were hijacked and the insured claimed under his policy. The insurers turned down the claim on the basis that the fact relating to the conviction had not been revealed at the time the insurance was taken out. McCarthy J. stated:

> In my view, if the judgement of an insurer is such as to require disclosure of what he thinks is relevant but which a reasonable insured, if he thought of it at all, would not think

> relevant, then, in the absence of a question directed towards the disclosure of such a fact, the insurer, albeit prudent, cannot properly be held to be acting reasonably. A contract of insurance is a contract of the utmost good faith on both sides; the insured is bound to disclose every matter which might reasonably be thought to be material to the risk against which he is seeking indemnity; that test of reasonableness is an objective one not to be determined by the opinion of underwriter, broker or insurance agent, but by, and only by, the tribunal determining the issue.

This judgement placed considerable emphasis on the fact that the duty of good faith applies to both the insured and the insurer. This is something that has not been emphasised in the past. Despite this case, most commentators seem to consider that the judgement will only be applied in a small number of cases although they do not state the nature of those cases.

It is clear from this judgement that the test is an objective one. Although evidence may be presented concerning whether a fact would be considered reasonable, the final arbiter is the court, who will consider the reasonableness of the requirement that a material fact should be revealed.

In the *Aro Road* case it was held that a reasonable insured would not have considered a conviction 20 years before to be relevant and therefore, in relying on the non-disclosure of this fact, the underwriter was being unreasonable. In view of this, the policy was not considered void.

It would appear from the case law that, if a proposal form is completed, the insured must answer the questions truthfully and reveal all material facts requested in the form. If he fails to complete the form correctly, this constitutes a misrepresentation. Where there is no proposal form, the insured has to comply with the duty laid down in the *Aro Road* case.

Despite the judgement in the Supreme Court case of *Aro Road*, the High Court case of *Curran v. Norwich Union Life Insurance Society Limited* (1987) followed traditional English law lines. In this case, the plaintiff applied for a universal life policy closely connected with savings and investments. The element of life assurance was very small. He signed a declaration on 16 February 1985 to the effect that "to the best of my knowledge and belief, I am presently in good health and I am not in receipt of medical treatment".

In March 1984 the insured had suffered a severe head injury that necessitated hospitalisation for about six months. But after this, he made a complete recovery and suffered no further symptoms until two days before he signed the proposal when he suffered a severe attack of shivering while he was asleep. His wife noticed this attack but he himself was unaware of it and so, awaking in the morning, he seemed none the worse for the attack. The wife was worried about the attack and, against her husband's wishes, she contacted her family doctor who informed her that the attack was a mild form of epilepsy, which had been connected with the accident. The medical practitioner was of the view that this type of attack might never happen again but did require medication for a year as a precautionary measure. The doctor visited the insured and informed him of his view and prescribed the necessary tablets. The insured refused to take the medication. On 28 June 1985, the insured died in his workplace and the widow claimed the sum insured under the policy. The insurers refused to meet the claim on the basis that there had been a failure to reveal a material fact.

Barr J. referred to the *Chariot Inns* case and stated that the standard of care required by the proposed in revealing material facts was stated by Kenny J.:

> A contract of insurance requires the highest standard of accuracy, good faith, candour and disclosure by the insured when making a proposal for insurance to an insurance company. It has become usual for an insurance company to whom a proposal for insurance is made to ask the proposed to answer a number of questions. Any misstatement in the answers, when they relate to a material matter affecting the insurance, entitles the insurance company to void the policy and to repudiate liability if the event insured against happens. But the correct answering of any questions asked is not the entire obligation of the person seeking insurance: he is bound, in addition, to disclose to the insurance company every matter which is material to the risk against which he is seeking indemnity.

What is to be regarded as material to the risk against which the insurance is sought? It is not what the person seeking insurance regards as material. It is a matter of circumstance, which would reasonably influence the judgement of a prudent insurer in deciding whether he would take the risk and, if so, in determining the premium, which he would demand. The standard by which materiality is to be determined is objective and not subjective. In the last resort the matter has to be determined by the court: the parties to the litigation may call experts in insurance matters as witnesses to give evidence of what they would have regarded as material, but the question of materiality is not to be determined by such witnesses.

The first issue was something that would reasonably affect a prudent underwriter and also a reasonable insurer should have been aware that the fits were material, bearing in mind that a medical practitioner had prescribed medication. The declaration relating to the state of health of the proposer was relevant to the question of medical treatment and the deceased failed to reveal that medical treatment had been prescribed and therefore the signing of the declaration was a misrepresentation. This fact was on that a reasonable and prudent underwriter would expect to be revealed. It was a fact that would affect his judgement concerning acceptance of the life assured.

Once the insurer has accepted the proposal and a contract comes into being, the requirement of utmost good faith falls away. If anything occurs that is material to the risk between the time the proposal is completed and the acceptance of the offer, the underwriter must be informed. Once the insurance has been accepted, this requirement falls away until the next renewal date — that is to say, until the policy expires and the insured requests renewal. Most policies are issued on an annual basis and consequently the requirement relating to utmost good faith will arise annually. At the end of the policy period, the contract comes to an end and therefore a new agreement has to be negotiated. Normally the insurers invite renewal at existing or adjusted terms by means of a renewal notice, forwarded to all insureds whose policies they are prepared to renew. If that offer is accepted by the insured, a new contract comes into existence. **Figure 5.1** presents examples of facts that have been held to be material and those that have not.

Figure 5.1: Examples of Material Facts in Insurance Contracts

---

Material Facts:

- Previous claims history.
- Any refusal of cover by an insurer.
- Previous convictions of the proposer.
- Dangerous material on site.

Facts which need not be disclosed are:

- Facts that the proposer does not know.
- Facts that diminish the risk.
- Facts within the knowledge of the insurer.
- Facts that the insurer has waived his rights concerning knowledge thereof.

Insurable Interest

Before insurance can be granted on any property or person, the party who is taking out the insurance must have an insurable interest in the property or person to be insured, i.e. the subject matter of the insurance. An early definition of insurable interest occurred in *Lucena v. Crawford* (1806) as follows:

> A man is interested in a thing to whom advantage may arise or prejudice happen from the circumstances which may attend it.

Insofar as life assurance is concerned, the requirement for insurable interest was first brought into the law by the Life Assurance Act, 1774, which was extended to Ireland by the Life Assurance (Ireland) Act, 1866. This was aimed at preventing the practice of insuring the lives of well-known persons even though the person insuring would not have suffered a loss as a result of their death. This Act provided that the insured must have an insurable interest in the life assured to be able to benefit under the policy.

Prior to the Life Assurance Act, 1774, the Marine Insurance Acts, 1745 and 1788 provided that insurable interest was required on policies of insurance covering ships and their cargoes. Under both the Life Assurance Act and the Marine Insurance Acts, policies entered into without insurable interest were null and void. The position in respect of marine insurance is now governed by the Marine Insurance Act, 1905, which states that policies without interest are void.

Church and General Insurance v. Patrick Connolly and Patrick Joseph McLoughlin (1981) is an important case on insurable interest. Connolly and McLoughlin were on a committee that ran a youth group. They had leased premises and insured it and its contents against fire. Some time thereafter, a fire broke out and the premises and contents were destroyed. The insurers refused to meet the claim on the basis that the committee had no insurable interest. The court did not enter into a discussion concerning the liability of the lessees to the lessors for the building hired. The sole discussion was based on the committee's property rights. It was held that the committee had an insurable interest in the building and this was their right to occupy the premises as tenants of the owners with responsibility to pay rates and for care and maintenance of the premises while in their possession. The court went on to state that, despite the limited insurable interest of the insured, the insurers had to pay a sum of money to the insured that was sufficient to reimburse the owners of the building. In other words, the insurance policy could be effected, provided that the insured had some form of limited interest in the property. There is no legal rule that a tenant is responsible for damage to the building, unless this has been expressly included in the contract. In this particular case, it would seem from the facts that the committee intended to insure the landlord's interest and the judge recognised this fact and held that the insured could insure the property on behalf of the landlord, as this was the intention of the parties in entering into the insurance contract.

In the United Kingdom, in 1845 the Gaming Act extended the requirement of insurable interest to other types of insurance by declaring that all contracts of agreement by way of gaming or wagering are void. A policy of insurance covering property in which the insured has no interest is a gaming contract and therefore void. The relevant Irish Act is the Gaming and Lotteries Act, 1956.

Ever since these Acts, the definitions of insurable interest has expanded but the main requirements appear to be the following:

- There must be some property, right, liability, interest, life or limb, which is capable of being insured.

- These must be the subject matter of the insurance.

- There must be such a relationship between the insured and the subject matter of the insurance that the insured stands to benefit by its safety or be prejudiced by its loss.

- This relationship must be recognised at law. This is illustrated in the Irish case of *O'Leary v. Irish National Insurance Company Ltd.* (1956). The proposer completed a proposal form for the insurance of a motor vehicle stating that he was the owner of the car. This was not the case as a third party was the owner. After an accident, which damaged the vehicle, the proposer submitted a claim but this was repudiated on the grounds that the proposer had no insurable interest in the vehicle as he was not the owner. Again the interest of the driver of the vehicle as bailee was not considered.

- The relationship must be an enforceable one. The mere hope of acquiring an interest is not enough. This is illustrated in *Macaura v. Northern Assurance* (1925). Macaura secured insurance on some standing timber on his estate. The timber had been sold to a company of which Macaura was the sole shareholder. After the insurance had been arranged, the trees caught fire and were destroyed. Macaura submitted a claim but this was rejected on the grounds that he had no insurable interest in the standing timber, he did not own it or have any other interest in it. Macaura had an interest in the company limited to the shares of the company but this did not extend to the assets of the company. Therefore, he had no insurable interest in the trees and could not claim under his policy.

Therefore, a person has an insurable interest in the property he owns but not in the property of another, unless he can demonstrate some special relationship with that property. There is an insurable interest in the liability that may be incurred as a result of negligence or another tort. The tortfeasor stands to lose by their action in that they will be required to pay damages to an injured party. A creditor has an interest in the life of their debtor. If the person who owes money dies, the creditor may suffer a loss. It may be a very difficult or impossible to obtain the debt from the deceased's estate and therefore they have an insurable interest and can arrange life cover on the debtor. A wife has an insurable interest in her husband. If he dies, she will lose his financial support. Parents do not have an insurable interest in their child merely because of the parent/child relationship. It is possible that the parent is dependent on the child and, in that case, there will be insurable interest but not otherwise.

Shareholders have no interest in the assets of their company, only the company has. The shareholder does not own the assets or stand in such relationship to the assets as to suffer a loss. It is the company that suffers the loss. This is the position in England but, in other common law jurisdictions, a contrary view has been adopted.

Insurable interest must exist at different times dependent on the type of insurance involved. In the case of marine insurance, insurable interest need only be proved at the time of the loss while with other policies, other than life and accidental policies, interest must be proved at the time of the loss and at the time of taking out the insurance. In the case of life assurance and personal accident insurance, insurable interest need only exist at the time the policy is taken out. This is illustrated in the case of *Dalby v. India and London Life Assurance Co.* (1854), where the plaintiff was a director of a company that insured the life of the Duke of Cambridge. This risk was reinsured with India and London Life. The original policies were cancelled but the company went on paying the premiums until the Duke died. The company claimed on their policy but the reinsurers refused to pay on the grounds that insurable interest did not exist at the time of the loss. The court found in favour of the plaintiff on the basis that the 1774 Act only required interest to exist at the time of effecting the policy and not at the time of the claim.

Identifiability of Subject Matter

The subject matter of the insurance must be identifiable — that is to say, it can be ascertained by description. The subject matter of the insurance must be in existence. An insured cannot insure something that has already been destroyed by peril. Some of these conditions can be altered by express conditions in the policy itself or by the conduct of the parties.

Express Conditions

An express condition is one included in the policy, either in writing or orally. When considering conditions, a distinction has to be drawn between warranties and conditions and also between merc conditions and conditions precedent.

Warranties have to be complied with strictly. They are a fundamental term of the insurance and, if breached, insurers are entitled to repudiate the contract, i.e. consider it void. The breach does not have to be connected to the loss for the insurer to repudiate any claim that may be forthcoming. For example, in *Dhaahn v. Hartley* (1786), a marine policy covered a ship and its cargo sailing from Africa to the West Indies. It was warranted that the vessel would sail from Liverpool with 50 hands on board. In fact, it sailed with 46, although it took on a further six hands in Anglesey. It was held that the insurer could avoid liability in respect of any claim that might occur, despite the fact that the claim might have nothing to do with the fact that the ship was short-handed for a short period.

When a breach of warranty occurs, insurers are placed on election and must decide whether they are going to ignore the breach or rely on it and vitiate the contract. They must void the contract as a whole if they decide to take advantage of the breach and not just repudiate any claim that may be forthcoming. If they merely refuse to meet a claim following a breach of warranty but do not avoid the contract, they are considered to have waived their rights to vitiate the policy and will have to meet the claim, unless they can show other grounds to avoid liability.

Warranties are promises that the insured will do certain things or not do something else. For example, the insured will agree to clean up waste in a factory every night and the waste will be placed in fireproof bins.

The courts will view the warranty very carefully and will interpret it strictly. For example, an insurance policy contained the warranty that "the insured's machinery, plant and ways are properly fenced and guarded, and otherwise in good order and condition". The insurers argued that this was a promissory warranty, but the judge disagreed and said if that was the case the future tense would have been used in the warranty. The warranty merely applied to the time the policy was taken out.

Conditions Precedent

If a condition is one upon which the insured's liability depends, then it is a condition precedent. If there is a breach of a condition precedent, the insurers are entitled to dispute liability. For example, a policy providing an indemnity in the event of embezzlement contains a condition that requires the insured to inform the police and take all steps to ensure that the person committing the alleged crime is prosecuted. If this is not done, the insurers can refuse to meet any claim arising from the incident.

On the other hand, in *Re Bradley v. Essex and Suffolk Accident Indemnity Society* (1912), a workman's compensation policy contained the following conditions that purported to be conditions precedent:

1. The premium was to be regulated by the amount of salaries and wages paid by the insured.

2. The keeping of a proper wages book.

3. The insured must supply information to the insurers regarding wages and salaries.

The insured was a farmer who only had one employee, his son. He failed to maintain a proper wages book and the insurers relied on this to deny liability for a particular claim. The court held that the condition was not a condition precedent.

In both of these cases the policy stated that the condition involved was a condition precedent to liability, yet the court came to different conclusions. From this, it would seem that the court will look at the construction of each condition to ascertain its purport.

Mere Conditions

These conditions are neither warranties nor conditions precedent and, in the case of a breach, the injured party has only a right to damages.

Examples of Conditions

Various standard conditions will be discussed at this point and consideration will be given as to their nature. Most policies include the following conditions but, before assuming that this is the case the policy should be checked.

The Alterations Clause

"The insured shall give the company immediate notice of all or any alterations that materially affect the risks covered by the policy including any alteration in the nature of the business or of the property insured."

This clause provides for the disclosure of any alterations that affect the risk. The duty of disclosure normally ends once a policy is entered into. This clause is a condition precedent and if breached would allow the injured party to vitiate the contract.

The Claims Condition

"On the happening of any destruction or damage, the insured shall forthwith give notice thereof in writing to the company and shall within 30 days after such destruction or damage, or such further time as the company may in writing allow, at their own expense, deliver to the company a claim in writing, containing as particular an account as may be reasonably practicable, of the several articles or portions of property destroyed or damaged and of the amount of destruction or damage thereto respectively, having regard to their value at the time of the destruction or damage, together with details of any other insurances on any property thereby insured. The insured shall also give to the company all such proofs and information with respect to the claim as may reasonably be required together with (if damaged) a statutory declaration of the truth of the claim and of any matters connected therewith. No claim under this section shall be payable unless the terms of the condition have been complied with."

This is clearly a condition precedent. The last sentence makes abundantly clear that the payment of a claim depends on the fulfilment of the terms of this particular condition.

The Contribution Condition

"If at the time of any destruction of, or damage to, any property hereby insured, there be any other insurance affected by or on behalf of the insured covering any of the property destroyed or damaged, the liability of the company thereunder shall be limited to its rateable proportion of such destruction or damage."

This is a restatement of the corollary of indemnity contribution. The common law rule will be discussed later. Most policies contain a clause similar to this or ruling out contribution completely.

Indemnity

In the case of *Castellain v. Preston* (1883), it was held:

> The very foundation, in my opinion, of every rule which has been applied to insurance law is this, namely, that the contract of insurance contained in a marine or fire policy is a contract of indemnity and of indemnity only . . . and if ever a proposition is brought forward which is at variance with it, that is to say, which either will prevent the assured from obtaining a full indemnity or which gives the assured more than a full indemnity, that proposition must certainly be wrong.

This statement illustrates that the principle of indemnity is a cornerstone of insurance law.

Indemnity means to place the insured in exactly the same position financially after the loss as they occupied immediately before the loss. For example, if the insured had a safe containing €2,000 and the money is stolen, then the insurer must give the insured €2,000 cash to indemnify them. This is a simple case but the case of the owner of a 20-year-old piece of machinery is not so easy; how does an insurer indemnify him? The only way to do so is to establish the cost of a similar piece of machinery, which is 20 years old. To pay for a new machine is to over-indemnify, while to pay for something less than the machine he had is to under-indemnify. A true indemnity would be to ascertain the market price of a similar machine of the same vintage and in the same condition.

Methods of Indemnification

Insurers use a variety of methods to indemnify their clients:

- **Cash:** The simplest and easiest way is to provide a cash payment. In other words, to give to the insured a cheque for the value of the goods lost.

- **Replacement:** A further method is to purchase a similar article to the one lost or damaged and provide this to the insured. In the event of a 1997 Ford Mondeo being stolen, the insurers can purchase the insured another 1997 Ford Mondeo.

- **Repair:** In the event of the subject matter of the insurance being damaged, the insurers can arrange for its repair. Thus, if a car is damaged, the vehicle can be sent to a panel-beater who will beat out the dents caused by the accident.

- **Reinstatement:** Reinstatement is used in two contexts in insurance. Firstly, it refers to the rebuilding of a building following a fire or the occurrence of some other peril. In this case, the building is restored to the same position it was in prior to the loss. Once the rebuilding commences, it must be completed regardless of cost. Another difficulty is that in the event of the builders not carrying out the job properly, the insurers can be held responsible. The second manner in which the term is used concerns the reinstatement of a building as new. In most fire policies, buildings and their contents are covered so that if they are burnt down they are rebuilt as new. This is commonly called the reinstatement clause. This is an amendment to the indemnity principle in that the insured will gain by his loss. He is obtaining a brand new building in exchange for the old.

Modification of the Indemnity Principle

A number of clauses on the policy can modify the indemnity principle. It is quite common to include in the policy a clause that provides that the insurers will also pay for any improvements required by local authorities' building regulations. It could well be that the building insured is very old and does not comply with present building regulations but, if it was destroyed, it would have to be rebuilt so that any regulations are complied with. The insurance policy will provide additional cover to take into account this possibility.

In some householders' policies, cover is provided so that the replacement cost is paid in the event of property being lost or damaged. Thus, despite the age of the insured furniture or other contents, the insured will be paid the price of the article at the time of the loss as opposed to the depreciated value.

Indemnity Limit

All policies provide a limit over and above which the insurers will not pay. In the case of property insurance, the limit that insurers will pay is the sum insured. If this is insufficient to meet the loss, the insurer will not pay in excess of the figure included in the policy.

Liability policies and vehicle policies provide for a limit of indemnity. This has no connection with value but is a limit under the policy. The limits may be annual limits, limits per item or site, or limits per claim.

Excess or Deductible

Some policies provide for a first amount payable to be met by the insured in the event of a claim. This is quite common on a motor policy. Thus a policy might provide for an excess or deductible of €1,000. In the event of a claim where the total loss is €15,000, the insured will only receive €14,000.

Franchises

In this case the policy provides that the insurers will not meet a claim unless it exceeds a specific amount but, once that amount has been exceeded, the whole claim will be met. Thus, if a policy contains a franchise of €1,000 and a claim occurs for 4500, the insured will receive nothing but, if the claim is for €1,250, the insured will receive the full amount.

The Average Clause

In most fire policies and householders' and houseowners' policies — that is, policies covering the contents of the home and the building — there is a condition known as the average clause. This states that, should the sum insured be less than the value at risk at the time of the loss, the insured will be considered their own insurer for a proportion of the loss. There are other types of average clauses but this is the most common.

Non-Indemnity Contracts

Life assurance contracts, personal accident policies and some guarantee policies are not contracts of indemnity. The reason for life assurance and accident policies not being contracts of indemnity is that it is impossible to ascertain the value of a human life or a part of a human body. In view of this, there is no legal restriction concerning indemnity in such policies although insurers will try to ensure that, when they underwrite such policies, the sums insured are not excessive.

Corollaries of Indemnity

As a result of the operation of the principle of indemnity, a number of problems arise. For example, in the event of an accident where both parties have material damage and legal liability, the persons involved in the accident can, theoretically, claim from their insurers the cost of repairing the damage to their vehicles and also claim the cost of the same damage from the negligent party.

Subrogation

The doctrine of subrogation gives the right of one person who has indemnified another to stand in the shoes of that other and avail themselves of all that other's rights and interests. Thus, an individual will only be able to claim from their insurers who will then avail themselves of that individual's rights and claim against the other individual to recover their outlay.

The leading case on this point is *Castellain v. Preston* (1883). The facts were that Preston was selling his house to R and, during the course of the sale, it was damaged by fire. A claim was submitted to insurers and they met the claim. In the meantime, R paid the full price of the house to Preston in terms of the contract of sale. The risk of loss was with R. The insurers discovered this and recovered their payment from Preston on the basis that the insured had profited by his loss and the insurer was entitled to recover from R, but this had already been done by Preston so they recovered from their own insured. It was stated by the judge that:

> As between the underwriter and the assured, the underwriter is entitled to the advantage of every right of the assured, whether such right consists in contract, fulfilled or

unfulfilled, or in remedy for tort capable of being insisted on or already insisted on, or in any other right, whether by way of condition or otherwise, legal or equitable, which can be or has been exercised or has accrued, and whether such right could or could not be enforced by the insurer in the name of the assured, by the exercise for acquiring of which right or condition the loss against which the assured is insured, can be or has been, diminished.

The doctrine can only be exercised once the insurer meets the claim submitted by the insured. This particular common law provision is normally amended by a general policy condition that provides the insurer with a right of subrogation as soon as a claim has been made.

Contribution

The next case to consider is contribution. This rule deals with the case where two policies covering the risk are in existence. If the insured could claim against two insurers, he would benefit by his loss and the principle of indemnity would be breached. The common law provides that, in the event of two policies being in existence, which cover the same risk, any claim that is forthcoming will be divided between the insurers according to their rateable proportion. The insured is entitled to submit his claim against any one of the insurers or all of them at once but he is never allowed to retain more than his loss. In the event of contributing insurers paying more than their rateable proportion, they are entitled to proceed against the other insurers to recover any amount paid in excess of their proportion so that each has paid their rateable proportion.

In order for the doctrine of contribution to apply, the following requirements must be met:

1. The insurance must have a common subject matter.

2. The loss must be common to a peril common to both policies.

3. The same interest must be covered by both policies. Thus, in the case of a mortgagee insuring his interest in a building and a mortgagor insuring his particular interest, the doctrine of contribution will not apply as there are two different interests.

4. Both policies must be enforceable.

Again, the policy document may well alter the common law position. In fact, it is the practice of most companies to include in their policy some clause relating to contribution, either restating the common law position or amending it.

An interesting Irish case concerning contribution is the unreported judgement of *Rohan Construction Ltd. and Zurich Insurance Co. Ltd. v. Shield Insurance Company Ltd.* (1985). In this case, two employees of Q were travelling in the same vehicle in the course of their employment when an accident occurred, caused by the negligent driving of D, one of the two employees. S, the second employee, was badly injured and succeeded in obtaining an award of damages against D. Q was vicariously liable for D's negligence but, if damages had been awarded against them, they could have recovered them from D. Q were the holders of a motor vehicle policy that covered third party liability arising out of the use of a vehicle in connection with company business and an employer's liability policy covering their liability to employees. Thus, on the face of it, both policies covered this loss, and contribution between the companies should have applied. Gannon J. was of the view that contribution did not apply in this case, as the interest was not the same and neither was the insured. In the case of the car policy, the insured was the driver of the vehicle, D, while in the case of the employer's liability policy, it was Q. The latter covered Q's liability, not D's.

Proximate Cause

To be able to submit a claim under a policy, an insured must be able to show that the loss was caused by an insured peril. The test that is used to meet this requirement is whether the loss was proximately caused by the peril. This is the general rule but it can be altered by the policy terms.

The proximate cause is the active efficient cause that sets in motion a train of events, which brings about a result without the intervention of any other intervening force. In the case of a fire started by a dropped cigarette igniting waste paper, it is obvious that the fire caused the damage to surrounding furniture and also to the buildings. But what about the damping down that the fire brigade has to carry out in order to ensure that the fire does not spread or reignite.

In this case, there is no intervening cause; the fire started and, as a result of this, the fire brigade was called, who, as a result of the fire, damped down the premises. If it was not for the fire, the water damage would not have occurred. Suppose a wall had been weakened by the fire and was blown down by the wind a week later; has there been an intervening cause? In this case, it is submitted that there has been an intervening cause and it cannot be argued that the fire caused the wall to fall down, despite the fact that the fire may have weakened it. The insured has had sufficient time to make safety arrangements. So it can be said that the storm was a new cause and the wind blew the wall over after it stood for a week. In the case of the wall being blown down within a few hours of the fire, the result may be different. It can be argued that the fire weakened the wall and, as only a few hours had elapsed, there was insufficient time for a new cause to operate.

Although it is very difficult to suggest rules relating to proximate cause, the following appear to apply:

- Once the risk operates, any further damage caused in order to mitigate the loss will be covered. Therefore if a fire occurs and the fire brigade is called to put out the flames, any damage caused by the fire brigade is covered.

- An accident facilitating the loss must be distinguished from an accident causing the loss. Thus, in the case of thieves breaking into a warehouse under the cover of an air raid, the proximate cause of the loss is the thieves. The air raid facilitated the occurrence, by making it easier for the thieves to commit the crime, but the theft was the proximate cause of the loss of goods from the building.

- There must be no *novus actus interveniens*. An intervening cause must not interfere with the original cause. If it does, there is a new cause. Thus, if a fire occurs and thieves steal goods during the course of the fire, the proximate cause of the loss of stolen goods is not the fire but the theft. The thieves are a new intervening cause.

- This rule covers another rule whereby it can be argued that, if a human agency is competing with a natural agency for the causative factor, then the human agency would be considered to be the proximate cause. Thus, if a storm occurs and a human fails to take reasonable precautions to mitigate his loss, it can be argued that the ensuing loss is a result of the human failing to reduce the possibility of loss as opposed to the storm.

- Death-blow cause: If the natural cause follows a series of events begun by a human, the proximate cause is the human agency.

INTERPRETATION OF INSURANCE CONTRACTS

In order to interpret an insurance contract, there are certain basic rules to bear in mind. Normally reading and understanding the words used can interpret the contract but, due to the imperfections of language, there may be certain ambiguities. The insured may have meant one thing and the insurer another. In order to deal with these ambiguities, there are certain rules of interpretation developed by the Courts.

The Golden Rule

The golden rule of interpretation is that the intention of the parties must prevail. The whole object of reading any contract is to try to ascertain the intention of the parties. In order to ascertain the intention of the parties, there is a rule of evidence which is known as the parole evidence rule which states that, to interpret the contract, regard may not be given to particular facts that occurred at the inception of the transaction or during the negotiations. Attention may be given to other surrounding circumstances such as the nature of the transaction and the known course of business and the forms in which such matters are carried out. The effect of this is that, if the contract is in writing, as is normally the case with insurance contracts, then only the insurance policy may be used to ascertain the true intention of the parties.

If one of the parties believes that the document does not contain the true intention then that party must apply to the court for rectification of the contract before any attempt is made to interpret the incorrect document. If the applicant can prove that the document does not contain the intent of the parties, the court will alter it.

Order of Importance

The insurance contract is normally in printed form but sometimes this is amended by a typewritten document, normally an endorsement. If there is any conflict between a printed document and a typewritten one, then the latter takes precedence. If the document was amended by hand, the handwriting takes precedence over both the printed and the typewritten words.

Construction of Words

The words used in a document must be interpreted as having their normal and natural everyday meaning. Thus, a fire does not mean an explosion although, technically speaking, an explosion could be considered a fire as there is normally ignition. A further example is a policy, which excluded death by the hands of the insured, has been held to include death caused by drowning.

Technical words or words that have acquired a particular meaning must be interpreted as having the meaning that has been acquired. Thus in *Clift v. Schwabe* (1946) it was stated that:

> Terms of art, or technical words must be understood in their proper sense, unless the contract controls or alters their meaning; ancient words may be explained by contemporaneous usage, and words which have acquired a particular sense by usage in particular districts, occupations or trades, must be read in their acquired sense.

If a word is defined in a statute, that word will retain that meaning provided it is intended to mean the same as in the Act. For example the Interpretation Act, 1937 provides meanings of a variety of words used in statutes in Ireland. The courts would most probably assign these meanings to the words used in an insurance contract.

The *Ejusdem Generis* Rule

Where general words are linked with particular words, the former must be construed as limited to the same *genus* (type of thing) as the particular word. For example, if a policy is worded to exclude watches, jewellery, gold, silver and other valuable articles, this would not include furs. Although furs are valuable, they would not fall into the same class as the other articles and therefore cannot form part of the exclusion. The words "valuable articles" can only mean "valuable articles of a like nature". If the whole class of goods is exhausted, that is to say the list includes everything in a particular class, then the *ejusdem generis* rule cannot apply.

If it is clear from the words that, despite a host of exclusions, words are used to exclude the operation of the rule, then the rule cannot be applied. Thus if the words "or from any cause whatso-ever" are used these would exclude the operation of this rule. Again the all-important point is the intention of the parties.

Construction as a Whole

The policy must be construed as a whole. One cannot isolate one clause from the rest of the document. Before making any attempt to ascertain a meaning, the policy must be looked at in its entirety. In order to reach this meaning, the words used must bear their natural and ordinary meaning unless they are intended to mean otherwise.

In some policies, words are given meanings in the document. For example, the term "all other contents" is usually defined in a fire policy so that wherever it is used it bears that meaning. In other policies, various other terms will be defined so that wher-ever they are used in the policy they must bear that meaning unless it can be shown that it was not the intention of the parties for the word to bear that particular meaning in that context.

Ut Res Magis Valeat Quam Pereat

This is translated as: "It is better for a thing to have effect than to be made void". The document must be construed so that it is an effective legal document. Thus all attempts will be made, despite the difficulty in interpreting the words used. So, words will not be given a meaning, unless absolutely necessary, that will make the policy void or unenforceable.

Contra Proferentem Rule

If a clause is drawn up so that it is ambiguous and has at least two meanings, one interpretation of which benefits the party who drew up the contract and the other which benefits the other party, the in-terpretation used is the one that benefits the party who did not draft the contract. In the case of insurance, it is normally the insurer who drafts the policy and, therefore, if there are any ambiguities in the document drawn up by them, those ambiguities should be construed against the insurer and in favour of the insured. This will only apply if there are ambiguities in the construction after considering the document as a whole. If the meaning becomes clear after perusing the whole of the policy, this rule cannot apply.

Table 5.1: Key Insurance Terms

Assurance/ Insurance	Assurance is cover against a certainty — e.g. life assurance. Insurance is cover against an event that may never happen, such as an accident at work.
Average Clause	Does not apply to EL policies but worth noting. Applies to property cover. Basically, it means that if you insure premises for €100,000 and it is worth €200,000, you will be regarded as having under-insured and will only receive €50,000 in the event of a claim. In other words, the payment due will be reduced in proportion to the amount by which the premises is under-insured. Can also apply to other property, like plant, machinery, or motor vehicles.
Conditions (express)	A condition that is included in the policy, either orally or (more usually) in writing.
Conditions (mere)	A condition upon which the insured's liability (precedent) depends, such as a condition to keep the insurer informed of payroll cost changes.
Contribution	A principle that operates to ensure that the insured is not paid twice in respect of the one claim. So if an injured employee has a claim against, say, their employer and the owner of the vehicle that crashed into them, only the amount awarded can be recovered, split in whatever proportions the court decides or as has been agreed.
Cover note	A short document issued by the insurer, confirming that the risk is covered by insurance.
Endorsement	A note put on a policy to confirm a change in cover.
Exclusions	Matters set out in the policy on which the insurers will not provide cover.
Indemnity	The word used to cover the insurer's promise to pay the insured or, in the case of an EL claim, to pay the injured person, on the insured's behalf, so that the insured is not out of pocket in respect of the damages awarded and the legal costs incurred. It does not cover what safety practitioners refer to as the uninsured costs, such as management time.

Insurable Interests	The insured must have an interest in the subject matter of the insurance and employers are deemed to have an interest in the safety and well being of their employees.
Material Facts	Facts that may influence the insurer's decision to accept or decline to accept the risk, such as previous refusals of other insurers to grant cover. In certain circumstances, this could extend to a past refusal to grant cover to directors or senior managers.
Peril	A word sometimes used to denote the occurrence being insured against.
Policy	The document that sets out the terms of the insurance cover.
Proposal	The proposition put by the person seeking insurance to the insurer, giving details of the cover sought and disclosing all material facts that may influence the insurer's decision as to whether or not to provide cover. Usually, but not always, made by completing a proposal form.
Proximate Cause	The insured must be able to show that the loss was caused by a risk that was insured against.
Subrogation	Gives the insurer the right to step into the shoes of the insured and claim against another party against whom the insured may have rights.
Utmost Good Faith	Often referred to by the Latin tag *uberrima fides*, this doctrine is the fundamental principle of insurance. An insurance contract is deemed to be a contract of the utmost good faith. This requires the potential insured to disclose any material fact that may influence the insurer's decision to accept or decline the risk or decide the rating to be attached to it.
Warranties	Are fundamental terms of an insurance policy and, if not complied with, can, invalidate the policy at the option of the insurer. A warranty is a guarantee by the insured that they will take some specific action, such as, say, putting a guard on a machine.

LIABILITY INSURANCE

Difference between Employers' and Public Liability Insurance

Insurers provide a range of liability policies to cover different eventualities. These policies indemnify insured in the event of their becoming legally liable to third parties who suffer loss or damage or personal injury or disease as a result of a tort committed by the insured. All the policies provide for payment of compensation awarded as a result of accidental loss or damages to property or personal injury or disease. The policies are subject to a limit of liability, which is the maximum amount payable in compensation to the injured party. Cover extends to include legal fees incurred in order to defend an action and investigation costs over and above the limit of liability. The policy provides that the insurer has the right to take over any claim made against the insured and deal with it, as they deem fit. Thus once the insured has received a claim, insurers generally deal with it on their behalf. It must be emphasised that the policy is one that covers the insured's legal liability, therefore payment will only be made to a third party in the event of there being an actionable tort. Despite this, insurers will define actions on behalf of their clients and meet all costs incurred.

There are four main classes of liability policy:

- General liability.

- Employers' liability.

- Product liability.

- Professional liability.

The general liability policy covers loss or damage to property or persons arising out of the activities of the insured. It excludes liability to employees whilst they are acting in the course of their employment, loss or damage caused by a product and liability arising out of the giving of advice or the provision of incorrect designs or specifications. The first exception is covered by the employers' liability policy, the second by product liability and the third by professional liability policies.

These policies all contain a number of important conditions, relating to contributions, subrogation, claims procedure and a reasonable precaution condition. This last provides that the insured shall take all reasonable precautions to prevent accidents and to maintain the premises. The wording may differ depending on the policy and should be consulted. In *Frazer v B.N. Furman Productions* (1967), a particular reasonable precaution clause was discussed. It is instructive to study the words of Diplock L.J. in his judgement:

> It is the insured personally who must take reasonable precautions . . . the obligation is to take precautions to prevent accidents. This means in my view to take measures to avert dangers, which are likely to cause bodily injury . . . 'reasonable' means reasonable as between the insured and the insurer having regard to the commercial purpose of the contract. . . . What, in my view is 'reasonable' . . . is that the insured should not deliberately court a danger, the existence of which he recognises. . . . The purpose of the condition is to ensure that the insured will not, because he is covered against loss by the policy, refrain from taking precautions which he knows ought to be taken.

Now that liability in policies in general has been considered, we will deal with the general liability policy and the employers' liability policies in more detail.

Generally, a distinction is made between employers' liability and public liability insurance. Case law confines employers' liability to an individual who has a contract of service, whereas public liability relates to anybody who renders service under other arrangements.

However, unlike Great Britain, in Ireland there is no statutory obligation on employers to arrange employers' liability insurance to ensure that a basis of compensation exists should the employee receive actionable injuries while at work. Indeed, this issue was litigated in *Sweeney v. Duggan* (1991). The plaintiff sought to lift the veil of incorporation and sue the managing director of the company that employed him on the basis that he had failed in his duty to him as an employee by not ensuring that employers' liability insurance was in place. The High Court (Barron) held that a general duty on the employer to protect the economic well-being of his employees did not exist at common law and therefore the case could not succeed.

Scope of Employers' Liability Insurance

The subject matter of employers' liability insurance is the amount of damages that an employer may be liable to pay his employees in respect of accidental death or injury, including disease, caused during the period of insurance and arising out of, and in the course of, employment with that employer in connection with his business.

- While there is no such thing as a standard insurance policy, there is what is referred to in *Tolley's Health and Safety at Work Handbook* as a "typical policy". The typical policy will:

  ◊ Indemnify the employer against the payment of damages and legal costs when employees are injured or suffer occupational ill-health during the course of work, as a result of the employers' negligence.

  ◊ Contain a limit on cover of €12,700,000 (IR£10,000,000).

  ◊ Normally limit cover to a defined state: e.g. Ireland, although, in some policies, temporary travel outside Ireland may be covered.

  ◊ Require the insured to notify the insurer of all accidents and incidents.

  ◊ Grant the insurer the right to settle claims.

  ◊ Contain an exclusion clause.

- In some policies, the definition of employee has been extended to cover those who are gaining work experience and even self-employed persons working on the employers' premises. He also notes that many policies insure against the costs and expenses of defending proceedings brought under the Safety, Health Welfare at Work Act, 1989. Safety practitioners should read the exclusion clause carefully, for it is the area that is most likely to give rise to a dispute between the insured and the insurer (apart from a dispute over whether all relevant material facts were disclosed at the proposal stage). O'Regan Cazabon (1999) notes that "although an EL policy is an extremely straightforward document, an insured should be vigilant to examine specific exclusions thereunder".

- Because insurance policies cover only what is agreed and set out in writing in the policy and because exclusion clauses can give rise to difficulties, safety practitioners should seek a *pro forma* copy of the intended policy before the insurance contract is finalised. They should read it very carefully, to see that cover as is envisaged is provided. If it is not, extra cover should be negotiated. Examples of extra cover that may be required are cover for employees who are working abroad or cover for employees who are working from home.

- The insurers may include a provision that entitles them to cancel the policy where certain specified changes occur. These generally include the winding up of the business or an alteration to a system of work that makes it more risky.

- Insurers often include a right-of-recovery condition within the policy, which allows the insurer to seek to recover the indemnity paid under the policy in situations where the employer did not take reasonable steps to protect employee's from injury.

In the case of *Frazer v. B.N. Furman (Production) Ltd.* (1967), the Court of Appeal considered a reasonable precaution condition in an employer's liability insurance policy. Diplock C.J. identified three considerations to be borne in mind when interpreting this condition:

- It is the insured personally who must take reasonable precautions. Failure by an employee to do so would not represent a breach of the conditions.

- The obligation of the employer is to take precautions to prevent accidents, which means taking measures to avert dangers that are likely to cause bodily harm to employees.

- "Reasonable" in this context means reasonable as between the insured and the insurer, having regard to the purpose of the insurance contract.

Most employers' liability policies give wide coverage in terms of the business definition. The business definition will usually include the provision and management of canteens, social, sports and welfare activities. It will also include private work carried out with the consent of the insured.

Common exclusions in employer liability policies include any work of demolition, pile-driving, quarrying or the use of explosives, the construction of roads, work on roofs and the loading or discharging of vessels.

In terms of the employees covered, the following categories of persons are commonly deemed to be individuals under a contract of service: a labour-only sub-contractor; self-employed persons; persons hired or borrowed by the insured from another employment; voluntary helpers; persons under work-experience schemes and FÁS trainees. It also includes regular full-time employees.

The insurer will generally not be liable under an employers' liability policy to indemnify the insured employer if the employee received their injuries from a situation not arising out of, and in the course of, employment. The British Court of Appeal in recent years has held that the test as to whether an employee is acting "in the course of his employment" is not a strict test of whether the employee at the relevant time performed duties specified by the employer. The employee may be in the course of their employment where they acted in a casual, negligent or disobedient manner. Employees may be considered to be acting outside the scope of employment where they are in a jaunt of their own. This may be for example using a firm's vehicle to take their family on a picnic or leaving the premises to go home.

IBEC has produced a set of guidelines that employers should follow when taking out employers' liability insurance. These are presented in **Figure 5.2**.

Figure 5.2: IBEC Guidelines on Employers' Liability Insurance

---

- It is essential to have full disclosure of the organisation's activities and to describe accurately the business when completing the proposal form.

- All material facts that may affect the insurance must be communicated to the insurer, including the full details of accidents. (The accident history of the organisation)

- There is an obligation to inform the insurer of changes to the risks that they carry. This could include new employees, new plant or equipment.

- The policy wording should adequately include the activities of the business and the employer should be aware of any conditions precedent, which affect the policy.

- Any exclusions to the policy should be checked and clarified with the insurer. IBEC recommends that there should be no exceptions to the type of injury or disease for which cover is required.

- The policy should cover all locations of the business including foreign locations. It is too cumbersome to secure special cover for each foreign visit.

- It is recommended that cover should specifically include the operation of medical and first aid facilities, sports and leisure facilities, EAP programmes and any other welfare arrangements.

- Any cover sought should contain a provision that indemnifies directors, senior management, and first aid personnel, who may be pursued in an action for damages.

- It is recommended that special or unique activities within the business should be brought to the attention of the insurers so as to confirm that they are covered.

The Nature of Public Liability Insurance

The reason for an organisation taking out public liability insurance is to obtain an indemnity in respect of its liability to third parties where injury, death or loss or damage to their property occurs. Public liability policies generally cover two broad fields of liability:

- Risks arising from the ownership, occupation or management of a business premises.

- Risks arising from the activities of employees or agents to third parties.

The purpose of a public liability policy means that the insured cannot recover anything under the main indemnity clause or make any claim against the underwriters until the insured has been found liable and so sustained the loss. Public liability, therefore, has an indemnity limit attached, which is not the case with employer's liability insurance. The policy usually provides that the insurer will indemnify the insured against all sums that the insured is legally obliged to pay as compensation for accidental death, personal injury or illness or disease of any person or loss or damage to property.

The following conditions are usually found in public liability insurance policies:

- Insurers usually place a condition in the policy to the effect that the insured must not make any admission of liability or seek to compromise or settle any claim made against them without the specific consent of the insurer.

- The insurer will usually place a limit on their liability in relation to any one accident or occurrence. In the former, "accident" will be construed from the claimant against the insurer's point of view, whereas the word "occurrence" is used in the clause limiting the liability of the insurer. This will be construed from the insurer's point of view.

- The policy will usually specify the claims procedure to be followed by the insured. The requirement may be limited to forwarding every written notice of claim received. It may also specify the forwarding of policies and documents received immediately.

Scope of the Liability Policy

These relate to contractual liabilities, professional negligence, product liability and injury or death of employees. In the first situation, it refers to liability for any amount of penalties that arise because of a contract. Professional negligence is outside the scope of public liability insurance and product liability issues are also excluded. The public liability insurance policy will exclude liability arising from the death or injury, illness or disease contracted by any employee of the insured. **Figure 5.3** presents a set of guidelines for employers considering taking out public liability insurance.

Figure 5.3: IBEC Guidelines on Public Liability Insurance

- It is advantageous to have the same underwriter for employers and public liability, particularly where the incident gives rise to a claim under both areas.

- The insured should be aware of any excess clause in the policy and its precise implications.

- The cover should indemnify directors, senior managers and first aiders who might be pursued in an action for damages.

- Special cover arrangements to deal with, for example, contractors would need some specific discussion with insurers.

- There should be adequate cover for all locations and activities where the company may be exposed to the risk of a claim for injury.

- In all cases, the company should not make any admissions, or offer promise of payment, to any person arising from the incident without prior agreement with the insurers.

- The policy excludes property in the custody or control of the insured.

SELF-INSURANCE

There is a growing tendency for organisations to self-insure, that is to say, to finance their own losses in the event of liability being incurred. In this case, the organisation may finance all their losses or avail of a deductible. This latter means that the insured agrees to pay the first €100,000 or first €1,000,000 and an insurer deals with liability incurred above this amount. There are many inventive ways in which organisations can now provide finance in the event of a loss instead of purchasing insurance. For details of these, it would be wise to contact a good insurance broker with a risk management department.

If an organisation decides to self-insure, it is important that the following factors are taken into account:

- It is important that resources are available to manage claims and provide for reserves in respect of outstanding cases.

- The company should adopt specific measures that discourage claims. These may include the provision of expert medical treatment to injured employees. However, IBEC cautions that care needs to be exercised in order to avoid the prejudicing of future claims.

- There is a need to create a claims management team whose role it is to provide expert advice on liability issues, claim values, the assessment of medical reports and specific engineering advice. It may be possible to hire this on a consultancy basis if required.

- Employees should be made aware that the company does not have conventional employers' liability insurance, therefore the company has to bear the full cost of any claims made by employees.

- The company should adopt a policy whereby accident claims are settled sooner rather than later.

- The company should provide systematic training to management in the costing of accidents, the conduct of accident investigations and specific preparation for court appearances.

There is much concern at national level about the cost of employers' liability insurance. The European Foundation for the Improvement of Working and Living Conditions has published a report, *An Innovative Economic Incentive Model for the Improvement of the Working Environment in Europe*, in which it recommended that there should be a compulsory industrial insurance with bonuses for companies that improve working conditions. The higher the health and safety standard, the larger the bonus.

CHAPTER ROUND-UP

- This chapter considered the subject matter of insurance in terms of its key principles and it focused on two specific types of insurance that have direct relevance to health and safety: employers' liability and public liability insurance.

- A contract of insurance is any contract whereby one party assumes the risk of an uncertain event, which is not within their control, happening at a future date, in which event the other party has an interest, and under which contract the first party is bound to pay money or provide its equivalent.

- A contract of insurance comes into existence when there is an offer, acceptance and intention to contract. A number of additional elements are also required, specifically a contract of insurance is a contract of utmost good faith. This means that any failure to reveal a material fact will void an insurance contract from inception.

- Before insurance can be granted on any property or person, the party who is taking out the insurance must have an insurable interest in the property or person to be insured. The insurable interest constitutes the subject matter of the insurance. The insurable interest must be some property, right, liability interest, life or limb that is capable of being insured. There must also be a relationship between the insured and the subject matter of the insurance. This relationship must be recognised by the law.

- Contracts of insurance typically contain a range of conditions including an alterations clause, a claims condition, a contribution condition and an indemnity clause.

- There are no statutory obligations on Irish employers to take out employers' liability insurance. The High Court has held that a general duty on the part of the employer to protect the economic well-being of their employees does not exist at common law.

- The subject matter of employers' liability insurance is the amount of damages that an employer may be liable to pay employees in respect of accidental death or injury, including disease, caused during the period of insurance and arising out of and in the course of employment with that employer.

- Employers generally take out public liability insurance in order to obtain an indemnity in respect of their liability to third parties where injury, death or loss or damage to their property occurs. Public liability policies usually cover liability arising out of the ownership, occupation or management of property or from the activities of employers or agents causing injury or damage to third parties or their property.

Chapter 6

REGULATING THE ENVIRONMENT: ENVIRONMENTAL AND WASTE MANAGEMENT LEGISLATION

INTRODUCTION

Environmental issues are not generally dealt with in a book on health and safety. However, developments in recent years have created a realisation that the activities of the business environment can have significant implications for the quality of the natural environment. It is quite common now to find large companies reorienting and renaming their health and safety departments to include environmental issues. It is therefore appropriate to consider some of the more relevant pieces of legislation in this area and consider their impact for organisations.

This chapter will consider a number of issues related to environmental law in Ireland. It does not, however, consider planning law as this is beyond the scope of the handbook. The chapter will focus on five important issues in this context:

- The influence of the EU on Irish environmental law.

- Remedies available in the courts for environmental protection in Ireland.

- The nature and role of environmental impact assessment.

- The Environmental Protection Agency Act and the law on waste disposal in Ireland.

- The issue of access to information on the environment.

THE EUROPEAN COMMUNITY INFLUENCE ON ENVIRONMENTAL LAW

The development of national policy on the environment in Ireland can largely be attributed to the influence of the EU. Until 1989, no national policy existed and the majority of the measures introduced were simply complying with EC requirements or in some cases, responding to political pressures. Scannell (1995) points out that there was a singular failure to integrate environmental issues into other sectoral policies and programmes and this lack of integration has led to many environmental problems. She cites as an example the granting of planning permission for housing developments incorporating open fireplaces. This led to a significant increase in smoke levels in urban areas.

Since 1989, the development of environmental law has been extensive and the most significant influence has been the level of activity at EU level in the environmental sphere. The Treaty of Rome is largely silent on environmental issues, although Article 2 calls for the harmonious development of economic activities. In 1973, the Council of Ministers declared that such harmonious development could not be achieved without concern for the protection of the environment. The first programme of action of the European Community on the Environment was adopted in 1973 and five further programmes have since been adopted: in 1977-81, 1982-86, 1987-92, 1993-2000 and 2001-03.

These action programmes provide the basic policy framework within which each member state's actions are taken. The first two programmes tended to focus on serious environmental problems such as pollution. The third programme changed direction significantly and placed an emphasis on prevention. The fourth programme further reinforced the prevention theme, whereas the fifth and sixth programmes placed an emphasis on sustainable development. They give priority to six key areas:

- Sustainable management of natural resources.

- Integrated pollution control and the prevention of waste.

- Improving mobility management.

- Improved public health and safety.

- A reduction in the consumption of non-renewable energy.

- The adaptation of measures to improve environmental quality in urban areas.

The fifth programme focused on five sectors: manufacturing, energy, transport, tourism and agriculture and broadens the range of instruments to effect the programme to include legal measures, market-driven instruments, financial supports and other supporting instruments such as the analysis of data, education and training initiatives and research and development. Existing European Community environmental initiatives are driven by principles of environmental management, which were articulated in the first action programme. These principles are presented in **Figure 6.1**.

Figure 6.1: Principles of Effective Environmental Management

- Prevention is better than cure.
- Environmental effects should be considered as early as possible in the decision-making processes.
- Avoid the exploitation of nature and natural resources.
- Improve scientific and technical knowledge.
- The polluter should pay the costs of pollution.
- The state itself should not contribute to environmental degradation.
- Member states should take account of the interests of developing countries.
- Member states should participate in international organisations dealing with environmental matters.
- The level of environmental awareness should be continuously improving.
- For every category of pollution, it is necessary to establish an appropriate level of action.
- Natural environmental programmes/policies should be co-ordinated within the EU without hampering progress at national level.

THE IRISH RESPONSE TO EUROPEAN UNION
ENVIRONMENT INITIATIVES

The first major recognition of environmental issues in Ireland occurred in 1978 when the then Minister for the Environment established an Environmental Council, now defunct. It was charged with
the development of a national environmental policy and produced
a policy document, *Towards an Environmental Policy*. This rather
slim document considered a number of policy considerations and
made very little reference to EC environmental policy. A second
policy document for the environment was published in 1980. This
was more specific in nature and placed an emphasis on better controls, better environment, better monitoring and the collection of
data on pollution. The document remained largely unimple-
mented, although the Coalition Government in its Programme for
Government 1981-86 did make reference to it and put forward
plans to deal with the protection of the environment. Very little
happened, however.

The next significant development came in 1985, when the Environmental Awareness Bureau was established. A major report on
the state of the environment was published by An Foras Forbartha
in the same year. 1987, the European Year of the Environment, was
used as a mechanism to increase the level of environmental
awareness amongst businesses and communities in Ireland.

The Fianna Fáil–Progressive Democrat Coalition Government
decided in 1989 to place the environment high on its policy priorities list. A new office for the protection of the environment was established and the establishment of an Environmental Protection
Agency was proposed. In 1990 the then Minister for the Environment, Pádraig Flynn, launched the first National Environmental Action Plan. This proposed the investment of £1,000 million on environmental programmes, the enactment of better pollution control
legislation, the preservation of the natural environment and the enhancement of amenities. It also included proposals on waste and
recycling. This action programme was significantly driven by EU
policy and represented the first co-ordinated attempt to put forward
a comprehensive and coherent national environment policy.

The Environmental Protection Agency Act was enacted in 1992
and is generally considered by most commentators to represent

the most significant development in Irish environmental law to date. The Programme for a Partnership Government 1993-1997 likewise placed environmental issues to the forefront and adopted the principles of sustainable development and the promotion of energy conservation. The National Development Plan 1994-99 places a similar emphasis on sustainable development.

THE NATURE OF EUROPEAN COMMUNITY ENVIRONMENT LEGISLATION

Ireland has, in general, adopted three specific mechanisms to give effect to EU environment legislation. These EU laws are generally implemented by statute, by regulations and by the use of administrative action. We will briefly discuss each of these in turn.

Statutes

Statutes are not frequently used in the Irish context. However when they are used, their use is confined to directives that have significant or far-reaching implications for the operation of Irish environmental law. In the case of *Meagher v. Minister for Agriculture (SC)* (1994), for example, the Supreme Court held that where a directive leaves the determination of matters of policy or principle to a member state, then the appropriate way of implementing it is through statute.

Regulations

Regulations are the most commonly used implementation measure in the Irish context. There is some debate about the constitutionality of regulations in Ireland. However, in *Meagher v. Minister of Agriculture* (1994), the Supreme Court upheld the constitutionality of regulations. Scannell (1995) argues that regulations are "inconvenient, confusing and misleading". She also argues that regulations may not create an indictable offence. The maximum penalty that can be imposed is €761 (IR£600) or €1,270 (IR£1,000) and/or six months' imprisonment.

Administrative Action

The administrative action route is legally appropriate where existing Irish law is considered adequate to meet the objectives of a directive. There is, however, some confusion surrounding the legal status of administrative circulars. Hogan (1987), for example, argues that administrative circulars cannot change procedural or substantive law and believes that they may be contrary to Articles 15 and 16 of the Constitution. The case law is likewise unhelpful on this matter. In *Browne v. An Bord Pleanála, Cork County Council and Merrell* (1989), the High Court pointed out that administrative circulars do not have the force of law unless the principles of the directive are already incorporated into Irish law.

REMEDIES FOR ENVIRONMENTAL PROTECTION

There are four sources of legal remedies in the context of environmental matters in Ireland: constitution, the law of tort, statute law and employment law.

The Constitution

There is nothing written in the Constitution on the matter of a clean and healthy environment. However, some commentators argue that such protections are available under Article 40, specifically 40(4)(2) and 40(3)(2) and Article 45. In two cases, *The State v. Frawley* (1978), and *The State (Richardson) v. Governor of Mountjoy Prison* (1980), the High Court acknowledged that the principle established in *Ryan v. Attorney General* (1965) could be extended to deal with any act or omission of the executive that, without justification, would expose the health of a person to risk or danger. The general view that holds is that a citizen would have some success in getting the Irish courts to declare that the citizen has a qualified right to a clean and healthy environment.

Tort Law

Tort law provides a range of remedies that have relevance to environmental damage. The law of tort allows a successful plaintiff to recover damages for loss suffered. Specific torts that are of relevance include: nuisance, negligence, trespass and the rule in *Rylands v. Fletcher* (1846).

*   Nuisance may be private or public in nature. Public nuisance is generally defined as: any act unwarranted by law or an omis-

sion to discharge a legal duty. This must significantly affect the reasonable comfort and convenience of the life of the public.

- Private nuisance is generally defined as any act of a wrongful nature causing or allowing the escape of deleterious material onto someone else's land. This could include water, smoke and fumes, gas, etc.

- Trespass to land: There is sufficient case law to suggest that pollution may constitute a trespass. Trespass is generally defined as causing a physical or noise disturbance or any object to cross the boundary of another's land or to come into physical contact with that land.

- *Rylands v. Fletcher*: This rule, established in 1846, imposes strict liability upon the occupier of land who brings on to it, and keeps there, anything liable to cause danger if it escapes. This has been deemed to include the collection of sewage, chemicals, landfill sites and the manufacture of explosives.

- Breach of statutory duty: Five conditions must be met by a plaintiff who wishes to succeed in an action for breach of statutory duty:

  ◊ The statutory provision in question must impose a duty, which is specifically owed to the plaintiff.

  ◊ The damage suffered must be of a type intended by the statute in question.

  ◊ There must be proof that the defendant had broken his statutory duties.

  ◊ The plaintiff must have suffered damage as a result of the breach.

  ◊ There must be a remedy available within the statute or at common law.

- An action for misfeasance of public office: This action may be taken where a public authority has made a decision or done something that is illegal or *ultra vires*. The Supreme Court case of *Pine Valley Developments v. Minister for the Environment* (1987) has classified the grounds upon which damages will be awarded for an *ultra vires* act. These include: where the act involves the commission of a recognised tort, where there is proof of malice or where there is evidence that the authority knew it did not possess the powers which it purported to exercise.

THE ENVIRONMENTAL PROTECTION AGENCY

The Environmental Protection Agency (EPA) was established under the Environmental Protection Agency Act 1992. This Act was enacted primarily in response to the perceived need to create specialist expertise to deal with complex environmental issues and a recognition that there was an inadequate system of control over the activities of local authorities that may have an impact on the environment.

Functions of the Agency

Section 52 of the Act sets out the general functions of the agency, which can be summarised as:

- The licensing, regulating and controlling of activities that are directed at environmental protection.

- The monitoring of environmental quality including the dissemination of environmental information (including access to it).

- The provision of support and advisory services to local authorities in relation to the performance of their functions.

- The promotion and co-ordination of environmental research and the provision of assistance and advice on environmental remedies.

- Ensuring effective liaison with the European Environmental Agency.

- Carrying out any other functions assigned by the Minister for the Environment.

Other functions of the EPA include the following:

- Providing environmental monitoring.

- Preparing state-of-the-environment reports.

- Maintaining records on environmental monitoring.

- Developing and maintaining a database on the environment.

- Preparing and publishing environmental codes of practice.

- Promoting environmental auditing.

- Preparing and publishing environmental quality objectives.

- Investigating and reporting environmental pollution incidents.

- Enforcing noise controls.

EPA Control Over Public Authorities

Generally local authorities are not subject to the types of controls that are imposed on the private sector. Specifically, they are not obliged to obtain planning permission nor are they obliged to obtain a permit for the disposal of wastes. The 1992 Act however has changed this somewhat and the Environmental Protection Agency now has specific powers over some activities of local authorities, as they relate to the environment.

Section 56 of the Act specifies that the EPA may, either on its own initiative, or the request of the Minister, give information and advice or make recommendations that are directed at ensuring environmental protection. There is an obligation placed on local authorities to take these communications into account in their decision-making processes. Scannell (1995) suggests that it is most likely that the EPA would give advice in areas such as the preparation of legal proceedings to enforce environmental controls, the preparation of guidelines and codes of practice, the monitoring of emissions and environmental management issues. The Act places a specific responsibility on the EPA to prepare and publish reports on the management and operation of local authority landfill sites and it has the power to put forward recommendations, if it deems it appropriate.

The EPA has specific powers in a number of areas:

- The EPA may require a sanitary authority to supply it with specified information about the monitoring of drinking water intended for human consumption.

- The EPA is obliged to specify and publish criteria and procedures for the selection, management, operation and termination of landfill sites for the disposal of domestic or other wastes.

- The EPA can, if it is of the opinion that a local authority has failed to perform a statutory duty in the environmental area, or if it has done so in an unsatisfactory manner, request a report from the local authority and can issue advice and recommendations to the local authority, as it sees fit.

Integrated Pollution Control

The (1992) Act gives the EPA the power to establish a system of integrated pollution control (IPC) for what it considers polluting industries.

Section 82 of the Act requires IPC for any new process development or operation. The Environmental Protection Agency (Licensing) Regulations (1994) specify that IPC will apply to the following industries: minerals and other materials, energy, mineral filters and glass, chemicals, food and drink, cement, waste and others. Manufacturers of pesticides, pharmaceuticals, or veterinary products or their intermediates are required to obtain an IPC licence where the number of employees exceeds 200. The licence is obtained by making an application to the EPA. Applicants are required to notify the relevant planning authority and other prescribed persons and the public of their intention to apply for a licence. The notice to apply must be published in the newspaper at least two weeks before the application is made. If an environmental impact statement (EIS) is required with the application, the notice must state that the EIS will be submitted with the application. If the EPA wishes to review a licence or a revised licence, it must give public notice of its intention to do so and inform the relevant planning authority and other relevant bodies.

In considering a licence application, the EPA will have regard to five key principles:

- Any relevant air quality management plan.

- Any relevant noise regulations.

- Any special control area orders.

- Any EIS submitted with the application and observations in relation to same that may have been submitted.

- Any other matters related to the prevention, elimination, limitation or reduction of environmental pollution.

The agency will not provide a licence for any activity unless it is satisfied that any emissions from the activity will not contravene any air quality standards, that the emissions from the activity comply with relevant quality standards for water and sewage effluents, that any noise from the activity complies with the noise regulations, that the emissions from the activity do not cause significant environmental pollution and that the best available technology will be used to prevent, abate or reduce emissions.

The EPA may, if it considers it appropriate, attach conditions to the licence. It has the power to impose charges for services and to require the licensee to pay monitoring costs. Because conditions are imposed, the EPA is obliged to consult with the relevant planning authority and may attach conditions specified by the authority.

Provision is also made in the legislation for objections to be made to the licence. Any person may object to the licence within 21 days of the publication of the notice. This objection must be made in time, must be in writing and must state the nature of the objection. The objection must clearly state the grounds for the objection and any arguments or reasons on which they are based. The Act requires a fee to be paid. It is also necessary to provide supporting documentation and other information relevant to the objection. The EPA is obliged to carry out investigations, if it considers them necessary in order to deal with the objection, and give its decision as quickly as possible, which is generally within four months. **Figure 6.2** presents an outline of the licensing process.

Figure 6.2: Outline of the IPC Licensing Process

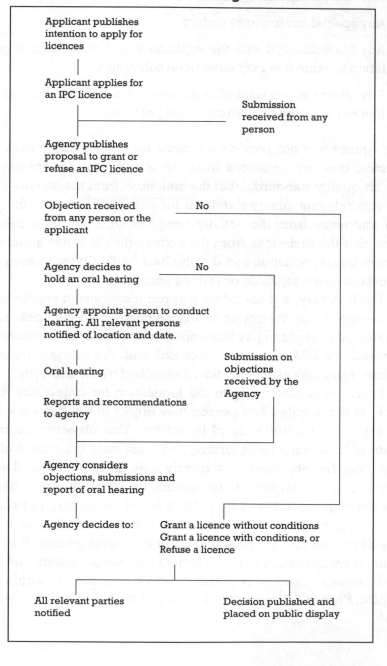

ENVIRONMENTAL IMPACT ASSESSMENT

EC Directive 85/337/EEC came into force on 3 July 1989. However its substantive implementation in Ireland did not take place until the Local Government (Planning and Development) Regulations, (1990). Article 2.1 of the Directive states that member states should adopt measures to ensure that, before consent is given, projects likely to have a significant impact on the environment are assessed in order to consider their effects. Article 5(2) specifies that the minimum information that must be contained in an EIS is as follows:

- A detailed description of the project, including information on its size, design and state.

- A description of the measures envisaged in order to avoid, reduce or eliminate adverse environmental effects.

- Data which supports and identifies the main effects that the project is likely to have on the environment.

- A non-technical summary of the above information.

The developer must supply this information. The provisions of Article 5 have been given effect through the European Communities (Environmental Impact Assessment) Regulations, (1989). Article 3 of the directive specifies that bodies assessing an EIS must consider: the direct and indirect effects of the protection on human beings, flora and fauna, its impact on water, air, climate and landscape, the interaction between these two sets of variables and its influence on the actual heritage.

There is little litigation in Ireland on whether an EIS complies with Article 3. However, in *Rehabilitation Institute v. An Bord Pleanála* (1988), planning permission granted for a lamb-slaughtering facility was quashed because An Bord Pleanála had not given the applicants an opportunity of submitting an expert report setting out the impact of the proposed developments on Rehab trainees occupying a building close to the development site.

Section 72(1) of the Environmental Protection Agency Act, 1992 specified that the EPA may prepare guidelines on the information to be contained in an EIS and that such guidelines must be taken into account when preparing and assessing an EIS. Such guidelines were issued in 1994.

The European Community's (Environmental Impact Assessment) Regulations 1989-1994 gave effect to the Local Government (Planning and Development) Regulations Act 1994. It implemented the most significant elements of the Directive. The European Community's (Environmental Impact Assessment) Regulations 1989-1994 require an Environmental Impact Assessment for all projects with the exception of motorways. Whether a project is subject to an EIA has been considered in three cases:

- In *Browne v. An Bord Pleanála, Cork County Council and Merell* (1989), Dow Manufacturing argued that a pharmaceutical facility was not an integrated chemical facility and therefore did not require an EIA. The Court did not, however, rule on this issue.

- In *Howard v. Commissioner of Public Works* (1993), O'Hanlon J. argued that he doubted whether an effluent-treatment plant for an interpretative centre came within the regulations.

- In *Max Developments Ltd. v. An Bord Pleanála* (1994), the issue in question was whether an EIS was required for a housing development involving an area greater than two hectares. Dublin Corporation and An Bord Pleanála decided that the area was not an existing urban area and this decision was challenged. The High Court held that it could not interfere.

A number of projects may be subject to an EIA if there is a likelihood that the project will have significant effects on the environment by virtue of size, nature and location. However, the 1989 Regulations list a number of projects that, irrespective of their size and location, are automatically subjected to a mandatory EIA. These include: mining and petroleum extraction, any installation involved in the production of chemicals and pharmaceutical products, and fish-meal and fish-oil production. For other projects, the key issue will be whether the project is located in an environmentally sensitive area or in an area of special cultural or historical importance. EIAs are also required for new activities that are subject to IPC licensing and the EPA may require or seek an EIS where there is a reconstruction or alteration of an existing activity or where this requires an application for the review of a licence or new licence.

The Integrated Pollution Prevention and Control Directive

The Integrated Pollution Prevention and Control Directive (IPPC) (EU/96/61/EC) represents the cornerstone of the EU's future pollution control strategy. The overall goal of the Directive is "to prevent emissions into air, water or soil where this is practicable, taking into account waste management, and, where it is not, to minimise them in order to achieve a high level of protection for the environment as a whole".

The activities listed in the First Schedule of the EPA Act 1992 are required to obtain an IPC Licence, i.e. one licence to deal with emissions to all environmental media. This directive adopts a holistic approach to environmental management.

The Directive:

* Covers installations rather than processes.

* Includes such activities as intensive livestock units and food and drink plants.

* Extends the scope of IPC Licensing by requiring the adoption of emission limit values and the application of BAT (Best Available Technology) with a view to preventing or, if this is not possible, minimising pollutant discharges.

* Recognises that emissions limit values are not the sole means of achieving environmental compliance with quality requirements in what are recognised to be environmentally vulnerable areas. The Directive requires additional protection and therefore stipulates that environmental quality standards must be taken into account in setting release limits in permits.

If the use of BAT is not sufficient, measures to be taken include limiting the number of polluting firms in a particular region and/or lowering the output of installations operating in the area. The activities requiring an IPPCL are listed in **Table 6.1**. The steps in the application process include pre-application discussions, site visits and the completion of a prescribed application form within a specified time frame. The application process is intended to be open to public participation, with submissions, objections and oral hearings heard throughout.

Table 6.1: Activities to be Licensed under IPPC Regulations

Minerals	Wood, Paper, Textiles, Leather
Energy	Fossil Fuel
Metals	Cement
Mineral Fibres, Glass	Waste
Chemicals	Surface Coating
Intensive Agriculture	Other Activities
Food and Drink	

The Directive refers to limits already set in existing Directives, such as hazardous waste, dangerous substances and landfill. The EU Commission compiles an inventory of information provided by each member state. After every three years, the Commission can intervene and set EU-wide emission limits if member states are not up to standard.

The essential components of the licensing system are the Environmental Management System (EMS) and the Annual Environmental Report (AER). The adoption of an EMS brings many benefits, both financial and operational, and it is an essential tool in working towards continued improvement of environmental performance. Each firm is required to establish and implement an EMS so that targets can be set to mitigate adverse environmental impacts.

While the Directive stipulates only the minimum environmental standards required, it is up to the individual firms to set targets for continuous improvement and demonstrate their attainment. These can be assessed through the use of "waste indices" (waste/production), which should be seen to decrease on an annual basis.

The AER provides a detailed annual assessment of the environmental impacts of the installation. All licenses granted are required to contain emission limit values for priority pollutants and are required to lay down requirements for environmental monitoring, data evaluation, and co-ordination with the competent authority.

Under the Directive, Irish industry must apply BAT/BATNEEC to:

- Prevent pollution.

- Avoid waste production.

- Recover waste.

- Use energy efficiently.

In other words, to ensure that "the necessary measures are taken, upon definitive cessation of activities, to avoid any pollution risk and return the site of operation to a satisfactory state" (IPCC Directive, article 3).

ACCESS TO INFORMATION ON THE ENVIRONMENT

EC Directive 90/313 and the Access to Information on the Environment Regulations 1993 deal with the issue of access to environmental information. Directive 90/313 is a short piece of legislation with seven main articles. Its core purpose is set out in Article 1: to ensure freedom of access to and dissemination of information on the environment held by public authorities. It also lays down guidelines on the terms and conditions under which information will be released. The requirement to release information is not absolute. The Directive recognises that information must, or may, be held in certain circumstances such as on grounds of public policy, public security, the application of the *sub judice* rule or where the information is in an incomplete state.

The definition of information relating to the environment is broadly defined to cover all actual or potential activities, and measures affecting environmental media. Public authorities are defined by Article 2 of the directive as any public administration with responsibilities for the processing of information relating to the environment. The Directive excludes bodies acting in a judicial or legislative manner. The Department of the Environment has laid down some non-binding parameters for organisations it considers to come under the control of public authorities. They include organisations acting for a public authority on an agency contract or other bases such as research institutes, professional consultancy services and private waste-management contractors.

Requests for Information

Any person may request access to information regardless of proof of interest. Such persons may be private individuals, community groups, non-governmental organisations or companies. Article 4(1) of the 1993 Regulations refers to the availability of information to any person who submits a request. Article 4(1) specifies that the request must be in writing and be as specific as possible about the information being sought. Where a request is felt to have been unreasonably refused or inadequately responded to, the applicant must be given the opportunity to seek judicial or administrative review.

Neither the Directive nor the Regulations specify the information that may be accessed, although the regulations permit public authorities to deny requests on procedural grounds where:

- Material is still in the process of completion.

- Internal communications are concerned.

- A request is manifestly unreasonable.

- A request is too generally formulated.

Where information is released, the public authority, having regard to the costs of making it available, may impose an appropriate or reasonable charge. Requests incurring insignificant costs should, in practice, be facilitated free of charge.

The Information Role of the EPA

The Environmental Protection Agency represents a unique development in the implementation of environmental law in Ireland. Its main functions concern licensing, monitoring and advising public authorities (section 52). While local authorities carry out similar functions, its specialised status and its clearly enunciated statutory powers distinguish the EPA. A further major distinction is the Agency's explicit information-dissemination role. Local authorities grant access to plans and registers, and to certain application documents. They do not usually, however, publish or disseminate environmental material in excess of their statutory obligations. In contrast, the EPA is called upon by the EPA Act, 1992, not only to process licences and monitor activities, but also to collect data, draw up reports and lay down guidelines. All of this information is to be published or opened to inspection, in effect making the EPA the institutional counterpart of the 1993 Regulations.

As the EPA has only been in operation since July 1993, and as regulations clarifying certain aspects of its functions have not yet been made, it is too early to assess its impact. However its potential is underscored by the large numbers of provisions in the EPA Act directly bearing on information gathering and dissemination.

The Agency is obliged to publish and provide for the public access to databases established and maintained for the purpose of monitoring environmental quality (section 52 (1)(b)). The Act specifies a number of monitoring and data-collection activities, to which publication requirements apply, including:

- All monitoring results (these are also open to public inspection) (section 67).

- Reports on the quality of effluents from sanitary-authority sewerage systems (section 61(3)).

- Hydrometric data (section 64(1)).

The EPA is required to publish an environmental quality monitoring programme (section 65); technical guidelines and management reports on landfill sites (section 62); reports on local authority monitoring operations (section 68); periodic reports on the state of the national environment (section 70); and reports on section 104 investigations. The following sources are to be made available for public inspection: the register of sources of environmental quality data (section 69); records on emissions of integrated pollution control of prescribed substances (section 96); and the noise prevention and limitation notices register (section 107).

The Act also gives the EPA the option, subject to ministerial intervention, to publish criteria and procedures on water or sewage treatment (section 60), and reports on section 105 inquiries. Where the EPA holds information but is not required to provide access — e.g. section 103, recommendations to the Minister on air and water pollution — it will be obliged to release that information in accordance with the (1993) Information Regulations.

POLICY ON WASTE MANAGEMENT

In 1995 the Government published a policy document, *Moving Towards Sustainability*, that sets out specific issues in respect of waste management. During the 1990s, substantial progress was made on the development of waste-management policies. There is an increased public awareness and concern about waste-disposal practices and there is a general view that waste must be managed in a planned and environmentally-acceptable way. The government has committed itself to:

• The development of comprehensive new legislation on waste.

• The formulation of new policies for waste management with a specific focus on recycling.

• A new programme of investment in solid waste management.

There is, however, general agreement that waste represents a significant area that is not well covered by establishing Irish legislation. Five particular measures have been introduced in the last seven years that have moved things along in a positive direction.

• Powers to control farm wastes are now contained in the Local Government (Water Pollution) Acts, (1977) and (1990).

• Controls on the incineration of solid or liquid waste are specified under the Air Pollution Act, (1977). These have, to a considerable degree, been superseded by participation provisions of the Environmental Protection Agency Act, (1992).

• Controls on the storage and disposal of radioactive waste are set out in the Radiological Protection Act, 1991.

• Integrated pollution control licensing under the Environmental Protection Agency Act, on the basis of best available technology not entailing excessive costs (BATNEEC). This applies to particular waste-disposal operations including hazardous and hospital waste incineration and it is intended to extend this to existing scheduled waste activities.

• The EPA also has a brief to publish criteria and procedures for the selection, management, operation and termination of use of landfill sites and for the management of domestic and other wastes, including those operated by local authorities.

In terms of recycling, a five-year recycling strategy was published by the Department of the Environment in July 1994. This set a target of 20 per cent for recycling municipal waste compared to the 1995 rate of 8 per cent. It is envisaged that this target rate will be achieved by the recycling of packaging waste, the diversion/composting of organic waste, the recycling/reuse of newsprint and other non-packaging wastes. The plan indicates that the number of collection points will be expanded from a figure of 200 in 1994 to a total of 500 in 1997, including 20 civic amenity sites for the reception of segmented waste from the public in the short term and 75 sites in the medium term.

In general, Irish waste policy in the future will try to reflect the primacy accorded to it in EU policy, specifically waste prevention, reduction and re-use. This emphasis on waste prevention and reduction is given special emphasis in the Waste Management Act, (1996), which we will discuss later in this chapter.

Figure 6.3 presents a summary of legislation currently in existence in Ireland.

Figure 6.3: Environmental Legislation in Ireland: A Summary

Air Pollution
Air Pollution Act, 1987: Defines air pollution, gives local authorities power to require information and to control emissions. Allows for licensing of industrial plant and the setting of air quality standards.
Air Pollution Act, 1987 (Air Quality Standards) Regulations (1987) (SI244/87): Specifies air quality standards for sulphur dioxide, suspended particulates, lead and nitrogen dioxide. Gives effect to EU Directive 80/779.
Air Pollution Act, 1987 (Licensing of Industrial Plant) Regulations (1988) (SI2666/88): Sets out procedure for obtaining licences for certain specified industrial plants.
Air Pollution Act, 1987 (Emission Limit Value for Use of Asbestos) Regulations (1990) (SI28/90): Specifies emission limit values for asbestos from industrial plants processing and/or manufacturing asbestos or asbestos products.
Air Pollution Act, 1987 (Municipal Waste Incineration) Regulations (1993) (SI347/93): Specifies emission limit values from municipal waste incineration plants.
Air Pollution Act, 1987 (Emission Limit Values for Combustion Plant) Regulations (1992) (SI264/96): Specifies emission limit values for polluting emissions of sulphur dioxide from large combustion plants. Gives effect to EU Directive 94/66 (SI33/99). Gives EPA power to assess ambient air quality. Thirteen different pollutants may be assessed. Gives effect to EU Directive 96/62.

Environmental Impact Assessment (Link to Planning)
European Communities (Environmental Impact Assessment) Regulations (1989) (SI349/89): These regulations, which have been amended a number of times (see below) should be read in conjunction with the Local Government (Planning and Development) Regulations, (1994) (see Planning below). The regulations give effect to EU Directive 85/337). These regulations and the regulations listed below are concerned with how Environmental Impact Assessments are carried out and how Environmental Impact Statements are written.
European Communities (Environmental Impact Assessment) Amendment Regulations (1994) (SI84/94), Amendment Regulations (1998) (351/98); Amendment Regulations (1999) (93/99): amend the original regulations and bring into effect EU Directives.

Environmental Noise

Environmental Protection Agency Act, 1992. Gives EPA and local authorities power to control noise (section 107).

Environmental Protection Agency Act, 1992 (Noise) Regulations (1994) (SI 178/94): In effect brings into force the noise control sections of the EPA Act, (1992). Allows local authorities and persons affected by noise to serve notice and go to court.

Integrated Pollution Control (IPC) Licences

Environmental Protection Agency Act, 1992: The concept of a single licence, an IPC licence, is introduced by Part IV of the Act. The Act deals with obtaining, granting, the effect of and conditions that may be attached to an IPC licence.

Environmental Protection Agency (Established Activities) Orders: (1994) (SI83/94). Order (1995) (58/95) Order (No 2) 204/95); Order (1996) (78/96); Order (1998) (SI460/98). Set dates after which operators of specified activities must apply for an IPC licence.

Environmental Protection Agency (Licensing) Regulations (1994): (SI85/94) (1996) (SI240/96). Concerns licensing requirements.

Planning Legislation (Link to Environmental Impact Assessment)

Local Government (Planning and Development) Regulations (1994) (SI86/94) and Amendment Regulations (1999) (SI 92/99): Concerned with the procedures for carrying out an Environmental Impact Assessment and the preparation and filing, in connection with a planning application, of an Environmental Impact Statement. The amended regulations require a local authority to give an opinion if required.

Waste and Packaging

Waste Management Act, 1996: Defines waste. Requires the EPA to draw up a national hazardous-waste management plan and in relation to non-hazardous waste requires local authorities to draw up local waste management plans. Organisations disposing waste must give it either to a local authority or to an authorised collector. Waste may only be recovered and disposed of at a licensed facility. Licences are granted by the EPA.

Waste Management (Licensing) Regulations (1997) (SI 133/97) and Amendment Regulations (1998) (SI 162/98): Sets out dates by which licences for the recovery/disposal of certain classes of waste are required.

Waste Management (Register) Regulations (1997) (SI 183/97): Concerns information to be kept by the EIP/ local authorities.

Waste Management (Packaging) Regulations (1997) (SI 183/97) and Amendment Regulations (SI328/98): Major producers of waste required to register with local authorities and to comply with certain duties imposed regarding recovery of waste.

Waste Management (Farm Plastics) Regulations (1997) (SI 315/97): Importers and distributors of farm plastics are required to register with local authorities, recover and collect farm plastic waste and provide purchasers with information.

Waste Management Act, 1996 (Use of Sewage Sludge in Agriculture) Regulations (1998) (SI 148/98): Sets standards for use of sewage sludge in agriculture.

Waste Management (Movement of Hazardous Waste) Regulations (1998) (SI 147/98): Concerns the movement of waste within Ireland.

Waste Management (Transfrontier Shipment of Waste) Regulations (1998) (SI149/98). Concerns the movement of waste into/out of EU.

Waste Management (Hazardous Waste) Regulations (1998) (SI 163/98). Deals with asbestos waste, batteries, waste oils and the records that a producer of hazardous waste must keep.

Waste Management (Permit) Regulations (1998) (SI 165/98): Allows local authorities to issue permits for specified waste disposal and recovery activities.

Water Pollution: In-Land and Off-Shore

Local Government (Water Pollution) Act, 1997 and Local Government (Water Pollution) (Amendment) Act, 1990: The Acts makes it an offence to pollute water, defines polluting matter, gives local authorities power to issue licences permitting discharge of effluent into water or a sewer, sets out procedures for applying for licence and sets out penalties for offences.

Local Government (Control of Cadmium Discharges) Regulations (1985) (SI 294/85). Local Government (Water Pollution) (Control of Hexachlocyclohexane and Mercury Discharges) Regulations (1986) (SI 55/86): Concerned with controlling emissions of substances mentioned in regulation titles.

Sea Pollution Act, 1991: Concerned with the prevention of the pollution of the sea by discharges of oil, noxious liquid substances, harmful substances, effluent or garbage.

Oil Pollution of the Sea (Civil Liability and Compensation) Act, 1998: Concerned with liability and compensation for damage to the sea caused by oil pollution.

Foreshore Act, 1933 and Foreshore (Amendment) Act, 1992: Concerned with the protection of the foreshore. Note that if any development is planned an Environmental Impact Assessment is required.

WASTE DISPOSAL IN IRELAND

It is estimated that over 30 million tonnes of waste products are disposed of annually in Ireland. Agriculture on its own accounts for 22 million tonnes, with industrial waste accounting for 5 million tonnes. Statistics compiled by the Department of the Environment for the period 1983-92 show that total annual production of hazardous waste is approximately 99,000 tonnes. Recovery/recycling is the principal means of management with some 54 per cent of total waste being dealt with this way. Approximately 19,000 tonnes are exported — 11,000 tonnes for incineration and 8,000 for recycling/recovery or other treatment. The statistics also show that Irish industry has a considerable incineration capacity, coping with 70 per cent of hazardous waste destined for incineration.

There is a plethora of EC Directives dealing with the issue of waste:

- European Communities (Waste) Regulation (1974).

- European Communities (Toxic And Dangerous Waste) Regulations (1982).

- European Communities (Transfrontier Shipment of Hazardous Waste) Regulations (1988).

- European Communities (Asbestos Waste Regulations) (1992).

- European Communities (Waste Oils) Regulations (1992).

- European Communities (Transformation Transfrontier Shipment of Waste) Regulations (1994).

These Directives have a number of important features:

- Unlike earlier Directives, which apply only to hazardous waste, the newer regulations cover all wastes.

- A distinction is made between controls applied to wastes going for disposal and those going for recovery.

- There are financial guarantees in place to cover regulation or problem consignments or the cost of disposal at alternative facilities.

Local authorities are responsible for the planning, authorisation and supervision of waste operations. However the type of waste over which they have responsibility is largely confined to household waste. Private industry is often responsible for the disposal of individual waste and there are no hazardous-waste disposal facilities in Ireland.

Public Waste Disposal

It is estimated that approximately 90 per cent of waste in Ireland is disposed of in landfill sites. This function is primarily carried out by local authorities, although private involvement has increased in the last five years. Local authorities have statutory responsibility for controlling waste disposal under the Local Government (Sanitary Services) Acts, 1878-1969. The legislation provides that sanitary authorities must provide suitable buildings and places for the disposal of waste. However, this does not include trade or industrial waste.

Planning authorities are obliged to take appropriate steps to ensure that, in their development plans, they provide sites for waste disposal. Such sites are subject to controls and the right of the public to object. Furthermore local authorities must not carry out their duties in respect of waste disposal in any way that would cause a nuisance. A public dump, for example, cannot cause a public nuisance. In *McGrane v. Louth County Council* (1983), the High Court concluded that the site had been selected with great care and therefore the dump would not create a nuisance. Local authorities have a number of important duties under other regulations:

- The larger local authorities have a duty under Article 4(2) of the European Communities (Waste) Regulations (1979) to prepare a plan setting out suitable waste disposal sites.

- The European Communities (Toxic and Dangerous) Waste Regulations (1982) specify that local authorities are obliged to draw up places for the disposal of toxic and dangerous waste. However they are not required to provide such sites.

- Under the European Communities (Waste Oils) Regulations (1992), local authorities have a responsibility to plan, organise and supervise the disposal of waste oils.

- The European Communities (Waste) Regulations (1984) specifies that any person (including a local authority) shall not cause or permit the discharge, dumping or tipping of PCB or materials/objects containing PCB in any manner that would endanger human health or harm the environment.

- The European Communities (Asbestos Waste) Regulations (1990-1994) specify that local authorities disposing of asbestos waste must comply with the requirements of the Regulation.

- The Environmental Protection Agency Act, 1992 obliges the EPA to specify public criteria and procedures for the selection, management, operation and termination of the use of landfill sites for the disposal of domestic and other wastes. These criteria may relate to site selection and design, the assessment of impact on the environment, the control of landfill gas and other issues. The local authority is obliged to comply with EPA requirements on monitoring and provide the results of such monitoring. It must likewise ensure that the management of landfill sites complies with EPA criteria.

THE WASTE MANAGEMENT ACT, 1996

The Waste Bill was introduced in May 1995, with the aim of providing a comprehensive and modern legislative framework for waste management in Ireland and was subsequently renamed the Waste Management Bill. Now enacted, it replaces older statutory provisions, which were based principally on the Public Health Acts and various regulations under the European Communities Act, 1972. It should be viewed in the context of a range of measures and initiatives designed to promote the concept of sustainable development relating to waste management. Some of these measures include:

- The EPA Act, 1992 and the introduction of IPC licensing to industrial activities.

- The development of criteria and procedures for the selection, management, operation and termination of landfill sites currently being carried out by the EPA.

- An ESRI study on economic aspects of solid waste management, which will be published shortly.

- The compilation of a comprehensive database of waste statistics being developed by the EPA.

- A commitment to levels of recycling of packaging and packaging waste to comply with the EU Packaging Directive and the Government Strategy document, *Recycling for Ireland*.

- A Cabinet sub-committee and a joint Oireachtas Committee looking at the whole concept of sustainable development.

These measures place emphasis on the prevention, minimisation, recovery/reuse and safe disposal of waste where no alternative is available. It is envisaged that landfill will remain the main disposal route for most wastes.

It seems clear from examining these measures that the management of waste, from its production to its final disposal is set to change, and that this change will be felt at all levels of society. Business and industry will be forced to look at all types of waste and to try to prevent it arising insofar as possible. The use of clean technologies will be encouraged. In doing this, there may be cost savings to be made. However, it is obvious that the cost of waste disposal is set to rise significantly above its present level.

The Waste Management Act, 1996 was introduced to provide a statutory basis for regulating the prevention, management and control of waste in Ireland. The Act seeks to make responsible for waste management not only "producers" but also "holders" of waste. The penalties prescribed in the Act for non-compliance with its terms are very prohibitive, in that they provide for fines of up to £10 million and imprisonment for terms of up to 10 years.

The Waste Management Act, 1996 incorporates the principle of "producer responsibility", which seeks to make producers, distributors and retailers responsible for the collection, recovery and disposal of goods even after they have left the factory. The Government's *Policy Statement on Waste Management in Ireland* indicates that regulations will be brought in, applying this principle to certain priority waste streams, in particular, batteries, construction/demolition waste, electric/electronic waste, end-of-life vehicles and rubber tyres.

Broadly speaking the Act provides for the following:

- The reorganisation of public authority functions in relation to waste management and the licensing of waste disposal, which will involve redefining the respective roles of the Minister for the Environment, the Environment Protection Agency and the local authorities.

- The introduction of a series of measures that will, in relation to waste prevention and recovery, place certain obligations on producers, distributors, retailers and consumers of waste.

- A statutory framework for implementing national and international requirements in respect of waste management.

Prior to the initiation of the Waste Act, waste control in Ireland was regulated principally by the Public Health Acts, and by numerous Statutory Instruments that implemented the terms of various EC directives into Irish law. As a result of the introduction of the Waste Act, all these enactments were repealed.

Provisions of the Waste Management Act, 1996

The Act is divided into seven parts; its main provisions are summarised below.

Part I: Preliminary and General

Part I of the Act provides for definitions, interpretations and other administrative matters such as the prosecution of offences and the penalties in respect of these offences.

Part I provides powers of certain "authorised persons" to enter premises where they suspect there is an immediate risk of environmental pollution taking place and to carry out inspections and tests once they are inside the premises. Provision is also made for the monitoring, by local authorities and the Environmental Protection Agency, of emissions to the environment as a result of the holding, recovery or disposal of waste. Furthermore, local authorities and the EPA will have authorisation to inspect any facilities where hazardous waste is produced.

Part II: Waste Management Planning

Part II of the Act provides for the development of waste management plans by local authorities and the EPA. Each local authority will be required to formulate a waste management plan and address all aspects of the prevention, minimisation, collection, recovery and disposal of non-hazardous waste within its functional area. These plans will be subject to review at least once every five years. The EPA, on the other hand, will be required to make a national hazardous waste management plan dealing with the prevention, minimisation, recovery, collection and movement of hazardous waste and also the disposal of such hazardous waste that cannot be prevented or recovered. The hazardous waste management plan should:

- Describe the type, quantity and origin of hazardous waste arising in the State, the movement of such waste within, into or out of the State, and facilities available for the collection, recovery or disposal of such waste in the State.

- Specify targets in relation to the prevention/minimisation of the production, harmful nature, and recovery of or disposal of such waste.

- Identify sites where disposal activities involving hazardous waste are carried out, assessing the risk of environmental pollution arising out of these actives and recommending cost-effective remedial measures to be taken in respect of such sites.

- Give effect to the "polluter pays" principle.

The EPA will review the hazardous waste management plan "from time to time".

Part III: Measures to Reduce Production, and Promote Recovery of Waste

Part III of the Act deals with waste prevention/minimisation and also waste recovery.

Firstly, in relation to prevention/minimisation, the Act enables the Minister for the Environment and Local Authorities to provide support and assistance (including financial assistance) for research and development projects carried out by any person in respect of the prevention or minimisation of waste. In addition, the Minister is empowered to make regulations for the purpose of preventing, minimising or limiting the production of waste. To this end, the regulations may incorporate a number of measures including requirements upon persons and business concerns to carry out waste audits and waste reduction programmes, and also may contain measures designed to prohibit, limit or control the production of certain specified materials.

The Minister may also specify in these regulations what constitutes the best available technology not entailing excessive costs (BATNEEC) for preventing or limiting the production of waste. The regulations may specify that persons or business concerns use BATNEEC in relation to waste control.

Secondly, in relation to the recovery of waste, the Minister or Local Authorities are enabled under the Act to provide support and assistance to persons carrying out research and development connected to waste recovery. The Minister is empowered to make regulations generally in relation to waste recovery and more particularly, may make many more regulations specifying any number of the following requirements:

- That products and packaging be designed and used in a certain way.

- That the importation, distribution, supply or sale of any product or substance in a particular container or packaging be prohibited, limited or controlled.

- That producers, distributors, and retailers operate a deposit and refund scheme in relation to products made, distributed or sold by them, and also that they arrange for the collection of any products, substances or any components or packaging related thereto after the purchaser no longer has any use for them (a take-back obligation).

- That owners/managers of supermarkets and service stations provide facilities for the disposal by customers of packaging from products or substances and that they provide waste collection receptacles for use by members of the public (such owner/managers may also charge customers for bags or containers that they provide to them).

• That producers of certain products or substances use recoverable materials or components in production.

• That a person must implement a source-separation programme for waste of a specified class.

Persons may be exempted from the provisions of such regulations if they participate in a voluntary waste recovery programme that has been approved by the Minister.

The Minister will be required to promulgate a programme with regard to the prevention, minimisation and recovery of waste arising from the performance by public authorities of their functions.

Part IV: Holding, Collection and Movement of Waste

Part IV of the Waste Management Act, 1996 contains a number of key provisions that can be summarised as follows:

• Section 32 imposes a general duty on a "holder" of waste. When the Bill becomes law, it will be prohibited for persons to hold, recover or dispose of waste in a manner that causes environmental pollution.

• Each local authority will be obliged to arrange for the provision of an adequate waste collection service for household waste only within its own functional area.

• Local authorities may collect or arrange for the collection of waste other than household waste, but is under no obligation to do so.

• Local authorities will be empowered to make bye-laws in respect of the presentation of household and commercial waste for collection.

• Persons who carry on the collection of waste for commercial gain will be required to obtain a permit from the relevant local authority.

- The Minister is empowered to make regulations to provide for the supervision and control of waste movement within, into or out of the State.

- The Minister will also be empowered to make regulations compelling holders of waste to take out an insurance policy covering them for liability in respect of injury to any person arising as a result of their holding of waste.

Part V: Recovery and Disposal of Waste

Part V of the Act requires Local Authorities to provide facilities for the disposal of household waste in their respective areas. It also provides that a waste licence must be obtained in respect of waste disposal or recovery activities taking place at a waste facility, either public or private, including local authority landfills. The EPA is the body responsible for the granting of waste licences. Certain activities are exempt from the requirement to obtain a waste licence and these include the following:

- Activities licensed under the Environment Protection Agency Act, 1992.

- Household waste disposal or within the curtilage of a house.

- The deposit of litter in a litter bin or at a civic waste facility.

- Water treatment sludges and certain agricultural wastes.

- The disposal of animal by-products.

Before a waste licence is granted, the Agency must be satisfied that the activity concerned will not exceed certain prescribed limits. In addition, the licence will cover waste activity in an integrated manner, replacing any relevant licences under the Air and Water Pollution Acts.

The Act contains various administrative provisions relating to the grant of a waste licence such as the procedures for application, review, transfer and surrender of the licence and also the fees in respect of these procedures. The EPA may only grant a waste licence subject to certain conditions and the licence may stipulate that these conditions be carried out before or after the activity to which the licence related has been commenced or has ceased.

Where the activity to which a waste licence relates has not commenced operation within three years of the grant of a licence, the licence shall cease to have effect.

The EPA may review a waste licence in any one of three circumstances:

1. On any one of a number of specified grounds (see below).

2. With the content of, or upon application of the holder of the licence.

3. At a time not less than three years from the date on which the licence was granted.

The grounds referred to in 1. above are as follows:

• Where the EPA considers that any emission coming from any activity to which the waste licence relates constitutes a risk of environmental pollution.

• Where there has been a change in the nature or location of the activity concerned or in the nature of the emission arising therefrom.

• Where there has been a material change in the condition of the environment in the area where the activity relating to the licence is carried on and which could not have reasonably been foreseen at the time at which the licence was granted.

• Where evidence has become available, which if available at the time the licence was granted, would have affected the decision to grant the licence.

• Where new standards relating to the control of the activity concerned have been prescribed by domestic or EU legislation.

As soon as may be possible after the review has been carried out, the EPA will grant a "revised waste licence".

Part VI: General Provisions Regarding Environmental Protection
Part VI of the Act contains provisions regarding the powers of local authorities, the EPA and the civil courts to take action in order to prevent or limit environmental pollution caused by waste.

The local authority may serve a notice requiring a person holding, recovering or disposing of waste to take specified action to prevent or limit environmental pollution. Where such a notice is not complied with, the local authority may take steps to remedy the situation and recover the cost from that person as a simple contract debt. Indeed, regardless of whether or not such a notice is served on someone, a local authority is empowered under the Act to arrange for the recovery or disposal of waste within its own area and then recover the cost from the person whose act or omission necessitated the recovery or disposal. In addition, the courts, on the application by any person, are empowered to order that a person, holding, recovering or disposing of waste, takes certain measures to prevent or limit environmental pollution and where appropriate, discontinues the said holding, recovery or disposal of waste.

The Act further stipulates that each local authority shall be responsible for the supervision and enforcement of the provisions of the Act in relation to the holding, recovery and the disposal of waste within its own functional area.

Part VII of the Act contains a miscellaneous collection of provisions relating to policy directives by ministers in relation to waste licensing, the movement of waste, the detention and forfeiture of certain vehicles and equipment and various amendments of existing legislation.

CHAPTER ROUND-UP

- Concern for the environment has increased in recent years with a parallel growth in environmental management departments within Irish companies. This emergence of concern for the environment can largely be attributed to the influence of the EU and the "green" movement. European Community environmental issues are driven by important principles of environmental management that include principles such as prevention is better than cure, avoiding the exploitation of nature and natural resources, that the polluter should pay the costs of pollution and that the state itself should not contribute to environmental degradation.

- Irish environmental legislation consists of statutes, regulations and administrative actions. Remedies for environmental protection can also be found in the constitution and tort law.

- The Environmental Protection Agency, established in 1992, is charged with the responsibility of monitoring environmental issues, licensing, regulating and controlling of activities that are directed at environmental protection, the monitoring of environmental quality, the provision of advisory services, the promotion and co-ordination of environmental research and carrying out functions assigned by the Minister for the Environment. An environmental impact assessment (EIA) is necessary for projects likely to have a significant impact on the environment. This assessment must contain a detailed description of the project including information on its size, design and state, a description of the measures envisaged in order to avoid, reduce or eliminate adverse environmental effects and an assessment, based on data, setting out the main effects of the project on the environment.

- The Waste Management Act, 1996 regulates the management of waste by Irish companies. The Act provides a comprehensive and contemporary legal framework for waste management. It addresses a number of important issues including waste management planning, measures to reduce production of waste and promote its recovery, the holding, collection and movement of waste, the recovery and disposal of waste and the protection of the environment. The Act incorporates the principle of producer responsibility, which seeks to make producers, distributors and retailers responsible for the collection, recovery and disposal of goods even after they have left the factory or shop.

PART TWO

BEHAVIOURAL DIMENSIONS OF HEALTH AND SAFETY

Chapter 7

HUMAN FACTORS AND SAFETY MANAGEMENT

INTRODUCTION

This chapter considers a range of human factors (individual characteristics) that are relevant to the study of safety behaviour in the workplace. The chapter concentrates on human factors such as attitudes, motivation, perception, memory and human information processing and their relevance to and influence on the management of health and safety. It gives particular attention to the issue of accident proneness and the role of the behavioural science in the management of health and safety in the workplace.

TRADITIONAL APPROACHES TO HEALTH AND SAFETY

Human factors are widely recognised as playing a significant role in improving the safety performance of organisations. The traditional approach to health and safety generally focused on engineering design issues in order to make environments, technology and industrial processes safer, thereby concentrating on physical design and its relationship to characteristics and limitations of employees, this representing the domain of ergonomics — the relationship between employees, work equipment and the environment. The engineering perspective kept the issue of safety on the industrial shop floor and was primarily the interest of engineers and ergonomists. Organisations have, however, begun to turn their attention to the cognitive errors of employees, and to consider accidents that result from subconscious factors such as forgetfulness, mental slips and lapses, rather than the deliberate conscious choice of inappropriate action. Organisations by focusing only on the cognitive errors of employees would seem to assume that unsafe acts are, in a sense, outside the control of those carrying them out. This assumption is not true.

The application of ergonomic, task, hardware and cognitive approaches has played a significant role in improving organisational safety in the past. Nevertheless, organisations continually find that employee accident rates, and subsequent employer liability insurance claims rates, level off after periods of continuing improvement. This lack of improvement in accident levels in Irish workplaces is reflected in the number and amounts paid out in employer's liability insurance claims since the introduction of the Safety, Health and Welfare at Work Act, (1989). It is argued that this factor alone indicates that traditional approaches to improving health and safety in the workplace are in some way inadequate, and highlights the need to consider other human factors and how they contribute to accidents, and in the assessment of the likelihood of accidents occurring in particular industries and job categories.

BEHAVIOURAL SCIENCE AND HEALTH AND SAFETY

The subject matter of behavioural science in an organisational context has three main aims: to describe, to explain and to predict human behaviour in a work/organisational context. In order to do this, it has developed models of particular aspects of human behaviour. These models are, in general, simplifications and cannot be considered perfect explanations of the way that individuals function. However, these theoretical explanations have some utility and can serve as a basis on which to make safety management proposals and implement effective courses of action.

It is generally accepted that occupational health and safety programmes, however well engineered and equipped with mechanical hazard protection, cannot be fully effective unless they address the agents most responsible for health and safety, the employees themselves. The psychological factors influencing health and safety must therefore be understood before an organisation can take the necessary steps to improve health and safety performance. The interaction of the individual with the physical dimensions of the workplace is commonly described as human factors. The overall contribution that behavioural science can make to safety management is advocated by Ridley (1993), who suggests that it allows the safety specialist to address the following issues:

- The types of hazards that individuals can spot easily and those they are likely to miss.

- The time of day and the sorts of jobs in which people are least likely to create hazards.

- The extent to which we can predict the sort of people who will have accidents and in what sets of circumstances.

- The question of why people ignore safety rules, or fail to use protective equipment.

- The types of changes an organisation can make in rules or in equipment in order to make it more likely that employees will use them.

- The types of knowledge employees must have in order to cope with emergencies and hazards.

- The influence of company payment, incentive and performance appraisal systems on employee safety behaviour.

- The role and value of training in making employees more safety conscious.

- The role of participation and work committees in developing a safety culture.

This is only a partial list of the issues but it captures the nature of the research undertaken to date on the contribution of behavioural theories to safety behaviour. Some of these issues will be given consideration in this and later chapters of this handbook.

THE NATURE OF HUMAN FACTORS

Human factors focus on human beings and their interaction with products, equipment, facilities, procedures and work environments. The emphasis is on human beings and how characteristics of the organisation influence employee behaviour. Chapanis (1976) argues that a human factors approach identifies and applies information about human behaviour, activities, motivations, limitations and other characteristics to the design of the workplace and uses it as an explanation of safety behaviour. Sanders and McCormick (1993) summarise some of the features that distinguish a human factor perspective on health and safety from other competing perspectives:

- A commitment to the idea that machines, procedures and systems are built to serve humans and must be designed with the user in mind.

- A belief that the design of machines, procedures and systems influences the safety behaviours of employees.

- A commitment to a systems orientation and a recognition that people, machines, procedures and the work environment do not exist in isolation.

- A reliance on the scientific method and the use of objective data to test hypotheses and generate basic data about human behaviour.

A fundamental element of the human factors approach is the notion of the human being as a system. Systems are defined as organised entities, characterised by distinct boundaries from the environment within which they operate. Sanders and McCormick (1993) suggest that systems have a number of important characteristics, specifically in the context of human-work environment interaction:

- Systems have a purpose: every system must have a purpose otherwise it is nothing more than a collection of odds and ends.

- Systems can be considered to be part of larger systems. These are sometimes called sub-systems.

- Systems operate in an environment. The environment is everything outside the boundaries of the system.

- All components of the system serve particular functions. Human systems have securing information, information storage, information processing and decision functions. Human beings also possess action functions.

- All components of the system interact and the system and its sub-systems have inputs and outputs.

Hale and Glendon (1987) consider the human being to be a system capable of taking in and processing information. Accidents and ill-health are conceptualised as damage that occurs to the system when one or more parts of the system fail. The human factor causes of accidents and incidents can be classified according to which components of the system failed.

Stranks (1994b) suggests a useful classification for human factors as follows: personal, job and organisational factors.

Table 7.1 provides examples of human factors under each of these headings. This chapter concentrates on the influence of personal factors as they relate to health and safety.

Table 7.1: Categories of Human Factors

Personal Factors	Job Factors	Organisational Factors	
		Structural	Contextual
• Attitude	• Equipment design	• Formalisation	• Size
• Attributions		• Specialisation	• Technology
• Motivation	• Machine systems	• Standardisation	• Environment
• Perception	• Job tasks	• Hierarchy	• Goals and Strategies
• Memory	• Characteristics of effective job	• Complexity	
• Human info. processing		• Centralisation	• Culture
• Physical ability	• Working height	• Professionalism	• Climate
• Personality	• Motion economy		
• Mental abilities	• Shift work		

The table illustrates that human factors, as a discipline, have strong links with the behavioural sciences. This is particularly the case when personal factors are considered, where much of the knowledge can be derived from psychological studies. Other behavioural sciences that aid an understanding of human factors include politics, ergonomics, economics, sociology, etc. This chapter will now consider specific human factors in terms of their relevance to health and safety management within organisations.

A FOCUS ON BEHAVIOUR OR A FOCUS ON ATTITUDE?

Two broad behavioural-based approaches exist: focus on changing safety behaviour or on changing attitudes to safety. We will consider both approaches in outline here.

The Behaviour-based Approach

The behaviour-based approach to safety places the focus on behaviour. It is suggested that approximately 96 per cent of all accidents, dangerous occurrences and near-miss events are attributable in some way to human error or behaviour.

The behavioural approach represents an alternative way of understanding why people behave as they do, and how they can be influenced to behave in ways that are safer. The behavioural approach to safety differs from "traditional" approaches in two important ways.

First, it concentrates on behaviour rather than attitude. Many safety campaigns concentrate upon trying to change people's attitudes, in the hope of thereby influencing their behaviour. The assumption underlying this approach is that attitudes cause behaviour. This assumption is considered inaccurate under the behaviour approach. There is considerable evidence showing that attitudes have a tenuous relationship with behaviour. Indeed, they often express how we think we would like to see ourselves behaving rather than how we actually behave. Another assumption is that the causal link is from attitudes to behaviour, that is, attitudes cause behaviour. There is evidence to suggest that behaviour can influence the formation and change of attitudes. These attitudes versus behaviour causation discrepancies explain why traditional approaches to safety have an inherent weakness. The improvement of safety via attitudes not only has to cope with the problems of the tenuous relationship between attitudes and behaviour, but also with the fact that attitudes are notoriously difficult to change. Concentrating on behaviour, on the other hand, misses out this weak link. Getting people to behave safely, and not by trying to change their attitudes, reduces accidents.

The second way in which the behavioural approach is different is its emphasis on the encouragement of desirable behaviour rather than the punishment of undesirable behaviour. The behaviour that needs to be encouraged should be very specific — for example, defining the wearing of hard hats and safety footwear in specific work areas. In many organisations, the emphasis of safety systems is often upon the use of discipline and punishment for non-compliance, rather than rewarding compliance.

Behavioural safety programmes use a variety of people-focused techniques including *inter alia* behavioural modification, goal setting, team building and skills training. The process of modifying behaviour by the planned manipulation of environmental factors is commonly referred to as operant learning. A psychologist named Skinner first discussed it in the 1930s. Skinner argued that people's behaviour is a function of their environment and can thus be modified by planned re-arrangement of the consequences of the particular behaviour (or sets of behaviours). He further argued that behaviour associated with positively reinforcing consequences, increases in frequency (e.g. increased earnings or reductions in the amount of effort required for task completion) whereas behaviour associated with negative consequences tends to decrease (e.g. loss of earnings or punishment). Several safety scientists have actively promoted Skinner's principles in the field of health and safety and have further suggested that "unsafe" practices persist in companies because they are, in some way, naturally reinforced — for example, the job may be completed faster if safety equipment is not used, resulting in either increased praise by managers or supervisors, or longer breaks away from the workplace. By contrast, many safe practices may appear to be penalised and the natural punishment or negative consequences of unsafe acts (i.e. accidents) may be delayed or occur at infrequent intervals. These principles have been recognised and the safety-related implications have been incorporated into many commercially available behavioural programmes both within the UK and the USA.

Goal setting is also a feature of many behavioural safety interventions. For example, recent studies on construction sites in the North West of England, funded by the UK Health and Safety Executive (HSE) have demonstrated how work behaviour could be influenced by training, feedback and goal setting. This work also showed the particular importance of feedback in the promotion of safe work practices. When feedback was temporarily withdrawn, it impacted negatively on the overall level of safety. Goal setting may also be usefully linked to risk assessment or personal profiles and action plans. This technique can be incorporated into behaviour programmes for individuals working in isolation as well as within teams.

Factors Influencing Behaviour

Human behaviour in the presence of danger is the result of a complex psychological process, not all steps of which are entirely conscious and deliberate, and whose complexity makes it open to numerous and diverse influences (see **Figure 7.1**).

The basic ingredients of the process are as follows. First, there is a perceptual stage (steps 1 to 3 in **Figure 7.1**). For someone to do something about the presence of danger, the danger must be perceived, either directly through the human senses or indirectly through measurement instruments.

Second, there is a psychological stage (evaluation and decision: steps 4 to 7). Once a danger is perceived, a person assesses a number of things: the level of danger, whose responsibility it is to take action, what the appropriate action is, the relevance of such action, the practical considerations about that action, then the person makes a decision by weighing up all of these considerations. It is only at this stage that the question of attitudes and conflicts of motivation intervenes. This point is discussed in depth in the next section.

Then, there is an action stage (step 8). This step involves mainly a person's reflexes, abilities, experience, psychomotor dexterity, physical condition, and so on. Finally, there is an outcome stage (step 9). By then the outcome is no longer dependent solely upon the person or persons involved, but also on situational factors such as timing of events, coincidence and chance.

What is important in such a process are the reasons why a "Yes" or a "No" answer is elicited at each stage. For example, what leads a person to evaluate something as dangerous or as not dangerous? What is it that leads a person to take preventive action or not to take preventive action? Why is it that some people assume responsibility for action, whereas others do not? Why is it that the same person will take charge in certain circumstances and not in others?

Figure 7.1: A Descriptive Model of Human Behaviour in the Face of Danger

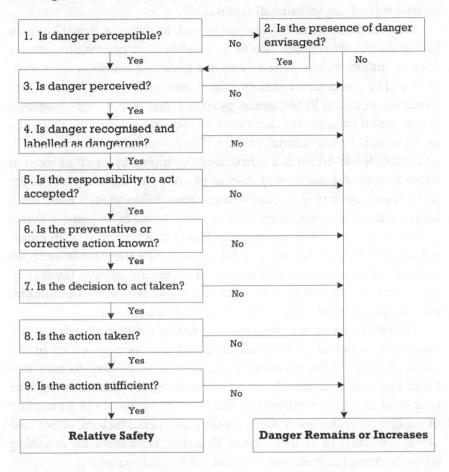

Much research has been devoted to studying personal factors that may influence a person's behaviour (task execution specifically or general behaviour) at work, in relation to workplace health and safety. It is largely recognised that factors such as age and experience usually improve the quality of task execution and decrease risk-taking behaviour. The behaviour-related factors most consistently associated with accidents were dexterity and psychomotor abilities. But the correlations were low, even when significant. Other explanations and factors had to be identified.

Other research yields additional factors and explanations. Ergonomics illustrate the importance of environmental factors such as workstation design and layout. This, coupled with research into the characteristics of successful safety programmes, reveals the crucial role of organisational factors.

Some of these factors, personal as well as organisational, may be favourable to workplace health and safety and prevention, others may be unfavourable. When there are personal factors both favourable and unfavourable to safety, this is referred to as an internal motivational conflict. When some personal and some organisational factors point in opposite directions as regards safety, this is known as an external motivational conflict. The behaviour that a person finally decides to adopt is a function of the interplay of all or most of these factors. A person may decide to adopt an unsafe practice for personal reasons (e.g. a desire to impress colleagues, a need for a better bonus pay, etc), despite an organisational environment that is generally favourable to prevention; this is one example of an external conflict. It may also be that the same unsafe practice is adopted because of practical considerations at an organisational level (e.g. poor workstation design, unavailability of the necessary equipment, etc), despite a positive general attitude towards safety.

For safe behaviour to be a near certainty, most or all of these factors, both personal and organisational, must be aligned or in the same direction. This situation is one that is conducive to safe attitudes and safe practices. Because of the interplay of both categories (personal and organisational factors) and because of the possibility of conflict between them, focus on only one set of factors, either one of them, is likely to be insufficient. This requires a more far-reaching strategy, aimed at both sets of variables simultaneously.

An Attitude-based Approach

An attitude-based approach starts from the proposition that attitudes influence behaviour. Some of the more important elements of this approach are as follows.

- Firstly, an attitude is basically a predisposition to react in a certain way (positively or negatively). It is not a guarantee that a certain behaviour will take place. Other factors, such as practical considerations, may intervene between the attitude and the behaviour. A person may have a favourable attitude towards something but may be unable to translate this predisposition into behaviour. An employee may be convinced of the necessity to wear personal protective equipment (positive attitude) but may at the same time be unable to do so because the appropriate equipment is not available.

- Secondly, an attitude has an object. People tend to react positively or negatively, mildly or strongly towards something or someone, that something or someone being the object of the attitude. In workplace health and safety matters, there are many objects towards which attitudes develop. People have attitudes towards accidents, injuries, risk factors, risk-taking, prevention in general and specific preventive measures in particular (of which there are many) and so on. For example, a person may have a favourable attitude to prevention in general, but also an unfavourable attitude towards a machine guard, the effect of which is to slow down the production rate. The person's output behaviour is the result, amongst other things, of an overall sum of attitudes towards related objects rather than the result to any single attitude. Moreover, practical considerations going one way take precedence even over relatively strong attitudes going the opposite way. This occurs, for instance, when a person has no real choice, or when a person is forced to do something. In such cases, the person who ends up doing something that goes against the grain of his or her basic attitudes will develop resentment, frustration, and other negative feelings.

- Thirdly, an attitude has two or three components. Most authors agree about an affective component (a tendency to like or dislike something or someone) and a cognitive component (a predisposition to rationally evaluate something or someone positively or negatively). Specialists disagree about a third component, i.e. a behavioural one (a tendency to act in a certain direction, all other things being equal) because this third component is difficult to isolate and to differentiate from the behaviour itself or from other psychological phenomena such as stereotypes.

The cognitive component of an attitude is the mechanism through which a person makes a rational evaluation (albeit at times a biased one) of the object of the attitude. This is the component of the attitude, which takes facts and figures into account. In contrast, the affective component is entirely emotional and can be irrational. This is the component that accounts for our likes and dislikes, even the ones we cannot explain.

The cognitive and affective components of an attitude can be aligned in the same direction, which makes for a fairly strong attitude. But they may also be aligned in opposite directions; this imbalance is known as dissonance, and makes for a relatively weak attitude, vulnerable to change.

Research has shown that the cognitive component of risk evaluation is a three-stage evaluation process. And the sequence of the three stages appears to be fairly constant across individuals, even though the evaluation is not necessarily done consciously. This process is illustrated in **Figure 7.2**.

Figure 7.2 : The Cognitive Component of an Attitude Towards Risk: A Three-Stage Process

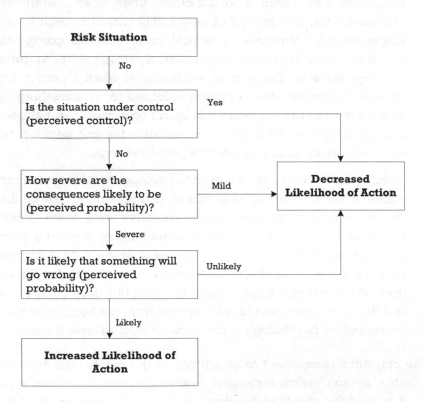

The first aspect of the risk situation that is evaluated is perceived control. The first preoccupation is to decide whether the situation is under our control or under the control of someone we trust entirely. When the situation appears under control, the process stops there, since there is no felt need for action. If control is perceived as insufficient, there results a feeling of uneasiness, which is likely to produce an urge to do something.

Perceived severity is the second aspect of the situation to be evaluated, but only insofar as control over the situation has been perceived as insufficient. The potential severity is assessed as a function of the type of injury or illness that may result, or the number or types of people potentially affected, and of the magnitude of potential damage. As far as consequences on health are concerned, death does not appear to be the ultimate fate; consequences which cause a severe loss of autonomy and reduction of the quality of life, such as the loss of sight of both eyes or paralysis of all four limbs, are sometimes rated as worse than death. The hazards generally rated as the worst are natural catastrophes, even though they are relatively infrequent occurrences, since they are totally out of control and cause severe and extended consequences.

The third and final stage is related to the evaluation of the likelihood of mishap. A couple of points need to be specified about this stage. Finally, the likelihood of an accident becomes a preoccupation only in the case of hazards about which control is perceived as insufficient and which may cause severe consequences; in other words, given that people often feel that being cautious is enough to be in control, this part of the evaluation is not performed very often. Secondly, just as in the case of the first two aspects, assessing the likelihood of an accident is relatively subjective and people are not very good at it. For example, research on gambling has shown that many people do not realise that their chances are exactly the same with ratios of 1:10 or 10:100; so if such simple odds pose difficulties, the difficulties are certainly not smaller with accident odds varying between 1:10,000 and 10:10,000,000! Finally, there appears to be a correlation between perceived control and perceived likelihood, likelihood being perceived as much lower when someone feels in control; this may have to do with self-confidence and confidence in one's own abilities.

Some of the most potent factors of influence are the attitudes of reference groups — the attitudes of formal and especially informal groups to which a person wants to belong; peer groups, group of friends, work teams, etc. Explicitly or implicitly, consciously or unconsciously, a person adjusts his or her attitudes to replicate those seen as prevalent among the members of the reference group. For instance, if a person feels a strong need to identify with and be accepted by his or her work team, and if the prevalent attitude of the other members towards the risk is one of bravado, then this person will tend to adopt a risk-taking attitude. And the closer the group, the more potent the influence. In other words, peers' attitudes tend to exert a greater influence than diffuse social values and attitudes, at least on a daily basis and in the short term. This phenomenon is crucial in understanding why some interventions in the workplace tend to fail and why others are generally successful. We will consider in more detail the subject of attitudes later.

Attribution Theory

The area of psychology that deals with how individuals decide the cause of people's behaviour is attribution theory. It is concerned with understanding how we attribute causality for people's behaviour.

Attribution theory suggests that there are two main types of explanation for the causes of behaviour. The first type of explanation is one that is accepted, almost without question, by the "man in the street". It is that a person's behaviour is caused by characteristics such as their personality or their attitudes. Thus, accidents are perceived as being caused by people being "accident-prone", "foolhardy", "negligent" or "having a poor safety attitude". In attribution theory terms, these explanations are referred to as internal attributions. Contrast this sort of internal explanation with the second type. This sees behaviour as being caused not by internal, but rather by external factors.

There is considerable evidence from social psychology and psychological experiments to show that there are a number of systematic biases that influence our attributions, both for our own behaviour and that of others. One such bias is the self-serving bias —

we tend to blame others for our failures, and take credit ourselves for our successes.

Perhaps the most important bias, however, is in our attribution of the causes of other people's behaviour. There is compelling evidence to show that, when doing so, we overestimate the influence of internal factors on behaviour, and underestimate the influence of external factors. When accidents occur, therefore, the evidence suggests that we concentrate too much on the personality and/or attitudes of the "culprit", and not enough on the external influences on their behaviour. For example, it is well known that there are accident "black spots" on the roads. If only "bad" drivers caused accidents, this would mean all bad drivers have their accidents on the same short stretch of road — statistically highly unlikely.

There is a strong tendency for us to see the behaviour of others as being caused by internal factors, however there are other strong pressures that may push us toward accepting such internal explanations. In a safety context, being able to place the blame on the weaknesses of an individual has its attractions. If the individual is to blame, the organisation is "off the hook". The fear of legal action, either criminal or civil, is largely removed, and the organisation need not look too closely at the possible contribution of physical or organisational factors to the accident. Internal explanations, however, are not without their problems. If behaviour is caused by such internal factors as "accident proneness" or "poor attitudes" there may be considerable difficulties in achieving any changes. As we will see, such internal factors are notoriously resistant to such change. For these reasons, behavioural approaches concentrate not on internal factors such as personality, but on behaviour. **Figure 7.3** presents a summary of behaviour and attitude oriented interventions.

Figure 7.3: A Summary of Behaviour and Attitude Oriented Interventions

---

1. Behaviour-oriented Incentive-based Interventions

This category of interventions is known as behaviour-oriented because its primary and only focus is to shape behaviours without using education or taking attitudes into account to any significant extent. In fact, the underlying assumption is that, by shaping behaviour, attitudes will realign in the proper direction by themselves.

A. Negative Reinforcement: Coercion and Disciplinary Sanctions

People are averse to punishment and to a coercive approach to behaviour shaping. Negative reinforcement of the undesired behaviour does not necessarily lead to the desired behaviour, but rather generates the development of punishment-avoidance behaviours. People still retain their old bad habits, but manage not to get caught in the process.

The use of negative reinforcement in order to shape behaviour is the approach that produces the highest levels of frustration in all those involved; no one likes receiving punishment, but also very few people enjoy administering the same sanction. Furthermore, this frustration is likely to have a spill-over effect onto the labour relations climate; when this occurs, short-term gains prove very costly when compared to much greater long-term losses.

B. Negative Reinforcement: Zero Tolerance

Negative reinforcement must be applied systematically, i.e. every time the undesired behaviour appears. The application of this principle to the field of safety has gained some popularity at the beginning of the 1990s under the name Zero Tolerance.

The notion of Zero Tolerance originates from the field of crime prevention. It has been, and still is, applied to such phenomena as drug abuse, marital violence and other such crimes, which a society seeks to eradicate. Crime repression involves coercion and punishment, negative reinforcement and disciplinary sanctions are the necessary way to go about it. Furthermore, this approach implies that negative reinforcement is applied every time an undesired situation occurs.

There are a number of problems with the application of Zero Tolerance approach to accident prevention. Firstly, such an application of the concept is tantamount to considering risky or even simply unsafe behaviour as a crime. This in itself is unfair, since unsafe behaviour, as pointed out in previous sections, may result from the fact that the person has no choice or may proceed from the best of intentions; neither of these cases fits the definition of a crime.

Secondly, identifying every undesired or unsafe behaviour and applying sanctions in every case is virtually impossible. Thirdly, unless extreme fairness is applied, frustration rises rapidly; yet it is almost impossible to obtain homogeneous application of the programme by any combination of five first-line supervisors, so absolute fairness and equity are almost impossible, therefore frustration is almost certain to occur. Fourthly, if the programme is to have even the slightest chance of success, it must not be applied in one way only. In other words, when a company does not tolerate any unsafe behaviour but does tolerate unsafe conditions and does not react quickly when a dangerous situation is reported, the Zero Tolerance programme is seen as yet another way for management to make the workers' lives miserable and rapidly falls into disrepute. Fifthly, most such programmes have suffered from basic flaws such as poor definitions of what constitutes unsafe behaviour, unfair balance between severity of the "offence" and severity of the corresponding sanction, and so on.

C. Positive Reinforcement: A Behaviouristic Approach

Basically this approach involves identifying a certain number of critical behaviours, defining a safe standard for those behaviours, and training supervisors to provide positive reinforcement (feedback, congratulations, etc.) every time they would witness the critical behaviours done correctly.

Some studies reported positive results in terms of near-perfect compliance with the set standards. But the DuPont project reported similar results in a control group not exposed to the project, and both experiments indicated that behaviour returned to its original, pre-experiment standard as soon as positive reinforcement ceased to be applied systematically.

Some research has concluded that discussing the potential outcomes of unsafe behaviour and improved supervisor-employee relations, rather than the actual reinforcement, might be the key variable at play. This would then shift the focus from the behaviouristic approach to one based on education and sound organisational environment. This is substantiated by the interventions in which those factors appear to be the keys to success.

D. Positive Reinforcement: Safety Contests

Safety contests are common. They have a lot of variety and they share at least two characteristics. First, they all involve some form of prize, meant to act as an incentive. Second, eligibility for prizes generally depends upon time spent without incidents.

These programmes have acquired a poor reputation for a number of reasons. For instance, when only a limited number of prizes were awarded among all those eligible, the chance factor or the deciding criteria soon came under heavy fire. Furthermore, they were rapidly seen as unfair, since people are rewarded or punished (denial of a reward is equivalent to a negative reinforcement) on the basis of something, i.e. accident experience, over which they do not have full control.

Two outcomes of such programmes have been demonstrated with a certain level of scientific credibility: 1) increasing frustration among those who do not win or who are not eligible through no fault of their own, and 2) under-reporting of minor (and sometimes not so minor) accidents. Moreover, companies with a good safety performance do not appear to rely upon contests to attain their results.

2. Behaviour-based Safety Management

Behaviour approaches based on positive or negative reinforcement have never produced exemplary and lasting results, but in some instances they have caused all sorts of other problems. Yet, despite all those mitigated results, a genuine preoccupation remains about the contribution of unsafe behaviour to accidents. And companies that reach world class status in safety mention that they approach the safety problem both from the angle of unsafe conditions and from the angle of unsafe acts.

The objective is to elicit safe behaviour. But the approaches have changed in at least two major ways. An important influence on workers' attitudes and behaviour is the managerial climate and an organisation should manage behaviours instead of trying to shape them behaviouristically.

New approaches are based on managerial styles instead of incentives. Second, in such a context, behaviour has become an indicator rather than an end in itself; whilst much attention is still devoted to safe or unsafe behaviour, this is no longer done in order to detect flaws in the individuals, but to detect flaws in the managerial system.

In these new approaches, safe behaviour is instrumental; the onus is on management. At least three major trends have been identified in this category.

A. *Zero Permitted Occasion*

This can be described in a number of ways. For example, in the strictest sense of the word, Zero Tolerance means that an action must be taken every time something wrong is detected. Zero Tolerance programmes that fail do so because they tend to:

- Over-simplify "something wrong" to unsafe behaviour, thus forgetting that "something wrong" could also mean an unsafe condition.

- Limit actions to be taken to disciplinary sanctions, thus overlooking the fact that taking action was also intended to mean consulting workers, finding solutions together, correcting unsafe conditions, etc.

Organisations are now moving away from Zero Tolerance and towards the concept of Zero Permitted Occasions. Although interpretations may vary from one organisation to another the general tendency is as follows. If an organisation is serious about workplace health and safety, it should not permit any exposure to danger, or any dangerous situation; the quickness of its reactions regarding a dangerous situation (an unsafe act, an unsafe or unhealthy condition, or a combination of both) is a measure of its seriousness about workplace health and safety. And the actions it takes are generally not (at least, should not be) negative reinforcements. Taking action should mean setting up a problem-solving process, much as in the case of continuous improvement in the field of product quality management.

These programmes are quite recent and some of the same problems as in Zero Tolerance seem to recur. For instance, if absolute zero unsafe behaviour is practically impossible, complicating the target to include zero unsafe conditions makes it even more impossible. So people tend to perceive this programme as utopian and lend it little credibility. In addition, there remains in some people a strong temptation to over-simplify again and to slip back towards the Zero Tolerance that means intolerance.

B. Behaviour Data Banks

One behaviour-based approach has been designed to attempt to avoid those problems. In this approach, behaviour is seen as an indicator of various potential flaws in the overall managerial system; inadequate or insufficient training, unsafe or unhealthy conditions, poor workstation design, unavailability of adequate equipment, and so on. Another basic assumption is that there is only one good way to do a job, and that the good way is the one, which is correct from the points of view of safety, of production and of quality.

One of the first steps in implementing such programmes is to train observers, both managers and workers. Trainees are taught to observe and identify dangerous situations without passing judgement, to discuss those situations with the people involved, and to identify satisfactory solutions together.

Among the satisfactory solutions, one consists of determining a way to do the job that is adequate both for safety and production, which then enables workers to avoid conflicts of motivation.

Even when specific dangerous situations are corrected on the spot, the results are nevertheless compiled into a data bank. The data bank is analysed periodically, as determined by the programme pilot committee or by the health and safety committee for instance, in order to identify trends which might suggest widespread needs in specific areas of workplace health and safety, or workplace health and safety programmes and activities that would address fundamental problems.

Reported results appear to be encouraging. It must be pointed out that this approach has not been widely documented in the scientific literature. From the available literature, however, it seems possible to identify some positive aspects. For instance, this approach does not rely on negative reinforcement. A real effort is made to involve workers at the shop-floor level, which ties in with an agreement discussed in the next section. In addition, the underlying approach is one of continuous improvement, which is compatible with quality improvement programmes, instead of aiming for goals that are perceived as unattainable.

C. Empowerment

Research indicates that one important barrier is the fact that workplace health and safety is seen by many as the domain of specialists; this is a phenomenon known as centralisation of safety.

In the light of research findings into organisational factors in workplace health and safety, it has gradually become obvious that the prevailing organisational context and managerial style might be another important barrier. The popularity of autonomous or semi-autonomous work groups, and managerial approaches based on employee empowerment, indicates that employees could responsibly take charge of production.

Two important elements underpin an empowerment approach. Instead of trying to find ways and means of motivating people so that they will get involved in workplace health and safety activities decided from above in the hierarchy, workers are involved from the start and allowed to make decisions, and it is this which generates motivation. The second common denominator is that traditional approaches to safety management can go only so far; a breakthrough can be achieved only by a fairly fundamental change in managerial style.

Little has been published on approaches based on empowerment, since these are fairly recent. So definite and very affirmative conclusions would be somewhat premature. Nevertheless this appears to be a very promising avenue for many reasons:

1. It appears to be very successful in eliciting safe behaviour and positive safety attitudes.

2. It avoids completely the apparent conflict between safety and production.

3. It succeeds in making employees active stakeholders in workplace health and safety activities.

4. It is totally compatible with other aspects of management such as continuous improvement, empowerment and autonomous work groups.

D. Training

Different types of training and education approaches have been tried, in an incredible variety of contexts. A number of findings emerge here.

First, the sessions should not be of the "general awareness" type. Motivational sessions designed to generate a drive in workers to get involved in safety activities of all kinds tend to make participants frustrated, particularly if they are convinced that the company is not serious about workplace health and safety matters. Experience shows that, if sufficient leadership is displayed in workplace health and safety matters, these sessions become irrelevant.

The training and education effort must reach all levels in the organisation, not just the workers. Obviously people at all levels have education and information needs. But these sessions can also be used very profitably as an opportunity for management and workers to exchange views and to get on the same wavelength. When done in this context, some remarkable results have been reported.

Safety training is no different from any other type of training in the workplace. Therefore, it must meet the same standards of planning, need identification, organisation, facilitating context and proper delivery as all other types of training. Active training techniques must be used to take into account that the sessions are addressed to adults who may have been out of school for many years. So all of the basics of adult educational techniques apply here too.

A continuous learning approach must be adopted. It is generally recommended that, beyond a solid initial session, reminder sessions should be organised on a regular basis until such time as the desired effect has become an irreversible part of the organisation culture; when presented this way, it becomes obvious that *one-shot deals* are far from sufficient.

In some instances, a training effort has been the only noticeable attempt to improve workplace health and safety results. Needless to say, training alone cannot do the job of the entire prevention system, and such attempts have been relative failures. Training and education must not stand alone, but must be a well-integrated part and an essential ingredient of a systematic workplace health and safety effort.

MOTIVATION, SAFETY AND HEALTH

An essential starting point in understanding human behaviour is consideration of employees' goals, objectives and motivations. In general, employees have multiple goals, some of which are short-term and others more long-term. These goals may conflict with one another and one goal or set of goals may significantly influence behaviour at a particular time. This can result in employees demonstrating inconsistent and contradictory behaviour from time to time. They may also demonstrate consistency in their behaviour.

The study of motivation has received a considerable amount of academic attention, partly due to the potential rewards that an understanding of the field could bring when utilised in a business context. An understanding of motivation has often (mistakenly) been equated with a complete understanding of how to control behaviour and thus motivation studies have often been the source of business "fads". Nonetheless, it is important to understand that although motivation is not the sole regulator of human behaviour, it does play a major role in influencing behaviour, and, therefore, much of the attention is justified. A useful way to understand motivation as a concept, is to view it in terms of a cyclical process, as shown in **Figure 7.4**.

Figure 7.4: A Simple Motivation Cycle

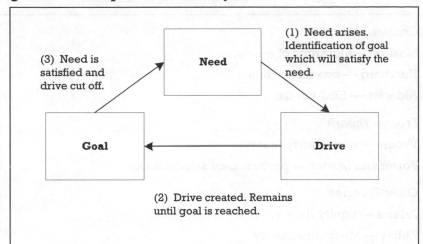

The cycle consists of three basic stages:

1. First, a need arises through some form of deprivation. Porteous (1997) defines a need as a psychological or physiological imbalance. Examples of such needs are sleep, when the body is fatigued, or affiliation, when the mind requires company. Once a need has arisen, the individual identifies a goal that will satisfy the need.

2. A desire to reach this goal follows, creating a drive (also labelled "motive"). This drive sets the need on course for fulfilment, and will remain until the goal is reached. However, the drive may be interrupted for a number of reasons. The need may change, the goal may conflict with other needs, or the goal may simply be unattainable.

3. If the goal is reached, by definition the need will become satisfied, and therefore the drive becomes redundant and is cut off.

Theories of Work Motivation

There is a considerable range of theories on work motivation, many far too complex to cover comprehensively in this handbook. This section will only attempt to provide an outline of the more relevant theories, which can be grouped into three categories, as shown in **Figure 7.5**.

Figure 7.5: Categories of Motivation Theories

Content Theories
Maslow — hierarchy of needs.
Herzberg — two-factor theory.
Alderfer — ERG needs.
Process Theories:
Vroom — expectancy theory.
Porter and Lawler — performance satisfaction.
Other Theories:
Adams — equity theory.
Kelley — attribution theory.

Content theories focus on identifying the basic needs, drives and goals that motivate individuals to put effort into work. Originally, based on the principles of scientific management, it was generally believed that money was the basic motivator. However, subsequent work by Maslow (1954) introduced the concept of lower order and higher order needs, which he summarised in his "hierarchy of needs". The hierarchy is a pyramid of steps — the needs contained in lower stages must be satisfied before higher needs can be satisfied.

Although Maslow's hierarchy was not originally designed to apply to the area of work motivation, it received much attention from managers in the business sphere. Herzberg built extensively on Maslow's higher order/lower order needs dichotomy to suggest his "two-factor theory". Put simply, Herzberg (1967) suggested that when applied to organisations, Maslow's lower order needs did not necessarily satisfy the individual. Rather, the absence of fulfilment of lower order needs resulted in dissatisfaction. Potential satisfaction of higher order needs, he argued, did act as a motivator. He therefore labelled Maslow's lower order needs "hygiene factors", and the higher order needs "motivators".

Alderfer (1972) subsequently introduced his ERG theory, an acronym for the needs of existence (physiological state), relatedness (affiliation) and growth (personal development). Although similar to Maslow and Herzberg in that the same needs are mentioned, the main departure was to suggest that there are no strict boundaries between the categorisations.

Process theories grew out of criticisms of content theories that argued that, though content theories were useful classification devices, they oversimplified the complexity of motivation, and were of little predictive value to managers. Process theories attempt to explore motivation in a dynamic manner, rather than as a set of fixed categories.

Vroom's (1964) expectancy theory was partially derived from utility theory, and aimed to provide a conceptual measure of an individual's level of motivation. However, the complex econometric nature of his model has made practical application by managers difficult. Porter and Lawler (1968) revised Vroom's model in their performance satisfaction model, which aims to represent Vroom's ideas diagrammatically, rather than mathematically. They also introduced a distinction between motivation (effort) performance (standard achieved) and satisfaction (fulfilment of the need which induced the effort).

Many other theories of motivation are derived from the field of social psychology, building on cognitive dissonance theory and attribution theory. Based on the ideas of Festinger (1957), Bem (1967) and Heider (1958), these theories suggest that perceptions play a major role in motivation. Adam's (1965) equity theory is based on the concept that, if individuals perceive they are being rewarded for their efforts in a manner equal to those around them, stronger motivation will result.

Kelley's (1971) attribution model of motivation suggests that both external perceptions (those of the environment) and internal perceptions (those of the self) are vital in understanding motivation. An example is the perception of the locus of control — the extent to which an individual believes that external factors or internal factors control their destiny.

Motivation Theories and Job Design

The area of job design has major implications for safety and levels of monitoring, and motivation plays an important role in many theories of job design. The concept of integrating motivation theories into job design has been widely researched, and a large number of theoretical models have been put forward, dealing with ideas such as job enrichment, job characteristics and goal setting.

Herzberg's two-factor theory has been directly applied to the work situation, in an effort to "enrich" jobs, with the aim of motivating employees to greater performance and safety standards. Hackman and Oldham (1976) developed a job characteristic model, which examined the link between the scope of the job and employee performance. The critical aspects of the link are considered to be the psychological states of employees arising from the job characteristics.

Locke (1968) and Locke and Latham (1990) suggest a goal-setting approach to job design aimed at improving motivation. This builds on both expectancy theory and other cognitive models of motivation. The basic tenet of their work is that goals are immediate, but not exclusive regulators, so performance will be improved if the goals of the job are understood and accepted by the individual. There is a more detailed treatment of the characteristics of "good jobs" in **Chapter 13**.

Safety Implications of Motivation Theories

The safety implications of motivation lie in the area of job design, because improvements in human performance should equate to improvements in safety. A proper safety climate in an organisation is a vital part of job enrichment, so as to ensure that Herzberg's hygiene factors are met. Similarly, proper consideration of safety when designing job characteristics is necessary, if employees are to have desirable psychological states. Thus frustration should be avoided as much as possible, by avoiding repetitive, monotonous tasks that lack variety, skill and autonomy.

There is evidence to suggest that goal setting and feedback have an important role to play in motivation and by association in improving safety consciousness (Marsh et al., 1995). Frustration often arises from the individual's inability to satisfy a goal, so management should make every effort to ensure job goals are realistic. Goal setting and feedback can be of particular value in safety management. McAfee and Winn (1989), for example, demonstrate that safety performance can be improved by systematically monitoring safety-related behaviour and providing feedback in conjunction with goal setting and/or training. Chokkar and Wallin (1984), in a study of US metal fabrication workers, demonstrated how safety performance with feedback and goal setting was better than only goal setting. Reber and Wallin(1984) found similar results in a study of machine operators. Marsh et al. (1995) found that goal setting and feedback can be used to produce significant improvements in safety performance at least over a period of several months. They concentrated their research on building sites.

Incentive schemes have also been demonstrated to improve safety performance (Aiken, 1992). However, Peters (1987) points out that, while they have been used successfully to improve safety behaviour in certain conditions, they are expensive. Group motivation is another important consideration, because peer pressure plays an important role (De Bobes, 1986). Propaganda can be a useful tool in ensuring that peer pressure is safety-oriented and thus beneficial. However, Wilson (1989) and Saarela et al. (1989) demonstrate that posters and informational safety campaigns designed to improve safety through increased safety consciousness are not consistently successful.

The value of motivation in understanding and managing safety-conscious behaviour is further supported by the research findings on the use of disciplinary action. The use of disciplinary action has shown limited success, largely because punishment is consistently held to be less effective than positive reinforcement. Punishment tends not to be effective if it is infrequent, delayed or of mild intensity. Supervisors are often reluctant to use punishment because of fear of resentment, which may lead to lower morale and lack of cooperation and productivity. Further discussion on the role of motivation will be considered in the next chapter, when the focus is on accident theories.

EMPLOYEE ATTITUDES AND SAFETY

In the search for new methods and approaches to improving health and safety and reducing risks, an interest in psychological factors and in particular in safety attitudes and climate has grown significantly. A major study carried out during the mid-1980s by the Safety Research Unit for British Steel demonstrated a clear correlation between attitudes and safety performance (Canter and Donald, 1990). Since the early work, the SRU has conducted research developing the measures of safety attitude and has carried out interventions in over 60 organisations in the UK and mainland Europe in the chemical, steel and power generation industries. As a result of this and other research, it is now reasonably well accepted by practitioners and researchers in the field, as well as in organisations, that attitude and organisational culture together play a very significant part in accidents.

To understand the difference between traditional approaches and that taken in relation to safety attitudes, it is helpful to examine the questions focused upon by each. The basic premise of the safety attitude approach is that a large number of accidents are under the control of those involved in them — that is, the behaviours that lead people to have accidents are intentional — they are aware of what they are doing. Naturally people do not usually intend to have an accident, but equally the actions that lead to accidents are often not momentary lapses of attention nor unconsciously mediated activities. This suggests that much behaviour that result in accidents are intentional acts. This does not mean that people intend to have an accident. However, what is shown in previous research by the relationship between attitudes and accidents is that people are aware of the factors involved in safe and unsafe behaviour. Because of this awareness, it can be suggested that people's actions are under their control.

There are direct organisational implications that stem from this finding. For example, rather than dealing with the unintended factors, i.e. the slips and errors, what is necessary is to create a safety culture where the dangerous actions and unsafe behaviour of which employees are aware are not carried out. Clearly this requires more than technological solutions such as control room design, and what is necessary here is to consider the more human aspects of safety and risk management by looking at employee attitudes to health and safety, and seeing how such attitudes are related to their behaviour in the workplace — the degree to which an attitude is acted upon.

The Nature of Attitudes

The concept of attitudes is difficult to define. However, the common thread that runs through the many and varied definitions is that an attitude is seen as a relatively persistent tendency to feel or behave in a particular manner, when faced with some object or situation. Attitudes fall somewhat along a continuum from negative via neutral to positive, in that individuals are predisposed to have negative, neutral or positive feelings about an object or situation, and tend to react accordingly.

Attitudes are often ascribed the status of a cognitive (mental) force which has the potential for either good or evil. Sometimes this force remains within an individual's mind, while at other times it is manifested as observable behaviour. In other words, attitudes have the potential for influencing behaviour on the assumption that some form of thought process always precedes action (Glendon and McKenna, 1994).

Attitudes may be considered as being located somewhere between deep-seated values and beliefs — which may well remain unchanged over a lifetime, and relatively superficial views and opinions — which may change frequently depending upon the information we have most recently been exposed to.

An attitude can be defined as a "learned tendency to act in a consistent way to a particular object or situation" (Fishbein and Ajzen, 1975). This definition indicates that attitudes:

- Are learned through social interactions (culture) and other influences (they are not innate) — for example, there is evidence that attitudes to safety in the construction industry differed depending upon whether the worker had ever personally experienced an accident or injury.

- Are a tendency to act but are by no means a guarantee that a person with a given attitude will actually act in particular way.

- Have an element of consistency about them; individuals tend to have clusters of attitudes that are consistent with one another.

- Are specific to a particular object or situation — they should not be thought of as being generalised to other objects or situations.

Thus, attitudes in the field of safety need to be seen as specific to particular aspects of safety. Virtually everyone would say that they are in favour of high standards of workplace safety (i.e. people generally have a "positive" attitude towards health and safety) but this does not tell us anything useful. Thus, we need to specify what particular aspects of health and safety influence people's attitudes.

Attitudes are commonly broken down into three basic components: the affective, cognitive and behavioural components.

- **Affective** — concerned with feeling and emotions. For example, someone who has witnessed a serious accident is likely to feel more strongly about safety than a person who has not learned through such an experience. This is because of the powerful impact of the memory of how they felt when seeing the accident.

- **Cognitive** — concerned essentially with the thinking aspect of an attitude; for example, having an attitude as to whether something is or is not dangerous. This is where our risk cognition or risk perspective apparatus come into play.

- **Behavioural intention** — this is the tendency to act, and is the one on which the utility of the concept of attitude stands or falls. If attitudes can predict behaviour, then this behaviour intention component has utility value. Behavioural intention is an important component of attitudes, and can relate to specific items, such as intending to acquire further training if you consider that a job or task you are doing is dangerous, or intending to use better personal protective equipment the next time you do it. However, even knowing that workers hold positive attitudes towards health and safety issues does not mean that we can necessarily predict their behaviour in situations that might require them to act in a particular way. Therefore, being able to predict behaviour does not always match the positive or negative behaviour. Why this might be so will be outlined later when looking at the attitude/behaviour link and theory.

Attitude Dimensions

The main characteristics of attitudes, sometimes referred to as attitude dimensions, are:

- **Valence** — the way in which the object of an attitude is evaluated, the degree of positive or negative feeling; this is what attitude scales or questionnaires are often designed to measure.

- **Multiplicity** — the degree to which an attitude is differentiated from other attitudes, for example, the degree to which attitudes about safety are differentiated from attitudes about health.

- **Breadth** — the number of attributes that characterise the object of the attitude, from the very broad (e.g. workplace health and safety) to the very narrow (e.g. a particular brand of ear defender).

- **Intensity** — the strength of feeling about an object (e.g. an accident that has been witnessed).

- **Stability** — how resistant is the particular attitude to change.

- **Centrality** — how much the attitude is part of an individual's self-concept or the extent to which a person feels it reflects their identity (e.g. a safety or risk manager feeling that holding safe attitudes is part of their self-concept).

- **Salience** — the degree to which an attitude occupies a person's awareness from total preoccupation to complete absence (a safety or risk manager might be considering safety issues all the time at work, while most other people would not be).

- **Interrelatedness** — how related is the attitude to other attitudes (e.g. to form a cluster of attitudes towards safety issues).

- **Behavioural expression** — the degree to which an attitude is acted upon.

- **Verifiability** — the extent to which an attitude can be checked against evidence (e.g. attitudes towards using personal protective equipment or machine guards can be verified by observing the use of PPE and machine guards).

The Functions of Attitudes

A basic question when studying attitudes is to ask what purpose they serve. Katz (1960) identified four functions: (a) social-adjustive function; (b) ego-defensive function; (c) value-expressive function and (d) knowledge function.

The social-adjustive function relates to the manner in which individuals adjust to the influence of those around them. Individuals develop attitudes towards family, friends, colleagues and authority figures, which help them to "fit" with the social environment in which they find themselves.

The value-expressive function allows individuals to use attitudes to communicate a desired "self-image" to those around them. It allows individuals to see themselves as unique and special. In order to enhance this self-image, individuals may adopt extreme attitudes in certain areas, to differentiate themselves from the "ordinary". In a health and safety context, this can be dangerous because certain employees may adopt very negative attitudes towards safety measures in order to match their desired self-image.

The ego-defensive function enables individuals to protect their self-image. This is achieved by developing attitudes that justify actions taken to project their self-image. For instance, an employee who has a self-image of being a skilled operator may view accidents as the direct result of sloppy work. Thus, their attitude may be that only unskilled workers need to wear protective equipment. They then project their self-image of being a skilful operator by not wearing protective equipment, an action justified by their attitude.

The knowledge function allows individuals to make sense of the world around them. Individuals build attitudes into a value system, which enables them to subjectively interpret, organise and make use of sensory information gathered through experience. Value systems tend to be fairly robust, providing individuals with a sense of stability in an ever-changing world.

Attitude Formation, Development and Change

Individuals form and develop attitudes throughout life, primarily as a result of their everyday experiences. The socialising influences of family, education, friends, peers and authority figures moderate the attitudes formed. Many attitudes are formed as a result of early life experiences, and tend to remain fairly stable throughout the rest of the individual's life. However, as individuals constantly have to reconcile their everyday experiences with their existing attitudes, these may gradually develop further or become slowly eroded over time.

Usually, rapid and radical attitude change is achieved only through some form of active intervention, encouraging the formation of alternative attitudes. Success in encouraging attitude change is relatively difficult to achieve, because attitudes usually contain strong barriers to change. According to Porteous (1997) the two basic barriers to change are prior commitments and insufficient information. If individuals are already committed to a particular course of action based on their existing attitudes, they will be unwilling to change their attitudes, as this will necessitate a reciprocal change in the course of action. Similarly, individuals who are provided with insufficient information as to why they should change their attitudes will be reluctant to do so. Available techniques to encourage rapid attitude change include the following: provision of new information; use of fear; use of dissonant information; influence of respected individuals and co-option.

Providing individuals with new information about a situation may alter their attitudes by first changing their beliefs. Many attitudes are strongly linked to beliefs, which in turn are based on the individual's perception of reality. If new information alters the individual's perception, it may eventually also alter their attitudes.

Festinger (1957) developed a theory labelled cognitive dissonance theory, which is concerned with the reactions of individuals when faced with contradictory items of information. He suggested that, when faced with such inconsistent or opposing pieces of information, the individual feels uncomfortable — he experiences dissonance. To reduce this discomfort, the individual is faced with a number of options. They may simply ignore the information, or make an attempt to adjust existing beliefs, knowledge, skills, attitudes and values. By implication, presenting the individual with dissonant information may induce attitude change, but a balance must be achieved lest the degree of dissonance encourage the individual to ignore the message.

Dissonant messages are more likely to be accepted (and thus more likely to create attitude change) if the source of information is a respected figure. Friends, colleagues and other persons whom the individual is already favourably disposed towards will find it easier to induce attitude change, as they have an existing basis for credibility. Persons whom the individual dislikes will often find their messages are ignored.

In certain circumstances, fear has also been found to increase the degree of attitude change. As a general rule, arousing a low level of fear is unlikely to induce attitude change as individuals tend to ignore gentle warnings. Similarly, arousing a high level of fear is also unlikely to produce the desired outcome, because strong warnings are viewed as threatening, confusing, or incredible, and are thus rejected. However, moderate levels of fear arousal do seem to alert individuals to danger, and thereby successfully encourage attitude change.

Co-option involves inducing change by providing the individual with the responsibility to remove dissonant information. If this task is particularly difficult, the individual may find it easier to change their attitudes so that they become consistent with the information, rather than removing it altogether. For instance, an employee who is unhappy with the organisation's levels of safety may change their attitude, if given the task of trying to improve upon complex safety procedures.

Attitudes and Behaviour

In terms of the relationships between attitudes and behaviour, Glendon and McKenna (1994) suggest the following propositions:

Attitudes Influence Behaviour

Attitudes influence behaviour, and thus if we know a person's attitude to something (e.g. the chances of an accident occurring), we can sometimes influence or predict their behaviour towards it with a reasonable degree of certainty. This theory therefore implies that, if we are able to change a person's attitude to something, toward a particular aspect of health and safety, then this will also influence — and, by implementation, also change — the relevant behaviour. However, merely expressing positive or negative attitudes towards something is not in itself sufficient to change people's behaviour, although it is one component of the desired behaviour change. Evidence suggests that we should be cautious of any simplistic "attitudes influence behaviour"-type theory as a complete explanation of the attitude-behaviour link.

Attitudes and behaviour mutually reinforce each other so, if we change either one, it is likely to lead to change in the other. While it is true that attitudes and behaviour are likely to be mutually consistent, in order to influence them it is necessary to address both independently — to influence deliberately attitudes on the one hand and behaviour on the other, in a consistent way.

Behaviour Influences Attitudes

This theory is a straight reversal of that described above. Thus, if we wish to change someone's attitude towards something (e.g. using PPE), we can achieve this by obliging them to behave in a particular way (e.g. by passing legislation or making a rule and enforcing it). It is this type of theory about the nature of the attitude-behaviour link that can provide the basis for certain types of legislation in relation to health and safety. Thus, it is assumed that, if ways can be found to change people's behaviour, their attitudes will change to correspond with that behaviour.

In the case of legislation, an attempt is being made to change behaviour directly here in Ireland with regard to health and safety by the setting up of the Health and Safety Authority, responsible for the enforcement of the policies and requirements set out in the Safety, Health and Welfare at Work Act, 1989. Over a period of time, attitudes may change as a result of a change in behaviour in respect of workplace safety, partly as a result of such legislation. According to the *cognitive consistency theory*, if we are obliged by law to behave in a certain way, then whatever our initial attitude towards the topic of the legislation, in order to remain consistent, we change our attitude to correspond with the newly required behaviour. This is not always the case, however, especially when the behaviour-attitude link is weak as a result of the relationship between them being only at a level of compliance. While it is difficult to demonstrate conclusively that any given piece of legislation influences a person's attitude, it is likely to be among the factors involved in attitude formation.

Bem (1967) offers an alternative interpretation of this type of theory, stating that we frequently determine what our attitudes are by observing our own behaviour (self-perception). For example, if people repeatedly take various safety precautions at work, they may conclude that they possess a positive safety attitude, as the self-perception theory maintains that a person forms attitudes through observing their own behaviour.

Mutual Influence Theory

A third view of the attitude-behaviour link is that attitudes influence behaviour and behaviour influences attitude. All that was said in respect of the first two theories therefore applies to this theory. This theory represents an advance and is characterised by the notion of consistency between attitudes and behaviour. This notion of consistency underlies such theories as those of Festinger (1957) on cognitive dissonance, the basic premise being that people strive to make their attitudes and behaviour consistent. **Figure 7.6** presents a summary of two theories.

Influence of Other Factors

In this theory, the importance of cognitive consistency is acknowledged, but the possibility of additional factors that could influence both attitudes and behaviour is also considered. For example, a safety campaign may be designed to address both attitudes and behaviour of a section of the workforce. An example might be incentives in the form of bonuses for achieving a certain safety score. This may be a combination of a given housekeeping level as revealed by successive workplace inspections and an accident rate target achieved. To reinforce this attempt to influence behaviour, a reminder system is used, for example a poster showing an appropriate message. Such a campaign would be a variant on the marketing approach to influencing consumer behaviour whereby advertising messages are designed to influence attitudes towards a product by promotional activities such as price reductions.

Attitude Levels

In considering the social influences that impact upon individuals in respect of whether they will adopt particular attitudes and behaviour, it is also useful to consider the levels at which attitudes and behaviours are formed. Kelman (1961) categorises the levels of attitudes as:

Figure 7.6: The Effects of Behaviour on Attitudes: Two Theoretical Explanations

---

Cognitive Dissonance Theory

The theory of cognitive dissonance, developed by Leon Festinger (1962) has been one of the most influential theories in social psychology. Festinger's fundamental assumption, for which there is considerable evidence, is that people like to see themselves, and be seen by others, as being consistent. This also applies to the relationship between attitudes and behaviour. What interested Festinger, therefore, was the situation in which there was a contradiction between a person's attitude and the way they behaved – in other words, when a person recognised, cognitively, that their attitudes and behaviour were in dissonance – hence the title of his theory. According to Festinger, a discrepancy between attitudes and behaviour will produce psychological tension. This tension will then produce a psychological drive, the purpose of which will be to reduce, or eliminate, the tension.

The lesson that cognitive dissonance teaches us is seen by some as being counter-intuitive – contrary to common-sense. If you want to induce attitude change, get the person to undertake behaviour at variance with their attitude, but in doing so, make as little use of external inducements as possible. In this way the person will not be able to justify their behaviour to themselves in terms of the inducements. Their only option is to change their attitudes.

Self-Perception Theory

Proposed by Daryl Bem, self-perception theory takes an alternative, and also perhaps counter-intuitive, approach to the nature and change of attitudes. Bem's theory is based on the way that we infer the attitudes of other people. As we have stated above, it is impossible to observe directly someone else's attitude. Bem suggests that we infer our own attitudes in much the same way as we infer the attitudes of others — by observing our own responses to the attitude object and then inferring what our attitudes must be! Unlike Festinger, Bem sees attitude change as a system of rational inference, not the result of psychological tensions. These two theories generated much research, often directed at trying to determine which one was correct. Recent studies suggest, however, that both are correct, but that they cover different situations.

- **Compliance:** Here an individual accepts the influence from another party because they hope to achieve a favourable reaction from them. In the field of safety, an example would be a worker using a particular type of PPE either because they wanted to please the supervisor or because there were strict rules about wearing it and sanctions, including eventual dismissal, for not using it. However, the attitude-behaviour link in this case is not strong because there is always the possibility that, once the reasons for compliance are removed (e.g. the rules are less strictly enforced because of increased production pressure), the wearing behaviour will tend to lapse because the attitude-behaviour link is basically weak — the behaviour results from external pressures rather than from internal beliefs.

- **Identification:** This refers to a situation where an individual adopts behaviour derived from another party because of their relationship with that party. A good example would be the operation of group norms, whereby a person uses PPE because others in the group do and the person values their relationship with the group members. So this behaviour is likely to continue as long as the individual remains in that group. However, if they transfer to another job and become part of a different group that has different norms, again the behaviour will be susceptible to change in response to changing circumstances. The second level of attitude is therefore dependent upon external factors — in this case, social relationships (the cultural context within which the attitude is formed).

- **Internalisation:** In this case, an employee adopts a particular safety behaviour because of its functional value or because it is in accordance with their existing belief system. It is at this level that the attitude-behaviour link is at its strongest since, whatever the external factors operating, an individual engages in the behaviour because they believe that it is correct — irrespective of rules or what others choose to do.

Attitudes and Safety Management

What relevance do attitudes have to health and safety issues? Primarily, safety specialists should be concerned about employee attitudes because of the potential correlation between negative attitudes toward safety and unsafe behaviour in the workplace. De Bobes (1986) argues that attitudes are an important aspect of accident prevention but points out that attitudinal behaviour is subject to change according to human needs. Mayo's (1933) Hawthorne study demonstrated the changeability of behaviour as a result of attitudes. This experiment points out that the extra attention given to employees had a positive impact on employee attitudes. Vernon and De Silva (1986) demonstrate that the attitudes of employees have a distinct effect on accident rates. They observed that the accident rate among women fell 60 per cent when certain measures were taken that improved job satisfaction levels. Light and Keller (1979) demonstrate that a team approach, allowing employees greater control over their own activities, resulted not only in increased production but also in improved attitudes to work and safety performance.

Recent studies have begun to provide examples of attitudinal and climate-based interventions that have led to safety improvements. As part of the project carried out for British Steel by the Safety Research Unit (Canter and Donald, 1990), safety attitudes were used as the basis for introducing safety initiatives that resulted in improvements in the safety performance of the company. Such improvements included the achievement of zero lost time accidents (LTA) in a number of hazardous plants. The initiatives were also later successfully tied into the company's TQP, total quality performance programme, during the latter part of the 1980s. The use of goal setting as a way of increasing safety performance has also been reported (Cooper et al., 1994). Further, the relationship between safety and total quality management (TQM) has also been discussed (Cooper and Philips, 1995).

The work in this area represents a fundamental shift in the approach to safety. Rather than it being addressed as a hardware, task-oriented method of shop-floor intervention, it has become an issue of management. Clearly, if safety is about such organisational characteristics as climate, culture and attitude, it becomes something that has the potential to be managed. The importance of management, if not the critical role that psychology has to play, has also been recognised in the law. There are numerous examples to illustrate the importance of management's attitudes both positively and negatively. When management's attitudes towards safety are positive, so are the results, and the positive side-effects extend to other, sometimes unsuspected areas as well, such as an improved labour relations climate, improved productivity, and so on. Conversely, when management's attitudes are negative, or even only neutral, positive results fail to materialise even despite noticeable efforts from the workplace health and safety committee, the workplace health and safety professionals or other dedicated individuals. Many accounts of successful safety programmes insist on the importance of top management's active involvement. Smith et al. (1978) relate such involvement among the most important success factors for safety programmes.

Research by the Surrey SRU in more than 40 companies over six years, has identified three principal elements in safety attitudes: organisational role, behavioural modality and safety object. That is, who, what and how?

- **Organisational Role:** When enquiring about a person's attitude towards safety at work, not only are the individual's attitudes important, but so also is the individual's perception of the attitudes of others within the organisation. The perceived attitudes of four groups are particularly relevant: workmates, supervisors (or the equivalent), higher management, and safety representatives.

- **Safety Object:** When people hold an attitude, it has to be towards something. In the area of safety the objects are usually activities or issues, such as safety training, the use of committees, or the provision of information. The Surrey SRU research has found that different objects within a safety system can be divided into two broad categories: passive and active safety referents. Passive referents include routine safety activities, such as checking equipment, wearing the appropriate safety clothing and carrying out housekeeping. Active referents go beyond the routine safety activity and require greater involvement and effort, such as finding out the results of safety inspections, making suggestions and seeking information.

- **Behavioural Modality:** This element of safety attitude is related to the concept of attitude as it is used within psychology. Essentially attitudes are seen as consisting of three aspects:

  ◊ cognitive — what people know.

  ◊ affective — what they feel.

  ◊ instrumental — what they do.

Figure 7.7 provides a summary of the factors that influence attitudes of management to safely.

ATTRIBUTION THEORY AND SAFETY

When psychologists seek to understand why individuals behave the way they do, there are two major types of explanation that people use. Behaviour can be perceived as being caused by factors that are either internal or external to the individual. Internal factors are those that can be seen as being "within" the individual. Examples include things such as personality traits, attitudes, and moods. In fact, the original title for these factors was "dispositional". An explanation of a person's behaviour using an internal attribution would see the behaviour as being caused by, for example, their negligence, or their being foolhardy, or even "accident-prone".

External factors, on the other hand, are those that are part of the external "situation". Behaviour that is perceived as being caused "externally" would place emphasis on the individual reacting to events in the environment, rather than being driven by their personality or attitudes. For example, many people use the situation to explain any mistakes they make while driving— "the road signs were inadequate" — rather than their own carelessness — "I wasn't paying attention".

Figure 7.7 : Factors Influencing Managers' Attitudes to Safety and Health

Negative Factors

Lack of Awareness: Many managers are unaware of the far-reaching consequences, or of the enormous costs, of occupational accidents and illnesses, or of the noticeable benefits of prevention. This is not surprising, considering that the focus on what is called the "indirect" costs of accidents is relatively recent, and that those costs are generally spread across other budgetary items.

Lack of Accountability: In some instances, the lack of knowledge about the costs of accidents is fostered by a lack of accountability. Accountability for compensation costs has brought about a marked change in workplace health and safety efforts.

Centralisation of Safety: Many managers think that workplace health and safety is a specialist matter. Therefore, they tend to "delegate" workplace health and safety matters to specialised personnel. In a way, such a point of view, and the resulting mode of functioning, suits everyone. Managers welcome the opportunity to do away with what they perceive as a chore, and specialised personnel see this as a justification of their jobs. Centralisation of safety, however, is counterproductive; it doesn't lead to satisfactory results, at least not to good, lasting results. These occur only when everybody in the organisation, from managers to all workers, including staff personnel, are deeply involved in workplace health and safety matters.

Improper Evaluation of Safety: When an organisation evaluates and measures something, the underlying, implicit message is that what is being evaluated is important. Absence of evaluation conveys the opposite message: if it is not measured, it must not be important. In many cases safety performance is not evaluated, or it is evaluated improperly. It is generally recognised that the focus on lost-time accidents alone as a measure of performance is inadequate. At a company level, it yields an incomplete picture of the safety situation. At an individual level, using accident frequency and severity to assess a person's safety performance can lead to injustice. For instance, first-line supervisors whose safety performance is being evaluated on the basis of whether there have been accidents to their employees see it as unfair that they should be rewarded or penalised for events over which they do not have full control; therefore, they tend to see safety as a necessary evil. Many companies have become aware of these problems and are in the process of developing proactive safety performance measures, such as quantitative and qualitative measures of workplace health and safety activities.

Lack of Knowledge: In some cases, there may be a positive attitude towards safety, maybe even a willingness to get involved, but also a lack of knowledge of how best to do things. But this is no longer a matter of attitude, and can be remedied by training and education as discussed later in this chapter.

Positive Factors

Influence from Corporate Level: The importance of a strong safety culture at the company level is now widely recognised. Probably the best-known example of this is the DuPont story. This company has had an uncompromising safety culture for nearly two centuries. Their results speak of themselves. When a plant in that company shows poor safety results, the managers of that plant must report about it to head office; the message is quite clear. The literature also cited another similar example, that of Proctor and Gamble.

Public Image: More and more companies are careful about their image of good corporate citizens. Environmental groups such as Greenpeace use this to raise the level of environmental awareness. One paper was found that discussed the influence of public expectations on companies as regards workplace health and safety.

Partnerships: Another interesting concept is gradually emerging. In various ways business relationships between companies take safety into account more and more. At least three examples can be quoted.

For instance, when entering into a joint venture, the DuPont company will select its partners according to their safety records and practices, among other things, and will provide some expertise transfer in that field. Managing contractors is a growing practice whereby a company will have workplace health and safety requirements and provide safety training and facilities to the contractors it hires. These are good examples of how safety-conscious companies can exercise leadership and have a positive influence.

Benchmarking: The practice of benchmarking is also gaining in popularity. Companies will exchange best workplace health and safety practices without being involved in a business partnership as such. Again, this is an interesting concept, but one that must be used carefully, for applying someone else's ready-made recipe without careful analysis as to whether this is the right solution to the right problem at the right time, can be counter-productive.

Awareness of Consequences: As noted earlier, lack of awareness of the enormous consequences and impacts of accidents and illnesses at all levels can explain why managers fail to adopt a positive attitude towards workplace health and safety. The opposite is also true; when managers have been confronted with facts, figures and examples of such consequences, some dramatic changes have been reported.

Equal Importance of Safety and Production: Not all levels of management are sensitive to the same arguments. For example, top management may be sensitive to arguments related to the public image of the company, or to the staggering costs of poor workplace health and safety results. These arguments are not quite as potent with middle management and first-line supervisors. Middle- and first- line managers appear to be more sensitive to the explicit or implicit message that the company sends them as regards workplace health and safety. If they are held accountable for their workplace health and safety performance, if their performance is evaluated, for bonus or promotion purposes for instance, if they are asked about the safety situation as often as they are about the production situation, if well-performed safety activities provide as many points as production parameters in their personnel record, then they receive a clear message that safety is as important as production volume, and they behave accordingly. If they do not receive such clear messages, they conclude that safety is a necessary but unimportant evil, and they concentrate on what the organisation lets them know *is* important.

How people make such attributions, and the factors that influence the attributions they make, is a complex process. However, there appears to be certain "biases" that predispose people towards the making of certain attributions. When asked to describe the causes of their own behaviour, people are more likely to provide an explanation in terms of their reacting to a situation. As evidence for the validity of this explanation, individuals will often point out that other people, as well as themselves, regularly undertake this pattern of behaviour. The reason for using the behaviour of others as evidence for an external cause is simple. If most people, despite their differing personalities and attitudes, behave the same way in the same situation, then the cause is likely to be external.

The "actors" are likely to use external factors as influencing their behaviour, especially when that behaviour is seen as being undesirable. Outside observers, on the other hand, also seeking to explain the same behaviour are more likely to suggest an internal explanation, such as "carelessness".

This common bias has been called, "the fundamental attribution error". Put simply, there is a strong tendency for people to underestimate the effects of the situation when seeking to explain the behaviour of others (but not themselves). This bias appears to have some cultural determinants. It is more pronounced in the highly individualistic Western economies, with their emphasis on personal responsibility.

Applied to safety, the fundamental attribution error manifests itself in a tendency to seek explanations that emphasise individual responsibility, rather than situational variables, as the prime cause of accidents. The role of "situational" determinants is correspondingly downplayed. Organisational and legal pressures further strengthen this tendency. If a particular individual can be held personally responsible for an accident, e.g. they were "negligent or careless", the organisation and its safety systems are "off the hook".

This desire to blame a person rather than the situation is apparent after disasters. When the official reports into the sinking of *The Herald of Free Enterprise* or *The Marchioness* were published, it was interesting to note the reaction of the victims' relatives. In each case there was a chorus of complaints to the effect that the reports were inadequate, linked with a demand that "someone" be identified whose actions "caused" the disaster.

Recognising this natural tendency to underestimate the power of the situation to influence behaviour, a behavioural approach to safety adopts a predominantly external approach to the causes and cures of accidents. It places a major emphasis on those factors in the situation that either encourage or discourage behaviour likely to lead to accidents. It correspondingly places far less emphasis on internal factors such as personality or attitudes as determinants of behaviour.

In seeking to explain the causes of accidents in terms of situational factors, the behavioural approach draws on the body of psychological theory known as Organisational Behaviour Modification. This is based on the theory that, if a particular pattern of behaviour is rewarded, it will occur more frequently. If it is punished, it will occur less frequently.

Accidents continue to happen, despite the expressed desire of management to reduce them. One possible reason lies in the way that company policies influence the way people behave. Despite the best of possible motives, the system of rewards often encourages the very behaviour that management would like to discourage.

Companies are, quite rightly, put under pressure from regulatory authorities to reduce accidents. The most common measure of this is "lost time accident-free periods". While this is important as an ultimate objective, there is a view that it is not where the emphasis should be placed. As a result of the use of this measure, the goal on the shop-floor becomes "report as few accidents as possible", and it pressures the workers to turn a blind eye to minor accidents, and especially near-accidents. Even the reporting of fairly serious injuries may be discouraged. This pressure is intensified by the common practice of rewarding such "accident-free periods". Following a minor incident (or a potentially major incident that came to nothing), all the pressures influence the worker not to report it to management.

Firstly, it should be ensured that the organisational systems are not, inadvertently, rewarding the very behaviour they are seeking to discourage, and *vice versa*. Secondly, and perhaps most importantly the organisation should concentrate on specific, observable behaviour, and not ultimate objectives.

"Traditional" approaches to safety try to encourage the goal of accident reduction. The behavioural approach concentrates on encouraging safe behaviour. This should then lead naturally to a reduction in accidents.

Organisations often believe that they do indeed encourage desirable behaviour (i.e. a good accident record) but this is often counterproductive. The behaviour to be encouraged should be very specific, e.g. the wearing of hard hats, safety footwear, etc.

Individual managers, charged with the responsibility for ensuring good safety practices, often use discipline and punishment for non-compliance, rather than rewarding compliance. Managers rarely congratulate an individual for wearing their hard hats, but instead punish those who do not.

For rewards to be effective in maintaining behaviour, they need occur only every so often. Punishment, on the other hand, has to fulfil two criteria if it is to be effective: it must occur every time the behaviour occurs, and as soon as possible after the behaviour.

It should be apparent that conditions for using punishment or discipline effectively are very limited. Managers and other individuals with responsibility for enforcement are rarely in a position where they can monitor all the time. The difficulties associated with the effective use of punishment suggest that schemes should concentrate on the encouragement of desired behaviour rather than trying to use discipline to eliminate the undesirable.

PERCEPTION

The Nature of Perception

The term perception refers to the product of a set of complex, interactive cognitive processes that enable the individual to interpret incoming sensory information into a meaningful depiction of surrounding reality. Fundamentally, perception is the result of two dynamic processes:

- Awareness (perceptual selectivity).

- Interpretation (perceptual organisation).

As much individual behaviour is guided by perceptions, an understanding of perceptual processes is central to developing human factors based on safety measures. A crucial point to note here is that as "perceived reality" is essentially the individual's approximation of "objective reality", the two can and often do differ greatly. In a safety context, this can lead to well-intentioned behaviour inadvertently compounding an already dangerous situation.

Luthans (1995) suggests a useful categorisation of the processes involved in perception. **Figure 7.8** illustrates this categorisation.

The first process is one of confrontation, whereby raw sensory information is generated via the stimulation sense organs by energy present in the individual's environment. Secondly, registration occurs, during which sensory and neutral mechanisms "register" the raw data. A process of interpretation follows, where the incoming information is reconciled with existing psychological information such as learning, attitudes and motivation. During this stage, the raw sensory data may be filtered, modified or radically altered to produce an understanding of reality acceptable to the individual. A process of feedback may then occur, in an effort to validate or clarify this newfound understanding. Feedback can involve kinaesthetic or psychological verification of the perception — the individual may use an alternative sense organ to confirm the perception, or logically analyse the accuracy of the perception.

Figure 7.8: An Overview of the Perception Process

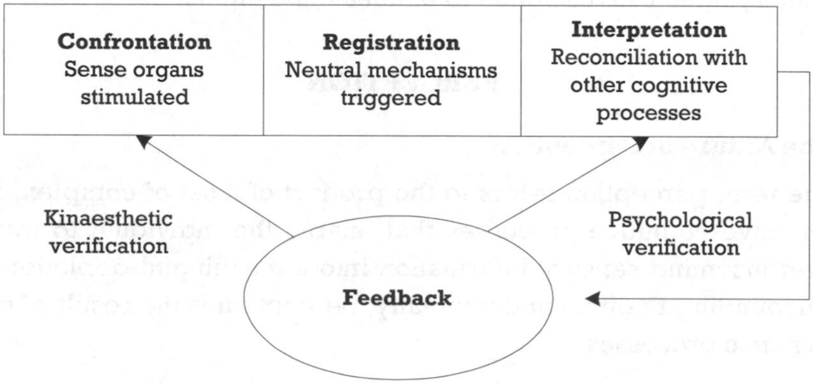

Perceptual Selectivity and the Perceptual Set

All individuals are continually being bombarded by various stimuli, due to the dynamism and complexity of the world. However, perceptions are usually concentrated on only a few of these stimuli at any one time, as various cognitive processes filter much of the incoming information. This filtering of information or perceptual selectivity is affected by a number of factors, known as the individual's perceptual set. External factors consist of environmental influences on the individual, whereas internal factors consist of existing cognitive influences based on motivation, learning and personality. **Figure 7.9** outlines some of the factors that make up the perceptual set.

Perceptual Organisation

Once the process of perceptual selection is complete, the data that has gained the individual's attention must be organised into a useful format, if it is to be interpreted meaningfully. This process of organising and interpreting sensory information is known as perceptual organisation. Luthans (1995) summarises various forms of perceptual organisation.

Figure 7.9: External and Internal Perceptual Set Factors

External Set Factors	Internal Set Factors
Intensity	Learning
Size	Unconscious or conscious motivation
Colour	Personality
Tone	Attitudes
Contrast	Expectations
Repetition	Span of attention
Motion	Fatigue
Novelty and familiarity	Sensitisation

Perceptual Grouping

The Gestalt school of psychology suggested that individuals organise information by attempting to group information from several stimuli into a recognisable pattern. Individuals use a number of ways to group such information.

Closure refers to the Gestalt concept that individuals will perceive stimuli as a patterned whole, even where none exists. Cognitive processes "close" the gaps in sensory information to form associations that are not necessarily present. *Continuity* is a similar concept to that of closure. However the tendency here is not to fill in missing stimuli, but instead to perceive stimuli as an extension of an existing pattern. *Proximity* refers to the tendency to view a number of closely located stimuli as a whole pattern, or as parts belonging together. *Similarity* refers to a situation where, as the stimuli increase, the propensity to perceive a common group or pattern increases.

Perceptual Constancy and Context

These are more sophisticated forms of perceptual organisation that allow the individual to develop a sense of stability and introduce meaningfulness to a dynamic, complex world. Perceptual constancy is closely linked to learning, and is the ability to perceive a consistent pattern even where sensory information is changing. To illustrate this, consider viewing an object such as a work tool from various angles, but the pattern is constantly perceived as the same work tool. Without perceptual constancy, reality would appear as a fluid chaotic mess, making everyday life impossible. The most sophisticated form of perceptual organisation is that of context. It allows individuals not only to recognise, but also to give meaning to identifiable patterns or groups. Meaningfulness can only be achieved if the individual has some "context" in which to place the pattern. A simple example of this is the ink patterns on this page — the reader can only interpret them as words within a "verbal context".

Perceptual Sensitisation and Defence

Perceptual sensitisation and defence are particularly important forms of perceptual organisation with regard to safety. Perceptual sensitisation occurs where the individual becomes "sensitised" to certain stimuli — those that are considered more important, valuable or meaningful to the individual. Thus the individual will react to the sensitised stimulus in preference to other stimuli. During perceptual defence, the opposite occurs, and the individual blocks or refuses to recognise stimuli that are considered stressful, culturally unacceptable or threatening. The individual builds perceptive defences in a number of ways, illustrated below with the example of a worker being encouraged to wear protective breathing equipment. **Figure 7.10** presents examples of perceptual defences.

Perceptions and Hazard Recognition

Perceptual selectivity and organisation are especially pertinent to health and safety when we consider an individual's ability to recognise and avoid hazards. First, a stimulus indicating a hazard may be "selected out" by the individual for two basic reasons:

- The stimulus may be unable to penetrate the individual's external perceptive set (it may be of weak intensity, the wrong size, colour or tone, etc.).

- The stimulus may be masked by other elements of the perceptive set (e.g. other external stimuli or by internal set factors such as fatigue or expectations, etc.).

Figure 7.10: Examples of Perceptual Defences

Defence	End Perception
Denial	Wood dusts do not cause respiratory problems.
Modification or distortion	Wood dusts only cause problems for those with an existing respiratory condition.
Change in perception	Wood dusts could cause respiratory problems for all workers.
Recognition but refusal to change	Wood dusts could cause problems for me but I still don't need to wear protective breathing equipment.

This "selecting out" results in ignorance of the hazard, and subsequent inaction to avoid an accident. Secondly, sensory data from the stimulus that does penetrate the perceptual set may become poorly organised, resulting in an inaccurate perception of the hazard, which may once again result in the wrong course of action to avoid danger. Such poor perceptual organisation or perceptual illusion can occur through:

- **Incorrect perceptual grouping** — confusion may arise due to closure, proximity continuity or similarity. Appropriate behaviour in one situation may be incorrectly transferred because of wrongly grouping the two situations together, e.g. incorrect first aid administered because of a confused diagnosis.

- **Incorrect assumptions of constancy** — an existing stimulus may increase in intensity but still be perceived as constant, e.g. a low level alarm may be upgraded to a higher level without the operators noticing the change.

- **Incorrect contextual placement** — a warning may be incorrectly interpreted as belonging to a particular context, e.g. a fire alarm may be interpreted as an intruder alarm.

- **Sensitisation** — can result in interesting superficial details being perceived before the fundamental meaning is established, e.g. operators may concentrate solely on the fire alarm to discover the source of the fire instead of noticing more obvious stimuli such as smoke pouring from a particular room.

- **Defence** — can result in the stimulus becoming ignored, distorted, or accepted without subsequent action, e.g. failing to register a warning signal or becoming paralysed by it.

PERSONALITY AND SAFETY AT WORK

In common with many concepts in the area of human factors and behavioural science, personality is a complex issue to define. There is much disagreement as to what personality actually is. This is fuelled by the fact that everyday connotations of the term differ somewhat from those held by behavioural scientists. The everyday usage of the term is usually associated with descriptive words about a person's characteristics and behaviour. For instance, people are described as polite, rude, clever, happy and so on. As Luthans (1995) points out, the problem for behavioural scientists is that over 4,000 such descriptive words exist, making a tight definition difficult.

Nonetheless, it is possible to identify similar elements within the varying behaviourist definitions. Firstly, personality is seen as each individual's unique pattern of measurable traits, and not a set of semantically vague descriptions of character. The term "trait" refers to the individual's typical ways of thinking, feeling and behaving. Secondly, these traits are seen as relatively permanent. Finally, the way in which the individual perceives and reacts to the environment is seen to be affected by their personality make-up.

There are two basic approaches to the study of personality: the Idiographic approach and Nomothetic approach.

The *Idiographic* approach, usually associated with Allport (1965), attempts to study personality from a holistic perspective. It aims to build portraits of various personality types, by extensively studying each individual's personality in its entirety. It can be classified as a systems approach, as it attempts to integrate personality into the wider context of the individual's environmental interactions, taking into account factors such as experiences, expectations and behaviour.

Though praised for its attempts to capture the unique nature of each individual's personality, the approach has been criticised for its lack of scientific rigour, as it tends to be overly qualitative. Furthermore, the cost of in-depth studies of specific individuals prevents large scale studies from being carried out, with the result that extrapolations of findings to the wider population may be unreliable.

The *Nomothetic* approach is diametrically opposed to Idiographic research, as it attempts to study personality by breaking it down into its component parts. It attempts to isolate significant variables or traits within personality, and to understand the relationships between traits and individual behaviour. The basic research method adopted is the quantitative measurement of large test samples under controlled experimental conditions, in the hope that identifiable and repeating patterns emerge.

The advantage of the Nomothetic approach is the scientific nature of its analysis, and its potential to predict behaviour among a particular sample of individuals. However, Lazarus (1971) suggests that despite its quantitative strength, the approach creates distortions by isolating traits and giving results that ignore the effects of the relationships between traits and behaviour. In addition, the predictive value of the approach is questionable because it is impossible to replicate all the potential environmental influences when designing experimental conditions. Therefore, results do not reflect the wide range of moderating influences the individual faces in daily life.

Along the ideographic–nomothetic spectrum, there are a number of possible perspectives from which to examine personality:

- Psychoanalytical perspective.
- Projective perspective.
- Trait perspective.
- Type perspective.
- Interpersonal/cognitive perspective.

Psychoanalytical Perspective

The psychoanalytical perspective is drawn mainly from the work of Freud (1938) on unconscious motivation. He structured personality into three components, which develop in childhood and slowly evolve during adulthood: the Id, the Ego and the Super-ego.

According to Freud, these components of personality struggle with each other to influence behaviour. The Id is the collection of instinctive urges, or desires for pleasure, that demand instant gratification. The strongest of these are sexual desires, the libido. In the newborn child, the Id reigns supreme, as the Ego and Super-ego have yet to evolve.

The Ego emerges in the developing child, as the mind learns to rationally assess how best to gratify the Id. The Ego is capable of logical reasoning and learning from experience. It has a policing function, initially balancing the demands of the Id, and later those of the Super-ego as well.

The Super-ego is awakened by the socialisation of the child, initially by parental influence. It is essentially a set of moral guidelines, which usually place restrictions on the gratification of the Id, so that the child learns to comply with socially acceptable standards of behaviour. However, these guidelines may be overly strict, resulting in great tension between the Super-ego and the Id, which must be resolved by the Ego.

In order to resolve this tension, the Ego has a number of defence mechanisms, outlined in **Figure 7.11** below. Freud's ideas were derived from patient observation, and attempted to integrate personality as a system of functioning parts into a wider understanding of behaviour, and thus could be classified as Idiographic in nature.

Figure 7.11: Defence Mechanisms of the Ego

1. It may **repress** the tension, by denying its existence and pushing the tension into the unconscious mind.

2. It may **suppress** the tension, by balancing the demands through conscious control.

3. It may **project** the tension onto other objects or persons by blaming them for it.

4. It may **fixate** the development of personality by refusing to accept the demands from the Id or Super-ego.

5. It may **regress** the individual's behaviour to an earlier stage of development, and use a coping device which used to work then, such as crying — the child's first coping device.

6. It may **form reactions** to the tensions created by the Id or the Super-ego whereby the pattern of behaviour adopted is the exact opposite of what is demanded by the tension.

Projective Perspective

The projective perspective is loosely based on analytical techniques and involves attempts to assess an individual's personality by interpreting information obtained from the subconscious mind. This information is generated by unstructured tests, where an individual is asked to "project" thoughts about ambiguous stimuli, such as vague visual images. The idea is to catch the ego off-guard, and allow information about unconscious motives and desires to emerge unchecked, which can subsequently be analysed to understand behaviour. Two of the more common projective techniques are the Rorschach Test (involving an ambiguous inkblot) and the Thematic Apperception Test (TAT) where respondents are asked to develop stories about pictures of varying degrees of clarity.

Trait Perspective

The trait perspective is Nomothetic, aiming to isolate dominant components of the individual's personality in order to predict behaviour. As mentioned earlier, a trait is a typical way of thinking, feeling and behaving. Identifying traits within the individual can give an understanding of their motives, abilities, temperament and characteristic behavioural styles (McKenna, 1994).

Cattell (1965) attempted systematically to isolate a set of fundamental traits that he believed would have an enduring dominant influence on an individual's behaviour. He used statistical techniques to derive "16 Personality Factors" that are considered to be "source traits" — those manifested in overly observable behaviour. For practical application, he developed a 16PF questionnaire containing 187 questions designed to identify traits within the respondent. Although widely used in industry as a predictive tool, its validity has come into question. There are a number of similar tests based on trait theory also in everyday industrial use, such as the Thurstone and Edwards Schedules, the Saville and Holdsworth Occupational Personality Questionnaire, etc.

Type Perspective

This perspective builds on trait theory in an attempt to categorise individuals who possess similar traits into large groups, known as personality types. Researchers such as Jung (1965), Eysenck (1987),

Sheldon (1954), Allport (1960), and Holland (1985) have developed such typologies, two of which are shown in **Figure 7.12**.

Figure 7.12: Examples of Trait Personality Typologies

Eysenck's Typology

Extrovert — sociable, has many friends, enjoys parties. Likes excitement, impulsive, active and optimistic. Can be short-tempered, unreliable and aggressive, does not like being alone.

Introvert — quiet, inward looking, reserved (except with close friends). Likes planning, order, ethical standards, but distrusts impulse. Tends to be pessimistic, but also reliable and emotionally controlled.

Neurotic — can become emotionally unstable, especially when placed under stressful conditions. Prone to anxiety and easily upset. Experiences disorders such as headaches, sleeping and eating difficulties.

Psychotic — can be extremely unstable, with serious conditions such as acute depression, schizophrenia, hysteria. May also have obsessions and phobias.

Sheldon's Typology
(based on the physical appearance of a sample of college students)

Endomorphic — soft round body, stocky, with large trunk and short legs, relaxed temperament, sociable

Mesomorphic — well-built, with rounded bone structure and muscle. Assertive, noisy and aggressive temperament.

Ectomorphic — fragile-built, inhibited, socially withdrawn, and with an inferiority complex.

Jung identified two broad personality types — the extrovert (outward-looking, scientific) and the introvert (subjective, philosophical, artistic). He then introduced the concept of "functions" that an individual carries out, namely: Sensing, Thinking, Feeling and Intuition. From using combinations of these, he was able to identify four specific personality types. The Myers–Briggs type indicator adapted Jung's work to identify personality types related to managerial decision-making (Myers, 1962).

Along with the development of his typology, Eysenck produced a personality inventory, which measures the dimensions of personality he identified. However, McKenna (1994) and other critics such as Peck and Whitlow (1975) are doubtful about the usefulness of practically applying Eysenck's work to predict behaviour among individuals or groups. Holland (1985) created a typology that was designed to demonstrate a link between personality type and career choice.

Interpersonal/Cognitive Perspective

This perspective encompasses ideas from a number of areas of psychology, placing an emphasis on the individual's perceptions of and interactions with the environment, particularly those involving human interaction. Thus personality is seen as an amalgam of influences on the individual including (among others) the following.

Self-concept (Rogers, 1951)

Self-concept refers to the pattern of values, feelings and perceptions the individual has about himself or herself. It is similar to Freud's views on personality, in that it suggests that an individual will feel tension if the "ideal self" (what the individual would like to be) does not match the "self-concept" (what the individual perceives himself or herself to be). However, the main departure from Freud's work lies in the focus on cognitive processes such as perception, rather than unconscious processes that are central to psychoanalytical thinking.

Personal Construct (Kelly, 1955)

Kelly suggested that, to be meaningful, personality descriptions should be based on an understanding of behaviour, and have a predictive value. He labelled such statements that an individual makes about their own personality "personal constructs", and argued that these change over time, depending on the accuracy of predictions based on the construct. For example, individuals who describe themselves as "happy" would expect to laugh often. If they subsequently find that they do not laugh at all, they may revise their construct to "unhappy".

Behavioural Aspects (e.g. Skinner, 1974)

Also labelled as "social learning", behavioural aspects are concerned with how an individual conforms to standards demanded by society. It therefore includes concepts such as reward and punishment, imitation and socialisation, and suggests that personalities are largely derived from the environment in which they live.

Locus of Control (Rotter, 1966)

This refers to the extent to which individuals believe external factors or internal factors control their destiny. Their expectations and behaviour will be coloured by the locus, and thus will react to reinforcement differently.

Personality and Safety Behaviour

There is a considerable body of work that has investigated the role of personality factors in accident causation. The studies have been of two types:

- Those that have searched for evidence of an accident-prone personality.

- Those that considered causal relationships between accidents and specific personality traits.

The accident-proneness theories hypothesise that some people are more prone to accidents because they have a specific set of personality characteristics. Accident-proneness theories consider accident proneness to be a permanent characteristic of people. The theory has a long heritage. It was first proposed by Greenwood et al. (1919). They showed that a small minority of workers had more accidents than they would have done if chance factors alone were operating. Newbold (1926) carried out the next major study and, in general, supported the Greenwood et al. findings. Farmer and Chambers (1926) were the first to propose accident proneness as a personal idiosyncrasy, predisposing certain individuals to a relatively high accident rate. They argued that it is possible to predict an individual's personal proneness regardless of environmental factors rather than considering the interaction between the environment and the individual as a possible explanation.

More recent authors such as McKenna (1983) have challenged these early statistical studies pointing out that, if one accepts accident proneness, then one has to accept the underlying assumption that all people in an organisation are exposed to the same job and environmental factors. This has led to a reformulation of the initial theory. Current thinking now suggests that, if the trait of accident proneness does exist, it is not a permanent, unchangeable feature. It is best treated as an attribute that is significantly influenced by a continuation of personal and environmental factors and it may vary significantly from one period to another. This has led to a consideration of factors such as age, hazard exposure and a range of other factors, which may cause an individual to be more liable to have an accident than others do.

Porter (1988) suggests that, if there is any stability in the concept, it is permanent for periods of at least 18 months. Her research suggests that accident proneness may relate more to abilities and issues such as attention. It is therefore unwise to treat accident proneness as a single personality trait. It more likely comes about as a result of a complex interaction with the environment.

A restrictive and perhaps more realistic view of accident proneness suggests that people are more or less prone to accidents in given situations and that this proneness is not permanent but changes over time. This is called accident-liability theory. The relationship between age and accidents is used as evidence of this theory. A number of important findings have been reported in the literature:

- Younger employees have higher accident rates than older employees (Slahane, 1987).

- Factors that contribute to younger workers having higher accident rates include inattention, lack of discipline, impulsiveness, recklessness, overestimation of capacity and pride (Lampert, 1974).

- Older employees (50–60) also show an increase in accident rates, although it is still lower than for younger employees

(Broberg, 1984). DeGreen (1972) suggests that this may be due to a deterioration in motor skills, sensory functions, mental agility and reaction time.

The other issue related to personality that research has considered is the relationship between particular personality dimensions and the likelihood of accidents. Shaw and Sichel (1971) used the Eysenck Personality Inventory to compare the personality profile of a group of South African bus drivers with their accident records. The good drivers had personalities characterised by thoughtfulness, peacefulness and calmness. Poor drivers were unstable extroverts with a tendency to be anxious, touchy, active and outgoing. Mackay et al. (1969) demonstrated that accident-prone drivers showed a mean extroversion score higher than the norms of the general population. Hansen (1988) also demonstrates that extroversion, locus of control, aggression and social maladjustment are all related to the occurrence of accidents. Sah (1989) carried out research on railway drivers and found that those with higher accident rates displayed more uncontrolled impulsiveness, aggression and greater display of emotion than more accident-free drivers.

It therefore appears that individual personality does influence accident rates but that such accident liability fluctuates with time and is specifically related to age. The notion that some people are naturally more accident-prone is, therefore, a less tenable position. Critics of the notion of accident proneness have highlighted problems with the perception of accident proneness as an inherent and constant characteristic of an individual. Boyle (1980) suggests that researchers of accident proneness should take into account how an accident is defined across studies; the completeness of the reporting and recording of accidents; whether the risk factors of job-centred and working conditions are equal; whether the duration of exposure of employees to the risk is equal across studies; and how the statistical analyses are carried out. Boyle highlights that many of the early studies on the concept did not control for these factors.

Arbous and Kerrich (1951) suggest that accident-proneness may be a factor of differences between the level of risk involved in different jobs. What was perceived to have been a characteristic of the individual may have been a feature inherent to the job being carried out. McKenna (1983) finds that a pattern of accident proneness may appear where the occurrence of an accident alters the probability of having further accidents in the future. This may occur where individuals think of themselves as being accident-prone after having being involved in one accident.

The concept of accident-proneness as a trait was also found to be unsustainable. Mischel (1986) posits that "highly generalised behavioural consistencies (over time and across situations) have not been demonstrated, and the concept of personality traits as broad response dispositions is thus untenable". Dunne (2000) suggests that researchers should now focus on the combinations of features of the individual's task relevant psychology and the work setting that give rise to accidents.

Research on the relationship between accident-proneness and personality has identified four distinct characteristics that differentiate accident repeaters from non-repeaters (Dunne, 2000). Accident repeaters generally have an external locus of control in terms of safety and safety-related matters (Jones and Wuebeker, 1985).

Locus of control with regard to safety refers to the extent to which individuals perceived themselves as being able to improve the safety level of their job or workplace. Those with an external locus of control hold the belief that accidents occur irrespective of their own actions but, if preventative measures can be taken, it is the responsibility of management to see to it. The severity of accidents appears to be related to locus of control, with the finding that those with a more external locus tend to have more serious accidents (Wuebeker *et al,*, 1985).

Repeaters tend to have a low level of awareness of the influence of interpersonal and performance aspects of their behaviour on safety (Hansen, 1988). When compared with non-repeaters, accident repeaters were found to be: impulsive, carefree and outgoing; indifferent to the rights of others; hostile and uncooperative, especially towards authority; emotionally reactive when put under pressure, becoming verbally and, sometimes physically, abusive; and likely to take unnecessary risks to prove a point to peers.

Repeaters often display high levels of anxiety, physical tension and indecisiveness (Hansen, 1988). Such individuals often feel nervous at work, become easily fatigued and view feedback as criticism.

Individuals regularly involved in accidents have a tendency to rate high on extroversion (Hansen, 1988). Extroverts are generally outgoing individuals who enjoy stimulation and excitement in the company of others. This has clear links with the interpersonal and performance aspects of behaviour described above. Dunne (2000) posits that high extroversion is only associated with accident repetition when combined with the characteristics listed — e.g. impulsiveness, etc.

It is argued that individual personality differences should be considered when selecting employees for specific occupations. To fit the best person to the job, employee specifications stipulating physical, mental, social and behavioural requirements must be established. An individual with average or above average intelligence is generally not a good candidate for a routine, monotonous job, because boredom itself leads to carelessness and risk taking. Emotional behaviour should also be considered when an unstable or immature employee might create a hazard to themselves or others.

MEMORY AND SAFETY AT WORK

Essentially, memory can be viewed as the brain's store of information. The inability of human operators to remember vital pieces of information from this store at crucial times is a common cause of safety lapses. Even trivial items, overlooked due to absent-mindedness, can prevent important safety tasks from being carried out. Thus memory plays a vital role in safe work practices and an understanding of it helps designers to create systems that can cope with human memory failures.

According to Wickens (1992), the "memory store" actually consists of two storage systems that accumulate information for use in different time frames. The working memory is a temporary store that has three basic functions. Firstly, it collects new high propriety information and retains it until it is used. A typical example of this is remembering a telephone number. Secondly, it is used as a sort of "mental notepad" to examine, compare and evaluate pieces of information. For instance, it is used during mental arithmetic, planning daily schedules, and evaluating decision options, etc. Thirdly, it is used to keep new information temporarily, until it can be encoded to fit more permanently into the long-term memory. As the name suggests, this second storage system retains information for long periods, keeping facts and the knowledge of how to carry out certain tasks until needed.

To be able to use items of information appropriately, the brain needs to encode information into a format that can be stored in, and retrieved from, the memory system. **Figure 7.13** provides a basic representation of the memory process.

Figure 7.13: The Memory Process

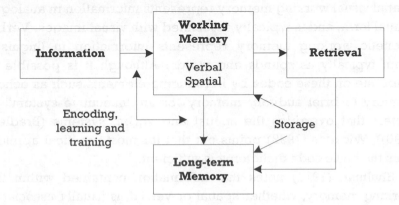

The various methods of encoding can be collectively referred to as learning. Training can enhance the efficiency of the encoding process — by using specific techniques to speed up and improve learning. Once information has been acceptably encoded into a verbal or spatial form, it enters the working memory, where it can subsequently either enter the long-term memory (after further encoding) or be retrieved to guide immediate behaviour.

Learning allows information from the working memory to enter the long-term memory by converting it into mental models, procedural knowledge or declarative knowledge organisation. A mental model refers to the way in which individuals organise their knowledge of how a system works or operates. Mental models tend to be very complex, and allow the individual to mentally "experiment" with options before coming to a decision. Declarative knowledge consists of information relating to a particular domain that is easy to verbalise, such as an organisation's safety rules (Wickens, 1992).

Procedural knowledge, on the other hand, is difficult to verbalise, as it is the knowledge of how to carry out a particular task.

Working Memory

Wickens (1992) breaks down working memory into two basic codes:

- Spatial visual working memory.

- Verbal phonetic working memory.

Spatial visual working memory represents information in analogue spatial form, and is typically associated with visual images. Verbal phonetic working memory represents information in linguistic form, typically as sounds and words. Although it is possible to elaborate on these codes by introducing elements such as echoic memory (a brief auditory memory) or an "executive system" (a system that overrides the spatial and verbal systems (Bradley, 1990)), Wickens (1992) points out that for most practical applications the basic code dichotomy is sufficient.

Shulman (1972) notes that information contained within the working memory, whether spatial or verbal, is usually associated with some form of meaning, so that the information has a semantic representation. This is essential if the information is going to be utilised effectively after retrieval, but it is possible to store information with little or no semantic representation, e.g. unfamiliar symbols or sounds may not be associated with meaning.

Wickens (1992) also discusses the importance of the distinction made between spatial and verbal codes. Firstly, the codes appear to operate relatively independently from one another, and thus are vulnerable to interference from certain forms of concurrent activities. Secondly, this potential for interference has implications for presenting information in verbal as opposed to visual displays. Thirdly, some individuals are better suited to verbal rather than visual displays and *vice versa* and this should be borne in mind when designing training techniques.

There is evidence to show that, in general, the verbal-phonetic and visual-spatial codes work co-operatively, despite being independent. Because of this, tasks that involve both codes are performed more quickly than similar tasks that require just one code

(Brooks, 1968). For instance, if a verbal question is given a spatial response (e.g. pointing), it will be answered more quickly than if the same verbal question is given a verbal response. This is due to time-sharing — as the two codes are independent, they can operate at the same time. A task requiring only one code takes longer because no time-sharing can take place. Healy (1975) and Klapp and Netcik (1988) also found that concurrent tasks that required only one code interfered with each other. The implication for the safety specialist is that task design should try to avoid such disruption. Tasks requiring a high spatial content should also have a verbal information processing element and vice versa. Stress can be reduced and performance increased when verbal tasks (e.g. editing) are carried out with spatial input (e.g. a mouse).

Working Memory Retrieval

Individuals often have difficulty remembering a new phone number, which suggests that the information retained by the working memory is kept for only a very short time. This restricted ability of the working memory has been widely researched. Experiments by Brown, et al. (1959) demonstrated that retention of simple sequences of three random letters dropped to nearly zero after a mere 20 seconds. Miller's work (1956) suggests that the limit of the individual's working memory span, i.e. the ability to immediately recall "items" of information, lies somewhere between five and nine items. An "item" here refers to what Miller labelled a chunk of information. A chunk can be a letter, a digit, a word or some other unit of meaning, which is closely grouped and recognised by the individual's long-term memory.

This limited capacity of the working memory poses many difficulties for safety specialists. Simple failures of working memory can have devastating consequences, so the notoriously unreliable working memory must be catered for in system design. It is possible to improve the efficacy of working memory if individuals are given reminders, e.g. a lasting visual message, but there is a trade-off to be considered. The reminder may clutter an individual's attention, and result in confusion because of information overload.

A more useful method of improving the reliability of working memory is chunking, whereby single items of data (such as individual numbers) are grouped into manageable chunks. The information is presented in stages with each stage not infringing the 5-to-9-chunk limit of working memory. The key to successful chunking is to find a meaning for each chunk that the individual is familiar with, so that it can be readily retrieved.

Chunking has two basic benefits. Firstly, it effectively reduces the number of individual items to be remembered, and thus allows more information into the limited store. Secondly, as the chunks have some form of meaning in the long-term memory, the information is much easier to transfer into it. In a safety context, chunking can be used to group specific tasks together, making working memory retrieval easier for operators.

In addition to capacity overflow and the passage of time, other factors can disrupt the accurate functioning of the working memory. Active interference from other brain activities can cause problems. This interference may be probative or retroactive, i.e. occur before encoding, or during retention. Confusion can also occur when similar pieces of information are inaccurately encoded.

Long-term Memory

Information is encoded from the working memory into the long-term memory via a process of learning. There are a number of ways in which learning can occur — random experience, formal teaching, practical experience and formal on- or off-the-job training, etc. To the safety specialist, formal training is of most interest, as a well-designed training programme can ensure the most efficient transfer by employees of safety information into safe work practices. Essentially, training speeds up the process of encoding information into the long-term memory, and can decrease the possibility of memory lapses. The topic of health and safety will be on long-term memory storage retrieval.

Long-term Memory Storage

The processes involved in long-term memory are broadly similar to those in the working memory, consisting of combinations of spatial, verbal and semantic characteristics. However, the key difference of the long-term memory lies in the organisation of these codes. Stored information is highly structured, defining the associations between various items of knowledge. As mentioned earlier, this knowledge can be organised procedurally, decoratively, or into a mental model.

This strong presence of structure in the long-term memory has an important implication for the safety specialist. If information is presented in a format that is incompatible with this structure, it will take time for new encoding and associations to be formed, and the learning process will be slowed down. On the other hand, if information is congruent with the existing organisation, then it will be absorbed more quickly, and actions taken on the basis of the in formation are more likely to be appropriate. Once again, training is of importance here as it can explicitly create specific mental models allowing safety information to be memorised quickly and accurately.

Long-term Memory Retrieval

After information has successfully been encoded and organised into the long-term memory, it needs to be retrieved at appropriate moments if it is to be of any use to the individual. If safety systems that cope with the shortcomings of memory are to be designed, it is vital for the safety specialist to understand the reasons why the individual's memory retrieval might fail. Wickens (1992) distinguished between two basic forms of memory retrieval — recall and recognition. During recall, an entire sequence of sterile information must be retrieved, but during recognition, only the fact of whether or not a particular piece of information exists in the memory must be acknowledged. Failures of recognition and recall can be attributed to the following:

- Interference — similar to interference in the working memory.

- Similarity — where similar items of information are confused.

- A lack of retrieval clues — external stimuli that trigger a memory.

- The passage of time — causing memories simply to "fade".

- Illness — some occupational conditions impairing memory.

Skill Retrieval

Particular attention should also be given to the area of skill retrieval. Although operators who are asked to perform a particular skill on a frequent basis will have little problem in recalling how to perform the task, a less frequently practised task can cause severe problems including safety problems. Typical examples are emergency procedures — unless regular training is devoted to the upkeep of skills required in emergency situations, memory failures can occur at crucial moments.

INFORMATION PROCESSING AND SAFETY AT WORK

It is generally agreed that the relative speed with which humans process information is a pre-condition of many accidents in the workplace. The response of an individual consists of two elements:

- Specific reaction time, which refers to the actual time it takes to perceive and process a response.

- Movement time, which refers to the time taken to execute the response adequately.

Generally people can only perform one task at a time and the speed with which this is done varies from person to person. This individual difference factor is significant in the context of accident causation. Where a task is well known or practised, the monitoring action of the brain can be reduced. This depends on the speed with which a person can respond to stimulation and not worker-specific movements or activities. Feedback is an important element of the monitoring process. High skill levels can be a hindrance and can destroy performance.

Information processing is divided into on-line processing and off-line processing. On-line processing refers to spur-of-the-moment decisions that individuals make in order to survive. However, it has limited capacity and is generally associated with jobs that consist of repetitive skills. Repetitive skills, which are developed over time, can be difficult to change due to the brain's lack of monitoring. Stranks (1994b) argues that this can be a significant feature in accident situations. Training may have a role to play in ensuring that employees have the correct habits.

Off-line processing is a process whereby people simulate in their minds the outcomes of different courses of action prior to taking them. This planning process is incorporated into many accident theories and is viewed as a significant predictor of accidents. Off-line processing is skill-based, contingent on individual knowledge, intelligence, experience of similar situations and the amount of skill practice. When considering the different outcomes, people attribute different values to various outcomes. These values are based upon a range of criteria and many are subjective in nature, influenced by the personality of the operator. The individual's level of arousal is also a significant factor. Arousal is defined as alertness and level of muscular tension. At lower levels of arousal, performance is poor and it tends to rise as arousal increases.

Compatibility

A major issue in human information processing is the concept of compatibility. This refers to the relationship of stimuli and responses to human expectation. It implies a process of information transformation or recording. It is suggested that the greater the degree of compatibility, the less recording must be done to process the information. High levels of compatibility are associated with faster learning, faster response times, fewer errors and accidents and a reduced mental workload. It is suggested that there are four types of compatibility:

- **Conceptual compatibility**: This conceptual capacity deals with the degree to which codes and symbols correspond to the conceptual associations people have. It concerns the meaningfulness of codes and symbols to people.

- **Movement compatibility**: Movement compatibility relates to the relationships between the movement of displays and controls and the response of the system being displayed or controlled.

- **Spatial compatibility**: Spatial compatibility refers to the physical arrangement in space of controls and associated displays.

- **Modality compatibility**: Modality compatibility refers to the fact that certain stimuli — response modality concentrators — are more compatible with some tasks than with others. Wickens et al. (1983) illustrates that the most compatible contribution for a verbal task is auditory presentation and spoken response whereas, for a spatial task, the most compatible contribution is visual presentation and manual response.

CHAPTER ROUND-UP

• Human factors are central to any discussion of health and safety management. Human factors are defined as characteristics of human beings. The concern is how they interact with work processes and the work environment. The particular characteristics of individuals of interest in the safety context include motivations, attitudes, perceptions and information processing capacities. A human factor approach posits that machines, systems and procedures should be designed to serve humans and have a user orientation in terms of design.

• Motivation is a much-studied concept and one that has received consideration in a health and safety context. The safety implications of motivation lie in the area of job design. There is considerable evidence to demonstrate that goal setting and feedback have an important role to play in motivation and are relevant in terms of improving safety consciousness. There is mixed evidence on the relationship between motivation and safety performance. There appears to be significant improvements in the short term at least.

• Attitudes are a useful concept in terms of managing health and safety. An attitudinal approach to safety represents an alternative to the behavioural approach. An attitudinal approach starts from the premise that a large number of accidents are under the control of those involved in them. It argues that the behaviours, which lead people to have accidents, are intentional. People are aware of what they are doing. This suggests that safety specialists should be concerned about employee attitudes because of the potential correlation between negative attitudes towards safety and unsafe behaviour in the workplace.

• Perception represents another individual characteristic that has relevance to health and safety management. Perception is a general term referring to the awareness of objects, qualities or events stimulating an individual's sense organs. Perception is an important feature of human behaviour, in that people behave in the way they perceive situations, people, places and the world in general. Failure to perceive and faulty perception represent two important causes of human failure and frequently result in accidents at work.

- Personality is likewise studied as an important variable in safety management. Personality involves the traits, ways of adjusting, defence mechanisms and ways of behaving that characterise an individual and, in particular, their relationship with people, events and situations. There is a debate about the link between individual personality and safety. However, it does appear that certain personality traits may contribute to accidents.

- Memory represents a process of retaining, recognising and recalling experiences. Memory represents a storage facility of the human system and can be both short and long-term. Memory represents an important dimension of human behaviour. Learning, past experiences, freedom from events and the individual's capacity to store information all influence it. Memory defects are sometimes associated with the concept of accident-proneness.

- Information processing capacity is also of relevance in the safety context. It refers to the relative speed with which individuals process information and is considered an important pre-condition of many accidents. Information processing can be on-line (spur-of-the-moment decision-making) or off-line (where individuals simulate in their minds the outcomes of different courses of actions). Capacity to act following a decision varies from one individual to another but is of considerable importance in explaining accidents.

Chapter 8

HUMAN ERROR, ACCIDENTS
AND SAFETY

INTRODUCTION

This chapter focuses on human error, accidents and safety. The reduction of human error and accidents and the improvement of safety is a top priority for most organisations and a key aim of a human factors approach to safety. This chapter first discusses the nature of human error and the types of intervention that can be made to reduce error. The remainder of the chapter discusses competing theories of accident causation, as well as considering the issue of human behaviour and accident prevention.

THE NATURE OF HUMAN ERROR

Human error is a common occurrence in human performance. Card et al. (1978) have estimated that operators engaged in word processing make mistakes or choose inefficient commands in 30 per cent of cases. Gopher et al. (1989), in a study of a well-run intensive care unit, found that doctors and nurses made an average of 1.7 errors per patient per day. Nagel (1988) has estimated that the proportion of accidents attributable to human error is considerably greater than that due to machine failure.

The study of human error in itself has only recently emerged as a well-defined discipline. This has resulted in attempts both to define error and categorise human errors. There is a considerable degree of debate about what constitutes a human error. Sanders and McCormick (1993) define human error as an inappropriate or undesirable human decision or behaviour that in some way reduces or has the potential to reduce productivity, system and safety performance. This definition puts an emphasis on the idea that error has undesirable effects. The error does not have to cause damage to be called an error; it is an error nonetheless.

Rasmussen (1979) argues that what is sometimes considered to be human error is very arbitrary because there may not have been a clear idea of what was considered appropriate until the error occurred. He likewise comments that the identification of an event as a human error very much depends upon the stop rule applied during an investigation. It is possible, in the case of an accident, to stop at the operator's actions and call the event a human error or, alternatively, one may go further and investigate what caused the operator to act in the way they did. It may be possible to identify causes that relate to faulty equipment, poor control practices and inappropriate procedures. This led Rasmussen to conclude that an action might become an error only because the action is performed in a poorly managed environment or culture that does not allow corrective action to be taken before the consequences of the error make themselves known.

Classification of Error

A wide variety of error classification schemes is found in the literature. In general, the schemes fall into two broad classifications: discrete action and information processing classifications.

Discrete Action Classification

Swain and Guttman (1983) suggest that errors fall into four categories: errors of omission, commission, sequence and timing. Errors of omission involve failure to do something. Errors of commission involve performing an act incorrectly. A sequence error occurs when a person performs some task, or step in a task, out of sequence. A timing error occurs when a person fails to perform an action within the allocated time, either performing it too fast or too slowly.

Information Processing Classification

Several authors have developed classifications using an information-processing model. Rouse and Rouse (1983) developed a scheme that follows the information processing assumed to occur when an employee operates and controls systems. They identify errors that can occur at each stage of information processing.

Figure 8.1: Human Error Classification Scheme

---

1. Observation of system state
- Improper (re)checking of correct readings.
- Erroneous interpretation of correct readings.
- Failure to observe sufficient number of variables.
- Observation of inappropriate state variables.
- Failure to observe any state variables.

2. Choice of hypothesis
- Hypothesis could not cause the values of variables observed.
- Much more likely causes should be considered first.
- Very costly place to start.
- Hypothesis does not functionally relate to variables observed.

3. Testing of hypothesis
- Stopped before reaching a conclusion.
- Reached wrong conclusion.
- Considered and discarded correct conclusion.
- Hypothesis not tested.

4. Choice of goal
- Insufficient specification of goal.
- Choice of counterproductive or non-productive goal.
- Goal not chosen.

5. Choice of procedure
- Choice would not fully achieve goal.
- Choice would achieve incorrect goal.
- Choice unnecessary for achieving goal.
- Procedure not chosen.

6. Execution of procedure
- Required stop omitted.
- Unnecessary repetition of required step.
- Unnecessary step added.
- Steps executed in wrong order.
- Step executed too early or too late.
- Control in wrong position or range.
- Stopped before procedure complete.
- Unrelated inappropriate step executed.

Rasmussen (1982) identifies 13 types of error and puts them in a form of a decision flow diagram. He suggests that the error depends on the type or level of behaviour involved. He identifies three types of error:

- Skill-based behaviour is controlled by subconscious routines and stored patterns of behaviour and would be typical of skilled operators performing routine activities. The errors involved are primarily ones of execution.

- Rule-based behaviour applies to situations where stored rules for co-ordinating behavioural sub-routines can be applied. The typical errors are ones related to recognising the relevant features in a situation and remembering and applying the correct rules.

- Knowledge-based behaviour occurs in unique and unfamiliar situations for which actions must be planned in relation to goals. The typical errors result from inadequate analysis or decision-making.

Norman (1988) and Reason (1990) make an important distinction between mistakes and step errors. They suggest that the human operator confronting a situation may not be able to interpret the evidence correctly and, given an interpretation, may or may not intend to carry out the right action to deal with the situation and may or may not exclude that intention correctly.

Errors of interpretation in the choice of intentions are called mistakes. Mistakes can actually result from the shortcomings of perception, memory or cognition. Reason (1990) likewise distinguishes between knowledge-based and rule-based mistakes. Knowledge-based mistakes are situations in which incorrect plans of action are arrived at because of a failure to understand the situation. Rule-based mistakes occur when the operator is more sure of their ground, but they misapply the rule, believing that it worked well in most cases but fail to notice subtle distinctions in the environment/context that indicate that the rule is not appropriate.

Quite distinct from mistakes are slips, in which the understanding of the situation is correct but the wrong action is accidentally triggered. A common category of slips are capture errors. These occur where:

- The intended action sequence involves a slight departure from a frequently performed routine.

- Some characteristics of the environment or the action sequence itself are related to the now inappropriate but more frequent action.

- The action sequence is relatively automated and not closely monitored by attention.

Another classification of error relates to lapses and mode errors. Lapses represent a failure to carry out an action. They are directly related to a failure of memory but are generally due to forgetfulness rather than knowledge deficiencies. Mode errors are a different component of memory failure. They come about when a particular action that is highly appropriate in one mode of operation is performed in a different and inappropriate mode. This occurs because the operator has failed to correctly remember the context. Mode errors usually come about because of a high workload and automated performance.

The Zeebrugge-Harrisburg Syndrome

Pheasant (1988) provides an interesting perspective on error. He argues that a deficiency in the design of a man-made machine interface makes the operator's task more difficult with an increased likelihood of more errors of omission and commission, incorrect designs, etc. The consequence of all of these errors may be catastrophic. In the case of the Three Mile Island incident, the display identified did not provide the operator with the information they required in a comprehensive manner.

Pheasant postulates that the likelihood of error increases significantly when the operator is under stress from unusually high pressure, when capacity is reduced, due to fatigue or other factors. He cites the example of the Chernobyl accident, which occurred at around 1.00 a.m. He argues that the time of day is a significant contributory factor, in that it reduces an individual's ability to cope with abnormal circumstances as they arise. **Figure 8.2** outlines the main components of Zeebrugge-Harrisburg Syndrome.

Figure 8.2: The Zeebrugge-Harrisburg Syndrome

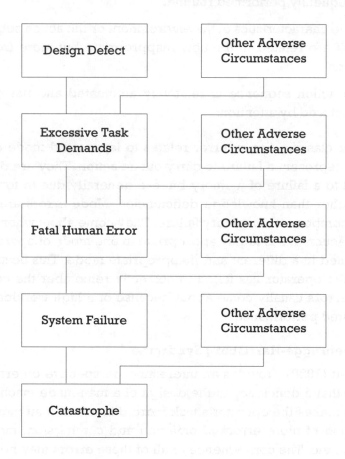

Dealing with Human Error

Error is inevitable, but there are a number of strategies that an organisation can usefully adopt in an effort to reduce or eliminate error. Five specific strategies are identifiable.

Task Design

Task design can be used to minimise operator requirements to perform tasks that impose heavy working memory load under conditions of stress. Sanders and McCormick (1993) suggest that there are three generic design approaches for dealing with human error:

- **Exclusion** designs that make it impossible to commit the error.
- **Prevention** designs that make it difficult but not impossible.
- **Fail-safe** designs that reduce the consequences of errors without necessarily reducing the likelihood of errors.

Selection

Careful selection of human resources with the capabilities and skills required to perform a job should result in fewer errors being made. This requires a selection strategy capable of identifying perceptual, intellectual and motor skills. However, it is not always possible to find such measuring instruments.

Training

Systematic job training can reduce errors. Lack of job knowledge is an important source of mistakes, although Reason (1990) has argued that error-free training should not be required. If operators are not practised at correcting errors that occur during training, they will not know how to deal with errors that are likely to occur in the work situation.

Assists and Rules

Assists and rules represent design solutions to error-likely situations. These may include memory aids or procedures. If rules are properly explained, logical and systematically enforced, they can reduce errors. However, Reason (1990) argues that rules may unexpectedly prohibit necessary behaviour in times of crisis, in a way that the person who designed the rules had not anticipated.

Error-Tolerant Systems

Rowe and Morris (1986) advocate the design of error-tolerant systems. Such a design attempts to avoid irreversible actions. For example, a command on a computer might not irreversibly delete the file but simply remove it and hold it somewhere else for a period of time.

ACCIDENTS AT WORK

One of the objectives of the human factors approach is to reduce accidents and make employees more safety conscious in their behaviour. This section will consider the term accident and outline a number of accident theories.

What is an Accident?

There is considerable disagreement about what constitutes and accident, although Suchman (1961) produced three indicators of an accident:

- A low degree of expectedness.

- A low degree of availability.

- A low degree of intention.

Meister (1987) defines an accident as:

> … an unanticipated event which damages the system and/or the individual or affects the accomplishment of the system mission or the individual's task.

Another definition by Stranks (1991) defines accident as follows:

> An accident is an unplanned and uncontrolled event in which the action or reaction of an object, substance, person, or radiation results in personal injury or the probability thereof.

Strank's definition applies to circumstances or conditions that create excess production cost, low volume, delay and spoilage as well as to events causing personal injury; also the causes and remedies for both are alike.

It should be noted that many researchers and practitioners prefer to use the term "incident" rather than "accident". The reason for this is that it eliminates the idea of "or the probability thereof", which is an important component of many definitions. An incident is defined as "an undesired event that could (or does) downgrade the efficiency of the business operation". The idea behind the definition of an incident is to include those things that occur that give organisations problems and cost them in terms of time, effort, money, etc., but do not result in actual injury to a person.

Figure 8.3 presents the International Labour Organisation Classification of Industrial Accidents.

Figure 8.3: Classification of Industrial Accidents (ILO)

Classification of industrial accidents according to type of accident

- Falls by individuals.
- Struck by falling objects.
- Stepping on, striking against or struck by objects excluding falling objects.
- Caught in or between objects.
- Over-exertion of strenuous movements.
- Exposure to or contact with extreme temperatures.
- Exposure to or contact with electric current.
- Exposure to or contact with harmful substances or radiations.
- Other types of accident, not elsewhere classified, including accidents not classified for lack of sufficient data.

Classification of industrial accidents according to agency

- Machines:
    - ◊ Prime movers, except electric motors.
    - ◊ Transmission machinery.
    - ◊ Metalworking machines.
    - ◊ Wood and assimilated machines.
    - ◊ Agricultural machines.
    - ◊ Mining machinery.
    - ◊ Other machines, not elsewhere classified.
- Means of transport and lifting equipment:
    - ◊ Lifting machines and appliances.
    - ◊ Means of rail transport.
    - ◊ Other wheeled means of transport, excluding rail transport.

◊ Means of air transport.

◊ Means of water transport.

◊ Other means of transport.

- Other Equipment:

    ◊ Pressure vessels.

    ◊ Furnaces, ovens, kilns.

    ◊ Refrigerating plants.

    ◊ Electrical installations, including electric motors, but excluding electric hand tools.

    ◊ Electric hand tools.

    ◊ Tools, implements and appliances, except electric hand tools.

    ◊ Ladders, mobile ramps.

    ◊ Scaffolding.

    ◊ Other equipment, not elsewhere classified.

- Materials, substances and radiations:

    ◊ Explosives.

    ◊ Dusts, gases, liquids and chemicals, excluding explosives.

    ◊ Flying fragments.

    ◊ Radiations.

    ◊ Other materials and substances, not elsewhere classified.

- Working environment:

    ◊ Outdoor.

    ◊ Indoor.

    ◊ Underground.

- Other agencies, not elsewhere classified:

    ◊ Animals.

    ◊ Other agencies, not elsewhere classified.

- Agencies not classified for lack of sufficient data.

Classification of industrial accidents according to the nature of the injury

- Fractures.

- Dislocations:
  ◊ Sprains and strains.
- Concussions and other internal injuries.
- Amputations and inoculations.
- Other wounds.
- Superficial injuries.
- Contusions and crushings.
- Burns.
- Acute poisonings.
- Effects of weather, exposure and related conditions.
- Asphyxia.
- Effects of electric currents.
- Effects of radiations.
- Multiple injuries of different nature.
- Other and unspecified injuries.

Classification of industrial accidents according to the bodily location of the injury

- Head.
- Neck.
- Trunk.
- Upper limb.
- Lower limb.
- Multiple locations.
- General injuries.
- Unspecified location of injury.

The ILO multiple classification system takes into account that an accident is rarely due to a single factor, but is generally the result of a concurrence of factors. The "type of accident" classification identifies the event that directly resulted in the injury; it indicates how the object, or substance, causing the injury entered into contact with the injured person and it is often regarded as the key to analysis of the problems. The classification according to agency may be used for classifying either the agency related to the injury or the agency related to the accident. Obviously, more instructive information can be obtained if industrial accidents are classified according to both concepts; however, for accident prevention purposes, the classification according to the agency causing the accident is more important. The classifications according to the nature and bodily location of the injury are designed to provide the necessary information for a detailed analysis.

In 1969, a comprehensive analysis of occupational accidents was undertaken by a study group chaired by Frank E. Bird, Jr., then Director of Engineering Services for the Insurance Company of North America. The analysis was made from 1,753,498 accidents reported by 297 co-operating organisations. These groups represented 21 different types of occupational establishments employing 1,750,000 employees who worked more than 3 billion manhours during the exposure period analysed.

The study revealed that, for every serious or disabling injury (as defined by the American National Standards Institute, 1967), there were 9.8 minor injuries and 30.2 property damage accidents reported. Part of the study involved 4,000 hours of worker interviews by trained supervisors about the occurrence of incidents that, under slightly different circumstances, could have resulted in injury or property damage. Results from this segment of the project added the 60 no-loss incidents to the ratio. Thus, the data gathered from the study resulted in what has become widely known as the 1-10-30-300 ratio (**Figure 8.4**).

Figure 8.4: The 1–10–30–300 Ratio

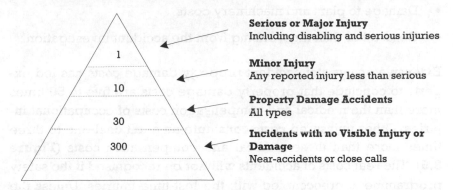

Costs of an Accident

There is a tendency to underestimate the costs of accidents or to hide them. Powell et al. (1971) considered the costs of over 2,000 accidents that occurred in four shop-floor settings. They calculated that the human resources loss through accidents was equivalent to the permanent absence of four people. Beacham (1976) divides accidents into three types:

• Lost-time accidents because of hospitalisation

• Non-lost-time accidents: they cause no loss to people but facilities, equipment and materials may be damaged

• Damage accidents: no injury is caused to humans but physical loss may be incurred.

Beacham also suggests that these three types of accident occur in the ratio of approximately 1:10:30:300. The costs of such accidents can be direct or indirect and include some or all of the following dimensions:

• Safety administration costs: accident investigation time

• Medical centre costs: medical time to treat injuries

• Welfare repayments: the amount of money paid to the injured employee while off work

• Cost of time of other employees: the time taken by the supervisor or other employees to assist the injured person

- Replacement labour costs

- Damage to plant and machinery costs

- Costs other than time, arising from the accident investigation.

Extensive analysis of accident property damage costs has led experts to conclude that property damage costs are five to 50 times more than the medical and compensation costs of occupational injuries. Other uninsured costs constitute an additional one to three times more than these medical and compensation costs (**Figure 8.5**). The real costs of accidents will not be recognised if the safety programme is preoccupied with the lost-time injuries. Unless the real costs of accidents are identified, actions to control them will not be implemented. When managers have inadequate information about their true costs and causes in this area, they are without any real controls for one of the most expensive parts of their operations.

Figure 8.5: The Accident Cost Iceberg

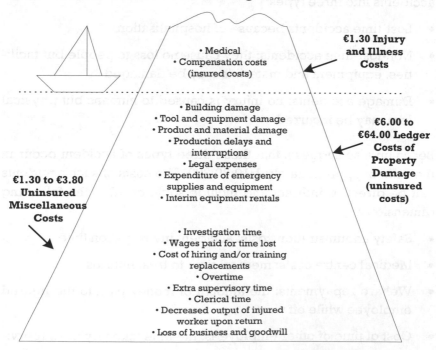

€1.30 Injury and Illness Costs

- Medical
- Compensation costs (insured costs)

€6.00 to €64.00 Ledger Costs of Property Damage (uninsured costs)

- Building damage
- Tool and equipment damage
- Product and material damage
- Production delays and interruptions
- Legal expenses
- Expenditure of emergency supplies and equipment
- Interim equipment rentals

€1.30 to €3.80 Uninsured Miscellaneous Costs

- Investigation time
- Wages paid for time lost
- Cost of hiring and/or training replacements
- Overtime
- Extra supervisory time
- Clerical time
- Decreased output of injured worker upon return
- Loss of business and goodwill

THEORIES OF ACCIDENT CAUSATION

A wide array of accident theories exists. It is possible to group the theories into a number of categories: domino or management theories, behavioural theories, physiological theories, job-role versus worker-capability theories and psycho-social theories. These will now be considered in some detail.

Domino or Management Theories

Heinrich's Axioms of Safety and Domino Theory

Heinrich (1930) presented a set of theories that he called the axioms of industrial safety. These axioms are presented in **Figure 8.6** and were the first set of principles ever laid down on industrial safety. The axioms have held up well and deal with some of the more important issues in managing industrial safety today. These issues can be summarised as follows:

- The theory of accident causation.

- The interaction of employee and machines.

- The relationship of frequency to severity of accidents.

- The underlying reasons for unsafe acts.

- The relationship of accident control to other organisational functions.

- The responsibilities for safety management within the organisation.

- A focus on the costs of accidents.

Heinrich argued that a preventable accident is one of the five factors in a sequence of results in an injury. The injury is caused by the accident and the accident is a result of something that immediately precedes it. (See **Figure 8.7**)

Figure 8.6: Axioms of Industrial Safety

1. The occurrence of an injury invariably results from a completed sequence of factors — the last one of these being the accident itself. The accident in turn is invariably caused or permitted directly by the unsafe act of the person and/or a mechanical or physical hazard.

2. The unsafe acts of persons are responsible for a majority of accidents.

3. The person who suffers a disabling injury caused by an unsafe act, in the average case, has had over 300 narrow escapes from serious injury as a result of committing the very same unsafe act. Likewise, persons are exposed to mechanical hazards hundreds of times before they suffer injury.

4. The severity of an injury is largely fortuitous — the occurrence of the accident that results in injury is largely preventable.

5. The four basic motives or reasons for the occurrence of unsafe acts provide a guide to the selection of appropriate corrective measures.

6. Four basic methods are available for preventing accidents — engineering revision, persuasion and appeal, personnel adjustment and discipline.

7. Methods of most value in accident prevention are analogous with the methods required for the control of the quality, cost, and quantity of production.

8. Management has the best opportunity and ability to initiate the work of prevention; therefore it should assume the responsibility.

9. The supervisor or foreman is the key man in industrial accident prevention. His application of the art of supervision to the control of worker performance is the factor of greatest influence in successful accident prevention. It can be expressed and taught as a simple four-step formula.

10. The humanitarian incentive for preventing accidental injury is supplemented by two powerful economic factors: (a) the safe organisation is efficient, productive, and the unsafe organisation is inefficient; (b) the direct employer cost of industrial injuries for compensation claims and for medical treatment is but one-fifth of the total cost which the employer must pay.

Figure 8.7: The Five Factors of the Accident Sequence

•	••	•••	••••	•••••
Social	Fault of	Unsafe act	Accident	Injury
Environment	Person	Mechanical or		
Ancestry		physical hazard		
•	••	•••	••••	•••••

One event is dependent on another and one follows because of another, contributing a sequence (a row of dominoes). If the sequence is interrupted by eliminating one domino, an injury cannot occur.

Figure 8.8: An Updated Accident Sequence

•••	•	•••	••	•
Lack of	Basic	Immediate	Accident	Injury
Control	Causes	Cause	Contact	Damage
Management	Origins	Symptom		Loss
•			•	••

Bird's Updated Domino Theory

Bird (1966) was first to update the domino sequence. He identified the five key loss control factors in **Figure 8.8**:

- **Lack of Control**: Bird used the term "control" to refer to the general regulation, curbing, restraint or holding back of losses. Loss control involves identification of work activities, establishment of standards for management performance in each activity, measuring performance and taking corrective action.

- **Basic Cause — Origins**: The absence of an effective loss-control system will permit the existence of personal and job-related factors, which are the basic or underlying causes of accidents.

- **Immediate Causes — Symptoms**: The most important factors to attack in the accident/incident sequence unsafe acts or conditions such as inadequate guards, poor housekeeping, operating without authority, bypassing safety devices.

- **Accident-Contact**: The accident is the undesired event that results in physical harm, injury or property damage.

- **Injury-Damage-Loss**: Where "injury" is used to broadly describe loss of many types, Bird uses: injury, damage and loss.

Adams's Updated Domino Sequence

Adams (1976) updated Bird's domino sequence. In Adams's sequence, the fourth and fifth dominoes remain essentially the same and he recognises Bird's refinements. The first three dominoes have been relabelled. Adams draws attention to the nature of unsafe acts and unsafe conditions within the organisation. Tactical errors in employee behaviour and work conditions are viewed as arising from operational errors made by managers and supervisors. These include administrative mistakes or omissions and are strategic in nature in that they affect the total organisation. All of these operational errors derive from the management structure. **Figure** 8.9 presents Adams's theory.

Figure 8.9: Adams' Domino Theory

•	• •		• • •	• • • •	• • • • •
Management Structure	Operational Errors		Tactical Errors	Accident Incident	Injury or Damage
•	Manager Behaviour	Supervisor Behaviour		•	• •

Weaver's Domino Theory

Weaver (1972) provides another update of the domino theory. He postulates that operational errors, which result in accidents and injuries, also result in an array of other unplanned and undesired results. These results are merely symptoms. In order to undertake corrective action:

• It is necessary to locate and define operational errors. All accidents and incidents are symptoms of operational errors.

• Behind any proximate cause, attributed to an incident, lie management practices.

• The organisation must ask why unsafe acts or conditions were permitted and whether supervisors had the safety knowledge to prevent the accident occurring.

Figure 8.10 presents Weaver's updated dominoes.

Figure 8.10: Weaver's Domino Theory

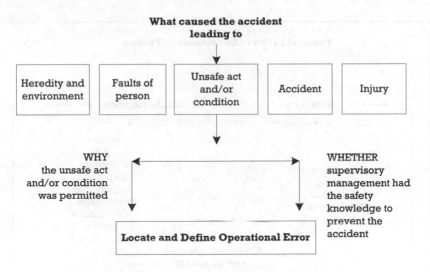

Zabetakis's Theory of Causation

Zabetakis (1977) provides a further update of domino theory of accident causation. While similar to others, it introduces the concept of the direct cause being an unplanned release of energy and/or hazardous material. The notion that accidents are caused by an unplanned transfer or release of energy is generally popular as an explanation. Zabetakis argues that many accidents are caused by an unwanted or unplanned release of mechanical, electrical, chemical, thermal, etc. energy or of hazardous material. These releases are in turn caused by unsafe acts and unsafe conditions. He likewise argues that the basic causes of accidents are traceable to poor management policies and decisions and to personal factors. **Figure 8.11** presents Zabetakis's theory of causation.

Figure 8.11: Zabetakis' Theory of Causation

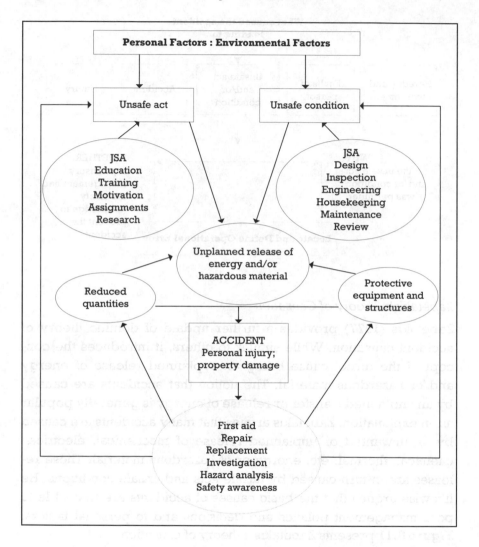

Personal Factors : Environmental Factors

Unsafe act

Unsafe condition

JSA
Education
Training
Motivation
Assignments
Research

JSA
Design
Inspection
Engineering
Housekeeping
Maintenance
Review

Unplanned release of
energy and/or
hazardous material

Reduced
quantities

Protective
equipment and
structures

ACCIDENT
Personal injury;
property damage

First aid
Repair
Replacement
Investigation
Hazard analysis
Safety awareness

The Stair Step Model

Douglas (1976) proposes an alternative model of accident causation that he calls the Stair Step Cause and Effect Sequence. This follows a logical series of steps: all organisational activities start with a stated purpose. Specific resources are required to accomplish this objective. There is an upper and lower limit in terms of resource use. The performance standards are set and these again will have lower and upper limits. Setting this standard at too low a limit may well result in negative outcomes such as physical or human loss.

Multiple Causation Theory

Multiple causation theory developed from criticisms of domino theories. The theory argues that, behind each accident, there are many contributing factors, causes and sub-causes. These combine in a random fashion to produce accidents. Thus those investigating accidents should be able to identify more than one unsafe act or condition that contributed to the accident. The theory criticises "domino thinking" for looking only at a symptomatic level, concentrating essentially on one proximate cause — an unsafe act or condition. Removal of the proximate cause prevents that particular accident from recurring, but does not diminish the possibility of similar accidents occurring, because the set of sub-causes that led up to the initial accident remain largely unchanged.

Multiple causation theory advocates the identification of as many proximate causes as possible. Subsequently, sub-causes for each proximate cause should be determined, and fault tree analysis carried out. These analyses should point to "root causes" that play a vital role in the accident process. The theory goes on to suggest that root causes often relate to deficiencies in the management system.

One such model is proposed by Sanders and Shaw (1988), which they call a contributing factor in accident causation (CFAC) model. This model puts an emphasis on management and sociopsychological factors and gives recognition to the human-machine environment system.

There is a strong body of research to support a view that many factors lead to accidents within a given organisation. Hayashi (1985) analysed 284 chemical industry accidents and identified a wide range of underlying causes. These are presented in **Table 8.1**.

Hayashi, however, made the mistake of attributing a single cause to each incident investigated and it is arguable that he fails to capture the complexity of the mechanisms involved. Sanders and Shaw (1988), on the other hand, found that in all of the mining accidents they investigated more than one factor contributed to the accident.

Table 8.1: *Underlying Causes of Accidents*

Inadequate standard operational procedure	19%
Error in recognition or confirmation	15%
Error in judgement	14%
Poor inspection	12%
Inadequate directives	10%
Inadequate communication of operational information	10%
Operational error	6%
Unskilled operation	6%
Imperfect maintenance	2%
Other	6%

Behavioural Models

Behavioural theories are popular explanations of accidents and demonstrate considerable variation in terms of explanation.

Accident Proneness or Unequal Liability Theory

This theory, discussed earlier, suggests that certain individuals possess relatively permanent idiosyncrasies, which increase their likelihood of having an accident. The reasoning behind this follows from an examination of accident statistics, revealing that many people have no accidents at all, while a very small percentage of people have multiple accidents. The proposed interpretation of these statistics is that employees with multiple accidents must have a specific set of characteristics that increases their accident potential.

However, there are three main arguments against accident-proneness as an explanation of accidents. Firstly, the unusually small percentage of those who are supposedly accident-prone can be explained by the fact that accident data could be expected to follow a Poisson distribution. According to a Poisson distribution, the vast majority of individuals would not have an accident, whereas a few would be involved in more than one. Secondly, despite numerous studies, no definite set of individual characteristics has been discovered which is predictive of accidents across different activities and time. Finally, studies of accident data appear to show that "accident-proneness" is a temporary phenomenon.

Seemingly, those who experience multiple accidents tend to have them concentrated in a relatively short time period and subsequently do not continue to have accidents. Refer to **Chapter 7** for more of the debate on this issue.

Life Change Unit Theory

The notion that "accident-proneness" could be temporary has led to a search for reasons why this might be so. The resulting theory suggests that certain life events put a strain on individuals, making them more susceptible to having an accident. Tables have been developed to allocate mean values or Life Change Units (LCUs) to certain life events, and the greater the total LCUs that individuals have at any one time, the more likely they are to be involved in an accident. Typical examples of these events are the death of a spouse, a divorce (high LCU ranking) or a change in eating habits, a holiday (low LCU ranking).

Risk Homeostasis

This theory advocated by Wilde (1982) proposes that people react to changing circumstances by modifying their behaviour in such a fashion that the level of risk to which they are exposed remain constant. People in effect have an internalised target level of risk that they seek to maintain. They do this by either risk-seeking or risk-avoidance activities, whichever the situation demands. This theory predicts that most safety initiatives taken by organisations are likely to fail.

There is some support for the theory and the role of behavioural compensation. Rummer et al. (1976) report that drivers who were provided with studded tyres to give them extra grip in icy conditions responded by driving faster. Perrow (1984) supports this tendency. His study involved the use of navigational equipment to increase safety levels. Instead, it was used to increase speed. Pheasant (1991) argues that, while the notion of an internalised target level of risk may explain many risk-seeking behaviours, he believes that other psychological explanations could equally apply. He suggests that employees are often prepared to accept risk in the interest of expediency. Therefore, many systems will be operated at the limits of their safety.

The Goals-Freedom-Alertness Theory

Developed by Kerr (1957), this theory suggests that increased alertness among individuals plays an important role in preventing accidents. Giving individuals the freedom to choose their own attainable goals, enriches their psychological climate, improves their work quality through increased awareness, and thereby reduces their liability to accident. Sanders et al. (1970) built on this theory with a Motivation-Reward-Satisfaction Model that includes other factors that might motivate individuals to superior work quality and fewer accidents. Accidents are viewed as low-quality work performance issues. They report that when decisions were decentralised in a coal-mine, when management was more flexible and innovative in trying out new procedures, and where morale was high, disabling injuries decreased.

Adjustment to Stress Theory (Arousal–Alertness Theory)

Kerr's (1957) adjustment to stress theory argues that negative stress increases an employee's liability to have an accident. Sources of negative stress may be internal or external to individuals, but are temporary in nature. Typical examples of these sources are temperature or lighting (external) and alcohol consumption and disease (internal). This theory suggests that proper consideration of human factors, aimed at eliminating negative stress, reduces accident potential.

The adjustment to stress theory suggests that accident rates will be higher in situations where the level of stress, physiological and psychological, exceeds the capacity of the employee to deal with it. There is, however, limited empirical support for a strong relationship between accidents and stressors. The relationship between a stressed worker's predisposition and accidents has not received comprehensive investigation. Verhaegen et al. (1976) quote a study that demonstrates that employees who had been responsible for an accident differed by their heavier psychological burden. This was defined in terms of worries about family, money, etc. Whitlock et al. (1977) demonstrate that accidentally injured patients had experienced more changes in their lives over the previous six months. Levenson et al. (1980) also studied patients and found that the patient group had experienced 25 per cent more life changes and 77 per cent more life stresses than a comparable control group. A related theory is called the arousal-alertness theory. This postulates that accidents are more likely to happen when arousal is too low or too high.

The Ferrell Model

This theory, like the domino theories, claims that accidents are the result of a causal chain. It suggests that the chain is initiated by human error. It builds on the adjustments to stress theory to identify situations where human error occurs. Three situations are identified as:

- **Overload** — where there is a mismatch of human capacity to the size of the workload.

- **Incorrect response** — where the employee has a basic incompatibility with the task, e.g. physical, educational, etc.

- **Improper activity** — where the employee deliberately takes a risk, or does so because of a lack of awareness of the risk.

Comparing individuals' sources of load with their innate capabilities highlights potential accident situations.

The Petersen Accident-Incident Causation Model

This model adds two additional concepts to the Ferrell model. Firstly, systems failure is recognised as an accident cause in addition to human error. Systems failure includes elements such as policy, responsibility, hazard recognition, selection, training, etc. Secondly, the model suggests that behind human error, there is a decision to err. This is not just a deliberate risk-taking or lack of risk awareness, but also includes unconscious decisions taken by individuals who have a subconscious desire to be injured.

Learning Theories

Learning theories put an emphasis on the individual's skills. A basic element of skill learning relates to reinforcement through feedback. Skilled performance is composed of a collection of skilled responses, but it is possible to incorporate inappropriate or dangerous behaviour into the employee's repertoire. Oborne

(1995) argues that safe behaviour is often negatively reinforcing in that it takes more time, it may involve the use of safe clothing and may be the subject of adverse comment from other employees. Unsafe behaviour is quicker, more comfortable and more socially acceptable. Winsemius (1965) demonstrates that experienced operators had learned to use unsafe behaviour patterns. This behaviour they viewed as easier and less time consuming and so it was positively reinforced. Safe behaviour led to fatigue, cost time and had no obvious rewards. This suggests that training alone is unlikely to reduce unsafe behaviour, unless there are sufficiently negative reinforcing aspects incorporated into the training programme. Unsafe behaviour is likely to become positively reinforced soon after training has ceased.

Memory Lapses/Absent-Mindedness

Memory lapses represent another behavioural explanation. Employees have limited capacity to retain information and forgetting important actions can cause accidents. The source of forgetting can relate to repression, the decay of memory over time, errors in storing or selecting material to be remembered. Memory breakdown is less likely to lead to accidents than memory recall. This happens, for example, when an operator carries out a sequence without awareness. Reason (1979) has studied absent-mindedness and suggests that it occurs in four ways: storage errors in which the original memory trace was incorrectly stored; lost errors in which an operator incorrectly checks the progress and outcomes of particular actions; discrimination errors in which they incorrectly identify the initial stimulus, and selection errors where they make an incorrect response. Reason concluded that absent-minded errors are more likely a problem for the skilled rather than the unskilled operator.

Withdrawal Behaviour

Hill and Trist (1953) suggest that employees may be motivated to have an accident so that they can take time off work. Their empirical research indicated that employees who were involved in accidents had a larger number of accidents than those who were free of accidents. Powell et al. (1971) show a relationship between accidents and absences for both men and women. However, the general conclusion is that there is limited evidence to support the proposition that employees consciously or unconsciously have an accident in order to avoid work.

Physiological Theories of Accident Causation

In general, physiological explanations of accidents suggest that accident causation is the result of the worker's body being unable to cope with the requirements of the task. Two particular dimensions of this category of theory are emphasised: physiological rhythms and the impact of drugs including alcohol.

Physiological Rhythms

We will consider this issue in more detail when we discuss shift work, but it is generally recognised that daily variations in human performance and efficiency occur. Folkard and Monk (1979), for example, demonstrate that the amount of information that can be remembered is significantly influenced by the time of day of presentation. The relationship between body, rhythms and accidents has received limited investigation. Colquhoun (1975) demonstrates a circadian variation in absent-mindedness and reaction time that suggests that the potential for accidents also varies with such rhythms. Folkard et al. (1978) demonstrate that the frequency of minor accidents varies during the day.

An area of major controversy relates to the existence of biological rhythms. Biorhythm theory suggests that there are cycles of 23, 28 and 33 days in duration, which govern physical, emotional and intellectual performance respectively. Each cycle has a positive and negative dimension. This theory postulates that accidents are more likely to occur on critical days, i.e. days when more than one cycle is in a critical phase or days when one cycle is in a critical phase and the others are in a negative phase (Wolcott et al., 1977). Khalil and Kurucz (1977) lend support to the view that there is no statistically significant correlation between the occurrence of accidents and biorhythms.

Alcohol and Drugs

There is a general finding that alcohol has a deleterious effect on performance, specifically because of its impact on vision, perceptual and motor functions, reasoning and memory. Only a small number of studies have examined the relationship between alcohol and accidents. Trice and Roman (1972) demonstrate that deviant drinkers have more accidents because of unsteadiness of hand, poor timing and motor responses and their reduced sense of danger. Brenner (1977) concludes that alcoholics are seven times more likely to become victims of fatal accidents than non-alcoholic employees. In general, it is difficult to draw a direct relationship between accidents and alcohol or drugs use because many other variables are involved.

Epidemiological Models/Systems Models

Epidemiology is the study of diseases, examining interactions between host, agent and environment. This approach is often applied to studying accident causation, where accidents are studied as diseases. In this context, the host is the accident victim, whose characteristics include age, gender, training, etc. The agent is the hazard that gives rise to the accident, and can be viewed in terms of an unplanned energy exchange. The environment includes characteristics such as the physical, biological, social and psychological settings of the accident.

Systems models study the inputs, interactions and outputs of the accident phenomenon. They are similar to epidemiological models in that they study the interactions of elements involved in the accident process, in an attempt to understand the output.

Decision Models

The Surrey Model

This model views the accident process as an individual progressing through three separate situations. The first situation is a secure one, the second is a dangerous one and the third is one where injury or damage occurs. The first and second situations are linked by a danger build-up, and the second and third situations are linked by a danger release.

Figure 8.12: The Surrey Model

Individuals will progress through the situation as a result of their behaviour. During both danger build-up and danger release, they are constantly being exposed to questions. If they answer them negatively, then the danger will grow to become a hazard — an imminent danger. If the answers are continually positive, then the danger will not grow, and the injury will be avoided. **Figure 8.13** presents the Surrey Decision Model.

Figure 8.13(a): The Surrey Decision Model — Cycle One

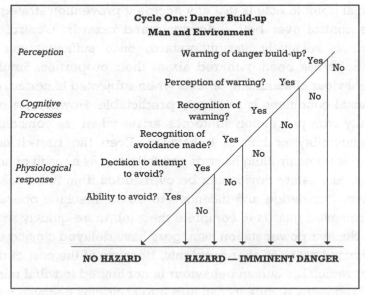

Figure 8.13(b): The Surrey Decision Model — Cycle Two

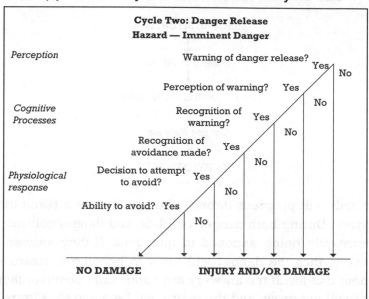

MOTIVATING EMPLOYEES TO BEHAVE SAFELY

A crucial point to note is that any accident prevention strategy requires control over both individuals and hazards. Control over
hazards is relatively straightforward, once sufficient scientific
knowledge has been gathered about their properties. Similarly,
the behaviour of inanimate objects when subjected to certain environmental conditions is relatively predictable. However, a major
difficulty with prevention strategies arises when we consider the
unpredictability of human behaviour. Even the best-designed
strategies for controlling hazards can fall apart as a result of human
actions. Any safety device can be overridden if an individual has
sufficient knowledge and incentive to do so. Machine operatives
have removed guards to complete their job more quickly without
them. Nuclear power station managers have delayed closing down
over-heated reactors after accidents, because of the cost of doing
so. Unpredictable human behaviour is not limited to wilful misconduct. Frequently, incidents can turn into accidents because people
panic, or simply because people do not have the skills, knowledge
or equipment to react appropriately.

Controlling human behaviour is of paramount importance in accident prevention. This is reflected in the emphasis placed on it in most accident causation models. Heinrich's second axiom is that the unsafe acts of persons are responsible for the majority of accidents. In fact, it can be argued that all accidents result from unsafe acts, if we define an unsafe act as one that permits a contact between a hazard and a body. However, the more common interpretation of an unsafe act is one whereby an individual ignores accident prevention measures and thus greatly increases the possibility of a contact. It follows, then, that organisations that have control over their employees are in a better position to avoid unsafe acts.

Although management cannot exercise complete control over any individual, behavioural theories suggest that management can exert some influence over employee behaviour. Marsh et al. (1995) suggest that there are three elements to behaving safely: the equipment to operate safely; the knowledge of how to operate safely; and the motivation to operate safely.

To ensure that employees have the right environment to operate safely, management must not only design machinery to control hazards, they must also explore contingencies to provide safety equipment appropriate to controlling hazards. A typical example of this is the need to provide appropriate fire-fighting equipment.

Knowledge

The knowledge of how to operate safely comes from a number of sources. Formal organisational training programmes can impart important facts about accident prevention, and employees often pick up knowledge from workplace experience. Alternatively, employees may have gathered safety knowledge from previous experiences, such as earlier jobs or education. Management can ensure that employees have the appropriate knowledge by including safety considerations in selection, induction, training and development procedures.

A common accident prevention technique used in conjunction with safety training is that of job safety analysis (JSA). Basically, job safety analysis involves breaking down a particular job into its component parts to identify the safest way of completing the tasks. Job safety instructions can then be developed to provide employees with the knowledge of how to operate safely. Ideally these should be merged into wider safety measures developed for the whole organisation.

Motivation

Motivating employees to act safely is a difficult element for management to control, and thus is considered the key to successful accident prevention. It is the aim of many behavioural approaches, which attempt to reinforce correct behaviours. Such approaches include employee incentives, disciplinary action, propaganda, goal setting and feedback.

Typically, propaganda in the form of posters and other informational material is used in an attempt to instil into individuals attitudes that increase their propensity to act safely. However, these are often met with inconsistent success, particularly if they involve error, are generalistic, or negative (Sell, 1977).

Marsh et al. (1995) suggest that, although incentives are sometimes useful safety motivators, they can be expensive, and only effective in the short term as they do not always result in the long-term adoption of safety attitudes. Furthermore, Makin (1994) points out that incentives often result in the under-reporting of accidents or near-misses. He also suggests that reward systems sometimes discourage precisely the behaviour they are trying to encourage. Consider the following example of conflicting incentives.

An organisation introduces an incentive of €50 to a machine operator, if no machinery accident occurs over a 12-month period. It also introduces a €100 productivity bonus for the same period, if the machine operator increased productivity by five per cent. As the operator can achieve the five per cent production increase by removing the machine's safety devices, there is a definite encouragement to do so. A subsequent scenario could be an accident caused by the removal of the safety device, halting production. Under this scenario, the operator's behaviour would have resulted in both an accident and a decline in production, the exact opposite of the intentions of the reward system.

Disciplinary action produces limited positive results. Skinner (1953) found that punishment tends to be less effective than positive reinforcement. Marsh et al. (1995) suggest that this is especially true where punishment is mild, delayed or infrequent. They also point out that managers are often reluctant to hand out punishment because of fear of resentment.

Marsh et al. (1995) cite examples of how goal setting and feedback improve safety behaviour. The findings on feedback suggest that when managers provide clear feedback on performance, it has positive effects on the further performance of employees. Similarly, when specific goals are set which employees agree with, performance tends to improve. This is because goal setting can focus attention on an issue to be tackled, and if the employees accept the goals, they can also act as motivation to behave as desired.

SOME PRINCIPLES OF ACCIDENT PREVENTION

What does Accident Prevention Involve?

A useful starting point to discuss prevention is a return to the discussion on accident causation. Bird (1977) proposed that the word accident could be better termed as a contact. This is because accidents usually involve a body coming into contact with hazardous energy.

The term "body" refers to a physical entity with a desired function. It includes both animate and inanimate objects, such as human individuals or physical structures. Hazardous energy is energy that will interfere with the desired function of the body should they come into contact. All bodies are vulnerable to a specific source and level of energy. Examples of potentially hazardous energy include kinetic, thermal, electrical, chemical and radioactive energy. For the sake of simplicity, we use the term hazard to denote a form of hazardous energy.

To illustrate these points, consider a situation where an individual is violently hammering two pieces of wood together, using a nail held between their fingers. The fingers are a body, as they are a physical entity performing a desired function of holding the nail. The kinetic energy behind the hammer is a hazard as, should contact occur between the two, it will injure the fingers and interfere with their ability to hold the nail.

Bird's observation points to a basic accident prevention principle. Accident prevention involves steps to avoid a contact between a hazard and a body. Therefore, it requires control over both bodies and hazards — the management of individuals, physical structures and energy within the workplace. This emphasis on control or management is reflected in synonyms for accident prevention — terms like "loss control" or "safety management".

Principles of accident prevention are guidelines which aid the development of effective accident prevention programmes which co-ordinate workplace bodies and energy sources to achieve organisational goals without accidents. However, before we discuss accident prevention principles, we must first establish the logic of accident prevention.

Why Prevent Accidents?

Accident prevention is viewed by some organisations as a nuisance activity imposed upon them by legislation. This is reflected in the fact that safety measures in many organisations set out only to achieve the legal minimum standard and to avoid possible fines or closure. However, there are two other compelling reasons for organisations to take accident prevention seriously. Firstly, there is the humanitarian consideration, and responsible employers will attempt to ensure the well-being of their workers to standards above the legal minimum. Secondly, there is an economic reason for preventing accidents. Direct financial losses are usually incurred when accidents happen, and if safety activities are ignored indirect costs can result from a deterioration of worker morale or company image.

As suggested by Heinrich, whom we discussed earlier, well-designed accident prevention programmes best demonstrate the benefits of accident prevention. Reductions in fatalities and occupational injuries, along with increased production, improved worker morale, and lower insurance premiums are commonplace among such organisations and can become a vital source of competitive advantage.

Developing Programmes of Accident Prevention

A comprehensive accident prevention programme avoids contacts between hazards and bodies by exercising control over both. To achieve this, the programme needs to be based around a number of important processes.

Identification of Hazards

If contacts with hazards are to be avoided, then all potential hazards should first be identified. This can be done in a number of different ways:

- Workplace hazard inspections.

- Management — employee communications.

- Hazard elimination.

- Safety audits.

- Accident statistics.

Workplace hazard inspections involve a comparison of all bodies and energy sources in the workplace to give an indication of where hazards may be present. Although most hazards are usually linked to bodies and energy sources directly involved in the production process, it is important not to overlook hazards that may nevertheless be present as a result of other activities in the workplace. **Figure 8.14** provides examples where hazards may be present.

An integral part of workplace hazard inspection is communication between management and employees, to obtain as much knowledge as possible about hazards. Similarly, Hazard Operability Studies (HAZOPS) are brainstorming sessions between workers and management from all areas of the organisation that aim to identify any potential hazard before new technology or new work practices are introduced.

Safety audits by recognised external experts are often also of value. This is not only because the auditors may have greater expertise and experience, thus spotting hazards that may otherwise have been overlooked, but also because it can be of benefit to the organisation's image as a responsible operator. Finally, careful analysis of accident statistics can uncover previously unrecognised hazards.

Figure 8.14: Types of Hazards

Potential hazards directly related to production
• Energy from the use of power sources for machinery such as electricity, gas, etc.   • Energy from plant and machinery.   • Energy from materials used in the production process, e.g. radioactive substances.   • Energy created by the production process, e.g. exothermic reactions.   • Energy from employee activities, such as machine operation and maintenance.
Potential hazards indirectly related to production
• Energy from power sources for maintaining the work environment, e.g. light, heat.   • Energy from unstable building construction, furniture and fittings.   • Energy from employee activities not related to production such as access to and egress from work, smoking, horseplay, etc.

Hazard identification should be an on-going and active search process, using creative thinking to develop hypotheses about where hazards may be present. It is especially important to consider latent hazards — those that are contingent upon other events, such as the hazards posed by flammable substances in a fire. A checklist is a useful tool to systematically carry out inspections, but should not be exclusively relied upon. The dynamics of any work process have the potential to create new hazards, and the compiler of the checklist may have overlooked hazards. Once potential hazards have been identified, some form of objective measurement should be attempted so that a balanced evaluation of control options can be made.

Measurements of Hazards

Measurement in an accident prevention context involves the gathering of facts pertinent to potential hazards. As accident prevention is both an art and a science, this measurement should include both quantitative and qualitative data, to reach a balanced conclusion on the extent of the hazard. Three sets of information should be sought:

• Information about the hazard source, revealing the type and amount of energy involved.

• Information about the likelihood of a contact.

• Evidence of the possible effects of a contact on workplace bodies.

A host of mechanical devices to aid data collection on hazards is available. However, the value of the data gathered from such devices is restricted by the circumstances in which they are used, and does not in itself provide conclusive answers. An element of judgement is necessary to decide which devices and techniques to use, and qualitative observations are often equally useful. This is especially true where latent hazards are concerned, as accurate estimates can only be achieved through correct assumption of the contingencies.

To reveal the probability of a contact, information from the hazard identification process (such as accident statistics, audit data) can be used to build mathematical formulae, using variables such as the frequency of hazard presence, strength of body, etc. Naturally, as with any operational research methods, the accuracy of the answer will depend on the accuracy values assigned, and the assumptions made during the development of the formula. When carefully designed, mathematical models can provide a useful guide to the possibility of a contact. Otherwise, managers must rely on purely subjective assessments about the likelihood of accidents.

Evidence of the possible effects on workplace hazards is usually derived from retrospective studies, experiments and on-going monitoring of the workforce. The effects of hazards on physical structures in the workplace can be relatively well predicted as a result of experiments during the design process, but, unfortunately, effects on human beings cannot be predicted as precisely. This, of course, is due in part to the variances in individual susceptibility, but also results from a lack of knowledge of many biological processes. The difficulty of obtaining accurate data is compounded by the reliance on retrospective studies, as complex ethical issues limit active experimentation. Consequently, there is often an unfortunate time lag between the creation of new technologies and the appearance of adverse biological effects, with workers being exposed to unrecognised hazards for long periods. Careful monitoring of employees can help to detect early signs of a problem.

Figure 8.15 presents the steps of accident prevention.

Figure 8.15: The Steps of Accident Prevention

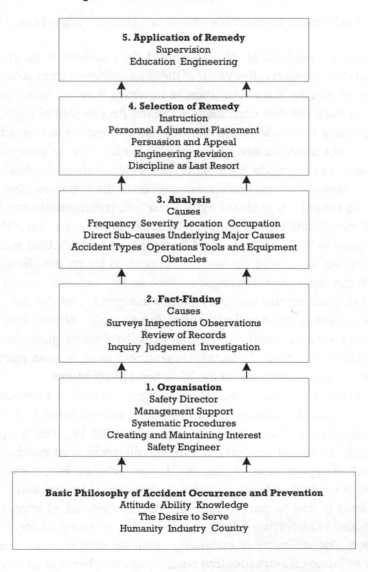

5. Application of Remedy
Supervision
Education Engineering

4. Selection of Remedy
Instruction
Personnel Adjustment Placement
Persuasion and Appeal
Engineering Revision
Discipline as Last Resort

3. Analysis
Causes
Frequency Severity Location Occupation
Direct Sub-causes Underlying Major Causes
Accident Types Operations Tools and Equipment
Obstacles

2. Fact-Finding
Causes
Surveys Inspections Observations
Review of Records
Inquiry Judgement Investigation

1. Organisation
Safety Director
Management Support
Systematic Procedures
Creating and Maintaining Interest
Safety Engineer

Basic Philosophy of Accident Occurrence and Prevention
Attitude Ability Knowledge
The Desire to Serve
Humanity Industry Country

CHAPTER ROUND-UP

- Error is a common occurrence in human performance and of relevance to explaining accidents at work. Human error is generally defined as an inappropriate or undesirable human decision or behaviour that in some way reduces or has the potential to reduce productivity, system and safety performance. Errors may have undesirable effects but an error does not have to cause damage to be called an error. Errors can be categorised as errors of omission, commission, sequence and timing.

- Organisations can implement a number of strategies in order to reduce or eliminate errors. Task design can be used to minimise operator requirements to perform tasks that impose heavy working memory load under conditions of stress. Careful selection of human resources with the capabilities and skills required to perform a job should help reduce errors. Systematic training can also be used to reduce errors, because lack of job knowledge is an important source of mistake. Assists and rules can also be used to help operators follow procedures and sequences.

- There is a degree of disagreement as to what constitutes an accident. It is generally accepted that it is an unplanned or uncontrolled event in which the action or reaction of an object, substance, person or radiation results in personal injury or the probability of injury. Accidents can be classified according to types of accident, agency, the nature of the injury or the bodily location of the injury.

- There exists a host of theories to explain accidents. Domino or management theories emphasise a sequence of events that immediately preceded the accident. Multiple causation theories argue that behind every accident there are many contributory actions, causes and sub-causes. Behavioural theories focus on issues such as accident-proneness, life changes, individual reaction to risk, alertness of individuals, adjustment to stress situations, and learning.

- Physiological theories suggest that accident causation is the result of a worker's body being unable to cope with the requirements of the task. Epidemiological models study accidents as diseases and consider characteristics of the individual such as age, gender, training, etc. Decision models conceptualise accidents as a series of decision phases.

- Accident prevention requires control over both individuals and hazards. Control over hazards is relatively straightforward, but the control of human behaviour is another matter. Human factor approaches suggest that management can exert influence over attitudes and behaviour. It is suggested that in order to get employees to behave safely, there must be the equipment to operate safely, the knowledge of how to operate safely and the motivation to operate safely.

Chapter 9

ERGONOMICS AND HEALTH AND SAFETY

INTRODUCTION

The modern organisation creates many conditions in which employees can become exposed to, or victims of, hazardous events in the workplace. Examples of such hazards include excessive noise levels, the impact of visual display units, visual defects and exposure to chemicals. The factors considered in this chapter generally fall within the subject matter of ergonomics, which is concerned with studying people at work and focusing on how they cope with their work environment. The chapter discusses the scope of ergonomics, visual perception, temperature changes, body posture and movement, seating, back pains and issues related to lifting.

THE NATURE AND SCOPE OF ERGONOMICS

Ergonomics is primarily concerned with the way employees interact with all aspects of their work environment, their equipment and their working situation. It is argued that an understanding of how employees behave at work and how they interact with their job environment at physical and emotional levels makes it is possible to design a work environment that meets the needs of the employee.

Oborne (1995) suggests that ergonomics seeks to maximise safety, efficiency and employee comfort by designing the work environment to the employee's capabilities. Ergonomics is sometimes narrowly referred to as the study of the man–machine interface. This interface is perceived as significant in the design of working layouts, safe systems of work and in setting work rates.

However, for the purposes of this book, a broader view of ergonomics is taken. Ergonomics is defined as referring to the total working system. This system is summarised in **Table 9.1**:

Table 9.1: The Scope of Ergonomics

Human Characteristics	Environmental Factors
• Body dimensions. • Strength. • Physical and mental limitations. • Perceptions. • Learning. • Reaction.	• Temperature. • Humidity. • Light. • Ventilation. • Noise. • Vibration.
Human-Machine Interface	**Outcomes of Work**
• Displays. • Controls. • Communication. • Automation.	• Fatigue. • Work Rate. • Posture. • Stress. • Productivity. • Accidents.

Person-Centred Ergonomics

It is suggested in recent literature that the employee and the work system are not equal partners at work. Therefore a person-centred view of ergonomics argues that it is the employee who controls the system, who operates it, shapes it and evaluates its effectiveness. Oborne et al. (1993) argue that, for the work system to be effective, it should be designed from the perspective of the employee. They reject the man-machine concept as too simplistic for the operation of modern organisations, which require the human resource to be given a central focus.

Eason (1991) suggests that a man-machine perspective does not adequately explain the interaction. He argues that it fails to recognise that interactions take place at many levels and that the totality of the interactions is greater than the sum of the component parts. Furthermore, the man-machine perspective fails to recognise the characteristics of the employee and the attributes they bring to the work system. The person-centred view of ergonomics, in contrast, considers the interaction to be one that is managed and guided by the employee. Employees bring to the system a complex set of characteristics (motives, experiences and expectations) that they use to interact with the system and change it. Such characteristics may have positive or negative implications for the system. Essentially, a person-centred perspective on ergonomics takes as its central tenet the need to accommodate human attributes and design the work system accordingly. A person-centred approach emphasises the need to create a work environment suitable for the effective functioning of the employee.

Oborne et al. (1993) identified four features of the employee, which they advocate fit within a person-centred approach:

- **Purposiveness**: Employees are not passive, they are active or "drivers". They have a specific purpose for their interaction with the work environment and such purposes must be understood when designing work systems.

- **Uncertainty reduction**: Employees aim to reduce uncertainty. They have a desire for control and autonomy. Such control and autonomy is a way of reducing uncertainty about the outcome.

- **Responsibility and trust**: Individuals act with responsibility when interacting with the system. This responsibility is directed towards the achievement of successful outcomes. Zuboff (1988) demonstrates that employees who lack trust in new technology are less likely to make effective use of it. There is, however, evidence to suggest that employees sometimes place too much trust in a work system and fail to interfere when appropriate (Lee and Moray, 1992).

- **Interest and commitment**: Some form of interest drives the employee, as an active agent. Increased interest leads to a reduced likelihood of boredom, errors and accidents. Branton (1983) demonstrates that reduced interest/boredom may lead to increased stress levels. This, in turn, may lead to panic that brings about error and accidents.

The person-centred approach argues that it is important to understand the factors that contribute to the employee's abilities, motives and expectations in order for the work system to be effectively designed. A person-centred approach emphasises that people are the central components within a working system in that they have ambitions and motivations for both the work and the system.

Man versus Machine

There is a considerable degree of debate about how functions should be allocated between the employee and the machine. Chapanis (1960) and Murrell (1971) for example, suggest that human beings are better decision-makers, have greater flexibility, can deal with unexpected events, are able to improvise, have a reservoir of past experience and have the ability to perceive and interpret complex forms. Machines, in contrast, are highly efficient at computing and differentiation, can deal with predictable events reliably and are effective in hazardous environments.

Some commentators, however, disagree with a simple man-machine comparison. A number of problems are highlighted. A general man-machine comparison is misleading because the nature of the system itself determines the effectiveness of its individual components. The situation may impact on the relevant balance of strengths and weaknesses. Second, the issue of which component can do a particular job better may not be a relevant question. Oborne (1995) argues that general comparisons between man and machine give no consideration to trade-offs. He suggests that the relevant question to ask is whether it is better to design a system that, because of size limitations, includes a human operator and fewer machines or more effective to reject the human component. **Table 9.2** does, however, summarise some of the basic comparisons between man and machine.

Table 9.2: A Comparison of Man and Machine in Terms of Capabilities

Advantages	Disadvantages
People	*Machines*
• Adaptable and flexible.	• Relatively inflexible.
• Can detect minute stimuli and assess small changes.	• Can detect if programmed, but not assess.
• Can interpolate and use judgement.	• Can do neither.
• Can synthesise and learn from experience.	• Can do neither.
Machines	*People*
• Can operate in hostile environments.	• Slow capability.
	• Slow response.
• Fast response to emergency signals.	• Can apply large forces coarsely.
• Can apply large forces smoothly.	• Easily distracted: limited short-term memory.
• Information storage: large short-term memory.	• Compute slowly and inaccurately.
• Perform routine repetitive task reliably.	• Suffer relatively soon from fatigue and monotony.
• Compute fast and accurately.	
• Can operate for long periods without maintenance.	

EMPLOYEES' VISUAL CAPABILITIES AND ACCIDENTS

The visual system gives rise to a number of visual capabilities that have important implications for the design of visual displays and for accidents at work. Three capabilities appear to be important: accommodation, vision acuity and contrast sensitivity.

Accommodation refers to the ability of the lens of the eye to focus the light rays on the retina. This allows a person to see details of objects where the accommodation capacity of the eyes is inadequate. It causes a condition called near-sightedness or farsightedness. Near-sighted individuals cannot see distant objects clearly, whereas far-sighted individuals cannot see objectives close up. With age, people tend to become far-sighted. This is caused by changes in the lens and the muscles that control its shape.

Visual acuity is the ability to discriminate fine details and depends largely on the accommodation of the eyes. There are different types:

- *Minimum separable acuity* refers to the smallest feature or the smallest space between the parts of a target that the eye can detect.

- *Smellen acuity* refers to the situation where a person can barely read at 20 feet what a normal (20/20 vision) person can read at 30 feet.

- *Vesmer acuity* refers to the ability to differentiate the lateral displacement, or slight offset of one line from another, that, if not so offset, would form a single continuous line.

- *Minimum perceptible acuity* refers to the ability to detect a spot from its background.

- *Stereoscopic acuity* refers to the ability to differentiate the different images or pictures received by the retinas of the two eyes of a single object that has depth.

Contrast sensitivity refers to a person's ability to discriminate objects or signs. Contrast sensitivity has been found to be a better prediction than standard visual acuity of people's ability to discriminate highway signs (Evans and Ginsburg, 1985) and is also believed to be a good prediction of air-to-ground search performance (Stager and Hameluck, 1980).

A range of factors is believed to influence visual acuity and contrast sensitivity. Six variables appear especially significant:

- **Luminance level**: Acuity and contrast sensitivity increase with increasing levels of light or background lightness and then level off.

- **Contrast**: When the contrast between a visual target and its background is low, the target must be larger for it to be identifiable with greater contrast.

- **Exposure time**: Under high illumination conditions, acuity generally improves with increased exposure.

- **Target motion**: The movement of the target, the observer or both tends to increase visual acuity.

- **Age**: Visual acuity and contrast sensitivity declines with age. Owsley et al. (1983) demonstrate that after age 40, contrast sensitivity declines.

- **Training**: Roscoe and Couchman (1987) report that training can improve acuity and contrast sensitivity significantly.

Visual Defects

A number of issues are of relevance here, specifically colour perception, lighting and glare, visual fatigue and the impact of age on visual performance.

Colour Perception

McKenna (1994) points out that the most common form of deficiency in discriminating between colours is the inability to discriminate between the colours red, green and blue. The colourblind individual sees only white and shades of grey. Oborne (1995) describes such an individual as monochromatic. There is, however, evidence to show that individuals with normal vision may have problems with colour because of certain diseases. Voke (1982) shows that a range of diseases can cause colour vision problems (see **Table 9.3**).

The human eye can likewise experience difficulty accommodating a variety of colours shown simultaneously on a display. This may result in fatigue. The research evidence suggests that this is more common when one colour is distant from another.

Table 9.3: *Diseases that Cause Colour Vision Problems*

Disease	Colour Vision Change
Diabetes mellitus.	Blue defects.
Multiple sclerosis.	Red-yellow defects.
Pernicious anaemia.	Green defects.
Addison's disease.	Blue-yellow defect.
Vitamin A deficiency.	Most colours.
Congenital jaundice.	Blue and green defects.
Malnutrition.	All colours.
Spinal cerebellar ataxia — Friedrich's ataxia.	Red-green defect first, then mostly green defect.
Brain tumour, trauma, concussion.	Red-green or blue-yellow defects.
Vascular accidents (stroke).	Various.
Cerebral cortex disease.	Blue defect.
Cortical lesions.	Blue defect.
Syphilis.	Red-green defect, blue defect.
Alcoholism and cirrhosis of the liver.	Blue defect.

Lighting

Lighting within the workplace has two major health and safety dimensions:

- The deterioration in an individual's visual acuity and consequent performance.

- The increased propensity of the individual to have an accident brought about by failing or incorrect perceptions.

Effective lighting within the workplace facilitates the effective performance of a job. The quality of light flowing from a source is termed the human's flux or light flow, or its more common term "illuminance". The lux is the metric unit of measurement for light. **Table 9.4** outlines average illuminances and minimum required illuminances for different types of work.

Table 9.4: Average Illuminances and Minimum Illuminances for Different Types of Work

	Application	CIE/ISO Range (lux)	Examples	BS 8206 (lux)
General lighting for areas used infrequently or having simple visual demands: 20-200 lux	Public areas with dark surroundings.	20-50	Walkways, cable tunnels.	50
	Areas for occasional access.	50-100	Storage areas, entrance halls.	100
	Rooms not used for continuous work.	100-200		
General lighting for working interiors: 200-2,000 lux	Tasks with limited visual requirements.	200-500	Rough machining, lecture theatres.	300
	Tasks with normal visual requirements.	500-1,000	Medium machining, offices.	500
	Tasks with special visual requirements.	1,000-2,000	Hand engraving, drawing offices.	750
Additional lighting for visually exacting tasks: 2000 – 20,000 lux	Very prolonged exacting visual tasks.	2,000-7,500	Electronic or watch assembly.	1,000
	Exceptionally exacting visual tasks.	5,000-10,000	Micro-electronic assembly.	2,000
	Very special visual tasks.	10,000-20,000	Surgical operations.	3,000

There are a number of qualitative aspects of lighting that are relevant in the context of health and safety in the workplace.

Glare

Glare is defined as the effect of light, which causes discomfort or impaired vision and is experienced when parts of the visual field are excessively bright relative to the background. Stranks (1994a) suggests that three forms of glare manifest themselves in the workplace:

- **Disability** glare, defined as the visually disabling effect caused by bright light directly in the line of sight. The effect on the individual is dazzle. This can have hazardous consequences, if the employee is involved in high-risk processes when driving or working at heights.

- **Discomfort** glare is caused by too much contrast of brightness between an object and its background. It is generally associated with poor lighting design and can cause visual discomfort, eye strain, headaches and fatigue.

- **Reflective** glare is defined as the reflection of bright light sources on shiny surfaces or wet work surfaces such as glass or certain metals. Its effect can be to conceal the detail in or behind the object that is glinting.

Glare has particular relevance in the context of VDUs. Glare can be compounded in this context by the quality of characters displayed on the screen. Laubli et al. (1982) report that where there are significant luminance contrasts between the VDU screen and its surroundings, and where characteristics on display vary in brightness, it can lead to annoyance on the part of the employee and significant irritation and redness in the eyes. In terms of reducing glare in the VDU context, it may be possible to position the screen correctly, put blinds on windows, use screen filters and have matt surfaces surrounding the VDU.

There are a considerable number of suggestions in the ergonomic literature on how to reduce glare. The suggestions made by Pheasant (1987) and Grandjean (1988) are particularly useful. They include the following:

- Ensure that there is uniformity of illumination within the working area. This can be best achieved by using diffuse lighting, reflecting from the walls and ceilings.

- Several low-power sources are generally better than one high-power source, provided that the light source is located in the correct position.

- The contrast ratio between the luminances of adjacent areas close to the centre of the visual field should not exceed 3:1. The task in effect should be brighter than its surround.

- The contrast ratio between the centre of the visual field and its periphery should not exceed 10:1.

- If the illumination on the visual task is set at 100 per cent then the illumination on the walls should be 50-80 per cent and on the ceiling 30-90 per cent. BS 8206 recommends that the reflectance of the walls should be 30-70 per cent, the ceilings at least 60 per cent and the floor 20-30 per cent.

- Light sources should not be placed within 60° of an employee's principal working line of sight, or within 30° of a person's horizontal line of sight when the eyes are in the working position.

- All light sources should be properly shielded.

- Fluorescent tubes should be mounted at right angles to the line of sight. Desks and fluorescent tubes should be at right angles to windows.

- The use of reflective surfaces should be avoided, particularly near the centre of the visual field. Where this is not possible, it is important not to reflect bright images off windows, etc. into the user's eyes.

In the US, there is considerable debate about the use of windowless offices and the design of lighting systems directly under the control of the operator. The general research evidence suggests that employees complain about the lack of daylight, the lack of awareness about the state of the weather and the lack of an external view.

Distribution, Brightness and Diffusion of Light

The distribution of light refers to its spread. It has significant health and safety implications. Poor light distribution may cause shadowed areas, which in turn can cause accidents. The evenness of illumination depends upon the ratio between the height of the luminance above the workspace and the layout of fittings.

Brightness or luminosity refers to a subjective sensation on the part of the employee. This presents measurement difficulties, although researchers have used the concept of brightness ratios. Brightness ratios refer to the ratio of apparent luminosity between a task object and its surroundings. Stranks (1994a) suggests that where there is a task illuminance factor of 1, the reflective values should be ceilings 0.6, walls 0.3 – 0.8, floors 0.2– 0.3.

Diffusion refers to the projection of light in many directions, with no one direction predominating. The directional flow of light can determine the density of shadows, which in turn may contribute to accidents. It is generally accepted that different lighting can limit the amount of glare.

Stroboscopic Effects and Colour Retention

Any light source that operates from an alternating current electricity supply tends to produce oscillations in light output. If it is considered dangerous, its reduction can be achieved by providing a high-frequency supply using high-frequency control equipment with tungsten lamps.

Some employees find fluorescent lighting a source of disturbance and complain that it gives them eyestrain and headaches. It is recommended that invisible flicker may be reduced by using an electronic device called a high-frequency solid state ballast. This device cuts the amplitude of the 100 Hz modulation to about 7 per cent. Wilkins et al. (1988) have researched the effectiveness of this device. They found that the incidences of headaches and eyestrain were reduced by more than half with the modified filter, which almost eliminated the invisible flicker.

Colour retention refers to the appearance of an object under a given light source. Colour retention enables the colour appearance to be correctly perceived.

Visual Fatigue or Eyestrain

Visual fatigue can arise due to either inadequate illumination or glare. The research evidence, likewise, demonstrates that keyboard operators may also experience visual fatigue when reading poor handwriting. The VDU screen may have an image that is unclear and unstable. This can result in a flickering image, which may lead to eyestrain or visual fatigue. Murray-Bruce (1982) points out that the severest form of visual fatigue has four general symptoms:

- Eyes that are sore and dry with itchiness.

- Eyesight that temporarily blurs, making focusing difficult.

- Photophobia, defined as an acute sensitivity to light.

- Headaches that spread to the neck and shoulder.

Visual fatigue can be aggravated by workplace conditions, such as overheating or a smoky and over-dry environment. The impact on employee performance is a general deterioration in the individual's ability to focus and concentrate on a visual task with consequent increases in error and increased accident potential.

The symptoms of eyestrain are primarily due to overuse of the muscles in and around the eye. The ciliary muscles are employed in accommodation and the orbital muscles in convergence, and visual fatigue is therefore considered by many medical practitioners as a special case of local muscular fatigue. Any working activity that imposes an excessive demand upon the muscles of the eye is likely to be a source of eyestrain. Examples include prolonged close work, poor lighting, and inadequate task controls, being confronted with blurred images, glare and reflectors.

Ostberg (1980) demonstrates that demanding VDU work causes an increase in dark focus distance and an increase in the magnitude of accommodation errors. This, he describes as, temporary myopisation. It is generally accepted, however, that the symptoms of eyestrain or visual fatigue are short-lasting and rapidly reversible and cannot cause permanent damage to the eyes.

NOISE AND VIBRATION

The Noise Regulations were discussed in the first section of this book, therefore the focus here is on the psychological and physiological implications of noise in the workplace. Noise is commonly defined as unwanted sound. Sound is defined as any pressure variation in air, water or other medium that the human ear can detect. Noise below 16 Hz is described as infrasound and can be produced by any pulsating or chronologic piece of equipment.

Six characteristics of noise are of relevance:

- *Sound intensity*, which describes the particular power of a sound or the level of sound energy with which it, confronts the ear.

- *Sound pressure level* refers to the magnitude of the air pressure variations or fluctuations, which make up sound. It is expressed in decibels (dB).

- *Frequency* is defined as the number of pressure variables passing a fixed point per second. It is measured in hertz (Hz).

- *Pitch* and *tone*. Pitch refers to the subjective quality of a sound that determines its position in the musical scale whereas the tone and quality of a note depends upon the harmonics that sound together with the fundamental note.

- *Loudness* is a function of the sound's intensity and its amplitude. It also depends upon frequency and the subjective perception of sound by the human being.

Continuous noise can have a negative effect on both individual and group performance. Crook and Langdon (1974), for example, found that aircraft noise produced differences in the teaching style of teachers. Intermittent noise is defined as a flurry of sudden large bangs or impulses from a machine and can have a significant effect on performance levels.

Noise and the Communication Process

Effective verbal communication in the workplace depends upon the ability of the communicator to provide the correct speech sounds, and on the listener's ability to receive and decode these sounds. There is a considerable body of research to demonstrate that a noisy work environment will interfere with the reception and decoding process. This process is known as masking. The research also shows that employees working in noisy environments develop coping skills supplemented by social and non-verbal cues to get over the existence of masking.

Speech itself is a significant source of noise. Nemecek and Grandjean (1973) report a study that showed that 6 per cent of employees who reported that they were disturbed by noise identified noise produced by conversation as the most annoying. Content was more disturbing than loudness. Waller (1968) points out that annoyance can be caused by overhearing conversations.

Non-continuous noise may also result in hearing loss. This noise may be intermittent noise from machines, impact noise or impulsive noise. Its general impact on hearing loss depends on the duration of exposure, its frequency and intensity.

In terms of the effect of noise on performance, Gawron (1982) reviewed 58 noise experiments and reports that 29 showed that noise hindered performance whereas 22 showed no effect and the remaining seven experiments produced inconclusive results. The variability is due primarily to the types of conditions in which the experiments were carried out.

Music and the Workplace

There is considerable debate about the impact of music on employee morale and their performance. Voke (1982) classifies music at work as either background or industrial music. Background music takes the form of light, quiet music or "wallpaper" music. Industrial music on the other hand may not be continuous and can be played at certain times of the day.

There is a theoretical argument to suggest that music can have a positive impact on cognitive functioning and productivity. The argument goes that music reduces boredom and fatigue where employees perform repetitive tasks. It is also argued that it produces a positive stimulating effect for the employee. Fox (1983) suggests that it may also contribute to increased quality and a reduction in errors. Oborne (1995) suggests two important questions that should be considered if music is going to be used in the workplace:

• When should the music be played?

• What kind of music should be played?

He suggests that it should take into account the daily variations in human performance and efficiency. Blake (1971) has shown that performance increases during the periods 08.00 and 10.30 hours and experiences a dip at 14.00 hours.

Hearing Loss and Performance

The evidence is very strong on the existence of hearing loss caused by noisy workplace conditions. There are essentially two forms of hearing loss: nerve deafness and conduction deafness. The former usually results from damage or degeneration of the inner cells in the ear. This hearing loss is usually uneven, manifesting itself at higher frequencies than at lower ones. The latter is caused by a condition of the outer or middle ear that affects the transmission of sound waves to the inner ear. It does not, however, result in complete hearing loss. Hearing aids are more useful in this type of deafness than in the case of nerve deafness.

In the occupational context, most hearing loss occurs from continuous exposure over time; however, exposure to non-continuous noise can also result in deafness. Temporary hearing loss may be experienced from continuous noise. The extent of temporary deafness depends on the amount of exposure although marked individual differences exist. Some people are more sensitive to high-frequency sounds, others to low-frequency sounds. Where there is permanent exposure to noise of sufficient intensity, permanent deafness will gradually appear.

Noise may be a source of stress and/or may interfere with the communication process. The nature and context of the noise, rather than its intensity, generally determines the individual's subjective response to noise. In stress terms, intermittent noises and noise with speech are much more stressful than continuous unstructured noise of a similar intensity, such as machine noise. All forms of noise are more stressful when an employee is trying to concentrate on something. **Figure 9.1** shows a range of noise levels related to particular environmental conditions.

Vibration

Vibration can be defined as any movement that a body makes about a fixed point. Oborne (1995) points out that this movement can be regular or random. Likewise, sound at the low end of the sound range is felt as vibration. There is a considerable body of research highlighting health and performance effects of vibration.

Health Effects

The health effects of vibration relate to the damage caused to body organs as a result of their being buffeted by high vibration levels. There is also the breakdown of body tissue resulting from the absorption of high-energy vibration. Griffin (1990), based on a review of over 100 studies, identifies one of the most frequently cited health effects as back problems resulting from spinal buffeting. Other common health problems include digestive and reproductive system disorders.

Figure 9.1: Noise Levels related to Particular Environmental Conditions

Sound Level — dB(A)

160	Blast from jet take-off, explosions, artillery fire, etc.
150	Rupture of ear drum
140	Shotgun (at ear)
130	Threshold of pain
120	Pneumatic hammer, chainsaw (at user)
110	Rock band (on stage or near speakers)
100	Jet flyover (1,000 feet)
90	Motorcycle (7 metres); personal stereo (inside ear)
80	Lathe, heavy traffic, noisy computer printer
70	Television, conversational speech at one metre
60	Noisy office (average level)
50	Typical office
40	Quiet office or residence
30	Quiet in the country, birdsong
20	Whisper at one metre
10	Soundproof room
0	Threshold of hearing

There are also health implications resulting from the frequency aspects of vibration. The most common ones arise where employees are required to use power hand-held machinery. Seidel and Heide (1986) point out that such vibration can cause structural damage to the peripheral blood and nervous system of the fingers. Its long-term effects include intermittent numbness, clumsiness, blackening of the fingers and a temporary loss of muscular control. Taylor (1974) refers to a condition called "white finger" as a consequence of vibration. It is now called Vibration Induced White Finger (VWF). The Industrial Injuries Advisory Council in the UK points out that there may be additional effects such as neurosis, damage to bones, joints or muscles and suggest that relief from these symptoms will come about after a period of prolonged rest.

Performance Effects

The performance effects of vibration occur primarily in the area of reduced motor control, such as reduced hand steadiness or difficulties in vision. There is little evidence to show that vibration affects intellectual processes.

In terms of its effect on vision, there is very little conclusive evidence. This stems largely from the methodologies used to measure the affects of vibration. Three combinations of conditions are possible.

- **Vibration of the object alone**: If the object is vibrating slowly, then the optical system can track it and maintain a stable image on the retina. However, if the vibration is above 1Hz, the ability of the human to track it diminishes considerably until about 2-4 Hz when it is almost non-existent.

- **Vibration of the observer alone**: The effects in this case are moderated by the characteristics of the body. There is mixed evidence. Griffin (1976) has demonstrated that in seated subjects, vertical vibration is likely to cause angular motions of the eyes.

- **Vibration of the object and the person together**: Barnes et al. (1978) have investigated this situation and found a marked reduction in the ability to read displayed digits at frequencies higher than 1Hz, with greater reductions for smaller-sized digits.

Overall the effects of vibration on visual performance are complicated and depend on whether the observer or the object is vibrating, the intensity and frequency of the vibration and the size of the object in question.

Vibration Syndrome

Vibrations transmitted to the arms and hands from using power-operated tools may result in a collection of symptoms called hand-arm vibration syndrome. It is typically found amongst employees who operate chainsaws, pneumatic drills, jackhammers, rock drills, rotary cultivators and other similar tools. The symptoms of vibration syndrome resemble the blanching of the fingers as well as suffering from pains, numbness and parastesia in the arms and hands, muscular weakness, a fatigue and peripheral nerve damage. Areas of brittleness may develop in the bones of the hand, wrist and forearm, but this is not a common occurrence.

The transmission of vibration from tool to hand increases with the gripping force applied. Research by Pykko et al. (1976) and Tesinger (1972) demonstrate that unskilled workers who grip a tool tightly are the worst affected. While gloves may reduce the vibration, thick gloves may require the user to grip the tool more tightly and have the effect of negating the beneficial effect of the gloves. The wearing of soft gloves appears to be more beneficial and is also likely to protect the user from cold. There is evidence to show that cold hands are more susceptible to the effects of vibration than warm hands. It is generally suggested that better organic design, which makes tools easier to grip and handle, is the best course of action.

Vibration, Reaction Time and Information Processing

The research (Weisz, et al., 1965; Warrick, 1947) demonstrates that reaction time is relatively unaffected by vibration. Shoenberger (1970) demonstrates significant performance effects of vibration; the interference, however, relates to peripheral rather than central interference. He demonstrates that the peripheral components of a task (in this case, perceiving the best letter and verbalising the response) were susceptible to vibration, although the central processing aspects (deciding to react) are not.

Shoenberger (1970) has likewise concluded that cognitive tasks are not affected by vibration. Simons and Schmitz (1958) found no effect in mental arithmetic and others have found similar results. Poulton (1978) argues that vibration at 5 Hz can act as an alerting mechanism to increase performance. Sommer and Harris (1970) demonstrate time-of-day effects in the relationship between vibration and mental performance. They found that performance varied considerably throughout the day.

Vibration and Comfort

Oborne (1975) suggests that vibration can affect comfort in one of three ways:

- It affects the individual's ability to perform motor tasks such reading, writing or eating.

- The vibration stimulus carries information to the individual. In the case of an aeroplane, passengers found the vibration assuring.

- It can result in motion sickness and headaches. Motion sickness causes considerable discomfort and performance loss.

IMPACT OF TEMPERATURE CHANGES

The body's temperature is controlled by a complex self-regulating system located in the hypothalamus section of the brain. Under ordinary conditions of rest, the temperature deep in the body is maintained within the normal range 97–99° F. At the same time, heat is constantly being lost from the body by radiation, convection and evaporation. Although skin temperatures may fluctuate over quite a wide range without significant damage to performance or health, the deep body temperature must stay within the 97–99° F range.

When the body needs to lose heat, hypothalamic activity causes the blood vessels to dilate, and sweat glands to produce cooling sweat. The body's respiration rate will increase and the metabolic rate will be lowered. Conversely, under cold conditions, the blood vessels will constrict and route the blood away from the extremities and increase the metabolic rate by inducing muscle activity (shivering). These processes allow the optimum body temperature to be maintained even when environmental conditions are adverse.

Hyperthermia (Heat Stroke)

If the body temperature reaches 108° F, an individual will be prone to heat stroke. This will manifest itself in a likely loss of consciousness, followed by a short period of weakness or confusion and irrational behaviour. This condition could lead to death unless corrective action is taken. Oborne (1995) suggests three reasons why the body may have difficulty getting rid of excess heat:

- The employee may be exposed to environmental conditions that are excessively humid, so that the body cannot reduce heat by evaporating.

- The insulating effects of protective clothing can cause heat stress. It arises because of impaired evaporation due to the heat-retaining properties of the clothing.

- Hyperthermia can occur when the environmental conditions are too hot but not dangerously so, and still interfere with the body's ability to produce sweat and the sweat's ability to cool the body.

Shibolet et al. (1976) argue that heat stroke is most likely to affect highly-motivated young individuals who are engaged in hard physical work, or military training. Wyndham (1966) suggests that it is a significant problem among miners and can be alleviated through adequate rest and liquid consumption. Bell et al. (1976) demonstrate that the more time the employee is exposed to the heat source, the more they will be affected by the incidence of heat stroke.

In terms of the performance effects of heat, there is inconclusive evidence. Kobrick and Fine (1983) show that many studies have produced mixed results, but that where performance impairment occurs, it usually happens at around 20–30° C (85° F). **Figure 9.2** presents some typical responses to temperature.

When analysing the effects of temperature on the employee, consideration must be given to air movement within the workplace. Air movement moderates the effect of high temperatures and makes the problems of low temperature more difficult to manage.

Figure 9.2: Typical Responses to Temperature

°F	°C	
100°	43°	Just tolerable for brief periods.
90°	32°	Upper limit of reasonable tolerance.
80°	26°	Extremely fatiguing to work in. Performance deteriorates badly and people complain a lot.
78°	25°	Optimal for bathing, showering; sleep is disturbed.
75°	24°	People feel warm, lethargic and sleepy; optimal for unclothed people.
72°	22°	Most comfortable year-round indoor temperature for sedentary people.
70°	21°	Optimal for performance of mental work.
64°	18°	Physically inactive people begin to shiver. Active people are comfortable.
60°	16°	Manual dexterity impaired (stiffness and numbness of fingers).
50°	10°	Lower limit of reasonable tolerance.
32°	0°	Risk of frost-bite to exposed flesh.

Heat Acclimatisation

Heat acclimatisation is defined as a physiological process of adaptation rather than simply a psychological adjustment to life in a hot environment. Generally it involves an increase in the capacity to produce sweat and a decrease in the core temperature threshold value from the inclination of sweating. Increased sweat production enhances the evaporative cooling capacity of the skin and, therefore, improves heat transfer from the deep body tissues to the periphery. Research demonstrates that the risk of dehydration and salt depletion is significantly reduced in an acclimatised person. It also reduces the skin's blood flow requirements, which in turn reduces the cardiovascular load during work in heat.

Studies by Diamond (1991) and Hanna and Brown (1979) demonstrate that an individual's ability to produce sweat depends on the climate experienced in the early years of life, apparently, the first 18 months. The body does not, however, have the capacity to acclimatise to dehydration.

Several other factors also influence an employee's ability to tolerate hot conditions. In terms of task factors, the most important variables are work rate, the provision of rest pauses, and protective clothing. Aspects of the thermal environment that appear important include the relative humidity, wind speed and temperature.

Four individual factors are of significance:

- **Age:** The very young and the very old are less tolerant than other age groups; older men are less able to tolerate high heat stress because of their lower skin temperature threshold.

- **Gender:** There is evidence to suggest that women begin sweating at a higher skin temperature and sweat less than men.

- **Physical Fitness:** Physical fitness improves heat tolerance because both rely on cardiovascular function and sweat production. Physically fit employees are generally less stressed by hot conditions.

- **Body Fat:** Excess body fat diminished real tolerance by increasing the mass-to-surface area ratio of the body and reducing cardiovascular fitness. Fat tissue contains less water than other tissue and has a lower heat capacity.

Radiation

Conditions that are very hot, due to heat being radiated from a heat source, can have a significant impact on an employee's comfort level and performance. Radiation is emitted by the heat source in the form of electromagnetic waves and, if it is severe, it can burn the skin tissue.

Humidity

Humidity is defined as an index of the amount of water vapour in the air and is normally measured using two mercury thermometers. If there is excessive water vapour in the air, it is likely to interfere with the efficiency by which sweat will evaporate from the skin. Personal discomfort is considered a normal consequence of both high humidity levels and low humidity levels.

Hypothermia

Small amounts of deep body cooling can lead to a condition known as hypothermia. This condition can come about due to accidental exposure to bad weather, short-term immersion in cold water or long-term exposure to slightly cold water. Hypothermia exists when the body's core temperature falls to 95° F. Death is likely at temperatures below 86° F. When the body is exposed to cold, its regulating system attempts to produce heat rapidly by increasing muscular activity, such as muscle tension and shivering. Violent shivering reaches a maximum at body temperatures around 95° F. During the shivering stage, the cardiovascular system responds to the cold by constricting the peripheral blood vessels and this increases the blood pressure.

The tolerance of individuals to hypothermia varies considerably. Timbal et al. (1976), for example, found that differences in response are primarily due to morphological factors such as the amount of fat around the body. Fat acts as a good insulating material. Hayward and Keatinge (1981) found that the individual's metabolic rate is also a significant factor. The individual's size and weight is also important because the degree of heat loss is related to the body's surface area and the amount of heat generated depends on the mass of active muscular tissue in the body.

Fox (1967) concluded that cold affects human performance in five key areas: tactile sensitivity, manual performance, tracking, reaction time and complex behaviours. In terms of motor performance, the limit temperature rather than the overall body temperature is more significant. It results primarily in a loss of muscular strength. Morton and Provins (1960) demonstrated that significant reduction in finger dexterity results at temperatures below 20–25° C (68–97° F). Clarke (1951) demonstrated that, the longer his subjects were subjected to the cold, the more their performance decreased.

As far as cognitive performance is concerned, the impact is not very clear. Coleshaw et al. (1983) demonstrate impaired performance and calculation speeds when core temperatures fell to between 34–35° C. Ellis (1982) likewise reports that large increases in error accompanied reductions in mean skin temperature. Reaction times were not affected. Gilsbreacht (1993) shows that 50–80 minutes of immersion in cold water (2–4° C) had no effect on simple tasks but adversely affected more complex tasks.

Overall, the research suggests that cold acts in the way of a general stressor.

BODY MOVEMENT AND POSTURE

Two proprioceptive senses, kinaesthetic and vestibular, are concerned with perceiving the body's own movement.

The Kinaesthetic System

The kinaesthetic system is primarily concerned with the feeling of motion and consists of senses in the muscles, tendons and joints. The senses serve the function of informing the individual of the relative positions and movements of limbs and the different parts of the body. The worker relying on kinaesthetic receptions is kept informed unconsciously of what the body is doing without every part of it having to be monitored. The kinaesthetic sensory receptors, located in the hand, arm and shoulder muscles, allow the operator to use their hands efficiently above the head or out of sight. These receptors also convey information about the extent to which a muscle is being stretched and the rate of stretching. Receptors in the tendons provide information about the degree of movement of the joints while others are sensitive to deep pressure. The kinaesthetic system is made up of a range of subsystems, all of which provide the operator with essential information about the position of the body.

The kinaesthetic system has a major role to play in the field of operator training, specifically in areas such as finger dexterity, reaction time and wrist and finger movement.

Oborne (1995) recommends that muscular activity should take place on an intermittent basis, but this is difficult to achieve given modern work patterns. Word processors allow more work to be done and may result in the operator experiencing muscular fatigue. This has led many commentators to recommend that prolonged work on VDUs should involve frequent posture changes between sitting and standing.

Repetitive Manipulative Tasks

Employees on modern production lines are generally required to perform any tasks that cannot be automated or are too difficult/expensive to automate. Many of these tasks are associated with forceful gripping and turning actions with the wrist in a deviated position. The turning actions may involve some or all of the following movements: flexion, ulnar/radial deviation, pronation/supination or some combination thereof. The negative impact of tasks with high repetition rates depends on the extent to which the job has other positive ergonomic features. It is suggested that higher repetition rates are more tolerable when forces are lower and the wrist is in a neutral position. The design of tools also appears to be important. Other features that help include changing the height of working surfaces, tilting the working surface and sitting the workpiece at an angle to the employee's body.

Lifting

Lifting is an area where considerable muscular activity is involved. There is sufficient evidence to show that people often suffer from backaches, ruptures and strained muscles as a result of lifting. The Chartered Society of Physiotherapy recommends that the maximum weight for safe lifting by an adult male is 120 lbs. However, when walking with a load, the maximum weight that can be lifted vertically is 20 lbs. The Society has issued guidelines for lifting, aimed at the individual worker. Hammond (1978) has added to this list. **Figure 9.3** presents the main recommendations.

Oborne (1995) suggests that there is a strong correlation between back injuries and handling, over a range of occupations. Back injuries are also most likely to be found among younger male workers, who value physical strength without adequate consideration of the inherent risks involved. Stubbs et al. (1983) reports that nurses are also a high risk group, most particularly from back pain as a result of handling patients.

Figure 9.3: Recommendations for Lifting

- The feet should be far enough apart so that there is a balanced distribution of the person's weight.

- The knees and hips should be bent and the back kept as straight as possible with the chin tucked in.

- The arms should be held as near to the body as possible.

- The whole of the hand should be used to grasp the object whenever possible.

- Lifting should be done smoothly without jerks or snatches.

- Avoid lifting and carrying above the level of the head.

- Avoid lifting or supporting a load in a vertical axis when the load is located any distance from the vertical axis of the body.

- Provide an intermediate platform where loads are lifted on to the shoulder or lowered from the shoulder.

- Eliminate features of design that impose awkward postures.

Lifting and Risks

Pheasant (1991) suggests that lifting involves three kinds of risk: the risk of accidental injury, the risk of over-exertion and the risk of cumulative damage. The research evidence suggests that the risk involved in lifting increases as a direct function of the weight of the load and the distance of the load from the employee's body. The distance dimension is very important because, for a given weight of an object, the loading on the spine and its muscles is greater, resulting in overexertion in some cases. The strength of the lifting action is less, with the result that the load may get out of control. The body is also out of balance and the trunk may be flexed.

It is suggested that a lifting action that stands at a distance and moves toward an employee's body is easier to control than one that starts close to the body and moves away. This ensures that the employee will be lifting the load into the region of greater stability provided by their footbase and into their region of greater strength. The stoop lift or back lift is generally considered to be negative whereas the crouch or leg lift is considered good posture. The latter lift is better because it keeps the lumber spine area closer to the safer middle part of its range of motion. The centre of gravity is also better positioned.

Asymmetrical or twisted lifting actions are very hazardous. Research by Kelsey et al. (1984) demonstrates that back pain and serious back problems are a major possibility of lifting and twisting. Asymmetrical lifting involves achieving a side bending, rotation or some combination of these but it may not involve any twisting actions. The twisting action is considered the most hazardous. We will consider some practical management steps to reduce these problems in a later chapter.

The Vestibular System

The vestibular system is located in the ear and its function is to maintain the body's posture and equilibrium. It allows the individual to maintain an upright posture and to control the body's position in space. It likewise provides information about the speed and direction of the body, the head's rotation and its position when static. Individuals may be prone to motion sickness in conditions of substantial motion. The vestibular system in the ear triggers the sensation of motion sickness.

This handbook will focus on three issues: seating and posture, human movement and body size.

Seating and Posture

Grandjean (1973) describes sitting down as a natural human posture. He maintains that sitting relieves the need to maintain an upright posture and reaches the overall static muscular workload required to lock the various joints of the body. He also suggests that sitting is better than standing for circulation because blood and tissue fluids in a standing person tend to accumulate in the legs. In a work context, sitting helps the operator to adopt a more stable posture, which is of considerable benefit when performing tasks that require fine or precise movements and it is advantageous in operations requiring good foot control.

Oborne (1995), however, argues that seated employees are disadvantaged in a number of ways:

- Their mobility can be severely restricted in that an employee who has to move around the workplace and move from a sitting to a standing posture will most likely experience fatigue.

- A seated posture, while ideally suited for performing fine manipulative tasks, is of little use when hand controls have to be operated with much force. In such a situation, the employees will have to rise from the seat to adopt the appropriate posture to carry out the task.

- Sitting down is a distinct disadvantage in a vibrating environment because these vibrations will be transmitted through the chair.

- While sitting may be healthy in terms of spinal loads and vascular performance (short-term), there is considerable research to demonstrate that prolonged sitting is not beneficial. Potter et al. (1969) demonstrated that prolonged sitting for more than 60 minutes produced swelling in the lower legs.

Orthopaedic and Muscular Aspects of Seating

The spine, the pelvis, the legs and the feet are the main body structures used by the sitter during sitting. When standing, the natural curved shape of the spine enables the body's centre of gravity to pass through the trunk to the feet. This, therefore, requires minimal muscular activity to maintain posture. Sitting upsets this arrangement. It increases tension in the muscles and ligaments in the lumbar region to compensate for the movement of the centre of gravity toward the anterior of the body. This has important implications for the design of a chair (see **Figure 9.4**).

Any alteration to the natural spinal shape produces corresponding stressors on the associated muscles. Floyd and Ward (1969), for example, report that muscular activity increases when seated. Sitting up straight without a back rest produces considerable activity in the lumbar region whereas a forward, hunchback posture causes more activity to occur in the upper back and shoulder regions.

Figure 9.4: Implications for Chair Design

Are You Sitting Comfortably?

Height

An optimum position is when the thighs of the sitter are horizontal, the lower legs are vertical, and the feet are flat on the floor (with appropriate adjustments for the short-legged person). The height of an easy chair (e.g. 38 to 45 cm) should permit the legs to be stretched forward, because this is a preferred relaxing posture and helps to stabilise the body. The height of a working chair (e.g. 43 to 50 cm) should permit the sitter to be in a more upright position with the feet flat on the floor. If a chair has to be higher to cater for a situation where a worker has to service a tall machine or sit at a high workbench, an adjustable footrest is suggested.

Depth

The sitter should be able to find support in the lumbar area from the backrest, and the seat should be able to accommodate even the shortest person. The suggested depth for an easy chair is 43 to 45 cm and 35 to 40 cm for a work chair. A backward sloping seat helps relax the sitter in an easy chair, and a forward sloping seat is generally more functional for a working chair. According to one authority, most work is carried out in a forward-bent posture. Therefore, a forward sloping seat is more appropriate. A backward sloping chair of even 5° would cause discomfort (Mandal, 1976).

Backrest

The suggested height is up to 48 to 63 cm (the distance from the shoulder to the underside of the buttocks) and 35 to 48 cm wide (shoulder width). The shape and angle of the backrest are extremely important in preventing fatigue of the spinal posture. It is often suggested that the backrest should have an "open" area or, alternatively, be designed in such as way that the lumbar area of the body fits into the backrest in order to accommodate the buttocks. Too high a backrest might prevent full mobility of the arms and shoulders in certain tasks (e.g. typing) where a small backrest supporting only the lumbar region is functional. The angle of the backrest (103 to 112°) serves two purposes: it prevents the sitter from slipping forwards; and it helps the body to lean against the backrest with the lumbar part of the back and sacrum supported.

Armrest

The armrest's main function is to rest the arm and lock the body in a stable position. The support provided can be of assistance when one wants to rise from the chair or to change the sitting position.

The disadvantage, particularly in a working chair, is the restriction of free movement of arms and shoulder.

Cushioning

Two important functions of cushioning are evident. First, it allows the pressure on the ischial tuberosities, caused by the weight of the sitter, to be distributed. This is important because this pressure will cause discomfort and fatigue if not relieved. Second, a stable body posture is maintained when the body is allowed to sink into the cushioning where it is supported. However, cushioning that is too soft should not be used because the buttocks and thighs sink deeply into the cushioning with little chance for the sitter to be able to adjust his or her position (Oborne, 1994).

SEATING AND BACK PAIN

Employees who suffer from back pain are less able to tolerate ergonomic failings in seat design. Back pain is a particular problem within certain occupations. Fitzgerald (1973) has studied air pilots who suffered from back pain with customised lumbar supports. When they were moulded to the individual's own spinal contour and worn beneath the pilot's outer flying clothes, the pilots reported a marked improvement in their comfort.

Pheasant (1991) has investigated the seating preference of employees with lower back problems. The employees were shown two pictures, one showing a person sitting with a fixed spine. Eighty per cent of employees chose the seated position as the most comfortable and more likely to relieve their symptoms. Seventy-four per cent of respondents indicated that it helped to put a cushion behind the lower part of the back, whereas others indicated that it helped to sit with the knees higher than the back or with the legs crossed.

Behavioural Dimensions of Seating

There is a considerable body of research in this issue. Grandjean et al. (1983), for example, show that people adopt different postures at computer workstations and that these postures have different physical consequences. The sitters' behavioural repertoires are likely to include activities such as fidgeting. Branton and Grayson (1967) demonstrate that the degree of fidgeting is an indicator of seat discomfort. Branton (1976) suggests a theory of postural homeostasis in which the sitter strikes a compromise between the need for stability and the need for variety. In practice, therefore, sitting behaviour is characterised by cycles of inactivity and activity and it requires an efficient and comfortable chair to accommodate these cycles.

Oborne (1995) suggests that individuals have three motives for sitting: for recreation, work and multiple purposes. These uses have implications for chair design; specifically, the following are relevant:

- The types and dimensions of the seat should be related to the reason for sitting.

- The seat dimensions should match the anthroprometric dimensions of the individual.

- The chair should provide both support and stability.

- The chair should allow for variation in posture and prevent slipping.

- The chair should be sufficiently firm to allow the distribution of body weight pressures.

MOVEMENT

Human movement involves other considerations than those that apply to sitting. McKenna (1994) points out that the emphasis is on the physical environment. He suggests a number of guidelines that should be observed:

- When employees are required to walk down passageways or between machines, the available space should be at least greater than shoulder breadth. There should also be allowances for arms and clothing characteristics.

- When movement is between machines, there is a need to be conscious of protruding controls that may come in contact with the employee and that may result in injury.

- Slipping is a major issue and a very common cause of accidents. The National Safety Authority has estimated that injuries resulting from slipping, tripping and falling account for up to 45 per cent of time lost due to accidents. If employees have to work on slippery surfaces, they will become fatigued and are more likely to slip or fall.

- Movement is also relevant in the context of stairs, ramps and ladders. Kales et al. (1985) for example, demonstrate that the provision of a handrail of 90 cm in height on a stairway can significantly reduce accidents.

- Falls from a height are a significant cause of accidents in Ireland. Dewar (1977), in an analysis of ladder accidents, found that in 66 per cent of cases, the accident happened when the person was working on the ladder, while the remainder were caused when the climber stumbled while climbing.

CHAPTER ROUND-UP

- Both blue-collar and white-collar employees are vulnerable to hazardous conditions at work. Many of these conditions come within the scope of ergonomics. Person-centred ergonomics argues that employees control the work system, shape it and evaluate its effectiveness. A person-centred approach assumes that employees are purposive, they aim to reduce uncertainty, they act with responsibility and trust and they have an interest in their work and commitment to the organisation.

- A selection of ergonomic issues in the work environment was examined. These relate to colour perception, lighting and glare, visual deterioration and fatigue, noise, vibration, temperature changes, and mechanical processes connected with the proprioceptive senses such as movement, lifting and posture. As well as purposeful action to contract hazardous work conditions, employees also engage in compensatory behaviour.

- Noise is a significant ergonomic variable and it can have negative effects on both individual and group performance. Noise may be continuous or intermittent in nature and both can influence performance depending on the types of conditions in which employees operate. Related to noise is the issue of music in the workplace. Music may be classified as either background or industrial music. It is argued that music may have a positive impact on employee morale, which, in turn, improves performance.

- Vibration represents another ergonomic variable the effect of which on employee health is well documented. It may cause change to body organs, result in the breakdown of body tissue, back problems, digestive and reproductive system disorders. The performance effects of vibration occur primarily in the area of reduced motor control such as reduced hand-steadiness or difficulties in vision.

- The temperature of the workplace may affect both performance and the employee's level of physical comfort. The employee may be exposed to environmental conditions that are excessively humid or may experience excessive cold. In both cases, performance is impaired, particularly in manual performance, reaction time, tactile sensitivity and complex behaviours.

- In the area of body movement, three issues were examined; lifting, seating and posture and seating and back pain. These variables all have implications for the design of the workplace and the layout of production systems and offices.

Chapter 10

HUMAN–MACHINE INTERACTION: DISPLAYS AND CONTROLS

INTRODUCTION

This chapter considers the issue of human–machine communications. The focus is on the nature and quality of information that passes within, and between, people and machines. The chapter first of all considers the communication process and then focuses on the issue of displays and controls and their effective design. Displays and controls are the interface through which human-machine information exchange takes place. The design of such displays and controls significantly influences the interaction between machine and person, the level of task difficulty and the probability of errors. The chapter also considers the issue of interface design and the consequences of deficiencies in this area for errors and accidents.

THE HUMAN–MACHINE COMMUNICATION PROCESS

One important function of ergonomics is to design the interaction between employee and machine, so that the chances are maximised of the transmitter and the receiver of information having a maximum common understanding. This communication process is, however, modified by a range of factors:

- **Personality**: If the receiver dislikes or mistrusts the transmitter, this can undermine the process of understanding. Negative opinions or motives can distort it.

- **Personal perceptions**: Bartlett (1950) argues that the mind continually fills in gaps in order to make something meaningful. This may result in the message being distorted by the receiver or placed in an incorrect context.

- **Interest and attention**: If the receiver is not attentive to the message, part of it may be missed or misinterpreted.

- **Capacity problems**: Messages can be distorted because of the human operator's limited capacity to process transmitted information. If a message is too detailed or too long, the consequence is overload to the memory system. The information may be lost or distorted.

Miller (1972) suggests that messages can be transmitted in three ways: verbal, vocal or physical. These issues will now be dealt with, although, as it is beyond the scope of this handbook, no detailed consideration will be given to the role of non-verbal stimuli in the communication process.

Perceptual Process in Written Communication

Research suggests that two features are important in written communication:

- The ways in which the eyes move over the information presented.

- The way in which information is integrated and organised.

Eye Movements

There is a strong body of research (Matin, 1979; Young and Sheena, 1975; Rayner et al., 1989) that demonstrates the existence of saccadic eye movement during reading. Two issues are of fundamental importance: the duration of each fixation and the number of fixations required. Rayner (1977) has established that the average fixation durations lie between 200–250 ms; however, he notes that there are significant individual differences. These relate to the individual's reading efficiency and the difficulty of the text. The greater the difficulty of the text, the greater the tendency for readers to fixate longer and to move their eyes a shorter distance. It also appears that typographical design is important. Bouma (1980) illustrates that the number of saccades is influenced by the size of the margin.

Perceptual Organisation

Rayner (1977) points out that eye movements are controlled by the reader's cognitive processes occurring at the time of reading. There is a complex interplay between a reader's perception of what is being read and eye movement control during reading. The Gestalt school of psychology has examined a number of principles of perceptual organisation. These are presented in **Table 10.1**.

Table 10.1: Principles of Perceptual Organisation

Proximity	The organisation of individual elements into groups varies on the basis of distance. The nearer the two elements, the more likely they are perceived as a whole.
Similarity	Similar items or the basis of colour, size or shape, will be grouped together. This principle can override the proximity principle.
Symmetry	In an attempt to interpret a stimulus array so as to maximise its meaning, various elements of the array will be included to form symmetrical or balanced figures.
Simplicity	Individuals will organise input into its simplest possible interpretation.
Closure	Individuals tend to organise elements so that they form simple, closed figures that are independent of other properties.
Good continuation	Elements will be organised into wholes if they produce few interruptions or changes in continuous lines.

The Gestalt principles suggest that individuals perceive stimuli in terms of how they arrange their perceptual organisation.

Visual Scanning and Search

Two sets of features are important in visual scanning and search: display and subject features. Display features relate to the position of the information in the material that is being searched. Wolford and Hollingsworth (1974) demonstrate that the further a character is displayed from the gaze-fixation position, the less likely it is to be identified correctly and the longer such identification will take. Studies also show that the initial fixation in a work situation is about a quarter of the way into the word from the right. Approximate spacing of displayed material may increase detectability of individual items of information. The ability to detect information is also influenced by:

• The complexity of the material.

• The number of different types of elements that make up the display.

• The colour features of the display; single-coloured or multi-coloured displays. The former is considered more efficient.

An important variable affecting the individual's processing performance relates to the type of information the operator wishes to abstract from the display. Buswell (1935) demonstrates that faces and hands are the most fixated areas in pictures containing people. Yarbus (1967) asked his subjects to view pictures and estimate the age of individuals in the picture. He found that most eye fixations occurred around the facial regions. When asked to describe social standing, they tended to focus on clothing and furniture. This led him to conclude that an individual's search and fixation process is significantly related to the search intention.

THE NATURE OF DISPLAYS

Rolfe and Allnutt (1967) argue that a display translates what is at first imperceptible to use into perceptible terms. It functions in one of the operator's five sensory modes: vision, hearing, touch, taste or smell. In general, it is possible to distinguish between visual and auditory displays. **Table 10.2** presents the relative merits of both forms.

Table 10.2: Merits of Visual and Auditory Displays

Visual Displays	Auditory Displays
• They are useful when information is presented in a noisy environment. • They are suitable when the message is long and complex. • If the message needs to be referred to later, visual displays provide a permanent record. • The auditory system is often over-burdened in organisations. • The visual message does not require an immediate response.	• They are most appropriate if an immediate response is required. • If there are too many visual displays or glaring conditions. • The information needs to be presented irrespective of direction in which the operator is looking. • When the message is short and simple. • Vision is limited by machine layout. • There are few restrictions in the use of auditory displays. • They make very suitable warning indicators. • When the origin of the signal is itself a sound.

Visual Displays

It is possible to distinguish between digital and analogue displays and qualitative and quantitative displays. Digital displays present numerical information directly as numbers whereas analogue displays make the operator interpret the information from the pointer's position on a scale, from the shape, position or inclination of a picture on the screen, or some other type of indicator.

Digital displays are generally considered superior when the following conditions apply:

- A precise numeric value or quantitative reading is required.

- The values presented remain visible long enough to be read.

- They are very accurate and precise.

Analogue displays have advantages in other circumstances:

- Fixed-scale moving-pointer displays are useful when the values are subject to frequent or continual change.

- They are useful when it is important to observe the direction or rate of change in the values presented.

- Analogue displays with fixed scales and moving pointers are superior to those with moving scales and fixed pointers.

Heglin (1973) suggests five criteria that should be considered when selecting analogue scales:

- A pointer moving against a fixed scale is preferred.

- If numerical increase is related to some other natural interpretation, it is easier to interpret a straight line or thermometer scale with a moving pointer.

- Do not mix types of pointer scale indicators when they are used for related functions.

- If manual control over the moving element is a requirement, there is less likely to be ambiguity if the control moves the pointer rather than the scale.

- If slight, variable movements or changes in quality are significant, they will be more apparent if a moving pointer is used.

Quantitative displays allow the operator to read a numeric value in precise terms. Both digital and analogue displays can be used to make quantitative readings. Sanders and McCormick (1993) identify important features of quantitative displays:

- They have a scale range, which is defined as the numeric difference between the highest and lowest value on the scale, whether numbered or not.

- The scale has numbered intervals, which represent the numeric difference between adjacent numbers on the scale.

- Each quantitative scale has some intrinsic numeric progression system that is characterised by the graduated intervals of the scale and the numbering of the major scale markers.

- The display has a scale unit, which is the length of the scale and represents the numeric value that is the smallest unit to which the scale is to be read.

- There is generally a scale marker for each scale unit to be read.

- The concept of interpretation usually applies to the estimation of specific values between markers when not all scale units have markers.

With qualitative displays, the user is primarily interested in the approximate value of some continuously changing variable or in a trend or rate of change. Qualitative displays are generally viewed as appropriate where the issue is to determine the status or condition of a variable in terms of a limited range of predetermined ranges (hot–cold), where the concern is to maintain some desirable range of approximate values or where the need is to observe trends and rates of change. Oborne (1995) argues that analogue displays may be more effective than digital displays in this context.

Many qualitative scales show a continuum of values that are sliced into a limited number of ranges. They may also use some form of shape coding to represent specific ranges. It may be a check reading scale where the instrument is used to ascertain whether the reading is normal. Sometimes qualitative information indicates the status of a system, a machine or a component. The most commonly used status indicators are lights and codes. **Table 10.3** presents a summary of guidelines on visual displays.

The Use of Colour

There is a debate about the use of colour in visual display design. People have a strong tendency to perceive similarly coloured objects as belonging together (Van Nes, 1968), as long as no more than three or four colours are used together. In general, colour can be used to provide conceptual grouping of text and to indicate things. Generally red is interpreted to mean "stop" or "danger", whereas green means "go" or that the system is running effectively. Orange, on the other hand, indicates caution. The use of colour is limited because approximately 5 to 8 per cent of people have colour vision defects. This manifests itself generally in the inability to distinguish red from green (they both look brown). It has, therefore, been suggested that the designers of equipment should use shape as well as colour for coding purposes.

Table 10.3: General Guide to Visual Display Selection

To Display	Select	Because
Go, No go, Start, Stop, On, Off	Light	Normally easy to tell if it is on or off.
Identification	Light	Easy to see (may be coded by spacing, colour, location, or flashing rate; may have label for panel applications).
Warning or Caution	Light	Attracts attention and can be seen at great distance if bright enough (may flash intermittently).
Verbal instruction (operating sequence)	Enunciator light	Simple "action instruction" reduces time required for decision-making.
Exact quantity	Digital counter	Only one number can be seen, thus reducing the chance of reading error.
Approximate quantity	Moving pointer against fixed scale	General position of pointer gives rapid clue to the quantity plus relative rate of change.
Set-in Quantity	Moving pointer against fixed scale	Natural relationship between control and display motions.
Tracking	Single pointer or cross pointers against fixed index	Provides error information for easy correction.
Vehicle altitude	Either mechanical or electronic display of position of vehicle against established reference (may be graphic or pictorial)	Provides direct comparison of own position against known reference or base line.

Table 10.4 presents a summary of the advantages and disadvantages of using colour in visual displays.

Table 10.4: Advantages/Disadvantages of the Use of Colour in Display Design

Advantages	Disadvantages
• Draws attention to specific data.	• May have little or no benefit to the 5 - 8% of the population who are colour-blind.
• Enables faster uptake of information.	• May cause confusion.
• Can reduce error.	• May cause fatigue.
• Can separate closely spaced items.	• May cause unwanted groupings.
• May speed reaction.	• May cause errors.
• Adds another dimension.	• Can cause after-images.
• Seems more natural.	• Appears more frivolous.

Auditory Displays

Vision is the most often used medium to present information to the operator, but there is a place for auditory displays as well. Colquhoun (1975) highlights that a combination of visual and auditory displays can often make the monitoring of performance superior to that achieved by relying on visual displays alone. Auditory displays are suitable when presenting qualitative information and may sometimes be used to present information on the state of a machine.

Sanders and McCormick (1993) suggest that four human functions are important in the context of the perception of auditory displays:

- **Detection**: This involves the determination of whether a given signal is present.

- **Relative discrimination**: The process of differentiating between two or more signals currently tied together.

- **Absolute identification**: The process of identifying a particular signal of some class when only one is presented.

- **Localisation**: The process of determining the direction from which the signal is coming.

The relative discrimination and absolute identification processes are usually made on the basis of several stimulus dimensions such as intensity, frequency and duration. Mulligan et al. (1984) suggest six procedures that may increase the detectability of a signal or noise:

- Reduction in the noise intensity in the region of critical band-walls around the signal's frequency.

- Increases in the intensity of the signal.

- Presentation of the signal for at least 0.5 to 1 second.

- Changing the frequency of the signal to correspond to a region where the noise intensity is low.

- Phase-shift the signal and present the unshifted signal to one ear and the shifted signal to the other.

- Presentation of the noise to both ears and the signal to only one.

Patterson (1982) suggests that the signal should be composed of four or more prominent frequency components (ranging from 1000 to 4000 Hz) because complex sounds are more difficult to mark than simple ones. There is a well-established set of principles relating to the use of auditory displays (Mudd, 1961; Licklider, 1961). These are presented in **Figure 10.1**.

Warning Sounds

A warning sign is one of the simplest types of auditory display. It essentially conveys information in an on-off nature. There is a limited amount of scientific evidence to guide the designer in choosing suitable warning displays.

Adams and Trucks (1976) have, however, tested reaction time to eight different warning signals (wail, yelp, whoop, yeow, intermittent hums, etc.) in five different environments. Across the small environments, the "yeow" and the "beep" were the most effective. The least effective was the "wail". They found that reaction time decreased with increased signal intensity.

Figure 10.1: Principles related to the Use of Auditory Displays

1. **General Principles**

   - *Compatibility:* Where feasible, the selection of signal dimensions and their encoding should exploit learned or natural relationships of the users.

   - *Approximation:* Two-stage signals should be considered when complex information is to be presented, consisting of:

     ◊ Attention-demanding signal: to attract attention and identify a general category of information.

     ◊ Designation signal: to follow the attention-demanding signal and designate the precise information within the general class indicated by the first signal.

   - *Dissociability:* Auditory signals should be easily discernible from any on-going audio input (be it meaningful input or noise). For example, if a person is to listen concurrently to two or more channels, the frequencies of the channels should be different if it is possible to make them so.

   - *Parsimony:* Input signals to the operator should not provide more information than is necessary.

   - *Invariance:* The same signal should designate the same information at all times.

2. **Principles of Presentation**

   - *Avoid extremes of auditory dimensions:* High-intensity signals, for example, can cause a startled response and actually disrupt performance.

   - *Establish intensity relative to ambient noise level:* The intensity level should be set so that the ambient noise level does not mask it.

   - *Use interrupted or variable signals:* Where feasible, avoid steady-state signals and, rather, use interrupted or variable signals. This will tend to minimise perceptual adaptation.

   - *Do not overload the auditory channel:* Only a few signals should be used in any given situation. Too many signals can be confusing and will over-load the operator. (For example, during the Three Mile Island nuclear crisis, over 60 different auditory warning signals were activated).

3. **Principles of Installation of Auditory Displays**

   - *Test Signals to be used:* Such tests should be made with a representative sample of the potential user population.

   - *Avoid Conflict with Previously Used Signals:* Any newly installed signals should not be contradictory in meaning to any somewhat similar signals used in existing or earlier systems.

- *Facilitate changeover from previous display:* Where auditory signals replace some other mode of presentation (e.g. visual) preferably continue both modes for a while to help people become accustomed to the new auditory signals.

Murrell (1971) suggests that, to be effective, the sound intensity should be at least 10 dB higher than the background noise. Sanders and McCormick (1992) argue that high-intensity, sudden onset signals are useful for alerting an operator, but the quality of the warning sound should differ from any other sound that the operator is likely to experience in the workplace.

A number of design recommendations, based on research carried out by Deatherage (1972) and Mudd (1961) can be made in terms of warning and alarm signals, as shown in **Figure 10.2**.

Figure 10.2: Designing Warning and Alarm Signals: Some Guidelines

- Use frequencies between 200 and 5000 Hz, and preferably between 500 and 3000 Hz, because the ear is most sensitive to this middle range.

- Use frequencies below 1000 Hz when signals have to travel long distances (over 1000 ft) because high frequencies do not travel as far.

- Use frequencies below 500 Hz when signals have to "bend around" major obstacles or pass through partitions.

- Use a modulated signal (1 or 8 beeps per second, or warning sounds varying from 1 or 3 items per second) since it is different enough from normal sounds to demand attention.

- Use signals with frequencies different from those that dominate any background noise to minimise masking.

- If different warning signals are used to represent different conditions requiring different responses, each should be discernible from the others, and moderate-intensity signals should be used.

- Where feasible, use a separate communication system for warnings, such as loudspeakers, horns or other devices not used for other purposes.

Table 10.5 presents the relative advantages and disadvantages of different types of auditing warning displays.

Table 10.5: Characteristics and Features of Different Types of Audio Alarms

Alarm	Intensity	Frequency	Attention-gaining Ability	Noise-Penetration Ability
Diaphone (foghorn) Horn	Very high	Very low	Good	Poor in low frequency noise.
Horn	High	Low to high	Good	Good.
Whistle	High	Low to High	Good if intermittent	Good if frequency is properly chosen.
Siren	High	Low to high	Very good if pitch rises and falls	Very good with rising and falling frequency.
Bell	Medium	Medium to high	Good	Good in low-frequency noise.
Buzzer	Low to medium	Low to medium	Good	Fair if spectrum is suited to background noise.
Chimes and Gong	Low to medium	Low to medium	Fair	Fair if spectrum is suited to background noise.
Oscillator	Low to high	Medium to high	Good if intermittent	Good if frequency is properly chosen.

CONTROLS

In order to communicate with machines and controls, the operator must use some device to input commands and data. These devices are known as controls. The primary function of controls is to transmit control information to some device, mechanism or system. The type of information to be transmitted falls into two broad categories:

- **Discrete information**: This information represents only one of a limited number of conditions such as on, off, high, medium, low.

- **Continuous information**: This information can assume any value on a continuum such as speed, pressure, position of a value or the amount of electric current. Visual display terminals often require the user to transmit to the system a special class of continuous information, which is called cursor positioning. The information relates to the optical location of the cursor on the screen.

The information transmitted by a control may be presented in a display, or it may manifest itself in the nature of the system response. **Table 10.6** presents some of the more common types of controls and their functions.

Effective Design of Controls

Size

Control size and dimensions need to relate to the dimensions of the limbs used to operate them. Size is also important in the context of the kind of action that the control requires, i.e. manipulation. Manipulative tasks usually range from gripping to non-gripping activities. In gripping activities, the fingers and parts of the palm form a closed chain and act in opposition to each other, whereas in non-gripping activities the forces are extended through all of the hands or through the fingertips. Catovic et al. (1989) demonstrate that the posture adopted when operating small hand controls has a significant influence on the gripping behaviour that can be used.

Feedback

Feedback refers to the information received from both outside and inside the body. This feedback facilitates the operator to assess performance, body position and provides information about the nature of the control being operated. It gives the operator knowledge of the control's feel. Burrows (1965) suggest that control "feel" occurs as kinaesthetic feedback from the muscles, and it is determined by the control itself, in terms of the amount of resistance to movement built into it.

Table 10.6: Types of Controls and Their Functions

Control Type	Discrete			Continuous		
	Activation	Discrete Setting	Data Entry	Quantitative Setting	Continuous Control
Hand push button	Excellent	Can be used, needs as many buttons as settings — not recommended.	Good	Not applicable	Not applicable
Foot push button	Good	Not recommended.	N/A	N/A	N/A
Toggle Switch	Good, but prone to accidental activation	Fair, but poor if more than three possible settings to be made.	N/A	N/A	N/A
Rotary selector switch	Can be used, but on/off position may be confused with other positions	Excellent, provided settings are well-marked.	N/A	N/A	N/A
Knob	N/A	Poor.	N/A	Good	Fair
Crank	Only applicable if large forces are needed to activate — e.g. open/close hatch	N/A	N/A	Fair	Good
Hand-wheel	N/A	N/A	N/A	Good	Excellent
Level	Good	Good, provided there are not too many settings.	N/A	Good	Good
Pedal	Fair	N/A	N/A	Good	Fair

Control Resistance

This refers to the control's resistance to movement, which fulfils a number of functions: it is a frequently used feedback mechanism and it can help guard against accidentally activating the control. However, it can lead to fatigue and performance decreases, if too much resistance is incorporated. Control resistance can take four forms:

- **Static and coloumbic**: where the resistance is maximal at the start of the movement but falls considerably with further force, e.g. on-off switch.

- **Elastic**: where the resistance is proportionate to control displacement, as in a spring-loaded control.

- **Viscous**: where the resistance is proportionate to the velocity of the control movement as in a plunger.

- **Inertia**: where resistance is caused by the mass of the control, as in a crank.

Morgan et al. (1963) suggest that for all hand controls, except push-buttons, resistance should not be less than 2-5 lbs because below this level the hand's sensitivity decreases.

Coding

Coding refers to the use of some mechanism to read the identification of the control. A wide range of coding mechanisms exist:

- **Shape coding**: This is particularly important where tactile sensitivity is valued. It is vital that controls are not confused with one another. Jenkins (1947) identified three broad classes of knobs: multiple rotation, fractional rotation and detent positioning. Multiple rotation knobs are used on continuous controls where twirling or spinning is required or where the adjustment range is a full turn or more. Fractional rotational knobs are used on continuous controls where the adjustment range is less than one full turn or where the knob position is not of critical importance. Detent positioning knobs are used on discrete setting controls where knob position is an important item of information in the control operation.

- **Texture coding**: Surface texture can act as an identification. Bradley (1967) has studied texture and proposes that three surface characteristics can be used to facilitate discrimination: smooth, fluted and knurled. Dirt and grime, however, can hinder discrimination in the case of knurled surfaces.

- **Size coding**: Size coding is useful in some cases. Bradley (1969) proposes that three diameters (¾, 1¼ and 1¾) and two thicknesses (³/₈ and ¾ ins) represent the optimum.

- **Location coding**: This is used in cases when the driver shifts from the accelerator to the brake. The research, in general, demonstrates that vertically arranged switches are best separated by more than 2.5 in (6.3 cm); for horizontally arranged switches, there should be a distance of at least 4 in (10.2 cm).

- **Colour coding**: Colour coding can be useful to identify controls, but it should be used in moderation. It is ineffective in situations where poor illumination exists or where the control is likely to become dirty. Colour can, however, be combined with other coding methods.

- **Label coding**: Labels are a very common method of identifying controls and, therefore, should be used because they do not require much time to comprehend. Seminara et al. (1977) report that most nuclear power stations' control rooms have walls of identical controls distinguished only by labels.

Other Factors Affecting Control Effectiveness

Oborne (1995) suggests that there is an additional set of factors that may affect the effectiveness of a control. These include individual handedness, the use of protective clothing, control shapes and the movements required for different controls.

- **Individual handedness**: This refers to the operator's hand preference. However, in reality, many employees may have different hand preferences for various actions and this can cause problems. Left-handed operators are presented with particular problems because controls and handles are often designed for use by right-handed operators. The research suggests that left-handed operators often experience fatigue and, possibly, accidents.

- **Protective clothing**: The type of clothing used by the operator may interfere with efficient control action. Gloves, for example, may inhibit the manipulation of controls and feedback. They can also affect manual dexterity. Cochran et al. (1986) examined the effects of gloves on grasp force using a leather glove, a leather glove with cotton backing, a cotton glove, a nylon stainless steel glove, a steel mesh over cotton glove and no glove at all. All of the gloves were found to diminish maximum grasp force by a range of 7.3 per cent to 8.6 per cent. Weidman (1970) has examined performance effects and found that gloves decreased performance by 12.5 per cent over bare-hand performance. PVC gloves decreased it by 64 per cent and leather gloves by 45 per cent. Bellingar and Slocum (1993) demonstrate that protective gloves reduce considerably the manipulative abilities of the operator.

Shoes have a similar effect where foot pedal controls are used. Warner and Mace (1974) demonstrate that the average brake response time of female drivers was increased by 0.1 of a second when wearing platform shoes as opposed to normal shoes.

- **Control shapes**: The shape of the control may affect operator posture and cause undue stress on the musculo-skeletal system. Pheasant and O'Neil (1975) demonstrate that muscular strength is minimal when using handles around 5 cm diameter. Fellows and Freivalds (1991), however, demonstrate that, if the increased diameter is created by using foam, it does not affect the pressure distribution to any great extent.

- **Body movements**: Different controls require different types of operation and this may significantly affect the effectiveness of the control when operated. It has implications for the speed and accuracy of the operator and the types of muscles involved. Mead and Sampson (1972) have measured hand-steadiness for different movements. The amount of tremor is considerably reduced when operators make ballistic-like in-out movements, rather than up-down movements. Furthermore, as the arm is extended the muscle orientation has to change. This means that finger control contact is diminished.

COMBINING DISPLAYS AND CONTROLS

Controls and displays are the means by which system inputs and outputs are made amenable to operators. An effectively designed interface that takes account of input-output relationships of the system, and is compatible with the operator's characteristics such as previous training and knowledge, should lead to higher performance, ease of learning, fewer errors and accidents. Shepherd (1993) points out that designers often fail in the task of control-display integration and create a "breaking the loop" problem. This happens when the design pays insufficient attention to what the operator actually does to effect the task in practice.

There is a considerable body of research demonstrating that errors result from deficiencies in interface design. As far back as (1947), Fitts and Jones examined pilot error. They asked pilots to describe critical incidents in which they had been involved. One category of incident they described related to the misreading of multi-revolution display instruments. The most significant error reported in this study was that of a substitution error, where the pilot confused one instrument for another. This type of error accounted for 50 per cent of all control errors and 13 per cent of all display errors.

Pheasant (1991) suggests that substitution errors are most likely to occur when two actions performed in a similar context have similar elements. They are also common where inconsistencies in the layout or function of controls arise from a lack of standardisation between products. Barber (1987), for example, notes the lack of standardisation in the layout and operation of special-function keys in the keyboards of desk-top computers and word processors. **Figure 10.3** presents a summary of the most common deficiencies.

Figure 10.3: Common Deficiencies of Interface Design

A	Displays
A1	Display not there (necessary information unavailable).
A2	Display gives incorrect information.
A3	Display unreliable (therefore ignored by operators).
A4	Display not visible/conspicuous.
A5	Display not legible (graduations, labelling, lighting, etc.).
A6	Display not intelligible (ambiguous, unclear, etc.).
A7	Display contrary to stereotype or convention.
A8	Confusion between inadequately differentiated displays.
A9	Display of irrelevant or poorly prioritised information leads to confusion.
B	Controls
B1	Control not accessible.
B2	Control too difficult to operate.
B3	Control likely to be operated accidentally (due to design and/or location).
B4	Control contrary to stereotype or convention.
B5	Control not compatible with displays.
B6	Confusion between inadequately differentiated controls (too close, too similar, inadequately labelled, etc.).
B7	Confusion due to inconsistencies in control layout.
B8	Inadequate feedback of control operation.

Bridger (1995) suggests a range of guidelines to optimise the integration of displays and controls:

- Proximity and similarity should be used in a constrained way so that controls are perceived to belong to their associated displays.

- Human beings are capable of retaining a visual image of a real object in memory and of manipulating this image in a manner analogous to the real object. The more the operator has to rotate the mental image to make some kind of decision about it, the more time it takes. Therefore the spatial correspondence between the two should be high.

- There is a body of research to demonstrate that humans have an inherent tendency to attribute meaning to the movements of objects and a limited understanding of cause-effect relationships. Displays and controls that behave in a manner consistent with a prevailing stereotype are said to be compatible. Barber (1987) talks about the clockwise-for-anything stereotype.

- People share expectations concerning the way in which objects are likely to operate. Such expectations are called motion stereotypes and they are generally learned rather than innate. There is a strong body of research on motion stereotypes. Pheasant (1986) and Murrell (1969) have produced a list, presented in **Figure 10.4**.

Figure 10.4: Motion Stereotypes

Actions of:

1. Turning a control clockwise.
2. Moving a control forward or to the right.
3. Moving a control downwards in the UK (and some other areas) but upwards in the US (and some other areas).

Are expected to result in:

1. Similar movements of physical objects or the pointers of displays (occurring in any combination of pair of planes).
2. Increase in some function quantity (e.g. speed, volume, time, etc.); the progression of a process through a sequence of stages.

Many of these stereotypes relate to the turning of controls, the movement of controls and progression through a sequence of stages. The general view is that such stereotypes must be considered in interface design.

- Indigenous culture, alphabets and symbolism appear to influence people's behaviour. Hsu and Peng (1993), for example, show that the Chinese differ from US subjects in their performance associated with the control-display relationship, on a four-burner range. Whereas US subjects mapped the left switch arrangement into an inverted U (i.e. far left, near left, near right, far right) the Chinese subjects preferred the inverted N (i.e. far left, near left, far right, near right). Courtney (1994) reports that, although the Chinese share many stereotypes with the West, they have many opposing stereotypes.

- Considerations of spatial memory and the operator's limited ability to process mental images can minimise unnecessary mental work.

CHAPTER ROUND-UP

- The human operator perceives things in many ways that are not accessible to consciousness. These perceptual processes organise information to maximise its meaningfulness. Visual displays have to take account of such processes in order to ensure a correct interpretation of the information. Failure to take account of such processes will lead to inappropriate designs. The same considerations apply to controls. The integration of displays and controls requires a consideration of general user expectations and population stereotypes. It is envisaged that information technology can facilitate a more flexible approach. Displays can be implemented using sophisticated software. The machine can present information to the operator through a variety of displays. Many types of displays are available, but the appropriateness of the displays depends on the nature of the task for which the information is to be used. The choice is between an analogue or a digital display, although within each category a number of presentational forms is available. In terms of auditory displays, the choice is more limited.

- Controls complete the communication link. The choice and design of controls is significantly related to the type of task, operator and protective clothing. There is a well-established set of principles covering the design of controls and their influence on employee performance. A wide variety of control and control mechanisms is available off the shelf, although the best design most likely depends on the particular demands of the task and the criteria used to assess performance. Numerous examples exist of inappropriately designed or selected controls, specifically in consumer products, nuclear power stations and heavy equipment design.

Chapter 11

WORKPLACE AND WORKSPACE DESIGN

INTRODUCTION

This chapter considers two dimensions of the human factors approach: workplace and workspace design. There is a tendency to concentrate on the individual's immediate workspace in the form of controls and displays and not give enough consideration to the overall workplace design. This chapter considers a number of issues including:

- The physical requirements of the workplace.

- Communication issues including auditory requirements.

- The social dimensions of the workplace.

- An ergonomic approach to workstation design.

- Design issues for standing and seated workers.

- Work surface design and the design of visual display terminals.

PHYSICAL REQUIREMENTS OF THE WORKPLACE

Oborne (1995) argues that the workplace must be designed to fit the human being's anthropometric dimensions. He identifies three particular workplace design issues.

Passageways

If operators have to walk down passageways or between machines, this has major implications for the space available to the operator. Damon et al. (1971) suggests the following as minimum dimensions for a range of different passageways:

- **Height**: At least 195 cm or 160 cm if stooping is permitted.

- **Width**: At least 63 cm.

Oborne suggests that, where there are space limitations, the passageway can be trapezoidal in shape (63 cm at shoulder and 30 cm at feet). In the case of gangways, the general recommendation is that the width should be increased by 50 cm for each person likely to walk about.

Stairs and Ramps

A number of studies have examined the physiological implications of stairs and ramps. Corlett et al. (1972) compared the average energy required to climb either stairs or ramps that had slopes ranging from 10 to 30 degrees. They found that the physiological cost of stairs was always less than that of a ramp of equal slope. They highlight that the stairs cause increased knee bending which for older, infirm people makes ramps easier to use.

In terms of the use of stairs, four issues are important: the riser height or the vertical distance between one step and another, the distance between the front and the back of the steps, the steepness or slope and the tread texture. Fitch et al. (1974) demonstrate that stairs impose an individual gait on the user because of the knee and pelvic angles required. If this gait is irregular or accentuated, it can cause discomfort and increase the expenditure of energy. Mital et al. (1987) show that a riser height of 102 mm along with a tread depth of 305 mm is optimum because it produces the least movement at the ankle, knee and hip-joints. In general, steeper stairs cause more energy to be expended. The research shows that almost twice as much oxygen is used in a 30 degree slope than in a 10 degree slope.

There is considerable evidence to demonstrate that the use of stairs can lead to accidents. This happens because of the absence of handrails. If handrails are used, they should be of appropriate diameter and height. Mital et al. (1987) demonstrate that a height of 90 cm is optimum from a biomechanical and personal preference perspective.

Ladders

Ladders are frequently used where space is at a premium, and there is clear evidence to demonstrate that ladders are more dangerous to use than stairs. Statistics in Ireland demonstrate that about 10 per cent of all falls from a height in industry involve ladders. Dewar (1977) analysed 248 ladder accident reports. Sixty-six per cent of accidents occurred when the ladder slipped during climbing or while the operator was working on the ladder; 34 per cent of ladder accidents were attributed to misplacing the feet or slipping when climbing. A number of factors, therefore, appear important in a health and safety context:

- The forces that restrain the ladder at the lower level.

- The operator's climbing action.

- The angle of the ladder.

- The climber's stature, which affects the knee and pelvic angles required to climb the ladder.

- The climbing style of the operator.

On the ladder issue, McIntyre and Bates (1982) demonstrate three distinct styles of climbing:

- The lateral gait with the arm on the same side as the moving foot used both for propulsion and safety. It is also moved at the same time as the foot.

- Four-lead lateral gait. In this case the hand moves slightly later than the foot.

- Two-diagonal gait patterns, which operate in a similar fashion to the lateral gait with the arm opposite to the leg moving.

THE COMMUNICATION DYNAMICS OF THE WORKPLACE

Communication within the workplace is both with machines and other operators and it may utilise sensory, visual or tactile senses. This means that the operator has visibility, auditory and movement requirements.

In terms of movement requirements, important machines should be placed within easy access of the operator. It is recommended that machines and workplaces should be grouped according to function and to ensure that operator movement from one machine to another follows the sequence of use. There is limited evidence on the effectiveness of layout. However, Fowler et al. (1968) report research that shows that, when controls and displays are arranged on the operator's console, and follow good design principles, performance time is reduced.

The issue of visibility is important. Operators should not be impaired visually in terms of both machines and other operators. Poor illumination levels, and lines of sight obstructed by other equipment/operators, can hinder visibility. Oborne (1995) suggests that effective workplace design can be achieved by mapping the operator's sight lines.

The nature of the visual environment has implications for visual strain and fatigue. Dainoff (1982) investigated the relationship between prolonged use of VDU and visual fatigue. He found significant fatiguing effects. Coe et al. (1980) found that creative workers report fewer symptoms than other workers. Full-time operators were more likely to report fatigue and irritations. Rey and Meyer (1980) found that VDU operators who worked 6-9 hours per day at their terminals were more likely to have visual problems and complaints than operators who worked less than 4 hours per day at a VDU. Ghiringelli (1980) found that there was an increase in eye irritation for workers who used terminals for more than 3 hours per day.

Oborne (1995) suggests that one of the reasons for the positive relationship between eyestrain complaints and VDU usage lies in the amount of work the eye muscles are expected to do. He points out that in order to perceive near and far objects the lens shape is constantly being altered — accommodating normal visual work the ciliary muscles in the eye are continually varying in the level of contraction and, therefore, pump blood to maintain an oxygen supply. VDU work does not allow this to happen because the copy and the screen are placed close to one another and the operator's eyes have little chance to vary their accommodation level. Starr et al. (1982) demonstrate that, if operators wear proper glasses, the incidence of complaints from VDU users significantly reduces. It is also clear that when the luminance contrast between the screen and the surrounding work environment is appropriate and the quality of the display characters is good, the problem is significantly reduced. High-contrast displays cause the most significant eye problems, and the greater the number of reflections off the screen, the greater the operator annoyance. However, it did not affect the number of eye complaints reported. If the characters have strongly oscillating luminances, it is more likely to lead to eye irritations and red eyes. It also has a significant impact on operator performance levels.

SOCIAL DIMENSIONS OF THE WORKPLACE

The workplace is an important social arena. The nature of the physical environment may, however, impact on the social environment and the level of social interaction, which takes place. There are a number of important dimensions of the social environment, including the requirements of personal space, territoriality, the influence of individual differences and the role of national culture differences in the workplace.

Personal Space

Sommer (1969) defines personal space as an area with invisible boundaries surrounding a person's body and into which other people may not enter. Savinar (1975) demonstrates that people have space requirements in both vertical and lateral directions and, if there is a lack of space in one direction, then the person's spatial needs will increase in the other direction. Hall (1976) suggests that the social space surrounding a person has four distinct dimensions: intimate, personal, social and public distance. The boundaries of each zone are not fixed and may vary depending on the circumstances. Furthermore, there are cultural differences. Hall suggests that the intimate distance is typified by physical contact that is restricted in many cultures. The personal distance is reserved for well-known friends and is viewed as a buffer zone between an area reserved for intimate acquaintances and one in which less personal contact takes place.

Most work-related business is conducted in a context where social distance is important. People who work together tend to use close social distance. However, there may be varying degrees of formality depending on the nature of the business transaction.

The behavioural consequences of an invasion of a person's space are significant. The research evidence suggests a number of important consequences:

- Sommer (1969) reports that individuals may experience tensions, discomfort, flight and other defence behaviour.

- McBride et al. (1965) report that flight is an extreme reaction to personal space invasion. Patterson et al. (1984) found that subjects engaged in blocking out and leaning away. Other research reports tensing-up and fleeing reactions.

- There is research evidence to demonstrate that an invasion of personal space can affect performance. Middlemist et al. (1976) demonstrate that space invasion can reduce performance, primarily because the individual's arousal level tends to rise above the optimum.

- Sinha and Sinha (1991) considered the effects of spatial infringements on employees performing either simple or complex cognitive tasks. The impact of invasion of personal space was greater when they were carrying out complex tasks.

The nature of the impact of the invasion of personal space appears to be moderated by factors such as personality, gender, age, culture, the status of the individuals involved and environmental factors. The key findings from this research are presented in **Table 11.1**.

Territoriality

Oborne (1995) suggests that territoriality is a concept that involves social, unwritten rules of behaviour, with infringement causing discomfort or other behavioural reactions. It differs from personal space, in that territories have fixed locations and do not move around with the person. The boundaries are quite visible and may be personal or interpersonal in nature. Fried and De Frazio (1974) demonstrate certain implicit by-laws with respect to territory. They found that:

- Seated passengers may not be challenged or deprived of their territory except under special circumstances.

- There was little verbal interaction between passengers, leading to the conclusion that many territorial markers are not used.

Table 11.1: *Influence of Moderating Variables on Invasion of Personal Space*

Variable	Researchers	Findings
Personality	Evans and Howard (1973)	• People with personality abnormalities need more space.
	Patterson and Sechrest (1970)	• Extroverts have smaller personal space zones than introverts.
Gender	Liebman (1970)	• Females have smaller personal space zones than males.
	Byrne et al. (1971)	• Males prefer to position themselves across from liked others, while females prefer to position themselves adjacent to liked others.
Age	Willis (1966)	• Peers approach one another more closely than they approach those who were older.
Culture	Hall (1976)	• Germans have larger personal space problems and are less flexible in their spatial behaviour than Americans.
	Sommer (1969)	• Dutch have slightly larger, and Pakistanis slightly smaller, personal space areas.
Status	Patterson and Sechrest (1970)	• External sources of threat such as meeting one who is not known or of a higher status leads to increased personal distance.
Environmental Conditions	Adams and Zucherman (1991)	• Quality of lighting and the direction of approach can affect personal space requirements. • Space requirements were lower in brightly lit rooms rather than dim rooms.

Little (1965) points out that people take account of environmental conditions when considering personal space requirements.

There are some interesting developments in the way individuals are now allowed to use the workplace. One such idea is the concept of the landscaped office (Brookes, 1972). This office is characterised by a lack of boundaries and the provision of spatial flexibility. Different work groups are scattered around without restriction by walls. The need for privacy and territory is accommodated by the provision of screens and providing employees with the flexibility to arrange desks as they feel fit. The layout of the workspace is supposed to reflect the pattern of the work processes and is arranged by employees rather than following a rigid supervised plan. It allows for the participation of all staff in the design of on-going work processes and it appears to have a significant impact on group cohesiveness. Brookes (1972) demonstrates that information flow between workgroups should increase in a landscaped office and employees seem to prefer brighter more colourful and friendly designs than landscaped office designs. On the negative side, there is evidence to suggest that it can result in a loss of privacy, increased noise, distraction, disturbances and interruptions and a perceived loss of control of the space around employees.

Sick Building Syndrome

A particular issue that has emerged in the context of workplace design is sick building syndrome. This refers to the feeling of a group or groups of employees that a part or the whole of their physical environment is unhealthy or psychologically unsuitable for their work processes. This may be due to faulty or inadequate air conditioning systems, noxious substances associated with their furnishings, or simply a distasteful atmosphere. Burge et al. (1987) identified ten symptoms of sick building syndrome including lethargy, blocked nose, dry throat, headache, itchy eyes, dry eyes, flu-like symptoms, runny nose and difficulty in breathing. Sick building syndrome *per se* exists where these symptoms occur more frequently than in normal buildings. Cribb (1992) concluded that up to three-quarters of all office buildings are affected to some degree by poor ventilation, poorly-serviced air conditioning or noxious fumes from furnishings or building materials. Bardana et al. (1988) and Burge et al. (1987) have identified a number of trends:

- Up to 80 per cent of the occupants of a building may be affected.

- Women are more frequently affected than men.

- Clerical and secretarial grades are more frequently affected by the syndrome than managers.

- Open plan offices are more susceptible to the syndrome than other configurations.

In terms of what causes the syndrome, few answers currently exist. Many causes are proposed, including microbiological contamination of humidifiers and pipework, high temperatures and low humidity, which dries out the mucous membranes. The recirculating of air in air-conditioning systems is specifically targeted because this may lead to an accumulation of mildly toxic contaminants and substances. Air ionisation is also highlighted as a contributing factor. It is argued that the presence of machines, plastics, etc. may create a change and positively ionise the air in offices. Positive ionisation can have detrimental effects on employee performance. There is also the suggestion that it may have a stress-related source.

WORKSPACE DESIGN

McCormick (1970) sets out four principles that are aimed at the elimination of wasted effort in the rationalisation of workspace layout. These principles are as follows:

- **Importance Principle**: This states that the most important items should be in the most advantageous or acceptable locations. This, for example, would include the location of emergency controls.

- **Frequency of Use Principle**: This states that the most frequently used devices should be in the most advantageous or accessible locations. In a workstation layout, the most frequently used components should be placed within easy sight and reach of an operator.

- **Function Principle**: This states that those items concerned with clearly related functions or actions should be grouped together. For example, on a panel it makes sense to group together displays and controls that are related to a specific function.

- **Sequence of Use Principle**: This states that items commonly used in a particular sequence should be grouped together and laid out in a manner compatible with that sequence. This allows the operator to follow the arrangement rather than work in an apparently random fashion.

ERGONOMICS AND WORKSPACE DESIGN

One of the aims of ergonomics and workspace design is to achieve an effective interface between the operator and the task so that the operator is not disturbed or inconvenienced by the equipment and workstation at which they are working. The design has to take account of task requirements as well as anatomical, psychological and anthropometric characteristics of the operator.

Characteristics of Users

Designers of work furniture typically design to ensure that 90 per cent of users are accommodated. Much office furniture is designed around a height of approximately 83 cm and assumes provision for a working height adjustable chair. Such a scheme allows short users to raise that chair so that the desk height approximates their sitting elbow height and the desk is high enough so that tall users can work comfortably and have space under the desk for their legs. If there are anthropometric mismatches, these can have significant consequences for operator comfort and efficiency. Short operators, for example, may have to raise their seat heights beyond knee height in order to gain access to the desk with the result that their feet no longer rest firmly on the floor. Therefore, the floor cannot be used by the legs as a fulcrum for stabilising and shifting the weight of the upper body.

Tall operators, on the other hand, may find desk heights of 75 cm too low, since the distance between the eyes and the work surface may be too great for comfortable viewing — causing the operator to slump over the desk when writing. Lack of footspace may also be a problem for tall workers. Ostberg et al. (1984) has recommended the use of height-adjustable desks for use with height-adjustable chairs in order to increase the range of operation accommodated by a workstation.

Seat depth is another issue for short operators. Chairs with deep seats may look more comfortable, but if the seat depth exceeds the operator's buttock-knee length, the back rest cannot be used properly. Short operators are often perched on the front edge of too-deep seats.

Backrest inclination has an impact on trunk inclination in sitting. Andersson (1986) suggests that a height-adjustable lumbar support is not necessary since the height of a fixed support can be optimised to contact the lumbar spines of a wide range of users.

Task Requirements

Three sets of task requirements influence workspace design: visual, postural and temporal. The position of the head is a major determinant of the posture of the body and is influenced by the visual requirements of tasks. If objects are placed above the line of sight, the neck is extended to lift the head backwards, which places a static load on the neck muscles. Brand and Judd (1993) recommend that frequently used displays should not be above the standing or sitting eye height of a short worker. Woodson (1981) pointed out that the eye is sensitive to stimuli up to 95 degrees to the left and right, assuming bifocal vision. He also suggests that the optimum position for placing objects is 50 degrees either side of the straight-ahead line of sight. Other issues to be considered include employee eyesight and the quality of lighting in the work environment.

The position of the hands, arms and feet is another issue. The working area of a desk or bench should always be close to its front edge and with unobstructed access. Rivas et al. (1984) demonstrate that, for both standing and sedentary workers, the redesign of the job to avoid excessive reach led to a reduction in back problems. The preferred zone for work objects lies in the front 210 cm of the bench or desktop.

The temporal requirements of tasks exert a moderating influence on the effects of other factors. Certain jobs impose a high degree of postural constraint as the position of the hand and head are fixed by, for example, a keyboard, documents or a screen. Eason (1991) illustrates that such highly constrained jobs are associated with health hazards.

Jobs may be categorised in terms of the degree of postural constraint that they impose on an employee. Highly constrained jobs require maximum flexibility to be built into a workspace to compensate for the lack of flexibility in the job itself. This has led to the view that frequent rests are required. **Table 11.2** summarises a set of factors that influence working posture.

Table 11.2: Some Factors that Influence Working Posture

Factor	Example
User characteristics	• Age. • Anthropometry. • Body weight. • Fitness. • Joint mobility (range of movement). • Existing musculo-skeletal problem. • Previous injury or surgery. • Eyesight. • Handedness. • Obesity.
Task Requirements	• Visual requirements. • Manual requirements (positional forces). • Cycle times. • Rest periods. • Paced/unpaced work.
Design of the Workspace	• Seat design and dimensions. • Work surface dimensions. • Workspace dimensions (headroom, legroom etc.). • Privacy. • Illumination levels and quality.

WORKSPACE DESIGN FOR STANDING AND SEATED WORKERS

Standing Workers

Bridger (1995) suggests that all objects to be used by standing workers should be placed between hip and shoulder height. This will minimise postural stress caused by excessive stooping or working with the hands/arms in an elevated fashion. If the work involves fine details, it is better to have a higher work surface. This reduces the visual distance and allows the operator to stabilise the forearms by resting them at the work surface. Ayoub (1973) recommends the following work surface heights but cautions that they should be taken only as a guide (**Table 11.3**).

Table 11.3: Recommended Work Surface Heights for Standing Workers (in cm)

Task Requirements	Male	Female
Precision work	109–110	103–113
Light assembly work	99–109	87–93
Heavy work	85–101	78–94

If the workspace is poorly designed, it may significantly increase the postural stress in standing workers. Burge et al. (1987) suggest four stress problems:

- Working with the hands too high or too far away can lead to compensatory lumbar lordosis.

- Working with a surface that is too low can lead to trunk flexion and back muscle strain.

- A constrained foot position due to a lack of clearance. If the worker is working at the corner of a bench, this may lead to a constrained foot position because of toes turned out too much.

- Having to work at the side rather than directly ahead may lead to a twisted spine.

White and Panjabi (1978) suggest a number of strategies that could be effectively used to relieve postural constraints. The provision of stools to enable workers to rest during quiet periods or to alternate between sitting and standing appears to be useful. The placement of one foot on a footrest or footrail also appears to be useful. Putting the foot on a footrest is believed to release the iliopsous muscle on that side and this helps prevent excessive anterior pelvic tilt and lumbar lordosis. Rys and Konz (1994) have investigated the ergonomics of standing. They found that the freedom to stand with one foot forward and elevated appears to be an important feature of a well-designed workplace. Stewart-Buttle et al. (1993) report that prolonged standing causes localised leg muscle fatigue and the use of footrests may relieve some of this. However, the provision of a rail to stand on does not reduce lower leg fatigue but may reduce discomfort in the lower leg, feet and back.

Seated Workers

In sedentary work, the flexibility required is for the worker to adapt both upright, forward-flexed and retiring positions. Ayoub (1973) makes some recommendations for work surface heights for sedentary work. However, for work that involves keyboards, the work surface is often 3–6 cm lower than a writing surface to allow for the thickness of the keyboard (**Table 11.4**).

Table 11.4: Recommended Work Surface Heights for Sedentary Workers (in cm)

Task Requirements	Male	Female
Fine work	93–105	89–95
Precision work	89–94	82–87
Writing	74–72	60–70

In terms of office chairs, a number of researchers have suggested that chairs should be designed with forward-tilted seats. It is argued that this type of chair allows the employee to sit with an erect trunk and less posterior curve because the tilt of the seat improves the angle (Brunswic, 1984; Bridger, 1995). **Figure 11.1** presents some important features of ergonomic chair design.

Figure 11.1: Key Features of Chair Design

1. Seats should swivel and have heights adjustable between 38 and 54 cm. Footrests should be provided for short users.

2. Free space for the legs must be provided both underneath the seat to allow the user to flex the knees by 90 degrees or more, and underneath the work surface to allow knee extension when the user is reclining.

3. A five-point base is recommended for stability if the chair has castors.

4. The function of the backrest is to stabilise the trunk. A backrest height of approximately 50 cm above the seat is required to provide both lumbar and partial thoracic support.

5. If the backrest reclines, it should do so independently of the seat to provide trunk-thigh angle variation and consequent variation in the distribution of forces acting on the lumbopelvic region.

6. Lumbar support can be achieved either by using extra cushioning to form a lumbar pad or by correcting the backrest. In either case, there must be open space between the lumbar support and the seat pan vertically below it to allow for posterior protrusion of the buttocks.

7. The seat back must have a slight hollow in the buttock area to prevent the user's pelvis from sliding forward. This keeps the lower back in contact with the backrest. The leading edge of the seat should curl downward to reduce under thigh pressure.

8. Armrests should be high enough to support the forearms when the user is sitting erect. They should also end well short of the leading edge of the seat so as not to contact the front edge of the desk. If the armrests support the weight of the arms, less load is placed on the lumbar spine.

9. Modern chairs tend to have a thin layer of high-density padding. Layers of thick foam tend to destabilise the sitter. The foam can collapse after constant use.

10. Cloth upholstery provides friction to enhance the stability of the sitter.

There is some research to demonstrate that users find forward-tilted seats to be uncomfortable.

The lack of agreement among the experts makes it unsurprising that so little real progress has been made towards a solution either in the office furniture field or in car seats.

There are at least two different problems associated with seating at the office:

- Static loading of muscles causes shortening and circulation problems. Seat evaluation by ergonomic studies is the recognised way to design for reduced muscle activity.

- Static loading of ligamentous structures (includes discs, capsules, ligaments, fascia, etc.) causes permanent deformation because all these structures behave plastically. To avoid this effect, lumbar support has been the recommended solution. In the office environment, this has not been particularly successful and is being superseded by the forward-tilted seat posture.

In car seats, this solution cannot be used because the knee is bound to be above the hip. The back must be supported directly. Many authoritative sources still recommend lumbar support for this purpose. It is suggested that the lumbar support should be adjusted to the apex of the lumbar curvature — probably at about L3, which is the centre of the lumbar spine.

Trends in Office Seating

The introduction of lumbar support chairs from about 1970 to 1985 in various industries where keyboard work was normal did not result in the improvements expected. In fact, in the paper, *Sitting Posture: An Old Problem and a New One* (The Ergonomic Society Lecture, 1986), the Society tried to seek an explanation for an increase, rather than a reduction, in problems where "good" lumbar support chairs had been introduced for keyboard work. In the last ten years, the main trend has been towards forward-tilted seats.

The main advantage of the forward-tilted seat is to open out the angle between body and thigh. At the same time, a trend in car seat design has been the anti-submarine seat, which effectively closes up this angle again with the raised thigh position.

WORK SURFACE DESIGN

There is a significant body of research to illustrate that the provision of tilt in work surfaces and the provision of document holders and free space in the working area can be beneficial from the human operator perspective. Mandal (1981) suggests that displays should tilt towards the user by about 15 degrees to encourage more upright posture of the trunk. There is evidence to demonstrate that tilted desktops do reduce the trunk and neck flexion of seated employees engaging in reading and writing and this reduces the load on the corresponding parts of the spine (Porter et al., 1992; De Wall et al., 1991).

It is also recommended that, for both standing and sedentary workers, work surfaces should be arranged so that the employee does not have to work continually with objects placed on one side or reach excessively to the side. The main working area should be directly in front of the worker's body to minimise any twisting of the trunk. Pearcy (1993) demonstrates that the twisting mobility of the human back is increased in sitting compared with standing. The increase essentially occurs because, in a flexed position, the morphology of the lumbar facet joints permits more axial rotation. The increase can be up to 38 per cent. The additional stress of twisting may result in high annular stresses, which may result in fibres rupturing. Pearcy warns that workers have to resist sudden, external twisting forces because they carry a high risk of injury.

Visual Display Units/Terminals

The design of workstations for the visual display unit operator is an issue of contemporary relevance and has received considerable attention in the literature. Numerous guidelines have been proposed that attempt to specify user space requirements and to define the appropriate working environment in functional and practical terms.

Grieco (1986) uses the term "postural fixity" to describe static postures of the head, neck and trunk that occur in VDU work. Fixed postures and cumulative trauma disorders (CTDs) are the main musculo-skeletal problems associated with VDU work.

In terms of workspace design, the key factor is the equipment. The equipment drives, for example, the position of the hands and the head (position of keyboard and screen). Grieco argues that an enforced eight-hours-a-day sitting should be regarded as an occupational risk factor. Static postures may result in depletion of local blood supply and increased fatigue. He also argues that a fixed posture is hazardous because it may interfere with the nutrient exchange mechanism of the body. **Table 11.5** summarises some design solutions for increasing the flexibility of VDU workstations. The literature in general advises a participatory approach as a way of designing features that are most beneficial to the employee.

Table 11.5: Product Features that Enhance VDU Work Station Flexibility

Workstation	Feature or Accessory
Source documents	• Document holder. • Book stand. • Tilted area of work surface. • Shelving. • Bulletin board.
VDU Screen	• Movable screen. • Tilt and swivel adjustment. • Screen holder.
Keyboard	• Keyboard detached from VDU. • Keyboard drawer.
Seating	• Footrest. • Armrest. • Lumbar pad. • Narrow backrest (permits trunk lateral flexion and rotation). • Lumbar and thoracic support. • Recline mechanism.
Desk	• Height adjustment. • Tilt adjustment. • Extensions for expanding surface area..

A number of minimum ergonomic requirements relating to equipment/environmental and operator/computer interface have been suggested by the HSA. **Figure 11.2** summarises these recommendations.

Figure 11.2: Ergonomic Requirements for VDUs

- **Display Screen:** Individual perceptions of screen flicker vary. The HSA has suggested that a screen that is flicker-free to 90 per cent of users would be regarded as satisfying the minimum requirement as it is not technically possible to eliminate flicker for all users. A change to a different display may resolve individual problems but persistent display instabilities, such as flicker, jump, jitter or swim may reflect basic design problems and the supplier's assistance should then be sought.

- **Brightness and Contrast:** Both negative polarity (light characters on dark background) or positive polarity (dark characters on light background) are acceptable but each have different advantages. With negative polarity, flicker is less perceptible, legibility is better for those with low acuity vision and characters may be perceived as larger than they are. With positive polarity, reflections are less perceptible, edges appear sharper and luminance balance is easier to achieve.

- **Screen Adjustability:** Tilt or swivel mechanisms allow the worker to obtain a natural, relaxed posture and avoid glare and reflections. They should be simple and easy to use and can be part of the screen or the furniture or provided by separate screen support devices.

- **Glare and Reflections:** Problems can arise through direct glare, e.g. from unshielded bright lights or bright areas in the workers' field of view; contrast glare, where the difference between brightly and dimly lit parts of the environment is too great; and reflected glare from reflections on the screen. Shading, shielding or repositioning sources of light; rearranging of workstation furniture; modifying the colour or reflectance of walls, ceilings, furnishings, etc., are all examples of methods to reduce problems of reflection and glare.

- **Keyboard:** Keyboard design should allow workers to locate and activate keys quickly, accurately and without discomfort.

- **Design of Work Surface:** Work surface dimension should take account of the range of tasks performed, position and use of hands for each task and use and storage of work materials/equipment, e.g. documents, telephones, etc.

- **Work Chair:** The primary requirement here is that the chair should allow the user to achieve a comfortable position — adjustability in height and seat back height and tilt are required.

- **Space Requirements:** Adequate clearance for thighs, knees, lower legs and feet under the work surface and between furniture components is necessary — the user must be able to find a comfortable working position and postural change.

- **Lighting:** Lighting should be appropriate for all tasks performed at the workstation. Any supplementary lighting provided for particular tasks or personal needs should not interfere with adjacent workstations. The level of lighting generally recommended for the use of VDUs is 300 to 500 lux.

- **Noise:** Impairment of concentration or interference with normal conversation should not occur as a result of equipment in use at the workstation — replacing, soundproofing or repositioning of the offending equipment should eliminate the problem.

- **Heat and Humidity:** Electronic equipment can be a source of dry heat that can affect the thermal environment at a work station — ventilation and humidity should be maintained at a level to prevent discomfort and problems with sore eyes.

- **Radiation:** So little radiation is emitted from current designs of display screen equipment that no special action by employers/users is really necessary to meet this requirement. Typically, users would not receive more than 1 per cent of the recommended maximum exposure. Accurate measurement is technically difficult anyway.

- **Task Design and Software:** Good task design can be as important as the choice of equipment, furniture and working environment. The General Application Regulations (1993) refer to the principles of software ergonomics.

CHAPTER ROUND-UP

- Workplace and workspace design is an important component of ergonomics. In terms of the workplace, two issues are relevant: the communication requirements of employees and the physical work setting and the issue of personal space and territory and how these may influence employee performance.

- In terms of workspace design, the overriding principles to consider are the arrangement of the components in terms of their sequence and frequency of use and their importance. Careful consideration should also be given to where displays should be placed in relation to other displays, controls *vis-à-vis* other controls and the relationship between displays and controls. Consideration of these factors should enhance the link between the employee and production processes.

- The reduction of postural stress is an important component in workstation design. The literature suggests that a multifaceted approach is needed to arrive at effective workstation designs for different categories of employees. The requirements of tasks and user characteristics must be considered when making options for workstation design. The workstation-task interaction is an important component of analysis in ergonomics.

Chapter 12

JOB CHARACTERISTICS, ORGANISATIONAL CULTURE AND SAFETY MANAGEMENT

INTRODUCTION

This chapter considers two important elements of a human factors approach to health and safety. These are:

- The influence of the job and shift work systems on human performance and safety behaviour.

- The organisational characteristics that influence safety-related behaviour at work and the development of a safety culture.

There is a considerable body of research emphasising the crucial role of job and organisational characteristics as key components influencing and helping to prevent human error and facilitating the emergence of a positive safety culture. There is also a tendency to consider human error at the level of the individual and the job without adequate consideration of organisational issues. This chapter will address the major issue of organisational culture and its specific influence on the development of a safety-first culture.

THE JOB AND SAFETY BEHAVIOUR

Successful management of human behaviour and, by extension, safety behaviour involves consideration of the design features of jobs and the degree of person-job fit. Fit occurs on two levels:

- Physical fit, which focuses on the design of workplaces and the work environment.

- Mental fit, which focuses on individual information and decision-making requirements as well as the perception of risk and danger.

These fit requirements raise important questions for the design of jobs. Stranks (1994) identifies eight factors in job design that should receive consideration within a safety management programme:

- The identification and analysis of key job tasks to be performed and the appraisal of likely errors.

- The evaluation of operator decision-making and the achievement of an optimum balance between human and automatic contributions to safety actions.

- The application of ergonomic principles to the person-machine interface.

- The design and presentation of procedures and operating instructions.

- The provision of correct tools and equipment to perform the job.

- The scheduling of work patterns including the operation of shift systems and the control of fatigue and stress.

- The advancement of efficient and effective communications while performing the job.

- The management and organisation of the immediate work environment and the creation of a safety culture within the organisation.

Some of these issues are addressed in this and later chapters, drawing where possible on the available research evidence.

MENTAL WORKLOAD AND ERROR

Mental workload is an important concept in terms of the interaction of the operator with a work process. Bridger (1995) suggests that an assessment of mental workload is important in terms of three issues: evaluating alternative job designs, evaluating the high-stress aspects of a job and evaluating operator performance. Two important measures of mental workload exist: physiological and psychological.

Physiological Measures of Mental Workload

Physiological measures generally assume that higher workload leads to an increase in the operator's state of arousal of the central nervous system. This increased arousal then leads to changes in particular physiological variables such as skin responses, heart rate, eye movement, and speech patterns. **Figure 12.1** summarises some of the key physiological measures of mental work overload.

Psychological Measures of Mental Workload

The main psychological methods for measuring mental workload are: (a) subjective opinions of employees and (b) measures of spare mental capacity by means of secondary tasks. Employee opinions about mental stress can be obtained using rating scales, questionnaires and interview. In aviation, rating scales such as the Cooper-Harper Scale have been developed to assess the handling quality of aircraft. The validity of these scales depends on the items included, how they were selected and the size of the sample on which the scale was validated.

Interviews and questionnaires are primarily supplementary sources of information on mental workload. In aviation, the de-briefing of pilots is commonly used, as is self-reported logging of stressful activities. Data from these sources can correlate well with other sources.

Measurement of spare mental capacity is based on the premise that an employee has limited capacity to process information. The greater the difficulty of the task, the more the employee's spare mental capacity is used up and the less will be available to allocate to other tasks carried out at the same time. This has led psychologists to suggest that measures of secondary task performance can be used as an index of primary task load. The tasks must, however, be capable of measurement in terms of the number of errors or performance time.

There are some reservations about the effectiveness of this method. Wetherall (1981) suggests that the technique is useful, if the secondary tasks are carefully selected *vis-à-vis* the primary task. He sees the key criteria as the minimisation of interference with primary task performance. He also recommends that other methods be used.

Figure 12.1: Physiological Measures of Mental Workload

GSR (Galvanic skin response): The electrical resistance of the skin changes when sweating increases, because of changes in the concentration of ions in the skin cells. GSR is often measured on the hand, foot, wrist or forehead. Changes in GSR have been shown to correlate with anxiety. In studies of driving, GSR has been shown to correlate with roadway events that increase workload. Although stressful situations do reduce the GSR, temperature, humidity, and physical workload can have the same effect and need to be controlled when GSR measurements are made.

Heart Rate: Heart rate does not necessarily change with mental workload, although it can increase under stress. Tea, coffee and cigarette smoking can also increase the heart rate. Heart rate variability measured on the basis of the instantaneous heart rate or of the interbeat intervals is sometimes used. Heart rate variability may decrease with mental workload, but it is also affected by changes in respiration rate, which can compound the results.

EMG (electromyography): Increases in forearm and forehead EMG have been correlated with high task loading in a variety of aircrew tasks.

EEG (electroencephalogram): The electrical activity of the brain can be measured using scalp electrodes. Semi-periodic activity in the EEG correlates with states of alertness (4 to 10 Hz — drowsiness or sleeping; 20 to 30 Hz — alertness). The EEG is an extremely complex signal that requires expert interpretation. Its use as an instrument for mental workload measurement is limited.

Eye Movement and Blinking: Fixation time, look-away time, and sequencing of eye movements can be used as an index of workload. Alertness and directed attention may reduce the blink rate. Over-arousal or emotional stress may increase the blink rate.

Speech Pattern Analysis: Changes in speech are detectable when a person is under stress (the modulation of speech may change, for example).

WORK CAPACITY

Work capacity refers to the employee's capacity to carry out physical work. A range of personal and environmental factors is involved including age, body weight, gender, alcohol consumption, motivation, air quality and other environmental variables.

Personal Factors

Some of the more common personal factors are:

- **Body weight**: Body weight influences all activities in which the employee has to move. It affects the person's oxygen consumption rate.

- **Age**: Age appears to have a significant influence on worker capacity. An individual's maximum oxygen uptake declines gradually after 20 years of age. This decline is due to a reduction in cardiac output and, in particular, the loss of muscle function.

- **Gender**: Women have a lower maximum oxygen uptake than men and have a higher percentage of body fat. They also have less haemoglobin than men.

- **Alcohol consumption**: Alcohol increases cardiac output thereby reducing cardiac efficiency. It also has an impact on liver function and can lead to low blood sugar levels.

- **Smoking**: Smoking reduces work capacity by reducing the oxygen-carrying capacity of the blood. It also causes chronic damage to the respiratory system. This has major implications for the transfer of oxygen from the air to the blood. In general, smoking has a depressing effect on the physical capacity of employees.

- **Training**: Special physical and job training interventions can enhance the work capacity of the employee. Training regimes can be developed which strengthen parts of the musculo-skeletal system.

- **Motivation**: Motivation is a very significant determinant of work capacity. We will consider this issue later in this chapter when we focus on the qualities of "good" jobs.

Environmental Factors

Many environmental factors affect work capacity. These include noise levels, the wearing of protective clothing and equipment, and work environment. These have been considered in other parts of this Handbook.

WORKING HEIGHT

In general, the best working height for activity is one that minimises the overall degree of effort required by the employee for the effective performance of the task. The research suggests a number of fairly well-established principles:

- Heavy tasks should be performed at well below the elbow height.

- Tasks involving fine visual discrimination should be performed as close to eye level as possible.

- Tasks that are manipulative in nature should be performed from 50 mm to 100 mm below elbow height.

- Tasks that are lighter and more delicate should be performed from 50 mm to 100 mm above elbow height, with the wrists properly supported.

- When the task involves lifting and handling, the ideal height is from the knuckle to a little above the elbow height.

- Where the task involves two-handed pushing and pulling actions, the ideal height is a little below elbow height.

- Where the task involves hand-operated controls, between elbow and shoulder height is the best height.

Pheasant (1986) has misgivings about adjustable workstations, primarily because employees often fail to adjust them and engage in unsafe work practices and because they may also cause back problems because of inappropriate support where the work surface is too low. He suggests that employees are much more likely to notice a work surface that is too high, primarily because upper-limb muscle fatigue comes on more rapidly than back muscle fatigue.

EFFICIENT WORKING

In job design terms, an efficient job action is one that achieves its ends with a minimum of wasted effort. There is a general view that employees seek to minimise the effort that they put into their tasks. This has led job design specialists to the belief that, if an organisation demands a safe working environment, the job must be designed so that the correct way of doing something is always the easiest way of doing it. Pheasant (1991) suggests that certain characteristics of jobs are inherently negative whereas others represent effective job design features. The negative features include the following:

- Performing any single activity continuously for a long period of time, especially where it is carried out in a sedentary position.

- Jobs involving explosive efforts at maximum intensity.

- Jobs requiring many repetitive motions or involving small muscle groups.

- Jobs requiring static muscle loading.

On the other hand, well-designed jobs are those that involve many changes in activity, involve dynamic work of moderate intensity, involve the large muscle groups, and have an appropriate balance between work and rest.

MOTION ECONOMY

Barnes (1963) formulated the concept of motion economy. He defined it as the optimisation of working efficiency measured in terms of the number of motions required and the time it takes to perform them. Barnes formulated nine principles of motion economy and these are summarised in **Figure 12.2**.

Figure 12.2: Principles of Motion Economy

1. The two hands should start and finish their motion at the same time.

2. The two hands should not be idle at the same time, except during rest pauses.

3. Motions of the upper limbs should be opposite and symmetrical (about the mid-line of the body).

4. Use the smallest body movement compatible with effective task performance.

5. Momentum should be employed to assist movement — but minimised if muscle action will be required to overcome it.

6. Smooth curved motions of the hands are preferable to straight-line motions involving sudden sharp changes in direction.

7. Ballistic (free-swinging) movements are faster, easier and more accurate than movements under continuous muscular control.

8. Work should be arranged to permit an easy, natural rhythm.

9. Eye fixations should be as few and as close together as possible.

These principles focus on the co-ordinated use of the hands, the exploitation of gravity and momentum, and free-swinging movement. The even distribution of workload between the two hands ensures that neither is disproportionally loaded. Finger movements are faster and more efficient than movements of the hand at the wrist, which, in turn, are more efficient than movement of the forearm. Pheasant (1991), however, differs from Barnes in that he contends that the first four principles are a prescription for fast repetitive movements leading to an overload of small muscle groups. This he sees as not differing in any significant way from a job design and ergonomic perspective.

CHARACTERISTICS OF A GOOD JOB

There is a comprehensive debate in the literature about what constitutes a good job in job design terms. The answer must take consideration of a large number of issues, primary among them, however, must be individual expectations and notions of work as a central life interest. Eklund (1988) provides a useful synthesis of the literature in this respect. He has developed a set of characteristics of a good job, primarily directed at the redesign of blue-collar jobs. It represents a significant contrast to the ideas put forward by Taylor and Ford (job simplification) and Marxist thinking on alienation from work. It incorporates many elements of the human relations school combined with other sound ergonomic principles. This list of characteristics is presented in **Figure 12.3**.

Figure 12.3: Eklund's Checklist: Characteristics of a Good Job

1. Variation; a job that consists of different subtasks.
2. Overview of the entirety of the production process.
3. Freedom to move around physically.
4. Long cycle time.
5. Self-paced work.
6. Influence on the choice of working methods and their order.
7. Influence on production quantity and quality.
8. Planning and problem-solving.
9. Control and adjustment of the results.
10. Few temporal deadlines (time pressure).
11. Few temporal constraints (time binding).
12. Continuous development of skills.
13. Freedom of action.
14. Responsibility and authority.
15. Participation.
16. Work demands in parity with ability.
17. Positive work management climate.
18. Group organisation.
19. Social support and interaction with colleagues.

Socio-Technical Systems and Work

Socio-technical systems theory has had a considerable influence on job design. This theory postulates that there is a technical and social subsystem, and the link between the machines and the social system is termed "work organisation". The best use of technology depends upon the design of an appropriate work organisation. This work organisation in turn determines the social organisation of the workplace and the nature of relationships between individuals. Cherns (1976) summarises the main design principles derived from socio-technical systems theory as they have been applied in many organisations. These principles are summarised in **Figure 12.4**.

Figure 12.4: Principles of Socio-technical Job Design

Compatibility: The way that socio-technical design is carried out must be compatible with the changes that are made. For example, if one of the reasons for change is to make the most of the cognitive skills of the workforce, these skills must be utilised in the process of change itself.

Minimal critical specification: In the design of new systems, no more should be specified than is absolutely essential. This leaves individuals with freedom to determine the precise details of how a task is to be carried out. It also leaves open options for change and improvement and enhances adaptability to unanticipated events. Strictly specified rules and procedures can inhibit an organisation's ability to adapt.

The Socio-technical Criterion: This principle states that variance in a system (the occurrence of unspecified and unprogrammed events) should be reduced by controlling it as close to its source as possible. Much of the system of supervision, inspection, and maintenance in industry is an attempt to reduce variance from a distance — to correct the consequences of variance, rather than control it. If operators carry out their own inspection, the size of the variance-control feedback loop is reduced.

The Multifunction Principle: This principle is aimed at increasing the adaptability of the organisation by allowing workers to fulfil more than one role, but designing jobs so as to reduce the interchangeability of people.

Boundary location: In all organisations, boundaries between different departments have to be drawn up. Such divisions are usually made on the basis of function, technology, territory, or time. For example, engineering products often pass through several different departments, such as milling or grinding shops, in the manufacturing process. Of the total time taken to manufacture a product, only a portion is spent with the item in contact with machines. Transport, storage, etc take up the rest. An alternative is the group or unit production method where each department makes a compete product. This approach has been tried, for example, in car assembly.

Information flow: This principle states that information should go where it is needed in the first instance rather than via senior management to subordinates. The tendency for information to filter down from above can have disadvantages as well as being inefficient. Managers may become preoccupied with matters for which their subordinates should be responsible. An information system designed according to socio-technical principles should direct information efficiently to those parts of the organisation where it is needed. It should also support two-way communication.

Support congruence: Administrative and management systems should be designed to reinforce those behaviours that the organisation wishes to encourage. If an aim is to encourage employees to take a more responsible attitude towards their jobs, then supervision and payment systems should be designed to be congruent with this goal.

Design and human values: This principle emphasises that systems must be designed to provide high-quality jobs. This is a difficult principle to apply — individuals may respond differently to changes in job design and have different needs.

Incompletion: Design never ends.

SHIFT WORK SYSTEMS

Shift work systems are an inevitable feature of modern industrial life. The ILO have estimated that between 15 per cent and 30 per cent of industrial workers in developed countries engage in shift work of some kind and other commentators estimate that 10–15 per cent of employees currently work nights. This makes the topic of shift work a relevant one in the context of the employee safety and health.

Circadian Rhythms

It is now accepted that the body has a clock, the nature of which is obscure but which is partially synchronised to the external world. Minors and Waterhouse (1985) have studied body temperature rhythm and this demonstrates a daily fluctuation of about 0.5°C on either side of the mean value of about 37°C. It hits its low point at approximately 4.00 a.m. Peak temperatures are reached between noon and late evening. From 10.00 p.m. onwards temperature begins to fall rapidly. Similar changes occur in cardiac, respiratory and renal functions. This body temperature rhythm is inextricably related to cyclical changes in arousal. This state of arousal determines an individual's pattern of sleep and wakefulness. It is well established that there is a more pronounced tendency to feel sleepy at certain times of the day (2.00–7.00 in the morning and 2.00–5.00 in the afternoon). These are described as periods of vulnerability in the cardiac cycle. (At these times, many individuals engage in microsleeps lasting a few seconds.) Mitler et al. (1988) suggest that these periods are characterised by inattention, forgetfulness and performance lapses. The sleepiness cycle has two peaks. The first one coincides with the body temperature cycle, whereas the other is called the post-lunch dip. Blake (1971) and Colquhoun (1975) demonstrate in their research that mental performance decreases in the early afternoon, despite the fact that the body temperature continues to rise.

Circadian rhythms have major implications for bodily functions. Some of the research findings can be summarised thus:

- Most deaths occur and more babies are born in the middle of the night (Mitler et al., 1988).

- Heart attacks tend to cluster around two peak periods, between 6.00–10.00 a.m. and 6.00–8.00 p.m.

- People with chronic back problems often tend to find the pain is worse in the morning or the evening (Baxter, 1987).

- Performance in a variety of work tasks follows the temperature rhythms fairly closely. Time-of-day effects are most pronounced in vigilant tasks and prolonged, simple, repetitive tasks (Folkard and Monk, 1985).

- Kerkhoff (1985) found that some people are morning types and other are evening types. Morning types have an earlier peak in their body temperature rhythms (up to three hours). He also found that morning types are likely to be introverts, older and female.

Shift Work and the Health of the Employee

The literature on shift work demonstrates that it has significant consequences for sleep patterns and general health.

Sleep Disturbances

Night shift workers are at odds with their body rhythms. Folkard and Monk (1985) demonstrate that the night shift worker never fully adjusts. Once normal daytime work is started again, the employee's normal daytime cycle reasserts itself. Carpentier and Cazamian (1977) report that over 60 per cent of night workers experience sleeping problems compared with 11 per cent of day workers. This effect appears to continue long after the shift work has ceased (Koller et al., 1978).

Psychological and Physical Health

Bohle and Tilley (1989) report research to demonstrate a significant increase in self-reported psychological symptoms. These include depression, loss of self-esteem and difficulties in concentrating. Morning types were more susceptible to these consequences. Trese and Semmers (1986) and Akerstedt and Torsvall (1981) report that shift workers are likely to experience mood disorders, gastrointestinal complaints and sickness, progressive states of chronic fatigue, loss of drive, loss of appetite, dyspepsia, constipation and other similar problems. Taylor and Pocock (1972) found a slight increase in mortality over a 12-year period in shift workers. There is also a strong relationship between shift work and coronary heart disease. Krutsson et al. (1989), for example, found that

11-15 years of shift work increased the possibility of heart disease significantly, but that it fell sharply after 20 years.

Individual Differences

Individual differences such as age, gender and personality type appear to be significant in terms of explaining the consequences of shift work. Tolerance of shift work generally decreases with age. Gender differences are not as pronounced. However, personality type appears to influence the ability to adapt to shift work both in the physiological and psychological sense

Social Factors

The social circumstances of the shift worker appear to be significant. The value that the individual attaches to his/her children and to leisure time, the need to participate in social groups and the extent to which the employee can experience isolation also appear to be relevant in how they experience shift work.

THE DESIGN OF SHIFT WORK

The physiological and psychological consequences of stress raise questions about how shift work systems should be designed in order to minimise their negative consequences. Pheasant (1991) suggests that there are two schools of thought on this issue:

- The **slow motion theory** argues that because physiological adaptation to night work takes several days, employees should change shift as rarely as possible. This allows for the maximum degree of adaptation to take place. Following this theory, it is generally safe to state that permanent night work is preferable to rotating shift systems and longer shift rotations are more effective than short ones.

- The **rapid rotation theory** argues that adaptation to night work is, at best, only partial, and that it makes better sense if it did not occur at all. This theory argues that employees should not be required to work more than two/three nights in a row. The rapid rotation theory is very much in the ascendancy at the moment. However, both theories argue that weekly rotations have the most severe consequences.

The more common rapidly rotating continuous shift systems are called the metropolitan rota and the continental rota. The former involves a continuous sequence of two early shifts, two late shifts, two night shifts and two rest days. The cycle is eight weeks in total. The continental rota yields a three-day free weekend every four weeks. The continental rota has one spell of three nights in a row every four weeks; however, it is viewed as generally satisfactory. Another category of shift system is the on-call system. Here the employee is "on call" at night It is a common pattern amongst nurses and engineers. Poulton et al. (1978) demonstrate that this is an ineffective system, from a performance and health point of view. In the case of doctors, he showed that their performance in mental tasks decreased significantly. **Figure 12.5** presents a summary of a variety of shift systems found in the workplace.

Figure 12.5: Types of Shift Work Systems

> • **Fixed or Permanent:** This is where an employee works only on the day, afternoon and evening, or night shift.
>
> • **Rotating:** Each employee works various shift patterns on a rotating basis. This rotation may be slow, where the person works on the one shift pattern for several weeks, or for simply one week. Rapid rotation would involve staying on the same shift for one to four days.
>
> • **Oscillating:** The employee works on days (or any other shift) for one week and nights (or an alternative shift to the initial shift) the following week and then back on days (or the equivalent).
>
> • **Split Shift:** The normal working day is split to cater for peak demands as in restaurants, or transport services.
>
> • **Relief Shift:** The employee who works relief can work on any of the above shifts, depending on whom they are filling in for.
>
> • **Alternative Types:** There are numerous other types of shifts, e.g. a four-day week, 10-hours a day with nine hours on the last day, this is usually combined with four days off thus it is an eight-day week, and so on.

The debate on the effectiveness of different shift system designs is not closed, however, and a number of findings appear to have validity:

- Employees adapt to a new shift system over at least a week and this must be allowed for in whatever design is implemented.

- Employees may never adapt effectively to a rapidly rotating system.

- It is advisable to minimise changes in working hours. If the number of hours is four or less, the general view is that employees can accommodate this.

- Where it is not possible to get voluntary permanent night shift staff, a rapidly rotating three-shift system is viewed as the best compromise.

- Shift work systems should consider social customs and the personal circumstances of employees.

- There is a considerable debate about the effectiveness of 12-hour shifts. Rosa and Bonnet (1993) investigated alertness and performance on 8- and 12-hour rotating shifts. The 12-hour shift shows considerable negative effects, in particular greater fatigue over the course of the shift.

- Williamson et al. (1994) investigated a 12-hour shift system that involved two 12-hour day shifts, followed by two 12-hour night shifts and followed by four days off work. They found that this 12-hour system produces positive changes in mental state and physical symptoms and improved sleep (quality and quantity). The 12-hour shift did not have a significant impact on absenteeism, staff turnover or productivity.

ORGANISATIONAL STRUCTURE, CULTURE, CLIMATE AND SAFETY

The Components of Organisations

Organisations consist of both a formal and an informal component. The formal component incorporates positions, roles and group relationships that are designed with the aim of efficiency and effectiveness in mind. The informal organisation incorporates the pattern of interpersonal and inter-group relationships that develop over time, especially where the formal organisation is considered ineffective or fails to meet the needs of the individual or group.

The formal organisation is in many ways deficient, in particular from a safety and health perspective. Stranks (1994) identifies a number of weaknesses:

- The formal organisation experiences many communication failures that prevent instructions and job roles being fully understood.

- The formal organisation ignores many emotional factors in human behaviour that have major implications for safety performance and behaviour.

- The formal structure may not be able to detect errors and failings within the organisation or it may choose to ignore them.

There is evidence to suggest that particular organisational characteristics are conducive to the development of effective safety attitudes, behaviour and performance. These characteristics include:

- The promotion of a positive culture and climate in which safety and health issues are viewed by top management and employees to be fundamental to organisational success.

- The development of policies and systems that take into account human capabilities and fallibilities.

- A commitment to the achievement of progressively higher standards in the area of health and safety performance.

- A continuous demonstration by top management of its active involvement in safety issues. This may manifest itself in the allocation of appropriate resources for safety, making managers accountable for health and safety performance, and rewarding positive achievement.

- Providing leadership, whereby an environment is created that encourages safe behaviour by all employees.

The Du Pont Corporation is considered a leader in terms of its approach to safety and health. It has formulated ten principles of effective safety. These are presented in **Figure 12.6**.

Figure 12.6: Du Pont's Ten Principles of Effective Safety Management

1. All injuries and occupational illnesses can be prevented.

2. Management is directly responsible for preventing injuries and illness, with each level accountable to the one above and responsible for the level below.

3. Safety is a condition of employment, that is, each employee must assume responsibility for working safely. Safety is as important as production, quality and cost control.

4. Training is an essential element for safe workplaces. Safety awareness does not come naturally — management must teach, motivate and sustain employees' safety knowledge to eliminate injuries.

5. Safety audits must be conducted. Management must audit performance in the workplace on a regular basis.

6. All deficiencies must be corrected promptly, either by modifying facilities, changing procedures, providing better employee training or disciplining constructively and consistently. Follow-up audits are to be used to verify effectiveness.

7. It is essential to investigate all unsafe practices and incidents with injury potential, as well as injuries.

8. Safety off the job is as important as safety on the job.

9. It is good business to prevent injuries and illnesses. They involve tremendous cost — direct and indirect. The high cost is human suffering.

10. People are the most critical element in the success of a safety and health programme. Employees' suggestions and their active involvement must complement management responsibility.

Organisation Culture and Safety Culture

Attitudes and perceptions are not simply the direct product of an isolated individual, but are grounded in the social and organisational system (culture) of which they are part. This reality demands that attention must, therefore, move more towards safety attitudes, climate and culture within and outside the organisation in attempting to solve health and safety problems in the workplace.

A majority of workplace accidents are a result of employees, armed with the right equipment and the correct information, failing to carry out the job properly. Organisations that take accident prevention seriously must look beyond ergonomics as the only component of a human factors approach and take a broader view considering the physical and cultural environment of the workplace. Hazards are both behavioural and conditional, and are thereby influenced by the prevailing organisational culture.

The *culture* of an organisation is defined as the set of values that helps its members understand what the organisation stands for, how it does things, and what it considers important. It is often described as the mix of shared values, attitudes and patterns of behaviour that give the organisation particular character. Put simply, it is "the way things are done around here" or the common ways by which an organisation's members have learned to think, feel and act. It has also been described as the:

> ... deeper level of basic assumptions and beliefs that are shared by members of an organisation, that operate unconsciously and define in a basic "taken for granted" fashion an organisation's view of itself and its environment (Johnson and Scholes, 1997).

A cultural perspective on management suggests that managerial experience and behaviour is likely to be based on "taken for granted" frames of reference that are brought to bear by a manager — or group of managers — and that impact how a given situation is perceived and how it is responded to. This taken-for-grantedness is likely to be passed on over time within a group.

Because of its intangible nature, culture is difficult to observe or measure. Nevertheless, it plays a major role in shaping managerial and employee behaviour. Culture can therefore guide behaviour of all members of the organisation. A strong positive organisational culture can be used to support health and safety issues in the workplace and help *shape employee attitude* to health and safety. In spite of individual differences, much behaviour in organisational settings is shaped by shared, socially-based factors. The formal and informal organisational context in which people work is critical in guiding employee attitudes and actions. Working within this context, and drawing on their experience of it, employees develop expectations about what is required of them. These interpretations and expectations are a function of, and are shaped by, their social group — the people with whom they work and interact.

Cultural features are complex, shared characteristics. These characteristics include: beliefs, values, attitudes, opinions, motivation, meanings, ideas, expectations, linguistic features, actions, rituals, ceremonies, quirks, symbols and responses. The more tangible aspects include buildings, uniforms, documents, liveries, logos, equipment and designs. Rousseau (1988, 1990) considers that organisational culture can be expressed at five levels:

- Artefacts — observable (e.g. company logo).

- Patterns of behaviour — observable actions.

- Behavioural norms — can be inferred from observed behaviour.

- Values — as expressed consciously by organisation members.

- Fundamental assumptions — core values, may not be articulated.

The Notion of Safety Culture

The concept of safety culture, therefore, has emerged from the earlier ideas of organisational culture and climate. It can be described as the embodiment of a set of principles that loosely defines what an organisation is like, in terms of health and safety or as the product of individual and group values, attitudes, perceptions, competencies, and patterns of behaviour that determine the commitment to, and the style and efficiency of that organisation's health and safety management system. The safety culture within the overall organisation culture can be described as the ideas and beliefs that employees share about risk, accidents and ill health. An effective safety culture should help communicate a sense that safety is valued and effective safety behaviour will be rewarded. Because individuals are subject to, and adopt, the attitudes and behaviours of the people with whom they share their context, their behaviour is likely to change if the context (organisational/safety culture) is changed. This suggests that an organisation with poor accident prevention in order to effect a change in attitudes and behaviour toward safety and health in the workplace must focus on changing its safety culture.

Dimensions of Safety Culture

Erickson (1997) identifies and quantifies those management characteristics that are conducive to high safety performance, and conclude that high performance can be achieved in two ways. The first of these is visible, continual management support for the health and safety effort and, second, management concern and support for employees. Erickson (1997) suggests that these routes are further subdivided into three factors: management support, management concern and employee setting. All of these components, by their existence or absence, combine and interrelate to serve as indicators of the prevailing safety culture within any given organisation.

Figure 12.7: Key Components of Management's Commitment to Safety

Management Support	Management Concern	Positive Employee Setting
• Written safety philosophy.	• Knowledge with regard to safety.	• Clean and safe environment.
• Location of health and safety in the organisational structure.	• Employee v. production concerns.	• Positive management action and behaviour.
• Priority of health and safety.	• Resources.	• Communication.
• Relationship to other organisational grades.	• Involvement in decision-making.	• Respectful treatment of employees.
• Design of tasks and work environment.	• No blame culture.	• Reward for innovative thinking.
• Employee selection and training.		• Management feedback.
• Continuing education.		• High employee commitment.
• Measurement of individual safety performance.		• High employee morale.
		• Good operational "fit" for employee.
		• Ethical considerations in management.

Pidgeon (1991) identifies three dimensions that are the essence of an effective safety culture: norms and rules (standards) for handling hazards; positive employee attitudes to safety; and the capacity for reflection on safety practice.

Pybus (1996) believes that there is an obvious lack of empirical data to provide a secure answer to the question: "What are the characteristics of a good safety culture?". This he attributes to the lack of studies broad enough to capture all the potential aspects of safety culture as defined within the various definitions. While expressing some caution with regard to the completeness of the definition as outlined by Pidgeon (see above), he points out that most of what Pidgeon refers to are related to social psychological processes and, in particular, social cognition and social construction of reality.

Earnest (1997) outlines the characteristics of proactive and reactive cultures, summarised in **Figure 12.8**.

Performance Measures

A proactive safety culture searches for ways to measure the system that produces the result. This does not mean that hard number results should be ignored, but rather that a firm must recognise that the manner in which results are obtained can be as important as the results themselves. In a proactive culture, key elements of the safety system are identified and a numerical rating system is devised.

Incident Investigation

In a reactive culture, the incident investigation system typically focuses on accident symptoms rather than basic or root causes. Accidents are often dismissed as isolated events that do not involve the management system. Consequently, system deficiencies may remain undetected — free to become the source of future accidents.

Figure 12.8: Distinguishing Characteristics of Proactive and Reactive Safety Cultures

Proactive Characteristics

- The primary measure of safety performance is based on the safety of the system.
- Incident investigation focuses on root causes and the management system.
- Management safety evaluation is based on improving safety systems.
- Activities are oriented toward improving key system elements and behaviour.
- Safety and health goals focus on improving the system.
- Employee safety meetings are planned and educational.
- Safety and health training is planned and linked to improved understanding of the system.
- Behaviour-based safe practices are developed based on hazard identification.
- Group recognition is based on improving safety and health.

Reactive Characteristics

- The primary measure of performance is based on system output.
- Incident investigation focuses on unsafe conditions and unsafe acts.
- Management safety evolution is based on the absence of injuries.
- Activities are oriented toward physical hazards, contests and gimmicks.
- Safety and health goals focus on improving system output.
- Employee safety meetings are not well-prepared.
- Safety and health training is largely conducted in response to regulatory requirements.
- Safe practices are developed in response to accidents and regulatory requirements.
- Group recognition is based on safe work hours without accidents.

A proactive approach to incident investigation recognises that the occurrence of accidents is likely a system problem. To truly address accident prevention, a firm must closely examine such factors as its reward/punishment system, safe practice enforcement, feedback systems, engineering, inspection/maintenance programmes, purchasing and training. Often, incident causes can be traced back to the management system. Thus, a company must go beyond the single-cause concept and take proactive steps to change the system.

Management Motivation

A firm that relies on after-the-fact measures to provide direction assumes that the absence of injuries means that safety system is functioning acceptably. This can demotivate management, causing supervisors to devote little effort to safety. A proactive culture evaluates and rewards a manager's safety performance based on what they contribute to the safety system. Has the system shown measurable improvement during that manager's tenure? Have they led safety efforts, including providing resources and time to detect, evaluate and eliminate hazards?

Safety and Health Activities

In a reactive safety culture, the safety system is not well-defined, and efforts are usually oriented towards physical hazards, contests and gimmicks. Within such an environment, the firm is looking for the next big promotion to provide a boost. If asked, "What is your safety programme", most managers would not be able to provide a concise answer.

In a proactive culture, activities focus on behaviour and system improvement. The key belief is that behaviours determine hard-number results. Thus, key elements of the safety system are structured so that performance measures reflect a behaviour bias. However, management behaviour, as well as that of employees, must be addressed, because a "one-sided" approach to behaviour based safety management can be counterproductive. Common activities include safe behaviour reinforcement and coaching skills; devising systems to measure safe behaviours and provide feedback; developing behaviour-based safe practices; and goal setting that focuses on system improvement.

Safety and Health Goals

Within a reactive culture, safety and health goals are either not established or are based solely on injury reduction; little attention is placed on strategies for achieving goals. Individual operating departments rarely establish their own goals, nor does site management require periodic progress reviews to ensure that goals are achieved.

Within a proactive culture, goals are established at both department and plant levels. These objectives focus on improving key elements of the safety system and fostering active employee involvement. Injury/illness reduction goals establish clear objectives, strategies and measures. Safety and health goals are aligned with overall company goals, progress is monitored by upper management and periodic reviews are conducted.

In addition, accomplishments and milestones are recognised and celebrated.

Employee Safety Meetings

The most visible manifestation of a reactive safety culture is employee response to safety meetings. Inadequate planning, coupled with a perception that management does not truly care about safety, can result in meetings that encourage employees to "vent" their feelings. The primary management objective is to "fill time".

Meeting content and quality are secondary. Preparation often consists of a hastily arranged video shown with little or no comment. Consequently, the meeting is not viewed as an opportunity but rather as a drain on time.

By contrast, a safety meeting in a proactive culture can be an exciting, educational event. Such a meeting is well-planned, is focused on improved understanding of the safety system and actively involves employees as partners with management.

Safety and Health Training

In a reactive culture, little safety training is provided beyond that mandated by regulations. To truly contribute to improving the safety system, employees must understand the scope, content and objectives of that system as well as how it functions. They should also understand how system components in their work area are evaluated. For example, if a department has a behaviour observation system (BOS), employees should participate in (or lead) these efforts. Such a process requires training commensurate with the level of involvement that employees will assume.

A proactive firm recognises the need for training beyond regulatory requirements, then schedules time and allocated resources to ensure that such training is provided. Training quality also reflects the importance that management place on safety. Thus, its primary focus is "key elements of the safety system". Objectives are established and methods devised to ensure that learning has occurred and that desired skills have been acquired. Those with safety leadership roles deserve training commensurate with assigned responsibilities.

Safety Practices

In a reactive culture, assuming that safe practices have been written, phrases such as "be careful", "watch out", "be alert" and similar non-behavioural, cautionary wording are often used liberally. These phrases do not yield information; they are merely used for emphasis. This is not surprising, however, since safe practices are often written in response to accidents. Unfortunately, some firms do not provide guidance on how to develop effective safe practices — or feel no need to write them down.

By contrast, a firm with a proactive safety culture develops safe practices based on a thorough evaluation of hazards inherent in the work area and implements safeguards before an accident occurs. These practices cover general, site-wide rules as well as operation-specific practices. Within such a culture, safe practices are written in clear, concise language and incorporate behavioural terms. Safe practices are: (a) known and understood; (b) readily available to all employees for reference; (c) updated when changes occur; and (d) used for training and employee safety performance evaluation.

Group Recognition

Group recognition of good safety performance is often based on criteria such as "safe work hours without an accident". Although such celebrations provide a break from the work routine and may be good public relations, they are linked to after-the-fact measurement of performance. Consequently, a celebration based on the absence of accidents rarely pinpoints or reinforces proactive safety efforts.

Practice recognition for group safety and health performance is based on system measures such as high BOS scores or job safety analysis. Recognition for contributions to improving a key element rating within the department helps ensure continuous improvement of the safety system — and consequently drives down accidents and associated costs.

Measuring the Safety Culture

In trying to measure the safety culture of an organisation, it is necessary, in the first place, to identify what actually constitutes safety culture. Ryan (1991) identifies four critical indicators of an organisation's safety culture:

1. **Effective communication**, leading to commonly-understood goals and a means to achieve them at all levels.

2. **Good organisational learning**, whereby organisations are able to identify and respond appropriately to change.

3. **Organisational focus upon health and safety** — essentially how much time, resources and attention is paid to health and safety issues.

4. **External factors**, including the financial health of the organisation, the prevailing economic climate and the impact of Regulations and how well these are managed.

The CBI (1991), in its report on safety culture, recognised the following factors to be important in assessing an organisation's safety culture:

1. The critical importance of leadership and commitment of the chief executive.

2. The executive safety role of line management.

3. Involvement of all employees.

4. Openness of communication.

5. Demonstration of care and concern for all those affected by the business.

Glendon and McKenna (1995) suggest that organisations with a positive safety culture can be characterised by "communications founded on mutual trust, by shared perceptions of the importance of safety and by confidence in the efficacy of preventive measures". The Institution of Occupational Safety and Health in the UK maintains that "organisations with a positive safety culture have competent people, strongly committed to safety who put their values into practice". This statement reinforces the view that a positive safety culture is central to effective health and safety management and can therefore be used as an indication of an organisation's determination and competence to control risks at work.

McCann (1996) also considers the following eight factors as being the most important components of organisational culture with regard to health and safety issues in the workplace:

1. **Worker involvement in safety issues***:* This refers to how much any particular person feels that they are really involved in the health and safety culture of an organisation. Low worker involvement can translate into more incidents and less accountability.

2. **Management commitment to safety***:* This refers to how much workers think that management is truly committed, viewing safety as a priority. It is usually found that there is a considerable difference between what workers think is commitment and what management thinks is commitment. Even if managers are very committed, it is irrelevant unless the message is getting across to the workers.

3. **Personal accountability***:* Within an organisation, how responsible do workers feel for their own safety?

4. **Performance management***:* How many performances are managed well in the working environment? This encompasses

feedback systems and performance appraisals dealing with both positive and negative health and safety issues.

5. **Co-worker support**: Peer support and proper feedback combine to make a very important impact on the organisational safety culture. If an organisation can harness it, then it can encourage people to start supporting one another to be safe and to reduce risks. However, sometimes co-worker support can do the opposite, both because employees do not perceive safety issues as necessary or important and because it can be seen as a siding with management.

6. **Training, equipment and environment**: Are people satisfied that they have the right working environment, that they know how to operate it and that it is safe?

7. **Organisational commitment**: This is also known as loyalty, the extent of the personal commitment of the workers to the organisation.

8. **Job satisfaction**: In general the higher the job satisfaction, the more committed the person within the organisation will be. A study conducted by Liberty Mutual showed that the second-largest factor in return to work by people who suffered lower back fractures was job satisfaction.

IBEC (1986) has likewise come to recognise the importance of a safe culture. It views the creation of a safety culture, concentrating on the four Cs:

- **Control** by individual enterprises in the management of safety.

- **Co-operation** through consultation and participation.

- **Communication** skills, external and internal.

- **Competence** in actions, decisions and advice from within enterprises and from external sources.

Figure 12.9: Characteristics of an Effective Safety Culture

- The acceptance of responsibility at and from the top, exercised through a clear chain of command, seen to be actual and felt through the organisation.

- A conviction that high standards are achievable as a result of proper management.

- Setting and monitoring of relevant objectives/targets, based on satisfactory internal information systems.

- Systematic identification and assessment of hazards and the devising and exercise of preventive systems that are subject to audit and review (in such approaches, particular attention is given to the investigation of error).

- Immediate rectification of deficiencies.

- Promotion and reward of enthusiasm and good results.

- Leadership and commitment from the top that is genuine and visible. This is *the* most important feature.

- Acceptance that it is a long-term strategy, which requires sustained effort and interest.

- A policy statement of high expectations and conveying a sense of optimism about what is possible supported by adequate codes of practice and safety standards.

- Health and safety should be treated as other corporate aims, and properly researched.

- It must be a line management responsibility.

- "Ownership" of health and safety must permeate at all levels of the workforce. This requires employee involvement, training and communication.

- Realistic and achievable targets should be set and performance measured against them.

- Incidents should be thoroughly investigated.

- Consistency of behaviour against agreed standards should be achieved by auditing, and good safety behaviour should be a condition of employment.

- Deficiencies revealed by an investigation or audit should be remedied promptly.

- Management must receive adequate and up-to-date information to be able to assess performance.

According to IBEC's explanatory document, a "safety culture" means that every business should have a coherent policy committed to the prevention of accidents and ill health at work. The policy should indicate that good standards of health and safety are a corporate aim, integrated into the mainstream of the organisation and managed in the same way as other matters vital to the operation of the business.

> The policy needs to be underpinned by a culture which promotes occupational safety and health and represents a mix of shared values, attitudes and particular behaviour that gives the enterprise its particular character.

Safety Climate versus Safety Culture

Safety climate has also received considerable attention in the safety literature. The distinction between culture and climate in the general organisational behaviour literature is unclear. Rousseau (1988) found considerable overlap between the two; however, she concluded that there were sufficient differences between the two concepts for one to be differentiated from the other. Rousseau characterises culture as a group phenomenon, manifested in the expression of strongly held norms, consisting of shared beliefs and values. She argued that it is possible to have organisations that do not have strong organisational norms, leading to the conclusion that organisations may not have an organisational culture at all. Rousseau (1981) and Broon and Holmes (1986) suggest that climate is best conceptualised as a descriptive term that applies to the organisation. Climate therefore refers to a situation and its links to thoughts, feelings, and behaviours of organisational members. It is generally viewed as temporal, subjective and often subject to direct manipulation. Denison (1996) argues that this is perhaps where it differs from culture. Culture refers to an evolving context and it is rooted in history, collectively held and of sufficient complexity to resist organisational attempts at manipulation. Denison does however acknowledge that, within the organisational literature, the distinctions appear to have disappeared and that the two concepts should be viewed as differences in interpretation rather than differences in phenomenon. He concludes that both concepts addressed a common phenomenon, which he defined as the creator and influence of social contexts in organisations. Moran and Volkwein (1992) appear to have come to the same conclusion. They conclude that climate and culture overlap as components of the expressive, communicative socially constructed dimensions of an organisation, but did point to a fundamental difference that argues that climate reflects the attitudes and behaviours of organisational members that are directly observable, whereas culture focuses on assumptions, expectations and perspectives that are taken for granted by organisational members but are not easily interpreted by outsiders.

Within the safety literature, the distinctions discussed so far have not been as clearly in evidence. Cox and Cox (1996), for example, suggest that there is a common tendency to describe safety culture in terms of values, beliefs, attitudes, social mores, norms, rules, practices and behaviour. They argue that such a perspective presents a danger that many definitions represent "catch-alls" and as a result they have tended ultimately in a research context to be of little value. It is observable, however, that many of the studies that propose to measure safety culture essentially only measure safety attitudes and pay little attention to norms and rules and whether an organisation has the capacity to reflect on safety practices.

Pidgeon (1995) argues that the search for safety culture has in effect been reduced to measuring individual attitudes and behaviours in a specific work context that more closely matches the concept of safety climate.

A number of attempts have been made to measure safety climate. Zohar (1980) concluded, based on questionnaires completed by over 400 employees, that safety climate consisted of dimensions such as the importance of safety training, the effects of safe conduct on promotion, levels of risk in the workplace and management attitudes to safety. Zohar identified eight dimensions in all. However, Brown and Holmes (1986), in an attempt to validate Zohar's safety climate model, found that the original eight-factor model reduced to three factors: employee perceptions of management attitudes, management actions and the physical risk perception of employees. A more recent study by Williamson et al. (1997) proposed a 67-item measure of safety climate. Factor analysis or a reduced scale revealed five items: personal motivation and safety behaviour, positive safety practice, risk justification, fatalism and optimism. The study did not, however, investigate how these measures related to accident rates.

Cox and Cox (1991), Alexander et al. (1995), Lee (1995), and Guest et al. (1994) have in contrast focused on safety attitudes as a measure of safety culture. Cox and Cox appear to have been the initiators of this line of research. They postulated the view that the idea of safety culture reflects the attitudes, values, beliefs and perceptions that employees share in respect of safety issues. They developed a conceptual model, which posits that the shared aspects of employee attitude to safety provide a partial description of an organisation's safety culture. They did not, however, seek to link these measures with safety metrics such as accident rates. A subsequent study by Alexander et al. (1995) also focused on safety culture and made attempts to link safety attitude with prior accident involvement. They concluded that a measure of safety culture could not be reliably demonstrated but did suggest six key factors that underpin safety attitude: personal need for safety, personal appreciation of risk, attribution of blame, conflict, control and a supportive environment. Lee (1995) conducted similar research on a sample of 5,295 employees at a large British nuclear plant. This study highlighted three factors of importance to risk and safety: risk taking, an assessment of perceived risks and the extent to which risks were perceived to be under personal control. The study did find major differences in attitude and perception according to job type, type of shift worked, gender, age and experience. They also reported that differences in perception and attitude to safety were linked with prior accident involvement.

Guest et al. (1994), in contrast, did not rely on a questionnaire methodology, but instead used in-depth interviews using critical incident technique, repertory grid and general questions. The study was conducted among British Rail employees following the Clapham Junction disaster. The study concluded that it was possible to identify a safety culture that was characterised by a belief in hierarchy and management, a belief in the value of technically sound and complex safety systems, a reluctance of employees at lower levels to accept personal responsibility and a sense of duty and commitment to running trains on time. The study in general did not succeed in linking safety culture and accident rates because there were few, if any, differences in perceptions of risk and safety performance between what was characterised "safe" and "unsafe" employees.

One can conclude that the dimensions identified from studies of safety climate appear to be related to employees' perceptions of the organisational conductions that impact upon safety whereas those dimensions associated with safety culture are more complex, diverse and personal. The findings on safety climate are, in general, consistent with definitions of climate constructs in the organisational literature (James et al., 1990; Schneider, 1990), in that individuals do attach meanings to and interpret the environments within which they work. The meanings and perceptions that they attach to safety climate then influence their behaviour. Hoffman and Stetzer (1996) and Jacobs et al. (1995), for example, demonstrate that employees who work for a supervisor who never mentions safety are likely to develop perceptions that safety is unimportant and, as a result, will not place a strong emphasis on safety issues. James et al. (1990) and Schneider (1990) provide support for the view that a strong safety climate has the potential to motivate employees to take greater ownership and responsibility of safety within the organisation and this in turn has the potential to influence their own propensity to behave in a safe manner.

PROMOTING EMPLOYEE INVOLVEMENT IN SAFETY

A key to the development of a positive safety culture relates to the creation of employee interest and involvement in safety. This is a difficult objective to achieve and rests on an understanding of a range of factors. One of the problems is that involvement in health and safety is often viewed by employees as boring, uninteresting and not really their concern. Therefore strategies that are motivational in nature are necessary in order to promote employee involvement in health and safety. **Figure 12.10** summarises some of the basic factors that may motivate employees to be concerned about safety and health in the workplace.

Figure 12.10: Some Elements of a Total Safety Culture

Principle 1	Safety should be internally — not externally — driven.
Principle 2	Culture change requires people to understand the principles and how to use them.
Principle 3	Champions of a Total Safety Culture will emanate from those who teach the principles and procedures.
Principle 4	Leadership can be developed by teaching and demonstrating the characteristics of effective leaders.
Principle 5	Focus recognition, education and training on people reluctant but willing, rather than on those resisting.
Principle 6	Giving people opportunity for choice can increase commitment, ownership and involvement.
Principle 7	A total safety culture requires continuous attention to factors in three domains: environment, behaviour and person.
Principle 8	Do not count on common sense for safety improvement.
Principle 9	Safety incentive programs should focus on the process rather than outcomes.
Principle 10	Safety should not be considered a priority, but a value with no compromise.
Principle 11	Safety is a continuous fight with human nature.
Principle 12	Behaviour is learned from three basic procedures: classical conditioning, operant conditioning, and observational learning.
Principle 13	People view behaviour as correct and appropriate to the degree they see others doing it.
Principle 14	People will blindly follow authority, even when the mandate runs counter to good judgement and social responsibility.
Principle 15	Social loafing can be prevented by increasing personal responsibility, individual accountability, group cohesion and interdependence.

Principle 16	On-the-job observation and interpersonal feedback is key to achieving a total safety culture.
Principle 17	Behaviour-based safety is a continuous DO IT process.
Principle 18	Behaviour is directed by activators and motivated by consequences.
Principle 19	Intervention impact is influenced by: amount of response information, participation and social support, and external consequences.
Principle 20	Extra and external consequences should not over-justify the target behaviour.
Principle 21	People are motivated to maximise positive consequences (rewards) and minimise negative consequences (costs).
Principle 22	Behaviour is motivated by six types of consequences: positive v. negative, natural v. extra, and internal v. external.
Principle 23	Negative consequences have four undesirable side effects: escape, aggression, apathy and counter-control.
Principle 24	Natural variation is behaviour can lead to a belief that negative consequences have more impact than positive consequences.
Principle 25	Long-term behaviour change requires people to change "inside" as well as "outside".
Principle 26	All perception is biased and reflects personal history, prejudices, motives and expectations.
Principle 27	Perceived risk is lowered when a hazard is perceived as familiar, understood, controllable and preventable.
Principle 28	The slogan "all injuries are preventable" is false and reduces perceived risk.
Principle 29	People compensate for increases in perceived safety by taking more risks.

Principle 30	When people evaluate others, they focus on internal factors; when evaluating personal performance, they focus on external factors.
Principle 31	When succeeding, people over-attribute internal factors; but when failing, people over-attribute external factors.
Principle 32	People feel more personal control when working to achieve success than when working to avoid failure.
Principle 33	Stressors lead to positive stress or negative distress, depending on appraisal of personal control.
Principle 34	In a Total Safety Culture everyone goes beyond the call of duty for the safety of themselves and others — they actively care.
Principle 35	Actively caring should be planned and purposive, and focus on environment, person or behaviour.
Principle 36	Direct, behaviour-focused, active caring is proactive and very challenging, and requires effective communication skills.
Principle 37	Safety coaching that starts with caring and involves observing, analysing and communicating, leads to helping.
Principle 38	Actively caring can be increased indirectly with procedures that enhance self-esteem, belongingness, and empowerment.
Principle 39	Empowerment is facilitated with increases in self-efficacy, personal control and optimism.
Principle 40	When people feel empowered their safe behaviour spreads to other situations and behaviours.
Principle 41	Actively caring can be increased directly by educating people about factors contributing to bystander apathy.
Principle 42	As the number of observers of a crisis increases, the probability of helping decreases.
Principle 43	Actively caring behaviour is facilitated when appreciated and inhibited when unappreciated.

Principle 44	A positive reaction to actively caring can increase self-esteem, empowerment and belongingness.
Principle 45	The universal norms of consistency and reciprocity motivate everyday behaviours, including actively caring.
Principle 46	Once people make a commitment, they encounter internal and external pressures to think and act consistently with their position.
Principle 47	The consistency norm is responsible for the impact of "foot-in-the-door" and "throwing a curve".
Principle 48	The reciprocity norm is responsible for the impact of the door-in-the-face technique.
Principle 49	Numbers from programme evaluations should be meaningful to all participants, direct and motivate intervention improvement.
Principle 50	Statistical analysis often adds confusion and misunderstanding to evaluation results, thereby reducing social validity.

The strategies that an organisation can use to create safety awareness amongst employees include:

Good Example by Management

Management, regardless of the size of the organisation, can eliminate the majority of its accidents. Most injuries result from a combination of physical hazards and human error, which can easily be corrected. The correction of either will usually prevent injury. Effective safety performance requires that all physical hazards are reduced to the minimum and every means is taken to control work habits and practices. Suggestions for accomplishing this includes:

- Providing a safe physical, mechanical and chemical work environment.

- Providing safe work methods, processes and procedures.

- Providing necessary training and qualified supervision.

- Providing protective devices and equipment.

Figure 12.11: Basic Factors Motivating Employee Interest in Safety

- **Fear of personal injury:** No one wants to be injured. Employees need to be informed of hazards and told how these hazards can result in injury.

- **Fear of economic loss:** Employees need to be advised of economic losses that result from injury and from physical suffering due to injuries; there are also wage losses, possible loss of future earning power and the threat to family well-being and security.

- **Desire for reward:** Employees appreciate being recognised for their accomplishments. Rewarding employees for good safe work procedures, extended periods of work without injury and other safety accomplishments, can ensure that their interests are aroused and maintained.

- **Desire for leadership:** Some employees have a greater desire and enhanced ability for leadership than others. Those who have this specific desire should be used to guide and be role models to others in promoting the safety programme.

- **Desire to excel and be outstanding:** This factor can be used in contests of many kinds where individuals and groups can prove that they excel in preventing accidents and the actual safety record of the organisation.

- **Protection to others:** No one wants, intentionally or unintentionally, to cause injury to a fellow employee or an innocent bystander. Employees need to be shown that, if they cause an accident or set a poor example, it might result in an injury to themselves or to others.

- **Creating a favourable impression:** Every employee wants approval. Management appreciation of the work done is important. Supervisors have a challenge to ensure that employees, who work for them, achieve safety. This effort will pay off in higher morale and production as well as in effective safety.

Good Example of Supervision

As representatives of management, supervisors are the key to the control of employee work methods and practices. They can promote safety among subordinates by the example they give in terms of their own attitude toward safety. Some methods used successfully by supervisors to promote safety are:

- Giving comprehensive safety instructions for each job.

- Setting a good example by wearing personal protective equipment or clothing and by following safe procedures at all times.

- Requiring workers to do jobs safely and to use protective equipment at all times.

Education and Training

The more that employees know about safety, the safer their behaviour will be. Knowledge of how to reach and maintain top safety performance is now available. Training in safe work practices is considered essential to good work performance. Regular safety training should be a priority.

Safety Promotion Meetings

Meetings are considered essential to the implementation of an effective safety programme. A great variety of safety pamphlets, talks and demonstrations are used to make such meetings interesting. They are helpful, if properly used and not overdone.

Contests

One of the oldest and most widely used means of promoting employee safety interest and effort is the safety contest. It is important that contest rules be clear and definite, and as fair as possible to all contestants. The purpose of such contest must never be forgotten. The greatest accomplishment comes from the progress made by the non-winners in improving their own safety performance.

Bulletin Boards

Every organisation, regardless of size, should have one or more bulletin boards. It is important that the board be well-made, attractive, well-finished and properly maintained. In addition:

- Material should be arranged neatly and outdated material removed regularly.

- Posters and notices should be rotated often.

- Lighting should be good.

- The board(s) should be located where all employees can easily view it/them.

Publications

In-house publications are valuable for promoting safety issues when they are informative, interesting and suitably written. Material should be timely and pertinent to organisational conditions. Humorous illustrations should make a point. Photographs of hazardous situations and of persons with safe accomplishments are considered valuable in promoting safety behaviour.

Signs and Slogans

These are widely used to promote effective safety practice. Properly used, they provide an instant image emphasising an attitude of readiness to do everything possible to prevent accidents at work. They should be simple, definite as to meaning and eye-catching.

CHAPTER ROUND-UP

- The design of jobs should be based on systematic task analysis of the actions required by the employee. In the health and safety context, task analysis provides the information to evaluate the suitability of machinery, tools and equipment, work processes and the employee's physical and social environment. Job safety analysis can be used to identify all of the accident prevention measures appropriate to a particular job or work activity. A job analysis approach is both diagnostic and descriptive in nature.

- Motion economy deals with the optimisation of worker efficiency, measured in terms of the motions, which are allowed for, and the time it takes to perform them. Motion economy deals with the co-ordinated use of hands, the even distribution of workload between the two hands, the exploitation and gravity of movements.

- Shift work represents a reality in many industries and there is a considerable body of evidence to demonstrate that shift work impacts on employee health and well-being. There are important individual differences. Only a minority of employees find that shift work has advantages. It has significant effects on sleep patterns, psychological and physical health including depression, loss of self-esteem, difficulty in concentrating, sickness absence, mood disorders and gastrointestinal complaints.

- The establishment, development and promotion of a positive safety culture is now considered a prerequisite to effective health and safety management and to ensuring compliance with health and safety legislation. The benefits of such a culture are considerable, including: reduced accidents, sickness, absence, lost time and insurance premiums, increased overall performance, morale and employee commitment. Safety culture represents the major contemporary management issue.

PART THREE

MANAGING HEALTH, SAFETY AND THE ENVIRONMENT

Chapter 13

THE MANAGEMENT OF HEALTH, SAFETY AND WELFARE

INTRODUCTION

Modern safety management encompasses, to a large extent, a complex set of factors. These factors must be effectively understood and carefully controlled in order to achieve maximum results in minimising accident levels and enhancing organisational safety. This chapter considers a wide range of safety management issues:

- The nature and scope of health and safety management.

- Organisational approaches to health and safety management.

- Alternative management strategies to achieve effective health and safety at work.

- The formulation of organisational policies on health and safety.

- The nature of organisational structure for safety management.

- The role of the Safety Officer within the organisation.

- Health and safety monitoring within the organisation.

- Effective training for health and safety.

- The costs of safety to the organisation.

THE SCOPE OF HEALTH AND SAFETY MANAGEMENT

Safety management is essentially concerned with the effective use of safety resources and measures in the pursuit of specified safety goals and continuous improvement. Safety management as an activity covers four areas:

- The management of health and safety operations, including the formulation of policies, the setting of objectives, organising, controlling and establishing accountability.

- The measurement of health and safety performance on an on-going basis.

- The motivation of managers and employees to improve standards of health and safety performance.

- The design of effective organisational structures and the creation of a safety culture that contributes to effective organisational safety performance.

The research evidence suggests four approaches to health and safety management: the legalistic, the socio-humanitarian, the financial-economic and the human factors approaches.

The Legalistic Approach

The basic premise of this approach is that the organisation should comply with the law and do no more. This represents a minimalist approach because the basic philosophy of the law is to articulate minimum standards, which it expects employers will build on and exceed. Those organisations that adopt a legalistic approach simply do so as a means of avoiding the clutches of the National Safety Authority.

The Socio–Humanitarian Approach

The socio-humanitarian approach is based on the premise that human resources are an important element of business success and, therefore, must receive protection and must not be exposed to risks, hazards or other dangers. This approach is also known as the welfare approach and is based on paternalistic principles.

The Financial–Economic Approach

The financial-economic approach starts from the perspective that all accidents, incidents and occupational ill-health cost the organisation money. Such costs can be avoided, so the motivation is to bring about an improvement in health and safety performance and reduce all safety-related costs. Many organisations ignore the costs of accidents and are not able to identify the elements of costs that apply to health and safety in an effective manner.

The Human Factors Approach

The human factors approach advocates that effective safety performance is contingent upon identifying those organisational and individual characteristics that influence safety-related behaviour. Five variables are important:

- The development of a culture and climate where health and safety is seen as important by all organisational members.

- The formulation of policies and systems that help to control risk.

- A commitment to continuous improvement in health and safety performance.

- A demonstration by senior management of its active involvement and interest in health and safety issues within the organisation.

- Effective leadership by all managers and supervisors within the organisation.

Figure 13.1 presents a set of tasks that constitute effective organising for health and safety.

Figure 13.1: *Organising for Health and Safety: Key Tasks*

The key tasks of policy makers include:

- Devising health and safety policy.

- Establishing strategies to implement policy and integrating these into general business activity.

- Specifying a structure for planning, measuring, reviewing and auditing health and safety policy.

- Specifying a structure for implementing policy and supporting plans.

- Agreeing plans for improvement and reviewing progress to develop both the policy and the organisation.

- Pursuing health and safety objectives with evident sincerity.

The major outputs of policy makers include:

- Written statements of general health and safety policy and strategic objectives.

- Written statements of the organisation for planning, measuring, reviewing and auditing.

- Written statements of the organisation for implementation.

- General plans containing specific objectives for each year.

The key tasks of planners include:

- Producing detailed plans to achieve corporate health and safety objectives.

- Establishing performance standards for planning, measuring, reviewing and auditing health and safety policy implementation.

- Co-ordinating the specialist advice necessary to ensure effective planning and implementation of policy — for example, the input of health and safety specialists, engineers, architects and doctors.

- Ensuring the participation and involvement of workers in compliance with the Safety, Health and Welfare at Work Act 1989, and supporting Regulations.

- Keeping up to date with changes in health and safety legislation, standards and good practice and with management practices relevant to the organisation.

The key outputs of planners include:

- Health and safety strategy statements and plans to support the policy.

- Health and safety operational plans that identify specific health and safety objectives to be achieved within fixed time periods.

- Performance standards, and supporting systems and procedures.

- Up-to-date documentation of plans, performance standards and systems.

The key tasks for implementers are:

- Implementation of operational plans, performance standards, systems and procedures and the provision of necessary physical and human resources and information.

- Provision of timely feedback on performance including successes and failures and any deficiencies in plans, standards, procedures and systems.

- Ensuring participation at all levels in health and safety activities

The key outputs of implementers are:

- Safe and healthy production and delivery of products and services.

- Products and services, which in themselves do not create risks to others.

FORMULATING SAFETY MANAGEMENT STRATEGIES

Safety management strategies can be either proactive or reactive in nature. Proactive strategies are primarily concerned with prevention, whereas reactive strategies are essentially post-accident strategies.

Proactive strategies are classified as either safe place or safe person strategies.

Safe Place Strategies

The objective of safe place strategies is to bring about a reduction in the physical danger to people at work. Such strategies underpin Irish legislation on safety and health, in that the legislation sets down minimum safe place requirements, which must be implemented by organisations. The main areas currently legislated for include: safe premises, safe plant, safe processes and materials, safe systems of work, safe access to and egress from work, adequate supervision, and competent and trained personnel.

Safe Person Strategies

Safe place strategies alone are ineffective without some consideration of safe person strategies. The focus of safe person strategies is the employee's perception of risk and danger. Safe person strategies depend upon the employee conforming to prescribed standards and organisational practices. Stranks (1994) suggests that safe person strategies focus on some or all of the following:

- Caring for vulnerable employees, in particular those exposed to toxic substances, radiation or dangerous metals.

- A focus on personal hygiene, particularly the risk of occupational skin conditions. The provision of washing facilities for use by workers prior to the consumption of food and drink is an example of a safe person strategy.

- The encouragement of safe behaviour and taking steps to prevent employees from indulging in unsafe behaviour or horseplay.

- The assessment of risks in the workplace, together with the implementation of actions to protect employees from such risks.

Reactive Strategies

Proactive strategies represent the backbone of any management effort to promote and ensure effective safety performance. However, at some stage, there will be a need to implement reactive or post-accident strategies. There is ample evidence to demonstrate that individuals are forgetful, they take short cuts and sometimes do not pay attention to organisational safety rules. Such behaviour often results in accidents.

There are three types of reactive strategies:

- Disaster/contingency/emergency planning.

- The development of feedback strategies, including the analysis of post-accident situations.

- Improvement/ameliorative strategies, including the minimisation of the effects of injuries using first aid services and rehabilitation services.

ELEMENTS OF THE ORGANISATION'S SAFETY MANAGEMENT SYSTEM

Dawson et al. (1983) put forward a self-regulation model as the basis of effective safety management within organisations. The notion of self-regulation is understood in terms of the development of strategies to control the particular hazards that characterise an organisation. When such hazards are unacceptable, positive interventions need to be made, either in anticipation of hazard realisation or in reaction to the harm or loss that has already occurred. Three main options for anticipative control are suggested: elimination, containment and mitigation. The combination selected will reflect the specific legal requirements and management judgements about the nature of the hazard, the probability of realisation, likely consequences, possible solutions and availability of resources.

The effects of the organisation's political context on these judgements are significant. Control is considered in terms of both technical and motivational controls. Technical controls are directed toward the identification and control of specific hazards and involve four stages: the identification of the need for control measures; the determination and prescription of control standards and processes which are going to be applied; their implementation; and finally their maintenance and adaptation. Motivational controls have a broader purpose and are essentially concerned with the development and maintenance of general safety awareness and commitment to technical controls. Three key elements of motivational control are important: the general objectives, culture and climate of the organisation; definitions of responsibility and authority; and mechanisms of accountability and performance measurement.

The basis of self-regulation is found in the development of efficient management systems based on line-management responsibility and specialist advice, on the one hand, and employee involvement, on the other. Neither efficient management nor worker involvement in health and safety can be taken as ends in themselves; they can only be appreciated in relation to the processes and outcomes that follow from them. Thus, self-regulation can be taken as an indicator of states of mind and action on the part of management and employees and their representatives that lead to the conscious development of strategies aimed at controlling the particular hazards that characterise an organisation. The results of these strategies can then be assessed in terms of their impact on various measures of health and safety performance.

The Control of Hazards

Hazards are endemic to many work activities and have their origins in the interaction between the basic elements of any workplace, specifically:

- The "hardware" of the working environment, including the characteristics of materials, plant, equipment and place of work.

- The characteristics of the people involved, particularly their knowledge, skills, attitudes, actions and beliefs.

Most managers have responsibility for work situations in which hazards are endemic, although the probability of their realisation and the severity of the consequences of their realisation vary considerably. Workplaces are likely to be characterised by hazards that are regarded in some way as unacceptable, whether legally, operationally or morally. When this is the case, positive interventions need to be made. Such interventions may also be taken in anticipation of hazard realisation. Alternatively, controls may be applied in reaction to the harm or loss that has actually occurred. Any such action will be directed at changing at least one of the basic constituents of all hazards — namely, characteristics of either the hardware of the working environment or people's attitudes, values and behaviour or, more often, the interface between the people and the working environment. The alternatives that can be followed in attempting to control hazard sequences in anticipation of their realisation are: elimination, containment and mitigation.

The first option is to eliminate the risk by acting upon the probability of the risk occurring. This may be achieved, for example, by finding alternative raw materials or changing machinery or plant design. This is a limited avenue and, even in relation to one specific hazard, the possibilities for complete elimination are likely to be few. Furthermore, even if it can be accomplished in relation to the specific hazard, unanticipated consequences may arise in the form of other hazards.

The second option is to control the hazards through containment, by reducing the probability of their happening. For example, ventilation equipment might be installed to control the risk of lung disease from dust. In another context, specific job training programmes might be instituted in order to reduce the probability of employees using machinery or substances in a dangerous way.

The third option is to take action directed towards mitigating the consequences of the risk of hazard realisation — for example, through the provision of knock-down water sprays, a round-the-clock nursing presence or the provision of personal protective clothing and equipment.

The Organisational Context of Hazard Control

The nature of the organisational controls used depends on specific legal requirements and on judgements that are made, however implicitly, about the nature of the hazard, the probability of its realisation, the likely nature of the consequences should it be realised, the nature of possible solutions and the cost and availability of the resources involved. The process of making such judgements varies enormously. At one extreme, they may result from completely "internal" or implicit processes within one manager's mind. At the other extreme, they may be made through a large and formal series of advisory and executive committees. Whatever their form, these judgements need to be understood within their organisational context.

When it comes to making decisions about the selection of hazard control strategies, many factors other than pure health and safety considerations may be involved. Some of the more important considerations that can affect the communication and judgmental processes are the availability and cost of scarce resources, particularly:

- Technical and specialist knowledge to generate and interpret information on hazards and to contribute to the identification of solutions.

- Capital and revenue monies to finance the search for the implementation of appropriate strategies.

- Time within busy work schedules to allow line management to play a full part in developing and implementing strategies.

The extent to which resources are made available for health and safety depends in part on economic, staff and time constraints. What happens is dependent on the "political" organisation context. In particular, the perceptions and interests of the different groups involved will be reflected in what they believe in and are prepared to champion. As regards health and safety, the key interest groups are likely to form around corporate management, plant management, technical specialists, first-line supervision and workforce representatives. Although none of these groups "wants" accidents or ill health, they may well have different views on what constitutes an "acceptable" level of risk to which different groups may be exposed. They may also attach different priorities to the expenditure of scarce resources to secure improvements in health and safety, especially when there are other pressing priorities. Shop stewards may place a higher priority on gaining improved terms and conditions of work for their members, while line managers may be more eager to invest in plant and equipment that will increase productivity rather than to alter other aspects of the working environment. The groups involved are not always equally matched in terms of their power and influence to advance their interests. Hence, sources of power and influence become another critical aspect of the organisational context that affects the development of health and safety strategies. This also explains why the commitment of senior management has been found to be so important in securing effective health and safety programmes.

Strategies to control hazards through elimination, containment and mitigation must be understood within the context of the organisation in which they originate. Concepts of "control" are central to the framework of self-regulation. Control can be conceived of as being technical or motivational. Technical controls are developed in respect of objectives to identify and control specific hazards, whereas motivational controls have a more diffuse coverage in terms of purpose and are concerned with the development and maintenance of a general safety awareness and commitment to maintain technical controls.

Technical Controls for Health and Safety at Work

Technical controls can employ and/or act upon the physical characteristics of the working environment, aspects of administrative and organisational systems, and/or the behaviour or attitudes of individuals. They are associated with a "felt need" to identify and control specific hazards and can be applied at the point of risk. They may involve:

* Modifying physical characteristics of the working environment, e.g. machinery guards to reduce the risk of physical injury or extraction and ventilation equipment to contain the accumulation of dust and fumes and so prevent chronic or acute respiratory problems.

* Modifying or requiring specific behaviour patterns from job holders, e.g. through training in kinetic handling to prevent back injuries.

* Structuring the way those at risk interact with their working environment, for example, permit-to-work systems.

Four stages in the process of selecting technical control can be identified:

* **The identification of the need for control measures.** This can be done in a fairly sophisticated way, for example, through hazard and operability studies. Alternatively, managers may rely upon their own experience and the guidance provided by trade journals, suppliers and other sources. Whatever the means employed to identify hazards, parts of the process are often far from scientific and involve a certain amount of guesswork of likely happenings. Ultimately, a decision has to be made about whether the presumed situation presents a potential for harm, significant enough to warrant the development of controls.

- **The determination and prescription of the control standards and processes to be applied.** Broadly, this involves considering which combination of the options of elimination, containment and mitigation is, within specific legal requirements, most feasible and appropriate, and then determining precisely what is to be done. For example, considering the hazards that originate in the interaction of people and toxic materials, it might be felt appropriate merely to warn people about the hazard. Alternatively, elaborate systems may be devised to contain hazardous interactions of people and materials. The standards of control that are decided upon will depend crucially upon assessment of the probability and consequences of hazard realisation as well as on specific legal requirements. Although these factors may be capable of systematic measurement, the choice of control standard remains essentially a subjective decision regarding the acceptability of the residual risk relative to the costs of further reducing it.

- **The implementation of control standards and processes.** There is little point in identifying the need for control, deciding upon standards and then not implementing these controls, although this sometimes happens. The third stage in the technical control process therefore involves the actual implementation of the standards of control that have been determined.

- **The maintenance and adaptation of control standards and processes.** Implementation of controls is not a once-off activity. Control systems that have been implemented in the past may, for a variety of reasons, cease to be effective. They may no longer be applied or may have been overtaken by changes in the way that people and the working environment actually interact. Attention must, therefore, be given to the maintenance of established and previously implemented standards of control, as well as to their adaptation, if new information suggests that they are no longer appropriate in their present form.

Motivational Controls for Health and Safety at Work

The traditional focus in terms of managing health and safety at work has firmly been placed upon the technical control system.

The specific problems and difficulties of identifying hazards and deciding upon the control standards to be implemented and maintained have occupied a considerable amount of management and specialist time within industrial organisations. When technical control is inadequate, this is often attributed to a lack of necessary knowledge and/or resources. For example, ill-health or accidents at work may be attributed to hazards that had not previously been identified or to situations where existing forms of control were wrongly believed to be sufficient to prevent hazard realisation. In other cases, people may be aware of hazards but lack resources to attempt effective control. Problems of knowledge and resources are, and will remain, a major obstacle to the development of effective technical control systems. However, the problem cannot be left there. Effective self-regulation depends on the creation of motivational controls. These controls are general, rather than specific in their objectives and are designed to engender and maintain a positive motivation to the technical control of risk. Such positive motivations are important for everyone at all levels in the organisation.

It is often argued that managers are naturally motivated to the maintenance of technical controls and feel that particular efforts in the motivational direction are unnecessary. Dawson et al. (1983) suggests that this naturalistic approach is based on two main arguments. First, that "efficient production is safe production" and that somehow an adequate control of risks is automatically achieved through the pursuit of efficiency. A second argument is that people's own sense of self-preservation and humanity towards their colleagues results in a natural aversion to creating harm and unnecessary risk at work.

Objectives, Culture and Atmosphere

A prerequisite "climate" of safety awareness is essential to success in hazard control, and this climate is substantially dependent upon the words and deeds of senior management. The degree of commitment to health and safety goals and objectives expressed by senior management is seen as a crucial determinant of motivation at other levels throughout the organisation. This commitment can be expressed in many ways. The willingness to allocate resources of a purely financial kind is the most obvious and concrete, although formal declarations such as those contained within the written safety policy also create an impact. Commitment can be further demonstrated in a more straightforward way simply by senior management frequently visiting its production areas and showing a keen and active interest in the efforts that are directed towards health and safety problems and hazard control.

Responsibility and Authority

Although senior management commitment forms an important element of motivational control, more specific and bureaucratic forms of control also have an important role in securing management motivation. In particular, the allocation of specific responsibility for defined elements of technical controls is essential, if key individuals in the organisation are to have a clear understanding of what is expected of them. Without such structures of responsibility, the overall picture of what is done in terms of risk control may be relatively haphazard and important elements may remain unfulfilled, since nobody recognises them as their responsibility. A natural partner of responsibility is authority. If individuals are allocated responsibility for certain aspects of technical control, they will need the necessary authority to enable the successful accomplishment of those responsibilities. Line management has a key contribution to make to the creation and maintenance of a healthy and safe work environment. Accordingly, the role of health and safety specialists can be largely defined as advisory rather than executive. Line management's role can be described as "creating awareness", "providing sufficient awareness", "ensuring rules are observed", "encouraging and co-ordinating safe working" and "maintaining high standards of housekeeping".

Mechanisms of Accountability and Performance Measurement

Accountability involves the generation and use of acceptable performance data in such a way that those concerned can be, and are, held accountable for specified areas of activity, and are rewarded or sanctioned accordingly. Mechanisms for monitoring performance are important for two reasons. First, they can lead to the identification of problems and, possibly, suggest solutions. Secondly, monitoring can provide information on performance with a view to motivating employees to maintain good, or to remedy poor, performance. Difficulties arise, however, when problem solving, performance measurement and motivation are in conflict. Since the information derived from monitoring is not neutral, but carries with it messages of success or failure, some people have suggested that monitoring information is best presented in its problem-solving form, and not as a basis for performance appraisal. Such an approach is unrealistic since health and safety objectives will not be achieved naturally, particularly when the means for their achievement compete with other priorities. Monitoring is important to solve problems, but it is also important as a basis for motivating those responsible for hazard control.

A crucial question is therefore: what data should be collected and how should it be used? The hazard outcomes of poor performance, as reflected in the frequency, incidence and severity of injury or loss, are obviously relevant data, but they are susceptible to social and cultural factors. In addition, they concentrate on the bad news of the results of poor performance and only tell the good news indirectly and incompletely. In addition to these hazard outcomes, one can also monitor control outcomes that are the everyday results of health and safety programmes (or their absence) in terms of working conditions, attitudes and behaviour as revealed in working practices and management processes.

These distinctions between hazard and control outcomes and technical and motivational activities provide managers with the opportunity to use four types of data for monitoring performance. Hazard outcome data is limited to the details of any particular accidents or incidents. Control outcome data is derived from investigating the way new machines and systems of work are being used and supervised. Data on technical control activity is derived from investigating whether the people using the new machines and materials are aware of likely hazards and the measures to prevent or mitigate their realisation (e.g. are they aware of the dangers of working with lead, the importance and means of preventing exposure, and what to do should exposure occur?); whether there was an effective procedure for "vetting" new machinery and/or materials to identify hazards introduced by such changes and, if so, to assess their nature and significance and to determine and implement control measures. If controls are thought to be necessary, were elimination, containment mitigation considered? If so, how and by whom was this consideration made? On the motivational side, attention would be focused on examining whether decisions to develop or apply technical controls are actually reflected in managerial policy and practice, and whether definitions of responsibility and accountability were established.

Once monitoring makes data available, it will be useful to the cause of improved health and safety only if it is to be used in problem solving and in management appraisals and developments. Although formal management appraisal systems are usually a feature of large organisations, it is rare for safety performance to be included as a criterion.

SAFETY MANAGEMENT AND POLICIES

The first stage in the process of managing health and safety is to ensure that the company adopts and develops an effective health and safety policy. The policy will need to be developed and supported by senior management if it is to have any effect on raising standards. It should be understood that the vast majority of accidents that occur in the workplace are caused by a failure in management systems. That failure often stems from the fact that health and safety is not *seen* to be given the same priority as other business functions, with the consequence that insufficient resources are made available. Major effort is normally required to reverse this trend. The first step is to examine any existing policies and statements to ensure that they convey the correct message.

Key aspects of safety policy define management's commitment to safety and demonstrate that sound health and safety standards are a core objective. This means that such a policy should be integrated into all other management activities and strategies and would, therefore, be managed as any other strategy vital to the business. Effective safety policy can drive the overall organisation to apply good principles in managing hazards and controlling risks. The health and safety policy statement is a reflection of what the organisation is trying to achieve with respect to health and safety.

The health and safety policy statement sets out what the organisation is doing to manage health and safety and contains three essential elements:

- A general statement setting out the broad policy that the company has adopted.

- What is being done to secure health and safety (the arrangements).

- The responsibilities and functions of individuals (the organisation).

A safety policy, however, in order to be most effective, needs to be underpinned by a culture that promotes effective health and safety procedures. Organisationally, the policy should establish the responsibilities and, where appropriate, the relationships within the workplace.

An effective policy on safety and health will include a number of important features. It will ensure that:

- The fact that health and safety has positive benefits to the organisation is recognised and that a high level of safety makes for good business sense.

- Appropriate levels of resources will be allocated to promoting health and safety within the organisation, as there are distinct benefits to be gained.

- A positive culture will be encouraged within the organisation and that this encouragement will be actively supported by senior management.

- All employees will be involved in the decision-making processes, whether on an individual basis or through their representatives.

- The approach to health and safety will be based on the identification and control of risks.

- Health and safety is a business function and must, therefore, continually adapt to changes.

- Continual improvement will be made to health and safety standards.

- Adequate planning, monitoring and review of the implementation of the health and safety policy will occur.

- The direction is set for the organisation by communicating senior management's values, beliefs and commitment to health and safety.

- The basis of the policy and how it can contribute to business performance (e.g. by reducing injuries and ill health, protecting the environment and reducing unnecessary losses and liability) are explained.

- The importance of health and safety objectives in relation to other business objectives is established.

- The organisation is committed to pursuing progressive improvements in health and safety performance, with legal requirements defining the minimum level of achievement.

- The responsibilities of managers and the contribution that employees can make to policy implementation are explained, while outlining the participation procedures.

- The organisation is committed to maintaining effective systems of communications on health and safety matters.

- The director or key senior manager with overall responsibility for policy formulation, implementation and development is identified.

- The leaders of the organisation are committed to supporting the policy with adequate financial and physical resources, by ensuring the competence of all employees and by the provision of any necessary expert advice.

- The leaders are committed to planning and regularly reviewing and developing the policy.

Figure 13.2: Examples of Statements of Health and Safety Philosophy

"A good safety record goes hand-in-hand with high productivity and quality standards."

"We believe that an excellent company is, by definition, a safe company. Since we are committed to excellence, it follows that minimising risk to people, plant and products is inseparable from all other company objectives."

"Experience shows that a successful safety organisation also produces the right-quality goods at minimum costs."

"Prevention is not only better, but cheaper, than cure. There is no necessary conflict between humanitarianism and commercial considerations."

"Profit and safety are not in competition. On the contrary, safety is good business."

"Total safety is the ongoing integration of safety into all activities with the objective of attaining industry leadership in safety performance. We believe: Nothing is more important than safety — not production, not sales, not profit."

RESPONSIBILITY FOR MANAGING SAFETY WITHIN THE ORGANISATION

Managing health and safety is concerned with ensuring that the appropriate management structure exists within the organisation. Because organisations vary in their operation, so will the structure for tackling health and safety. Senior management needs to ensure that the management structure is suitable to guarantee that health and safety is properly addressed at all levels of the organisation. In addition, they should ensure that individuals have sufficient time to carry out their responsibilities.

The overall aim of safety management is to create a culture in the company where all employees, managers and directors have a common purpose to reduce accidents and ill health to the lowest level that is reasonably practicable. The culture will normally take some time to develop and, like all others, will need to be management-led. Managers and directors must accept that managing health and safety is the same as managing any other function under their control and must accept responsibility for it. It is not sufficient that a few interested persons within the organisation alone should manage health and safety and directors should, therefore, be seen to actively promote a positive culture.

Managers, employees and directors all need to be seen to be accountable for their actions or inactions and this can only be achieved through the development of properly defined responsibilities. These responsibilities must be sufficiently detailed for the person to know what is required of him and when it is required. When assigning responsibilities, organisations should be concerned to ensure that:

- Persons will be competent to carry out the task.

- The responsibilities are clearly explained.

- People are aware of the consequences of failing to manage the responsibilities.

- People are aware of how often these tasks must be done.

Many different groups within the organisation have responsibility for managing health and safety. We will focus on the more important groups in our discussion here.

Senior Management

Responsibilities should be clearly defined from top management downwards. Assumptions about responsibilities should not be made, because everybody should be definite about what is expected from them.

The responsibilities of key stakeholders should be achievable, objective, and be possible to evaluate so that each stakeholder can accept them, understand what is expected of them and ensure that the business can objectively assess where there are any inconsistencies within the policy. This can be achieved in a number of ways:

- A reference to safety and health responsibilities in individual job descriptions.

- Formal performance review and appraisal systems that involve the measuring and rewarding of individual performance (including managers') in health and safety activities.

- Procedures to take action where poor safety performance occurs.

Figure 13.3 presents an outline of senior management responsibilities for health and safety.

Figure 13.3: Senior Management Responsibilities in Respect of Health and Safety

---

- Act as chair of the safety committee, where one exists.

- Advance the aims and objectives of health and safety at work throughout the organisation.

- Provide both the human and financial resources necessary to implement the organisations safety policy.

- Report to the board on: overall health and safety status; periodically report on accidents, statistics.

- Detail any statutory enforcement orders issued that apply.

- Inform of impending health and safety legislation that is likely to affect the organisation.

- Propose updates to safety statement for ratification by the Board, where appropriate.

Senior managers are expected to support the organisation's health and safety policy and, in particular, to ensure that:

- Safe working practices are followed.

- Defects in equipment, plant and machinery are corrected.

- Physical arrangements for safeguarding the safety and health of employees are in place.

- Accidents are properly reported and investigated.

- The disciplinary procedure is invoked in cases where breaches of safety rules occur.

- Regular safety inspections of their areas are carried out.

- Employees are properly trained and competent to undertake tasks assigned to them.

- Effective consultation with employees on health and safety matters takes place.

- The necessary resources are provided to meet health and safety requirements and, where approval at a more senior level is necessary in this regard, to ensure that such matters are brought to the attention of the appropriate senior manager.

- The causes of accidents and the conditions under which they are most likely to occur are identified.

- Safety factors are accounted for at the design stage — the building of safety into the system.

- Safety equipment and protective devices are designed and protective clothing is provided.

- Regular inspections and checks are carried out and action taken to eliminate risks.

- All accidents and incidents are investigated to establish the cause and to initiate corrective action.

- Records and statistics are maintained that will identify problem areas and unsatisfactory trends.

- A continuous programme of education and training on safe working habits and methods of avoiding accidents is conducted.

Figure 13.4 outlines a number of basic procedures that management can use to achieve effective safety performance.

Figure 13.4: Basic Management Procedures for Effective Safety Performance in Organisations

> - Procedure for approval of new machines, processes and materials before purchase.
> - Rules for handling/using/storing substances.
> - Training arrangements for new employees or for employees transferred to new jobs or to different departments.
> - System for informing employees, contractors, visitors and customers of safety rules.
> - The licensing of drivers of internal factory vehicles.
> - Action to be taken in the event of a fire or explosion including the calling of the emergency services.
> - Arrangements for medical examinations.
> - Procedures for safety inspections and checks.
> - First-aid and medical attention available on site.
> - Maintenance of accident-reporting procedures.
> - Rules on the use of personal safety equipment such as guards, face shields, eye protection, etc.
> - The regular maintenance of plant and machinery.
> - Implementation of a proper housekeeping plan — cleanliness, tidiness, provision of waste bins, etc.
> - System of permits-to-work in certain specified situations or areas.

Supervisors

Effective supervision complements the provision of information, instruction and training by senior management, in ensuring that health and safety policy is effectively implemented. Supervision has two key dimensions: task management and team building.

Task Management

The primary task is to ensure the achievement of specific health and safety objectives and safe working in accordance with performance standards. This involves the provision of direction, help, guidance, example and discipline, with the aim of ensuring that risks are fully understood and performance standards and supporting procedures and systems are consistently applied. Effective task management also involves local planning to achieve objectives; training and coaching in skills to develop individual competence; and monitoring to identify any existing performance standards that are inappropriate or inadequate and require revision. It involves the use of both formal monitoring systems and general monitoring through spot checks and continuous observation.

Team Building

This is another key task in which the supervisor encourages individuals to work together in pursuit of team health and safety objectives. The supervisor's role includes the leading of team activities such as "tool box" talks, team briefings, and problem-solving exercises. It involves coaching and counselling to encourage and support the participation of all team members. A particularly important objective is to secure a growth in understanding of the risks involved in the work of the group and how these can be either eliminated or better controlled.

Levels of supervision need to be the subject of positive management consideration and decision-making. The appropriate level depends on the risks involved and on the competence of employees to identify and handle them. In some cases, legal requirements stipulate the supervision of certain activities, e.g. in factories, young people working at certain dangerous machines have to be supervised by an experienced person until they have received sufficient training. Some supervision of fully competent individuals will, however, always be required to ensure that standards are being consistently met.

Health and safety supervision should not be reactive, involving only responses to requests for help. Supervisory regimes should be designed and organised as part of a proper system of active management control. Particular attention should be given to the problems of people working alone, job sharing and part-time working and continuity at shift changeovers.

Supervisors and employees need to exercise judgement and discretion, for example, when making decisions on when to seek help or guidance, when to report hazards, or when to halt work because they consider it too dangerous to continue. They should, however, exercise this discretion within the framework of control established at the top of the organisation. Although authority to act can be delegated to supervisors and individual employees, the ultimate responsibility for complying with the employer's legal duties cannot be delegated. It follows that management must ensure that those exercising discretion and judgement are competent to do so and have clear guidelines.

A growing number of organisations have developed new methods of team working that are often linked to the widening of job content and to flexible working. This can mean, for example, that:

- Some maintenance tasks become the responsibility of the work group, which may involve some maintenance workers joining production teams.

- Job variety for individuals is increased and they have to become competent in new tasks.

- Supervisors become responsible for areas of work that are not within their established expertise or experience.

In some cases the formal supervisory role may not be defined and "team leaders" may be allowed to emerge naturally or be elected by group members. There may also be a policy that there should be a minimum of direct supervision so that the groups are encouraged to identify and solve their own problems.

Such initiatives can have positive benefits, if group performance criteria cover health and safety. However, the health and safety implications need to be carefully considered, with specific steps being taken to deal with them. Team and flexible working usually increase the discretion available to supervisors and others. In situations where supervisors acquire wider responsibilities, they need to become familiar with new risks and with how these relate to the activities of the whole group and of other groups. Increasing the discretion and responsibilities of supervisors and others, therefore, needs to be accompanied by sufficient training and experience to develop their competence in the exercise of the relevant health and safety judgements.

Having examined the overall responsibility of management for health and safety, we will now look at other key roles (**Figure 13.5**) and, in particular, that of the safety specialist.

Figure 13.5: Roles of Other Stakeholders in Managing Health and Safety in Organisations

---

The Employee

The employee has the following responsibilities:

- To be personally responsible in the area of health and safety and to adhere to health and safety work practices.

- To comply with the employer's instructions regarding health and safety.

- To report potential dangers to responsible persons, e.g. supervisors (this is a legal requirement).

- To practise the right to make proposals relating to health and safety (based on the duty of employees — the right to criticise and the right to stop work where health is in serious danger).

The Training Officer

The training officer's brief is to:

- Mould employee behaviour to act responsibly in all aspect of health and safety through Induction Programmes.

- Act as a source of clarification on health and safety matters.

- Actively participate in the formulation of health and safety policies, procedures and programmes.

The Safety Representative

The Safety Representative has both legal and non-legal functions including:

- To consult and make representations to employers on safety, health and welfare matters.

- To support the prevention of accident and ill health.

- To highlight any potential health and safety problems and, where possible, identify means to overcome them.

- To investigate accidents and dangerous occurrences.

- The entitlement to consult a health and safety inspector.

- To carry out health and safety inspections and to identify hazards by; safety tours, safety sampling, safety surveys.

The Safety Committee

If the organisation has a safety committee, then its role is:

- To review unsafe work practices and conditions.

- To make suggestions on methods of improving health and safety performance.

- To assist in the formulation of health and safety policies, procedures and rules.

- To promote aspects of health and safety.

- To assist in carrying out occupational health programmes.

The Medical Officer

The medical officer has preventative and clinical dimensions to the role.

Preventative:

- To advise on health and safety precautions.

- To advise on conducting inspections and enquiries.

- To assist in establishing health standards.

- To conduct employee medical examinations.

Clinical:

- To deal medically with individual accidents and diseases.

- To advise on steps necessary to recover from injury or illness.

THE ROLE OF THE SAFETY SPECIALIST

The effective management of health and safety has major implications for the role of safety specialists. An emphasis on senior executives and line management does not mean that the specialists will, in time, become redundant but rather those complementary roles need to be developed. **Figure 13.6** shows a matrix of activities available to safety specialists involved in the technical control of hazards. The horizontal axis corresponds to the stages involved in the technical control of hazards (i.e. identification assessment, control and monitoring) and the vertical axis corresponds to different modes of operation from the highly reactive one of information processing, through giving advice and problem-solving, to the highly proactive one of taking direct executive action. Examples are also shown of the different types of activity that fall within each of the cells, so created.

Taking the horizontal axis first, it seems to be relatively uncontentious that safety specialists, whether individually or collectively, need to become expert in all activities associated with the control of hazards. This does not mean that they have individually to know everything about the identification, assessment and containment of all possible hazards, but they do need to be able to understand and articulate relevant information, whether from within their organisation or outside. Where more than one specialist is involved, they need to appreciate their colleagues' sphere of competence and learn ways of acting collectively to form expert multi-disciplinary groups.

It is ultimately the responsibility of line managers and supervisors to ensure that safe working practices are adopted, that recommended safety precautions are taken and that employees are made aware of the hazards and how best to control them. Pursuing these objectives often creates conflict with others — for example, the rate and quality of production, profitability and the stability and commitment of the workforce. These conflicting priorities have to be confronted and compromise reached. If the specialist assumes direct executive responsibility, managers may feel that they are absolved from responsibility; that they have "passed the buck" and can get on with those things they see as more directly relevant to their management role. This would be undesirable even if specialists tended to be fairly powerful people but, given that they are frequently relatively low on power and influence in the organisation, it would be a recipe for very poor self-regulation.

Figure 13.6: Safety Specialist Activities in the Technical Control of Hazards

Safety Specialists' Activities	Stages of Technical Control				
	1. Identification of Hazards	2. Assessment of Controls	3. Development of Controls	4. Implementation of Controls	5. Longer-term Monitoring and Adaptation
A. Processing information	Keeping accident statistics; processing hazard information	Calculating accident manufacturers' information and lists of products, etc.	Processing orders for safety equipment	Comparing accident statistics over time	Comparing accident statistics over time
B. Giving advice/ problem-solving					
B1 Passive adviser	Looking at work operations on request; investigating complaints	Answering questions about severity of hazards	Commenting on available controls which have been suggested	Commenting on effectiveness on requests	Investigating accidents; providing feedback on request
B2 Active adviser	Taking initiative in looking for hazards	Lobbying for appropriate standards and control limits	Recommending controls	Identifying short-falls and improvements	Making recommendations for update/ review of systems
C. Taking direct executive action:					
C1 Jointly with line management	Joint inspections and audits	Jointly deciding on standards	Jointly drawing up codes of practice	Joint supervision and approval or disapproval to jobs	Participating in reviews of arrangements
C2 Alone	Doing own inspections and audits	Deciding unilaterally what is safe/unsafe	Issuing instructions: specifying controls to be followed	Supervising job; exercising veto; physically stopping people working	Modifying procedures, etc. on own initiative

An important question then arises: how are safety specialists to influence senior executives and line managers and become a major force within an organisation, without actually assuming direct executive responsibility? Seven sources of power and influence are available to health and safety specialists:

1. Patronage of senior management.

2. Direct role in control process.

3. Coalition formed with safety representatives and/or safety committees.

4. Maintaining strong co-operative relationships with the HSA, especially Safety Inspectors.

5. Formal position in organisational hierarchy.

6. Personal qualities of charm, friendliness, leadership, etc.

7. Managerial dependence on specialist expertise.

The first is patronage — safety specialists should be aware that it is useful to get someone important on their side, whether this is demonstrated personally in support at key meetings or more formally through lending a name to a document. Secondly, the specialist's roles in policing the control process gives some power, but only within an organisation where health and safety are seen as important. There are, however, some problems involved for any safety specialist who tries to administer regulations, police activities and solve problems with the same group of people, not least because of unwillingness to share sensitive information. Other sources of power and influence can be derived through entry into coalitions — either internally with safety representatives and committees or externally with local officers of the regulatory enforcement agencies.

The safety specialist's official position in the hierarchy is measured by such indicators as job title, salary, grading and reporting relationships, while functional position is also important in determining power and influence. The specialist needs to be independent of line management and yet have their confidence. Reporting upwards, the specialist should reach someone who has the respect of senior executives on the "direct" operating side. The specialist can effectively be an operations person provided that they and the rest of the organisation are committed to establishing effective systems of hazard control.

Expertise is, in many ways, the most important source of power and influence for the long-term development of health and safety programmes. However, the extent to which the expertise of specialists actually provides access to real influence within a firm is dependent both on characteristics of the specialists themselves and of the management organisation with which they are associated. Nevertheless, qualifications and experience are important. Even if formally qualified or well experienced, the specialists still have to gain personal credibility with line managers and the workforce. This happens to the extent that stakeholders consider the specialist is providing an important service or performing an important control function, on which managers and workforce representatives depend. The nature of the relationship that prevails between managers and any specialist is much influenced by three inter-related factors:

- What the specialist can offer (and whether it is available from other sources).

- The importance of their offer to management.

- The basis for its importance, in particular, whether imposed from "outside" or developed "internally".

Thirdly, there are expert systems not directly geared toward the continuation of the primary production and distribution of goods and services but which are, nonetheless, seen as important for control and co-ordination. In organisations with improving safety performance, there is a noticeable move towards this type of relationship for safety specialists, as managers are considering seriously the meaning of their responsibilities for health and safety.

The fourth and weakest relationship does not derive internally but has its roots in the requirements and pressures of outside agencies. It is in this context that many specialists in health and safety actually work. The type of specialist role that develops reflects both the objective characteristics of the establishment and company and the prevailing attitudes within it. Where the technology, materials and working environment are stable and well-understood, access to a good data bank on established hazards and their controls may need only to be supplemented by a part-time specialist to oversee its operations, ensure the maintenance of administrative systems and draw attention to the safety implications of process or product changes. Alternatively, the use of sophisticated and changing technologies and new or toxic substances would arguably require a larger, more qualified and experienced specialist presence. The views and opinions of the managers and workforce representatives, which may be more or less tightly associated with "objective" issues, will also affect the specialist's position. It is only where line managers regard health and safety as an important aspect of their task, and take a broad socio-technical view of hazard origins and control, that specialists are well placed to perform a strong and advisory function.

It is important to remember that whether powerful or not, safety specialists usually to be found only in the larger Irish enterprises and establishments. Small retail outlets and construction firms, for instance, along with most other smaller establishments, simply do not employ specialists directly. In some cases, smaller firms may use the services of outside safety consultants or at least make use of specialist information available through trade associations and federations of employers. This, however, is by no means the norm. In the absence of specialist support, the argument that, ultimately a safe and healthy working environment must depend on the motivation and capacity of line managers to act, carries even greater force.

SAFETY MONITORING

Safety monitoring focuses on the measurement of safety performance and the taking of corrective action. Such monitoring should be active in nature and may involve:

- Indirect monitoring of performance standards, where managers check the quality and quantity of monitoring undertaken by subordinates.

- Procedures to monitor the achievement of objectives.

- The periodic examination of documents to ensure that standards relating to safety are being complied with.

- The systematic inspection of plant equipment and premises.

- Environmental monitoring and health surveillance.

- Systematic direct identification of work and behaviour.

Figure 13.7 presents a set of questions that should be posed in respect of health and safety monitoring.

Figure 13.7: Health and Safety Monitoring Guidelines

- Is there a manager's health and safety self-certification programme in place?

- If yes, what analysis of responses takes place?

- Does the internal audit department include health and safety in their work?

- Does it liaise with the organisation's safety officer on the matters audited?

- Are all managers aware that their health and safety performance may be checked by internal audit?

- What inspections take place in the organisation?

- Are they organised properly and are the terms of reference clear?

- Are the managers of those being reviewed copied on the inspection reports?

- Are managers of departments reviewed, required to respond formally to inspection reports describing the action programme with data?

A variety of approaches is available to the organisation in order to undertake this monitoring activity. These include the following.

Safety Sampling

This technique is designed to measure by random sampling the accident potential in a specific work area or activity by identifying safety deficiencies or omissions. The area of activity is divided into sections and a trained observer appointed to each section. A prescribed route through the area is planned and observers follow their itinerary in the time allowed, perhaps 15 minutes. During the sampling period, they note specifically identified health and safety aspects on a sampling sheet, which incorporates a limited number of points to be awarded for each aspect. Typical aspects for observation and assessment include: observance of fire protection requirements, the state of hand tools, evidence of damage to machinery guards, the operation of specifically-designed safe systems of work and chemical handling procedures.

The staff making the observations should be trained in the technique and should have a broad knowledge of the procedures and processes being carried out. The results of the sample inspections are collated by a specific manager or health and safety adviser and presented in graphic form. This system, in effect, monitors the overall effectiveness of safety management in various areas of workplace.

Damage Control

Damage control techniques aim at providing a safe place of work, and call for observation and co-operation by all staff who see or experience a condition that may lead to an accident, e.g. a damaged machinery guard or safety mechanism on a machine. Damage control relies heavily on the operation of a hazard reporting system, covering damage and defects in plant, machinery, structural items, etc.

Job Safety Analysis

Job safety analysis can do much to eliminate the hazards of a job. The analysis identifies every single operation in a job, examines the specific hazards and indicates remedial measures necessary. It involves the examination of a number of areas, including permit-to-work systems, influences on behaviour, the operator training required and the degree of supervision and control necessary. Job safety analysis can feature as part of a workplace risk assessment.

Safety Audits

A safety audit is a technique that submits each area of an organisation's health and safety activity to a systematic critical examination, with the principal objective of minimising loss. Every component of the total working system is included, e.g. management policy and commitment, attitudes, training, features or processes, safe systems of work, personal protection needs, emergency procedures, etc. An audit, as in the field of accountancy, aims to disclose strengths, and weaknesses in the main areas of vulnerability or risk. We will discuss safety audits in more detail in **Chapter 15**.

Safety audits should be designed on the basis of past accident experience, existing hazards and the need to improve individual attitudes to health and safety performance. One of the problems with safety audits is that, while they cover a comprehensive range of issues in most cases, the people undertaking the audit only examine the issues raised in the audit documentation. On this basis hazards can fail to be recognised due to the fact that the audit document does not incorporate any reference to them. In other words, a safety audit is only as good as the individual who prepared the audit format. In order to be 100 per cent effective, therefore, audit documents need regular updating and revision.

A team approach to the carrying out of safety audits is recommended, rather than the completion of the audit by any specific individual. Following a safety audit, a formal report should be prepared, incorporating short-term, medium-term and long-term recommendations for action. Implementation of recommendations should be closely monitored.

Safety Surveys

A safety survey is a detailed examination of a number of critical areas of operation, e.g. process safety, manual handling operations, or an in-depth study of the whole health and safety operations of workplace. A survey examines, for instance, health and safety management procedures, environmental working conditions, occupational health and hygiene arrangements, the wide field of safety and accident prevention, and the system for the provision of information, instruction and training for staff and other persons affected by the organisation's operations.

The outcome of a safety survey is generally the production of a safety survey report. In most cases, such a report is purely of a critical nature indicating, for instance, breaches of the law, unsafe conditions and working practices, inadequate management and administration of health and safety deficiencies in machinery guarding, etc. The report is generally written on an observation/ recommendation basis, recommendations being phased according to the degree of risk and the relative costs of eliminating or controlling these risks. The objective of a safety survey report is to present management with a phased programme of health and safety improvement covering a five-year period. Following the safety survey, regular revisits are made to assess progress in the implementation of the report, progress reports being produced for senior management indicating the degree of progress and any other issues that may have arisen since the report was prepared.

Safety Inspections

This is a scheduled inspection of a workplace by members of the management team and/or health and safety specialists. The inspection is generally broad in its application, covering plant maintenance standards, the operation of safe systems of work, cleaning and housekeeping levels, fire protection arrangements and other issues of specific significance in the workplace. This technique tends to be a more general examination of safety performance at a particular point in time, rather than the in-depth approach taken with a safety survey. The objectives of a safety inspection should be clearly defined and the outcome of the inspection should be a written report to individual managers with recommendations for action.

Safety Tours

A safety tour is an unscheduled examination of a work area undertaken by a selected group of staff, including the manager with direct responsibility for that area, members of a health and safety committee, supervisors, trade union and safety representatives and selected operators. A safety tour can examine predetermined health and safety aspects, such as housekeeping levels, standards of machinery safety, the use of personal protective equipment and the operation of established safe systems of work. Safety tours should be related to, and reinforce decisions made by, local management or by the health and safety committee. For maximum effectiveness, it is essential that action following a safety tour is taken immediately.

Project Safety Analysis

While existing risks may be identified and assessed by various forms of safety monitoring, project safety analysis is appropriate for large projects. Usually undertaken as a joint exercise by an engineering manager, architect, plant and equipment supplier and installer, health and safety specialist and other specialists, it helps to ensure that account is taken of accumulated experience, knowledge of the technology and best practice in the initial design of projects. Project safety analysis should be undertaken at the design stage of all projects, both large and small.

Hazard and Operability Study (HAZOPS)

HAZOPS is a technique applied in the assessment of potential hazards from new installations and processes. It is a technique used extensively in the chemical industry and in chemical engineering applications, along with other techniques, such as Failure Modes and Effect Analysis, Fault Tree Analysis and Event Tree Analysis.

The technique is defined as the application of a formal critical examination to the process and engineering intentions of new facilities to assess the hazard potential from incorrect operation or malfunction of individual items of equipment, and the consequential effects on the facility as a whole. It ensures that health and safety requirements are considered at the design stage of a project with a view to preventing the classic fire-fighting exercises, which commonly follow the completion of projects.

Failure Model and Effect Analysis (FMEA)

This technique is based on identifying the possible failure modes of each component of a system and predicting the consequences of that failure. For example, if a control valve fails, it could result in too much flow in the system, too much pressure, or the production of an undesired chemical reaction. As a result, attention is paid to these consequences at the design stage of a project and in the preparation of planned maintenance systems.

Fault Tree Analysis

Fundamentally, this begins with consideration of a chosen event, such as a major fire or an explosion, and then assesses the combination of failures and conditions that could cause it to arise. It is widely used in quantitative risk analysis, particularly where control over process controls is critical to meet safety standards.

Event Tree Analysis

Similar to fault tree analysis, this works from a selected initiating event, such as a pressure control failure. It is, basically, a systematic representation of all the possible states of the processing system conditional to the specific initiating event and relevant for a certain type of outcome, e.g. a pollution incident or a major fire.

Consequence Analysis

Consequence analysis is a feature of a risk analysis that considers the physical effects of a particular process failure, and the damage caused by these effects. It is undertaken to form an opinion on potentially serious hazardous outcomes of accidents and their possible consequences for people and the environment. Consequence analysis can act as a tool in the decision-making process in a safety study, which incorporates these features:

- A description of the process system to be investigated.

- An identification of the undesirable events.

- A determination of the magnitude of the resulting physical effects.

- A determination of the damage.

- An estimation of the probability of the occurrence of calculated damage.

- An assessment of risk against established criteria.

The outcome of consequence analysis is four-fold:

- To obtain information about all known and unknown effects that are of importance when something goes wrong in the plant and also information on how to deal with possible catastrophic events.

- To obtain information on how to minimise the consequences of accidents.

- To impart to employees an understanding of their personal situation and the measures being taken to protect them.

- To meet the requirements of legislation.

Professional technologists and chemists who are experienced in the actual problems of the technical system concerned generally undertake consequence analysis.

HEALTH AND SAFETY TRAINING

Competency Issues

Competence is an important issue in a health and safety context. The level of competence that individuals should possess will depend on their position within the organisation and the responsibilities assigned to them. The two issues of competency that the employer needs to address are to ensure that:

- Individuals, within or from outside the company, are appointed as "competent persons" to assist in undertaking the statutory duties and to assist in emergencies.

- Individuals are generally competent to carry out their specific allocated tasks.

The following points provide an indication as to some general skills and abilities that may be required in the organisation in order to ensure competency for individuals to carry out their specific allocated tasks:

- **Technical Knowledge:** the employer will need to assess whether persons have the necessary technical knowledge in order that they can adequately manage the issue. In the majority of cases, obtaining relevant literature and guidance notes will be sufficient. For more complex issues, expert assistance may be required.

- **The need to keep abreast of new legislation and guidance:** health and safety is a dynamic issue, with new regulations and guidance continually being issued. The employer will need to ensure that the competent person keeps abreast of such developments.

- **How and when to obtain expert advice:** every person has their limitations, and should recognise when to obtain specialist advice.

- **Training skills:** the level of training skills will vary according to the type of training to be provided. The employer should ensure that, if a large number of people are to carry out training (supervisors, etc), they possess basic training skills.

- **Interpersonal skills:** as for training, the level of interpersonal skills required will vary. For health and safety officers or other "competent" personnel, the ability to communicate effectively with all levels in the organisation and to deal with sensitive "conflict" situations is essential.

- **Management skills:** as a large proportion of work will fall to managers, they should be capable of applying basic management skills to health and safety issues.

- **Familiarity with statistical information:** this skill is only likely to be required in larger organisations with a significant amount of data to process

- **Specialist knowledge:** specialist knowledge can often be found within the workforce. The employer should ensure, however, that the level of knowledge is sufficient to control the risks.

Training can be defined as "the modification of attitudes, knowledge or skill to achieve pre-determined standards through a planned process of instruction and practice" (Glossary of Training Terms, MSC, 1981). It can include the provision of information and instruction. The primary aim of health and safety training is, therefore, to improve and enhance a person's skills, knowledge and/or attitudes to enable that person to carry out his work safely. This will help to ensure that an individual is competent to perform the work required of them. Provision of adequate training is an essential part of effective health and safety management and, for training to be successful, a considered planned approach is necessary.

Training helps employees to acquire the skills, knowledge and attitudes to make them competent in the health and safety aspects of their work — whatever their position in the organisation. It includes formal off-the-job training, instruction to individuals and groups, and on-the-job coaching and counselling. Ensuring that people are competent may demand more than training — for example, a period of supervised experience to practise and develop new skills. Training is therefore only one element in ensuring that people's health and safety performance is satisfactory.

Health and safety requirements should be integrated into job specifications for all employees, and training to meet those requirements calls for a similar approach to that for other business training.

Deciding if Training is Necessary

Training should not be used to compensate either for inadequacies in other aspects of the safety system, such as poorly-designed or insufficiently-protected plant, or for inadequate workstations and procedures that are not designed according to sound ergonomic principles. It may, however, be appropriate to use training as a temporary means of control pending improvements in such areas. Identifying whether training is necessary demands an understanding of job requirements and the abilities of individuals.

Identifying Training Needs

Job and task health and safety analyses help to identify health and safety training needs. With new jobs, this analysis can involve comparison with similar existing jobs, or possibly by reference to other organisations with similar jobs. With existing jobs, the analysis can involve:

- Consideration of accident, ill health and incident records relevant to those jobs to identify how such events have occurred and how they can be prevented.

- Information from employees about how jobs are done, the sequence of tasks involved and the tools, materials and equipment used.

- Observing and questioning employees to understand what they are doing and why. In complex process plans, the analysis must take account of all possible consequences of human error, including those that may be remote from the particular task in hand.

With management jobs, the analysis should cover both the job itself and the tasks of, and risks run by, subordinates so as to take account of the supervisory part of the job.

Analysis can be applied to complete jobs or subsidiary tasks. Complete analysis is essential for new starters but, with existing employees, the need may be to improve performance on particular tasks. Job and task health and safety analyses are detailed and resource-intensive. They can, however, support the safety management system in a number of respects as well as identifying training needs, including:

- Recruitment, selection and placement.

- The identification of critical tasks for which planning and monitoring activities should be a priority.

- The assessment of an individual's performance in a job.

- The assessment of the suitability of an individual for promotion or substitution to a job where health and safety factors are critical.

There are three main types of training needs: organisational, job-related and individual:

Organisational needs are common to all those in the organisation. They include knowledge and information about:

- The health and safety policy and the philosophy underlying it.

- The organisational structure and systems for:

  ◊ the control of health and safety.

  ◊ securing the co-operation of all employees.

◇   communicating health and safety information.

◇   ensuring the competence of individuals.

Job needs are of two main types: *management* needs and *non-management* needs. Management needs include:

- Leadership skills for directors and senior managers responsible for the whole organisation, health and safety advisers, managers and supervisors.

- Communications skills.

- Techniques of health and safety management.

- Training and instruction.

- Coaching and problem-solving skills relevant to health and safety.

- Understanding of the risks within a manager's area of responsibility, of the health and safety principles that underlie their control and of relevant legislation.

- Knowledge of the planning, measuring, reviewing and auditing systems.

For the last aspect, in particular, special consideration should be given to the needs of those who occupy key positions, including those who draw up performance standards, health and safety advisers, those who may have to report on accident, ill health and incident investigations, those involved in review and audit activities and those who have to implement emergency procedures.

Non-management needs include:

- An overview of health and safety principles.

- Detailed knowledge of relevant safety performance standards, systems, procedures and rules intended to control the risks of the job, and of the principles underlying them.

- Communication and problem-solving skills, to encourage effective participation in health and safety activities.

Individual needs are specific to an individual and are generally identified through performance appraisal. They may arise because an individual has not understood formal job training that has been delivered.

Training needs vary over time and regular assessments of needs should be made that cover:

- Inducting new starters, including part-time and temporary workers.

- Maintaining the performance of established employees (especially in the case of critical emergency procedures) and keeping them up-to-date with changes.

- Changing roles arising from job moves, promotion or the possibility of having to deputise for others.

- The introduction of new equipment or technology.

Figure 13.8 presents different sources of information about training needs.

Identifying Objectives

Having identified all the relevant needs, specific training objectives should be set. Using job and task health and safety analyses, together with an assessment of relative risks, objectives can be prioritised. Once set, objectives can be used as the basis for measuring the effectiveness of training. **Table 13.1** is an example.

Figure 13.8: Sources of Information about Safety and Health Training Needs

---

- *Consulting relevant legislation*: Reviewing the legislation relevant to the tasks being carried out may reveal specific requirements for certain types of training to be provided.

- *Consulting the risk assessment findings:* Examining the findings of the company's risk assessment should help determine what work activities require training as part of the preventative and protective methods required to reduce the risk.

- *Consulting records:* Examining accident and ill-health statistics may reveal a training need — for example, incidents involving damage to structure or stock caused by movement of vehicles such as a fork-lift truck may indicate that driver training is required.

- *Forecasting:* Potential training needs can be identified by looking ahead at likely changes in the tasks carried out by employees, the equipment they use, changes in systems of work, and the introduction of new technology.

- *Assessing the current position:* Examining employees' existing levels of training, knowledge and experience in relation to the nature of the jobs they do and tasks they carry out, can be used to provide an indication as to whether additional training is needed. This is known as job/task analysis, and it may involve observing and questioning employees in order to obtain information on how jobs are done, why they are done in a particular way, the tasks involved, equipment used, etc.

- *Consulting employees:* Requests from employees for health and safety training should be taken into account.

- *Health and safety policy:* The health and safety policy may state specific training requirements that the company expects to be met, which may be more stringent than the legal minimum. The policy should also state the health and safety responsibilities of managers, who may require additional training in order to discharge those responsibilities effectively.

Table 13.1: Training Needs

Training Need	Training Objectives	Training Content
Manual Handling	• To provide employees with an understanding of good handling techniques. • To equip employees with the ability to recognise potentially hazardous handling operations. • To familiarise employees with the proper use of handling aids. • To provide employees with an understanding of how to use and maintain necessary personal protective equipment.	• Explanation of how the mechanism of the back works. • Manual handling video. • Manual handling demonstration. • Group exercise. • Explanation and demonstration of the use of roll cages and pallet trucks, etc. • Overview of the Manual Handling Regulations. • Explanation of relevant company rules and procedures. • Procedures for reporting injuries, etc.

Deciding on Training Methods

Training can be carried out internally or externally. Internal training can involve in-house resources or the use of consultants. A range of equipment and activities may be appropriate depending on the nature of the subject. In general, there should be the maximum possible trainee participation.

Didactic learning involves trainees receiving information communicated to them, and understanding it. Examples of training methods incorporating passive learning include:

Lecture

• Effectiveness depends largely upon the ability of the lecturer to sustain the interest of the trainees.

- Useful for communicating information to large numbers of people, for example on legislation, company procedures or policies.

- Little opportunity for trainee participation and, as a result, trainees may easily be distracted.

- Can be time-consuming to prepare.

- Requires the use of visual aids to maintain interest.

Demonstration

- Usually involves a verbal explanation by the trainer, followed by a practical demonstration of how a particular task or activity should (and should not) be carried out — for example, the use of equipment, handling of materials, etc.

- Likely to prove more interesting for trainees than lectures, and can be used to train large groups.

- Important that the demonstration is effective and properly understood, and ideally trainees should be allowed to copy the demonstration themselves (under adequate supervision where necessary).

Active Tuition

- Similar to lectures but involves active as well as passive learning, in that trainees are required to discuss, question and debate the issues raised.

- This should help maintain interest, and the trainer can gauge to some extent whether the information being communicated has been understood.

Participative learning involves two-way communication between the trainer and trainee in that, having received the information, trainees then have to act upon it in some way, hence providing feedback for the trainer. Examples of training methods involving active learning include:

Discussion

- Can take various forms, and is often incorporated into training sessions involving other training methods.

- May simply involve the trainer discussing various principles, theories and policies with trainees in order to help them gain a better understanding of the issues.

- May also take the form of case studies, where trainees are encouraged to discuss a particular problem and present a suitable solution, or it may take the form of a trainee workshop whereby information is communicated and discussed, after which various exercises are given to trainees, either as individuals or in groups, in order to assess their understanding of the subject matter. The completed exercises would then normally be discussed and reviewed by the trainer and the other trainees. Similarly, syndicate exercises can be held, in which the main group of trainees is divided into sub-groups, each of which is given a set problem to work through and discuss.

- Useful in that it stimulates interest and participation, permits trainees' ideas and experiences to be shared, and enables them to apply theoretical principles to practical problems in order to devise appropriate solutions.

- Drawbacks are that it can be time-consuming, and some trainees may dominate the discussions to the detriment of those less forceful or poorly motivated.

Role Playing

- Can be viewed as an extension of discussion, in that trainees are presented with a particular problem or situation and then have to act out the roles of those involved — for example, with respect to procedures in the event of an emergency.

- Should produce a high level of interest and participation, as well as enabling trainees to gain a fuller understanding of the relevant safety issues and potential problems.

- Can be very time-consuming to prepare and carry out.

Project Work

- Usually set after (but sometimes before) a training session has taken place, in order to encourage trainees to apply the knowledge they have gained in a practical situation.

- Should stimulate interest and provide feedback for the trainer.

On- the-Job Training

- A common method of training, whereby the trainer (normally a supervisor or an experienced employee) explains and then demonstrates to a trainee how a particular activity should be performed, and then provides adequate supervision until the trainee is competent to carry out the activity alone.

- Is often carried out on a one-to-one basis.

- Has the advantage that the training relates precisely to the work activities being carried out, and the trainer receives immediate feedback on the performance of the trainee.

- It is vital, however that the trainer is competent and has the ability to deliver the training effectively and the time to provide the necessary supervision.

Carrying Out Training

In some cases, training needs may have to be met through closely supervised on-the-job experience. For some high-risk jobs and tasks, it may be necessary to arrange for such experience to be gained outside the real work situation, for example, at a training facility where simulation exercises can be mounted.

Evaluation and Feedback

The effectiveness of training should be measured against training objectives that have been set in advance. Formal evaluation should be undertaken after training, to establish if it has led to the desired improvement in work performance. The results of this evaluation can be used to improve the training process. The effectiveness of training can also be assessed as part of performance measurement activities that aim to identify the underlying causes of substandard performance.

Organisations achieving high standards of health and safety performance give a high priority to health and safety training and develop systematic and documented approaches to it. Resources are allocated according to need and are safeguarded from arbitrary cuts or modifications, such as those arising from cost reduction or rationalisation exercises. This is a reflection of the philosophy that regards people as the organisation's most important resource and good health and safety performance as contributory to business success.

Broad Categories of Safety & Health Training

Managing safety necessarily involves the organisation making sure that all those who are responsible have the appropriate safety-related training. While there will be certain industry or job-specific needs, broad categories are generally applicable. **Table 13.2** presents examples of different categories of safety and health training.

New Staff Induction

All new staff should receive training that ensures their safety both in normal working circumstances and in cases of emergency. This means that they must be trained to carry out their work responsibly and to use their buildings and the site with care. They must be informed, in no uncertain terms, of the safety rules and the disciplinary consequences of breaches of those rules. They must know when, where and how to get medical treatment. They must know the correct procedures in the event of fire or any emergency evacuation. They must know about the provisions for employee hygiene and health. Correct attitudes to health and safety must be initiated and developed from their first day, if not earlier.

Table 13.2: Determining the Type of Training Required

Type of Training	Training Points to be Included
Induction Training	General induction training should include: • Arrangements for first aid, fire and evacuation (these should be covered on an employee's first day). • The accident reporting procedure. • Introduction to the company safety policy, including employees' legal responsibilities. • Relevant health and safety legislation. • Workplace safety rules. • Who to contact in the event of a problem. • Welfare arrangements, e.g. toilets, catering facilities. • Conditions of employment, e.g. sickness or absence procedure, hours of work. In addition, health and safety training in matters specific to the tasks employees are expected to perform will often be required during induction, such as: • Information on relevant hazards, e.g. manual handling, exposure to chemicals. • How the risks presented by those hazards can be minimised, e.g. safe lifting and handling techniques, correct use and maintenance of PPE. • Specific training may also be required to comply with legal requirements such as the training of the lift truck operators. If new recruits are managers, additional training will usually be required on relevant subjects such as: • The safety management systems and any quality system in operation. • Legal responsibilities of the company and individual managers. • Training arrangements. • The company's risk assessment, and how hazards relevant to the manager's area of responsibility are controlled. • Disciplinary/grievance procedures.

Training/ Refresher Training	Such training could involve any of the subjects in induction training, perhaps in more detail, plus: • Safe working methods. • Training in technical matters, such as the identification and control of specific hazards. • The safe use of new machinery and technology. • How to follow a new work procedures, such as a permit-to-work system. • Specialised training for appropriate personnel, e.g. first aiders and competent persons.
Training for Managers	It is important to ensure that managers and supervisors receive adequate training as they will not only be responsible for supervising work activities, but also for: • Liaison and co-operation on health and safety with individuals and groups within the company. • Liaison and co-operation on health and safety with individuals and groups external to the company, such as enforcing authorities, suppliers, customers, contractors or the public. • The managers' duties and role in internal accident reporting and investigation, and statutory reporting of injuries, diseases and dangerous occurrences. • Effective supervision of employees, and identification of their training needs (managers need an appreciation of the risks present and control measures required). • Recruitment of employees, suitable for the tasks required of them. • Checking that work areas and work carried out under their control adhere to the company safety policy and to legal requirements. • How to carry out a risk assessment. It is vital that managers are given sufficient information, instruction and training to enable them to discharge their health and safety duties effectively. The level of training required will vary according to the extent of the duties and responsibility assigned to individual managers, the size of the company and the complexity of its operations.

Training for Non-Employees	Employers must ensure that adequate training is given to contractors, etc. who visit the site, on issues such as: • Risks to the contractor's health and safety on site. • Emergency procedures. • Safe working practices. • Persons responsible for evaluation. • Risks to employees from contractor's activities. The employer must also ensure that, where necessary, the contractor provides information and training where their actions may affect the health and safety of others.

Managers and Supervisors

Managers are prime targets for training, since they are the employer's representatives. It is they who are responsible for ensuring health and safety training and preventing breaches of rules, by disciplining if necessary. They must set a good example. It follows from this that they must know and accept their responsibilities. For example, for categories of staff who travel regularly as part of their job, the employer should stress their responsibility for ensuring adequate car insurance and maintenance, and for scheduling their day to avoid driving long distances after a full day of meetings.

Safety Representatives

The workforce elects safety representatives. They are the usual contacts for the factory inspectorate when the latter wishes to inform employees of action that should be taken. The inspectorate has a duty to inform employees of matters of fact that concern their health and safety. In practice, if the employer maintains good relationships with the inspectorate, seeks its advice and acts upon it, and also maintains good relations and communications with staff safety representatives, they should be able to take action together to improve safety.

If representatives' activities result in the setting up of safety committees, these can make either a substantial contribution or very little difference. The effectiveness of safety committees will vary considerably depending on the expertise of the safety representatives. Training is very relevant here. These committees will also, of course, be strongly influenced by the value placed on safety generally in the organisation (the underlying organisational culture or ethos), directly reflected in the level of support given to such committees.

Safety Officers

These may be full-time or part-time appointments. Training provided varies from none to a Masters Degree in health and safety. Safety officers need training and this is best carried out on specialist courses, off the job.

First Aiders

Employers are obliged to ensure adequate first aid provision for themselves and their employees. This includes training. Organisations are required to have a certain proportion of their staff trained and available to give first aid. Additional first aiders may be necessary, if shift working is operated. First aid kits must be maintained and their location known to all staff. Additional payments are often made as an inducement to staff to accept first aid training and responsibilities.

Temporary Visitors

Contractors are one example of "visitors", FÁS trainees are another, as are visitors in the more usual sense. Because such a high proportion of accidents involve "strangers" on sites, particular attention needs to be paid to raising the safety awareness of visitors and also to anticipating any hazards that they themselves may introduce.

Permanent Staff

One of the problems about long-serving employees is that they may stop noticing hazards. Entrenched attitudes may also be difficult to shift. Permanent staff need training to maintain and improve their health and safety consciousness. In part, this will come from careful enforcement of safety rules, but sometimes more will be needed. Sometimes a safety suggestion scheme can encourage interest in safety matters, as can the occasional visual reminder of just how hazardous some practices can be.

One type of training particularly useful to safety representatives, and indeed all employees, involves hazard-spotting training. This aims to make trainees more aware of the hazards surrounding the normal workplace.

Figure 13.9 presents some questions that should be considered when auditing health and safety training.

Figure 13.9: Health and Safety Training: Auditing the Organisation

- Does the organisation comply with its responsibilities as outlined in the Safety, Health and Welfare at Work Act, 1989?
- Does the organisation have documentary records to prove this?
- Who organises health and safety training for the organisation?
- Who carries out the training?
- Is there a formal written induction procedure?
- Does the procedure include a substantial health and safety element?
- Are there regular checks to the induction programme, and do new employees sign to confirm receipt of the training?
- What are the arrangements for refresher/repeat training?
- What special health and safety training do managers receive?
- What arrangements exist to upgrade the present health and safety training to cover the additional requirements imposed by new legislation?
- Does the company safety policy refer to safety training?

EFFECTIVE COMMUNICATIONS AND SAFETY MANAGEMENT

Good health and safety communication provides the organisation with: information on health and safety legislation, standards and authoritative guidance, technical and management information relating to risk control and development of a positive safety culture.

Effective internal communication is also essential. Systems are needed to communicate key information such as: the purpose of the health and safety policy; the commitment of senior management to its implementation; plans, systems and procedures relating to the implementation of the policy; and feedback on safety performance.

There are many functions that communication can play in the safety area. They can be summarised as follows:

- As an **instrument** to achieve or obtain a result such as improved safety performance or greater commitment to ensuring safe working practices.

- As a **control** to get someone to behave in a particular way, for example, to begin following a safe system of work.

- As an **informal way to establish facts** or, alternatively, to explain something to a person.

- As an **expression** of feelings, such as fear, anxiety, happiness, guilt, or to convey oneself in a particular way.

- As a **social contact** to enjoy another person's company.

- As an **alleviation of anxiety** through sorting out a problem or easing a worry.

- As **stimulation** to increase or raise the interest of an individual or group.

- Communication as a **role model** to give instructions, advice or a warning to a subordinate as the situation requires.

Communication has a significant role to play in health and safety as a participative process. The following aspects of communication are significant:

- **Safety propaganda:** The use of posters, films, exhibitions and other forms of repetition of a special message are important features of the safety communication process. Safety posters should be used to reinforce current health and safety themes — say, the use of eye protection or correct manual handling techniques — and should be changed on a regular basis. To have the most impact, videos and films should be used as part of scheduled training activities and not shown in isolation.

- **Safety incentive schemes:** Various forms of planned incentives directed at rewarding good safety behaviour, on the basis of formally-agreed objectives and criteria, have proved successful. Safety incentive schemes should not be based on a reduction in accident rates, however, as this can reduce or restrict accident reporting by employees. All safety incentive schemes must be accompanied by efficient communication of results and information surrounding the scheme. The effectiveness of the incentive depends on: the size of the incentive; the way in which it is calculated; the mechanism used to collect the safety data; the criteria on which the incentive is given; the frequency of the incentive and whether the target of the incentive is the individual or the team; the department of the organisation as a whole.

- **Effective health and safety training:** Health and safety communications featured in training exercises should incorporate sincerity, authority, confidence, accuracy and humour. Training of trainers in the various aspects of presentation can be helpful in making training more effective.

- **Management Example:** This is perhaps the strongest form of non-verbal communication and has a direct effect on operators' attitudes to health and safety. Management should openly display and promote, where appropriate:

  ◊ a desire to attain a common goal, such as clearly identified and agreed safety objectives.

  ◊ insight into ever-changing situations, particularly in the case of potentially hazardous operations.

  ◊ alertness to the needs and motives of others.

  ◊ an ability to bear responsibility for health and safety procedures.

  ◊ competence in initiating and planning action to bring about health and safety improvements.

◊   social interaction aimed at promoting the health and safety objectives of the organisation.

◊   communication, both upward and downward, through a wide variety of communication activities.

◊   clear identification by senior management of the health and safety promotional activities undertaken by the organisation.

◊   an example to staff, visitors and others at all times on health and safety-related procedures.

Verbal Communication on Health and Safety Issues

The legal duties of employers, including managers and supervisors, to inform, instruct, and train staff and others — in other words, to communicate — are clearly identified in current health and safety legislation.

Increasingly, supervisors and line managers are required to prepare and undertake short training sessions on health and safety issues for the purpose of briefing staff. If such training activities are to be successful and convey the appropriate messages to staff, the following matters need careful consideration:

- A list of topics to be covered should be developed, followed by the formulation of a specific training programme.

- Training sessions should be frequent, but not last longer than 30 minutes each.

- Extensive use should be made of visual aids — videos, films, slides, flipcharts, and so on.

- Topics should, as far as possible, be of relevance to the group.

- Participation should be encouraged, with a view to identifying possible misunderstandings or concerns that people may have (this is particularly important when introducing a new safe system of work or operating procedures).

- Consideration must be given to eliminating any boredom, loss of interest or adverse response from participants, so sessions should operate on as friendly and informal basis as possible. They should also take place in a relatively informal atmosphere, since many people respond adversely to the formal classroom situations commonly encountered in staff training practices.

A SAFETY MANAGEMENT CONTROL MODEL

The management control model is concerned with continuous improvement. The model is based on a number of important standards of performance. These are:

1. The company will ensure that arrangements are put in place for the effective planning, development and review of the health and safety policy statement.

2. Management will ensure that appropriate systems are developed and maintained for the effective communication of health and safety matters throughout the organisation.

3. The company will provide the necessary information, instruction and training to employees and others, including temporary staff to ensure their competence with respect to health and safety matters.

4. Management values health and safety rules equally with all other business functions and attaches equal importance to achieving health and safety targets.

5. The company will devote the necessary resources in the form of finance, equipment, personnel and time to ensure health and safety. The assistance of expert help will be sought where the necessary skills are not available within the company.

6. The company will liaise and work with all necessary persons to ensure health and safety standards are met. The company will also ensure that adequate arrangements are in place for ensuring the health and safety of visitors.

7. The company will liaise and work with all necessary persons to ensure health and safety standards are met. The company will also ensure that all relevant statutes, Regulations and Codes of Practice are complied with. The minimum standards that will be adopted are those required by law, although the company

will always seek to exceed these where there is a demonstrable benefit.

8. The company recognises that safety is the responsibility of everyone within the organisation and is not just a function of management. Managers will have specific duties and responsibilities to comply with the letter and spirit of company policy. Employees will have specific responsibilities to take reasonable care of themselves and others who could be affected by their activities and to co-operate with management in achieving the standards required. The company will ensure that health and safety management is an integral part of the manager's duties and will monitor their performance along with their other duties.

9. The company will ensure that health and safety is fully integrated into the management and decision-making processes within the organisation.

10. The company will set up a system to ensure that accidents and near-misses are fully investigated and appropriate action taken to reduce the likelihood of their occurrence.

11. The company will ensure that procedures are established to ensure that any equipment and plant provided for employees and non-employees is safe.

Details of these standards are set out below.

Management Control Standard 1: Effective Planning, Development and Review of Company Policy

To ensure that this objective is achieved, employers may wish to do the following:

1. Carry out a baseline audit to determine present strengths and weaknesses.

2. Select a horizontal audit or vertical audit or a mixture of both.

3. Determine what is to be achieved with respect to health and safety. The model "Management Control Standards" can be used as a guide.

4. Set the objectives to be achieved.

5. Establish priorities for action within the business.

6. Take into account both short and long-term planning. Short-term planning should concentrate on tackling the main risks identified within the company. Long-term planning should concentrate on maintaining and improving standards.

7. Set annual targets to be achieved. Such targets could include the number of people trained, number and frequency of audits, number of safety committee meetings, servicing and inspection frequencies for equipment and implementation of objectives within agreed time scales.

8. Assign specific tasks to individuals and hold them accountable.

9. Set aside time for monitoring to establish whether the targets and goals will be met. Develop procedures to take action both before and after things go wrong.

10. Establish procedures to review progress and check whether short and long-term goals are being achieved. Have procedures for reviewing: general levels of compliance with the policy, ensuring people carry out their duties; ensuring targets have been met; establishing positive and negative points within the policy. Build upon the positive points and take action to remedy the negative points.

11. Assign specific tasks of planning and review to key personnel. Incorporate a review of management performance into managers' annual performance reviews.

Management Control Standard 2: Effective Communication

To ensure that this objective is achieved, employers may wish to do the following:

1. Bring the safety policy to the attention of all employees.

2. Include reference to the safety policy and employees' duties in their job descriptions.

3. Detail managers' responsibilities in their job descriptions. This should be detailed enough to be meaningful.

4. Hold weekly "tool box" meetings between managers and employees to discuss specific health and safety issues.

5. Include health and safety as a standard item at all staff meetings.

6. Develop systems to ensure that all-urgent health and safety messages are communicated immediately to the relevant employees.

7. Ensure that instructions from senior management are communicated to all employees within a stated period. Checks should be made to ensure that this has happened.

8. Form a health and safety committee to discuss issues. Draw up terms of reference and membership with equal numbers from both management and employees.

9. Devise regular programmes for health and safety training.

10. Obtain specialist health and safety information from outside sources such as health and safety inspectors, trade journals, health and safety magazines, health and safety consultants, etc.

11. Summarise health and safety performance for the managing director.

12. Make health and safety performance statistics available to employees and at staff meetings.

13. Provide items for the company newsletter or notice boards.

14. Set up arrangements to action reports of safety inspections and audits.

15. Ensure that the most appropriate forms of communication are used to ensure that the right people are briefed in the right way at the right time.

Management Control Standard 3: Provide Effective Training, Information and Instruction

Training

To ensure that this objective is achieved, employers may wish to do the following:

1. Evaluate every job and establish what risks are exposed. This should form part of the risk assessment process. Identify training needs from this assessment.

2. Assess every employee as to their training needs (other training needs apart from health and safety could also be included)

3. Draw up an inventory of existing skills and a training skills programme based upon that inventory.

4. Establish what training can be given in-house and where external training is required.

5. Place priority on training that is required in areas of greatest risk.

6. List the type of training to be given on induction.

7. List the type of refresher training required and how often. Set up systems to ensure that the appropriate training is given when new machinery and processes are introduced.

8. Keep signed training records of the training given to individuals.

9. Examine the training records periodically to determine whether additional training is required.

10. Specify the training needed for managers to successfully manage health and safety.

11. Specify the training needed for the 'competent' person within the company.

12. Identify an appropriate director as the person responsible for identifying training needs of individual managers.

13. Specify that training will normally be carried out during work hours, subject to the availability of training courses.

14. Ensure that the necessary systems are established to provide the necessary training for temporary employees.

15. Ensure that all key personnel within the company have the necessary training to carry out their functions properly.

Information and Instruction

To ensure that this objective is achieved, employers may wish to do the following:

1. Provide information to every employee on how to carry out his or her job in a safe fashion. This could be either an oral or written instruction.

2. Provide written safe systems of work for the more complex and hazardous work activities. If the system of work is simple and the instructions can accurately be repeated at any time by anybody, it is unlikely that a written system of work will be required.

3. Attach the systems of work to the safety policy or refer to them in the policy and state where they are located.

4. Provide employees with copies of the safe systems of work.

5. Instruct employees on the safe systems of work to be adopted and provide them with written copies relevant to their work activities.

6. Explain that failure to follow these procedures will be treated as a disciplinary offence.

7. Develop a system of "permits-to-work". These are normally only required in hazardous situations, such as entry into confined spaces or working on dangerous machinery.

8. Establish whether all existing employees have received adequate information and instruction. If no records have been taken, the procedure should be repeated. Ensure that all work activities and employees are covered, including management.

9. Establish procedures for providing the necessary information to new employees and visitors such as maintenance personnel. The use of a checklist will ensure thoroughness and consistency of instruction.

10. Ensure that adequate information is given to temporary workers and their employment agencies concerning any special skills and qualifications required. Keep information requirements on the personnel file. Make copies of the information

requirements that can be forwarded to the person or agency before employment commences.

11. Ensure that supervisors closely monitor the work of employees, especially temporary employees, until they are considered competent. Use training record sheets to record this.

Management Control Standard 4: Ensuring Equal Importance for Health and Safety

To ensure that this objective is achieved employers may wish to do the following:

1. Include a statement in job descriptions to this effect.

2. When holding company strategy meetings, consider the health and safety requirements.

3. Develop a positive culture for health and safety.

4. Issue appropriate Mission Statements.

5. Develop a system of rewards for success and discipline for failures.

6. Ensure that all major projects, etc. make reference to health and safety implications.

Management Control Standard 5: Providing the Necessary Resources

To ensure that this objective is achieved, employers may wish to do the following:

1. Decide what capital expenditure is required each year and allocate the necessary resources. Use risk assessments to establish priorities.

2. Publish the anticipated planned expenditure in the company business plan.

3. Ensure sufficient supplies of personal protective equipment are available.

4. Regularly check suppliers of equipment.

5. Arrange priority delivery from a reputable supplier.

6. Carry out an inventory of critical safety equipment. Assess its condition and likely replacement date. Ensure that a request for replacement has been submitted or has been budgeted for.

7. Include equipment checks and condition surveys as part of regular safety inspections of the workplace.

8. Ensure that replacement equipment meets or exceeds original design specifications, such as resistance to chemicals or retraction rates.

9. Ensure that supervisors, etc. check equipment condition on a regular basis.

10. Ensure that all mangers are allocated enough time to effectively carry out their safety functions. Incorporate monitoring procedures to ensure that this is achieved.

11. Set aside training periods for employees.

12. Allocate specific tasks to key personnel. Decide whether sufficient time is available to carry this out or whether extra resources are needed to supplement.

13. Define the boundaries of what managers are realistically expected to achieve.

14. Specify when external help will be sought, such as for analysis or sampling for hazardous substances.

15. State what arrangements are in place for consultations with health and safety inspectors.

16. Ensure that there are sufficient numbers of competent persons available within the organisation. Consideration should be given to providing cover for persons while on leave or otherwise absent from the workplace.

Management Control Standard 6: Liaison Arrangements

To ensure that this objective is achieved, employers may wish to do the following:

1. Ensure two-way communication between management and employees.

2. Form a safety committee to discuss and promote issues.

3. Encourage employees to suggest improvements (suggestion box, staff meetings)

4. Set up systems for reporting defects in the workplace.

5. Set up teams of employees and management for solving specific problems.

6. Encourage team development between managers by joint working on projects.

7. Management meetings should include, as a standard item, issues on heath and safety.

8. The safety policy should be communicated in such a way that all employees will understand.

9. Establish arrangements for referring any unresolved issues to an independent third party such as a consultant.

10. Require managers to seek views of employees on a regular basis.

11. Establish regular workshops on health and safety.

12. Hold special staff meetings to explain safety policy, risk assessments, etc.

13. Provide feedback form for employees and mangers to complete.

14. Establish systems to ensure that managers consult the necessary people before undertaking specific projects, e.g. purchase of new machinery or refurbishment.

15. Arrange for joint safety inspections of the workplace.

16. Require contractors to submit their safety policy when tendering for work.

17. Require contractors to carry out and submit risk assessments prior to starting work.

18. Reject any work where contractors fail to demonstrate their commitment to safety or where assessments are not suitable and sufficient.

19. Ensure adequate liaison with contractors at all times.

20. Include in contracts any specific health and safety requirements that the contractor will be required to perform.

21. As part of risk assessments, determine the risks to visitors and members of the public.

22. Establish what control measures are required.

23. Inform visitors of the risks and the precautions they need to take to avoid those risks.

24. Closely supervise visitors at all times.

25. Train and instruct staff to watch over the public.

26. Carry out an audit of the premises, from the viewpoint of a member of the public.

27. Ensure that safety messages can be effectively relayed to the public (e.g. fire).

28. Cordon off certain areas of the premises to prevent public access if necessary (do not rely just on notices).

29. Assign responsibility for liaising with health and safety inspectors to one person.

30. Keep all documentation properly filed — for example, statutory inspection certificates.

31. Ensure that the premises are registered with the enforcing authority.

32. Define the circumstances in which the health and safety inspector will be contacted for advice.

Management Control Standard 7: Improving Health and Safety Standards

To ensure that this objective is achieved employers may wish to do the following:

1. Carry out regular audits of the premises to identify improvements that can be made.

2. Establish priorities for health and safety following the audit. Rank tasks or objectives according to priority.

3. Use the process of risk assessment to identify areas of improvement.

4. Set performance targets for staff. When these have been met, set higher targets.

5. Analyse information about incidents, such as accidents, lost time, sickness and the results of safety audits to identify improvement.

6. Keep abreast of developments by subscribing to specialist safety magazines, attending safety seminars or speaking to a local health and safety inspector.

7. Continually monitor and review the policy and procedures to ensure they are effective.

8. Encourage employees to suggest ways of improving health and safety within the company.

9. Set higher standards once all targets have been reached.

10. Establish what Regulations and Codes of Practice apply to the business. Obtain information from the health and safety inspector or trade organisations.

11. Seek clarification of legislative requirements that are not fully understood.

12. Ascertain what benefits will accrue from providing a higher standard than that required by law, such as staff morale, reduction in accidents, etc.

Management Control Standard 8: Health and Safety Responsibilities and Accountability

To ensure that this objective is achieved, employers may wish to do the following:

1. Agree and set priorities with managers.

2. Write down specific responsibilities in job descriptions.

3. Establish a system for ensuring that managers are held accountable for their responsibilities.

4. Bring the safety policy to the attention of employees on an individual or group basis.

5. Instruct employees on their general duties under health and safety legislation and their specific duties as they relate to their work activities. Record this training.

6. Develop disciplinary procedures for breaches of health and safety rules or for poor performance.

7. Develop a system of rewards for good health and safety performance against agreed standards.

8. Establish a monitoring system that will detect breaches in health and safety standards.

9. Encourage employees and management to report defects and suggest improvements. Develop a system to reward suggestions leading to improvements.

10. Establish deadlines for the completion of various tasks, following health and safety audits. Ensure that the deadlines reflect the priority of the tasks, and that the deadlines are realistic.

11. Ensure that separate tasks link in with others, where necessary, to build an integrated approach.

12. Include the successful completion of tasks as a performance indicator for managers.

13. Ensure that the tasks assigned to various individuals reflect a logical delegation of duties.

14. Ensure that all managers, directors and managing directors are assigned tasks to complete. This will help to install the necessary "culture" within the organisation.

15. Review individuals' performance at regular intervals.

Management Control Standard 9: Integration of Health and Safety into Management Functions

To ensure that this objective is achieved, employers may wish to do the following:

1. Include health and safety as a standard item in all management meetings.

2. Ensure that management is aware that a failure to manage safety according to the policy will be seen as a failure to manage.

3. Stipulate what disciplinary measures will be incurred if managers fail to comply with the safety policy and their specific responsibilities.

4. Ensure managers are held accountable for their responsibilities. Set up a system to regularly appraise their performance.

5. Detail health and safety responsibility in job descriptions.

6. Ensure all managers are made responsible for reviewing the health and safety performance of their staff.

7. Reward good performance.

8. Develop a league table similar to sales targets to encourage competition between sections and departments.

9. Establish performance standards for staff. These should detail the standard to be achieved, such as the minimum number of safety audits, etc.

10. Senior management should be made responsible for monitoring performance against these standards.

11. Overall performance should be reviewed at staff and board meetings.

12. Make the managing director responsible for monitoring the performance of his directors.

13. Make provision for ensuring that managers have the necessary knowledge and are competent to carry out their responsibilities.

14. Develop a purchasing policy that considers health and safety requirements and performance of equipment and materials.

15. Ensure that all proposals put forward to managers make suitable reference to health and safety (e.g. equipment purchase).

16. If contracting out work, ensure that the contractor submits his insurance policy at the tender stage.

17. Check that all equipment purchases will meet the necessary requirements for health and safety.

Management Control Standard 10: Investigation and Prevention of Accidents

To ensure that this objective is achieved, employers may wish to do the following:

1. Use accident investigation forms to record all details of accidents or near-misses and the corrective action taken.

2. Enter details of accidents and near-misses into the accident book.

3. Develop a system to ensure that all notifiable accidents, diseases and dangerous occurrences are reported to the appropriate enforcing authority. Keep records of those notifications.

4. Discuss accident trends and examples at staff meetings, safety committees, etc.

5. Use accident statistics to allocate resources.

6. Encourage employees to report near-misses and damage to equipment.

7. Establish systems to take immediate corrective action when the investigation shows that a recurrence is likely.

8. Set up a system to ensure that all recommendations resulting from investigations are followed up and action taken where this is reasonably practicable. The accident investigation form should not be signed off until this has been done.

9. Ensure that greater effort is placed on investigations where there is serious loss or injury or the potential to cause serious injuries.

10. Carry out risk assessments.

11. Carry out regular health and safety inspections.

12. Encourage employees to report defects and suggest improvements in working procedures.

Management Control Standard 11: Provision of Safe Equipment, Premises and Systems of Work

To ensure that this objective is achieved, employers may wish to do the following:

1. Develop a positive purchasing criterion for equipment by ensuring that it has the CE mark.

2. Ensure that a supervisor checks all equipment before it is used for the first time and makes sure that all of the safety features are present and working correctly.

3. Train and instruct staff in the safe operation of equipment before it is used.

4. Produce written safe systems of work for using equipment, if necessary.

5. Maintain equipment in a safe condition.

6. Develop a system for ensuring that faulty equipment is taken out of use.

7. Keep adequate records of equipment inspections.

8. Ensure that equipment is provided with a facility to isolate it from the power supply.

9. Provide warning devices/signs on equipment.

10. Develop a system for maintaining guards on equipment.

11. If building new premises, ensure that consideration is paid to designing for health and safety.

12. If converting or modifying existing premises, ensure that consideration is paid to the Workplace Regulations and any current Building Regulations.

13. Include checks on the premises as part of regular safety inspections.

14. Consider visitors and contractors who may be on site.

15. Arrange for periodic checks on the electrical systems and portable equipment.

16. If the premises have a fire certificate, ensure that its requirements are followed.

17. Ensure that safe means of access and egress are maintained. Specify how this will be done.

18. Carry out regular fire drills and alarm tests.

19. Develop written safe systems of work.

20. Revise these systems in line with risk assessments.

21. Train and instruct employees in induction.

22. Apply appropriate levels of supervision to employees, visitors and contractors.

23. Issue written instructions to contractors prior to starting work.

24. Supervise contractors' work to ensure their activities do not adversely affect employees.

25. Ensure that adequate co-ordination and co-operation exists between employers sharing the same workplace.

CHAPTER ROUND-UP

- Organisations that are successful in achieving high standards of health and safety have safety policies that contribute to business performance, while meeting their responsibilities to people and the environment in a way that fulfils both the spirit and the letter of the law. In this way, they satisfy the expectations of shareholders, employees, customers and society at large. Such policies are cost-effective and aimed at achieving the preservation and development of physical and human resources and reductions in financial losses and liabilities. Policies influence all other activities and decisions, including those concerning the selection of resources and information, the design and operation of working systems, products and services, and the control and disposal of waste.

- Organisations that achieve high health and safety standards are structured and operated so as to put their policies into effective practice. This is facilitated by the creation of a positive culture that ensures involvement and participation at all levels. It is sustained through effective communications and the promotion of competence, which enables all employees to make a responsible and informed contribution to the health and safety management process. The visible and active leadership of senior managers is necessary to develop and maintain a culture supportive of health and safety management. The aim is not simply to avoid accidents, but to motivate and empower people to work safely. The vision, values and beliefs become the shared common knowledge of all.

- Successful organisations in health and safety terms adopt a planned and systematic approach to policy implementation. The aim is to minimise the risks created by work activities, products and services. Organisations use risk assessment methods to determine priorities and set objectives for hazard elimination and risk reduction. Standards are established and performance is measured against them. There is a clear identification of specific actions required to promote a positive health and safety culture and to eliminate and control risks.

- In organisations that manage health and safety successfully, health and safety performance is measured against predetermined standards. This identifies when and where action is required to improve performance. The success of action taken to control risks is assessed through active self-monitoring involving a range of techniques. These include an examination of both hardware (premises, plant and substances) and software (people, procedures and systems) including individual behaviour. Failures of control are assessed through reactive monitoring that requires the thorough investigation of any accidents, ill health or incidents with the potential to cause harm or loss. In both active and reactive monitoring, the objectives are not only to determine the immediate causes of sub-standard perform-ance but, more importantly, to identify the underlying causes and the implications for the design and operation of the health and safety management system.

• Learning from experience and applying the lessons learned are important elements of effective health and safety manage-ment. This must be executed systematically through regular reviews of performance based on data derived from monitor-ing activities and from independent audits of the total health and safety management system. Commitment to continuous improvement involves the constant development of policies, approaches to implementation and techniques of risk control. Organisations that achieve high standards of health and safety assess their performance by internal reference to key per-formance indicators and by external comparison with the per-formance of business competitors. They record and account for their performance in their annual reports.

Chapter 14

SAFETY STATEMENTS AND SUPPORTING SAFETY PROCEDURES

INTRODUCTION

The Safety, Health and Welfare at Work Act, 1989 envisages the safety statement as a fundamental component of the effective management of the safety, health and welfare within the workplace. The safety statement is, in effect, a policy and procedures document, setting out the manner in which the organisation intends to manage safety and health in the specific workplace. The statement, as formulated in the 1989 Act, takes on board many of the criticisms of the Barrington Commission Report and incorporates the essential philosophy and approach of the EC Framework Directive. The safety statement has received some modification and enhancement as a result of Part II of the Safety, Health and Welfare at Work (General Application) Regulations, 1993. This chapter focuses on the formulation of the safety statement and issues relating to its implementation, review and specifically the formulation of safety procedures and control.

THE SAFETY STATEMENT:
STATUTORY REQUIREMENTS

The 1989 Act specifies that all employers and the self-employed must prepare a written safety statement, setting out how they will provide for the safety, health and welfare of employees and other persons in the place of work. The contents of the statement must be brought to the attention of all employees and other individuals at the place of work who are likely to be affected by its contents.

The Act specifies a number of conditions that the safety statement must meet:

- There is an obligation to specify the manner in which the employer will secure the safety, health and welfare of employees and other individuals.

- There is a clear obligation to base the statement on a systematic risk assessment. Section 12 (3) of the Act specifies that the risk assessment will identify and assess all risks to safety and health in the workplace to which the safety statement relates. The requirement for a risk assessment represents a significant departure in Irish legislation. Prior to 1989, hazard identification and risk assessment were considered good practice rather than being mandatory.

- The risk assessment requirements have been further amplified by Regulations 5 and 10 of the General Application Regulations, 1993. There is now a requirement to have a written risk assessment undertaken, as well as the periodic evaluation and revision of risks. The effect of the written risk assessment requirement essentially means that employers will have to produce appropriate and sound documentation to support the risk assessments that are made. The revision requirement is designed to reinforce the notion that simply writing the statement is not enough, it must be regularly updated to reflect changing conditions within the organisation.

- Section 12 of the Safety, Health and Welfare at Work Act, 1989 specifies that the safety statement must set out the manner in which the safety, health and welfare of employees will be managed. In particular, this relates to specific arrangements and resources as well as the level of co-operation required from employees in order to effectively implement the statement.

- There is an obligation under the Act to specify the names, including the names of authorised deputies, of the key individuals responsible for the performance of tasks assigned to them by the statement.

- The Act specifies that where a safety statement is prepared or revised and a safety inspector from the HSA is of the view that the statement is inadequate in a significant way, the inspector may direct that the statement should be revised. There is an obligation on the employer to comply with this instruction within 60 days of its issue.

- The Act places an obligation on public companies in the Republic of Ireland to include in the Directors' Report a statement of the extent to which the policy and procedures set out in the statement were implemented.

- Regulation 5 (c) of the Safety, Health and Welfare at Work (General Application) Regulations, 1993 places an obligation on the employer, having evaluated risks, to integrate all management and other measures into the ongoing work activities at all levels of responsibility within the organisation. This requirement places an obligation on all levels of management to be aware of their responsibilities under the statement and to give effect to them.

- Regulation 8 of the 1993 Regulations permits employers to delegate to specific employees the responsibility for implementing specific measures connected with the management of risks. There is a duty to ensure that such designated employees are competent and have sufficient resources to carry out their responsibilities. This, in effect, places an obligation on top management resources to implement the statement.

- The 1989 Act places a communication role on employers *vis-à-vis* the safety statement. The employer is essentially charged with communicating the content and terms of the statement to employees, safety representatives, contractors and others who may be affected by the terms of the statement.

THE COMPONENTS OF A SAFETY STATEMENT

Employers often see the production of a safety policy statement as a time-consuming process. Employers may be tempted to copy a policy statement from another employer. This is not recommended, as it is likely that the policy will need extensive modification in order to be relevant to the needs of the company. There will also generally be greater commitment to a document that has been produced internally as opposed to one that has been "borrowed".

The safety statement should contain four main components:

- **Component 1:** Statement of general policy on safety and health and welfare.

- **Component 2:** The employer's organisation for safety and health.

- **Component 3:** The employer's arrangements for safety and health.

- **Component 4:** Communication, review and revision.

Component 1: Statement of General Policy on Safety, Health and Welfare

An Opening Declaration

There is a general requirement that the statement should contain an opening declaration. IBEC suggest the following broad guideline as an opening declaration of the Safety Statement (see **Figure 14.1**).

Figure 14.1: An Opening Statement of Intent

Safety Statement of

_____Ltd.

To each employee, contractor, visitor:

This document sets out the Safety Policy of

_____Ltd.

and specifies the means provided to achieve that policy. Our objective is to endeavour to provide a safe and healthy work environment for all our employees and to meet our duties to contractors and members of the public who may be affected by our operations. The success of the policy will depend on your   co-operation. It is therefore important that you read the document carefully and understand your role and the overall arrangements for health and safety at

_____Ltd.

It is our intention to review this statement in the light of experience and developments on the _____. Staff and others are encouraged to put forward suggestions for improvement to the statement.

Signed _____   _____

                Chief Executive   Date

A Statement of Health and Safety Policy

There is a general requirement to formulate a policy statement on the overall company/corporate approach to employee health and safety. This policy statement should be drawn up by management and constitutes a significant declaration of company commitment to:

- Providing the resources required for ensuring the health and safety of employees in all workplaces under the control of the supervisor.

- Nominating a person with overall responsibility for implementing the corporate/company employee health and safety policy.

- Complying with the employers' duties set out in the legislation.

- Ensuring employee co-operation on all health and safety issues.

The policy statement is a document that can be used to demonstrate in a practical way how arrangements for safety and health will be managed within the workplace. This content demands that it should be clearly written and easily available to all employees.

An effective safety policy should incorporate four important components:

- **A statement of management intent**: The safety policy should indicate the approach to health and safety that the organisation plans to implement, and should make some explicit general reference to the responsibilities of directors, senior managers, line managers and employees, and identify the overall importance attached to safety and health within the organisation. An effective statement should seek to link safety and health to the organisation's mission statement and demonstrate how safety and health will contribute to the overall effectiveness of the organisation.

- **Organisation**: The safety policy should indicate management's approach to safety and health and specify who is responsible for specific tasks. In essence, the safety policy is concerned with people, their duties and accountabilities. It should include an organisational chart indicating the chain of command *vis-à-vis* safety and health issues as well as a clear statement that responsibility for safety and health rests with the Board/chief executive or senior management.

- **Safety rules**: The safety policy should indicate that management has put in place a set of general safety rules and that failure to comply with these rules will lead to disciplinary action.

- **Arrangements**: The policy statement should establish systems and procedures and the practical arrangements for their implementation. An effective policy statement will indicate the system for monitoring safety and publishing results. **Figure 14.2** presents an example of the types of issues that should be covered in this policy statement.

Component Two: The Organisation of Safety and Health

The second component of the safety statement is to detail the organisation that exists for ensuring health and safety in the workplace and concentrates on detailing individual responsibilities.

The responsibility in law for ensuring health and safety at work lies ultimately with the employer, although, in practice, many responsibilities will be delegated to individuals within the company. This delegation of responsibilities will most likely differ between companies; however, there are certain principles that are applicable in all circumstances:

1. Persons who hold senior positions within the organisation should take responsibility for controlling and directing a role with health and safety, as with other business functions. They must ensure that the company has the necessary structure in place to effectively manage health and safety.

2. Lower tiers of management should normally take a more hands-on approach to health and safety management.

3. There should be the widest possible involvement of managers to ensure "ownership" of the organisation's health and safety.

Figure 14.2: A Model Safety and Health Policy Statement

1. The company will ensure that arrangements are in place for the effective planning, development and review of this policy statement.

2. Management will ensure that appropriate systems are developed and maintained for the effective communication of health and safety matters throughout the organisation.

3. The company will provide the necessary information, instruction and training to employees and others, including temporary staff to ensure their competence with respect to health and safety.

4. Management considers that health and safety rules are equal in importance to all other business functions and will therefore attach equal importance to achieving health and safety targets.

5. The company will devote the necessary resources in the form of finance, equipment, personnel and time to ensure health and safety. The assistance of expert help will be sought where the necessary skills are not available within the company.

6. The company will liaise and work with all necessary persons to ensure health and safety. The company will also ensure that adequate arrangements are in place for ensuring the health and safety of visitors.

7. The company believes in constantly improving health and safety standards and performance. It will, to this end, endeavour to ensure that all-relevant statutes, Regulations, and Codes of Practice are complied with. The minimum standards that will be adopted by the company are those required by law, although the company will always seek to exceed these where there is a demonstrable benefit.

8. The company recognises that safety is the responsibility of everyone within the organisation and is not just a function of management. Managers will have specific duties and responsibilities to comply with the letter and spirit of company policy. Employees will have specific responsibilities to take reasonable care of themselves and others who could be affected by their activities and to co-operate with management in achieving the standards required. The company will monitor their performance along with their other duties.

9. The company will ensure that health and safety is fully integrated into the management and decision-making processes within the organisation.

10. The company will set up a system to ensure that accidents and 'near misses' are fully investigated and appropriate action taken to reduce the likelihood of their occurrence.

11. The company will ensure that procedures are established to ensure that safe equipment and plant are provided for employees and non-employees.

Persons assigned specific responsibilities must:

• Be capable of carrying them out.

• Agree and accept them.

• Be aware of the consequences of failure to discharge them.

Responsibilities should be assigned only to people who are competent to carry them out and have received adequate training and instruction regarding their duties. It is suggested that for each specific arrangement listed in the policy statement, an individual is made responsible for implementing that arrangement.

The responsibilities assigned to individuals will vary from organisation to organisation. Responsibilities will, however, depend on individual company structures, other management responsibilities and the number and type of arrangements. Wherever possible, agreement should be sought from the individuals concerned that they accept the responsibilities assigned to them.

The Safety Statement should describe the health and safety structure of the organisation through which safety and health performance standards are identified and achieved. The statement should emphasise the ultimate responsibility of top management for the health and safety performance of the company and should define the accountability of key management personnel for performance in all safety areas. Three key groups at a minimum should be addressed — employees, management and supervisors — although their exact titles may differ from one organisation to another.

Employees

In terms of employee responsibilities the statement should set out:

- Procedures for reporting accidents, illness and safety and health hazards; fire precautions; first aid.

- Arrangements for monitoring the atmosphere and maintaining high standards of hygiene for potentially harmful substances.

- Arrangements for instructing employees in safe working methods and for training employees in health and safety matters.

- Good housekeeping requirements covering storage facilities, adequate space for machinery and plant, the provision of gangways, and welfare arrangements.

- Special rules for work undertaken at a height, in confined spaces, on certain electrical equipment or on unguarded machinery.

- The maintenance of equipment and the provision of proper inspection and testing arrangements, including general rules on safe working habits; special rules for internal transport drivers; arrangements for checking new machinery and materials; safety inspections; the provision of personal protective equipment and rules as to its use, and suggestions on safety matters.

Management

The statement must clearly specify that management develops health and safety policies and procedures with the help of its medical and safety advisers. It must also ensure that the procedures are implemented, by making supervisors accountable for health and safety performance in their areas, and by providing them with appropriate help, guidance and training to carry out their responsibilities. Management must also set up information and control systems so that health and safety performance can be monitored and corrective action initiated when required.

IBEC recommends that it is essential to have a director with specific responsibility for health and safety matters. They envisage this job as consisting of advising the board on policies, ensuring that the agreed policies are implemented, and reporting back to the board on health and safety performance. They should also be responsible for the overall management of health and safety organisation.

Supervisors

It is generally accepted that supervisors can exert a significant influence on health and safety because they are in immediate control of employees and work processes. It is their responsibility to maintain a constant surveillance to reveal potentially unsafe practices or conditions. They need, however, all the support and encouragement possible from higher management to fulfil these responsibilities. If the emphasis from above is purely on output and cost reduction, supervisors can hardly be blamed if they neglect safety precautions. Exhortations on safety from management advisers are useless unless it can be demonstrated that health and safety considerations will be given priority if there is any conflict between them and the output and cost budgets.

Supervisors need training and guidance on their safety functions. The safety and training departments can provide this. However, the existence of well-defined safety rules and procedures should also help. **Figure 14.3** outlines the responsibilities of key roles within the organisation.

Figure 14.3: Model Responsibilities

Position	Responsibility
Managing Director	• Understanding the main requirements of the legislation. • Reviewing the performance of directors. • Allocating the necessary resources for health and safety. • Ensuring that the organisational structure is appropriate to manage health and safety. • Supporting directors in policy-setting. • Assuming ultimate responsibility for health and safety within the organisation. • Ensuring that the same management standards are applied to health and safety as to other management functions. • Ensuring that health and safety is integrated into the management structure. • Ensuring that equal importance is applied to health and safety as to other business functions.

Directors	<ul><li>Understanding the main requirements of the law.</li><li>Ensuring that competent persons are employed to assist in carrying out statutory responsibilities.</li><li>Setting company policy and direction.</li><li>Developing health and safety strategies and company objectives.</li><li>Reviewing company performance.</li><li>Ensuring that responsibilities are correctly assigned within the company.</li><li>Ensuring adequate resources are made available.</li><li>Ensuring that managers are trained and capable.</li><li>Ensuring the effective implementation of company policy.</li><li>Reviewing the effectiveness of the policy.</li><li>Ensuring the managing director is informed of progress and developments.</li><li>Ensuring that competent persons are appointed to assist in evacuation procedures.</li><li>Carrying out audits of their areas of responsibility/organising audits to be carried out.</li></ul>
Health and Safety Adviser	<ul><li>Understanding the main requirements of the law.</li><li>Ensuring that suitable and sufficient training is provided at all levels of the organisation.</li><li>Advising directors and management on the implementation of company policy.</li><li>Monitoring accident trends.</li><li>Joint investigation of accidents with line management/employee representatives.</li><li>Assisting in preparation of safe systems of work.</li><li>Co-ordination of company activities.</li><li>Reviewing and revising company policy.</li><li>Reviewing new legislation and guidance, advising senior management on their impact.</li><li>Reviewing training records.</li><li>Assisting in the auditing process.</li><li>Sitting on the health and safety committee.</li></ul>

Managers	• Ensuring supervisors are properly trained and instructed as to their duties and responsibilities.
	• Ensuring that supervisors carry out their assigned responsibilities and review their performance accordingly.
	• Making recommendations for improving performance.
	• Allocating the necessary resources within their control.
	• Ensuring that accidents and near-misses are recorded and investigated.
	• Drawing up annual action plans for health and safety.
	• Setting personal objectives and targets.
	• Monitoring of contractors.
	• Ensuring that the company policies and procedures are distributed.
	• Ensuring that appropriate equipment is available.
	• Ensuring that first aiders are trained and that cover is provided.
	• Monitoring the implementation of the policy.
	• Understanding company policies and procedures.
	• Maintaining relevant documentation.
	• Carrying out audits of their areas of responsibility and undertaking workplace inspections.
	• Ensuring that equipment, etc. is maintained in a safe condition.
Supervisors	• Ensuring that employees are adequately trained, instructed and informed.
	• Providing a suitable level of supervision.
	• Understanding company policy and procedures.
	• Allocating work in accordance with the employee's level of training.
	• Ensuring that defective equipment is taken out of use.
	• Reporting defective equipment.
	• Informing employees of their responsibilities.

	• Encouraging employees to report defects and suggest improvements.
	• Ensuring that correct work procedures are adhered to.
	• Carrying out regulator inspections of the workplace.
	• Reporting accidents and near-misses.
	• Assisting in the investigation of accidents.
	• Providing induction training.
	• Setting a good personal example.
Employees	• Working in accordance with company procedures.
	• Reporting defective equipment and dangerous situations.
	• Using safety equipment provided.
	• Avoiding horseplay that could result in injury.
	• Complying with management requests and instructions.
	• Not using defective equipment.
	• Not misusing equipment.
	• Not damaging equipment.
	• Exercising reasonable care towards themselves and others.
	• Not undertaking tasks that they are not trained for.

Component Three: Arrangements for Safety and Health

The term "arrangements" has two elements:

• The arrangements should define the responsibilities of managers and supervisors — the responsibility to identify hazards, evaluate risks and ensure that there are safe working practices defined and followed. It is this part of the arrangements that confirm the staff responsible for audits, for training, and all of the other elements that combine to form a safety management system. This can be represented as the health and safety components of job descriptions, or simply an organisational chart indicating that responsibilities flow along the hierarchy, with assistance from safety advisors and others.

- The second part of the arrangements section contains the key risk areas.

In terms of the specifics of this section, the following commitments must be made.

Hazard Identification

The company is obliged to outline its commitment to do the following:

- Carry out regular Hazard Audits internally, and identify in the statement the persons who will perform this task.

- Make use of the advice available through the National Safety Authority. Where necessary, to make use of competent consultants and bodies with special skills and services to augment the internal audits.

- Carry out Safety Audits concerning all aspects of operations and taking account of all of the potential hazards presented in **Figure 14.4**. **Figure 14.5** presents an example of a hazard inspection procedure.

- Specify the person who will undertake hazard audits. Define authorised deputies, and state that the person responsible for audits will advise a specified senior manager with responsibility for co-ordinating safety matters if there is a need for outside help in the area of hazard identification or risk assessment.

Engineering Out Hazards

The statement should specify that the organisation commits itself to dealing with the hazards identified — firstly, on the basis of their elimination by engineering means, be that machine guarding, replacement of hazardous substances with benign or less hazardous substances, provision of special tools or access arrangements, etc. This approach should take into account the norms in the particular industry, the expert advice available and external objective standards or guidelines where they are available. **Table 14.1** presents examples of hazards and their control.

Figure 14.4: Potential Hazards

- Access/egress problems, including floors, steps, ladders, etc.
- Machinery safety including both production and maintenance risks.
- Electrical safety, including standards at fuse boards, wiring standards, etc.
- Lighting, ventilation.
- Manual handling operations/posture.
- Handling of chemicals and storage of chemicals.
- Use of protective equipment.
- Noise and vibration.
- Heat and humidity.
- Systems of work.
- Internal transport.
- Maintenance operations.
- Fire safety.
- First aid.
- Housekeeping.

Instruction and Training

The safety statement should specify that the company recognises that, even with the best-engineered work arrangements, human resources may still need clearly defined safety procedures and instructions. This imposes a substantial commitment to identify safety-training needs, to carry out training and to measure the competence of trainees. Specific emphasis should be placed on safety and health aspects during all training exercises. The statement should indicate that the company expects employees to co-operate with and participate in the training provided. Certain tasks in operation require that strict safety procedures be followed. Where this arises, the statement should specify that the employees involved receive special instruction. It is essential that no person attempt a potentially hazardous task without instruction.

Figure 14.5: Example of Hazard Inspection Procedures

X LTD. sees hazard inspections as a necessity for maintaining a safe place of work and safe systems of work. Hazard inspections will be carried out by the Health and Safety Officer, the Safety Representative and the relevant Department Supervisor. These inspections will encompass all aspects of health, safety and welfare within the plant.

Definition

A hazard is a situation with a potential for human injury, damage to property or damage to the environment or any combination of the aforementioned.

Inspection Procedure

All hazards are to be identified during a plant tour. The Health and Safety Officer or their designate, during this tour, uses their training and experience to identify these hazards.

Frequency of Inspections

Hazard inspections will take place every month.

Hazard Elimination

Following identification of the hazards, the Health and Safety Officer will agree completion dates with the relevant personnel. They in turn are then responsible for ensuring that the hazard is eliminated before the completion date expires.

The person(s) responsible for training and instruction have responsibility to identify the training needs and report on the options available to carry out the training. They will present the options to an appropriate person within the organisation for decision.

Personal Protective Equipment

This is a key aspect of the Policy Statement. IBEC suggests the following wording:

Table 14.1: Example of Hazard Analysis

Hazard	Risk	Controls	Responsibility
Sequencer chains	• Entanglement in chains	• Safety covers, feeders	• Shift Supervisors
Radial m/cs	• Entanglement in the machine	• Safety guards, interlocks	• Shift Supervisors
VCD m/c	• Entanglement in the machine	• Safety guards, interlocks	• Shift Supervisors
Combos	• Entanglement in the machine	• Safety guards, interlocks	• Shift Supervisors
Board loader /unloaders	• Entanglement in the machine	• Safety guards, interlocks, light curtains	• Shift Supervisors
Sanyo	• Entanglement in the machine	• Safety guards, interlocks, light curtains	• Shift Supervisors
Screen printers	• Entanglement in the machine	• Safety guards, interlocks, safety edges	• Shift Supervisors
SMD glue m/cs	• Entanglement in the machine • Contact with glue	• Safety guards, interlocks, safety edges • Personal protective equipment	• Shift Supervisors • Shift Supervisors
SMD ovens	• Exposure to fumes	• Toxic extraction	• Department Supervisor
Soltecs	• Molten solder • Chemical contact • Fire • Solder fumes	• Personal protective equipment • Personal protective equipment • Chemical containers • Fire-fighting equipment • Toxic extraction	• Shift Supervisors • Shift Supervisors • Department Supervisor • Health and Safety Officer • Department Supervisor
Touchup	• Fume inhalation • Burns • Solder splashes	• Toxic extraction • Iron holders • Training • Supervision • Tip cleaning sponges	• Department Supervisor • Department Supervisor • Training Manager • Shift Supervisor • Department Supervisor
Test	• Entanglement in the machine	• Safety interlocks, guards	• Department Supervisor • TDV Supervisor
US welder	• Exposure to noise	• Acoustic enclosure	• Department Supervisor
Socket presses	• Entanglement in machine	• Safety guards • Operating instructors	• Shift Supervisor • Shift Supervisor

Through experience and on the advice of competent health and safety specialists, the company has developed a policy on the use of personal protective equipment. The policy to date is set out at _____ and is obligatory for all personnel at the plant including management, staff and visitors. The company intends to review this policy regularly and to update it as required. The review will consider the experiences to date, changes in work arrangements and the use of new chemical substances and processes.

It is the policy of the company to provide the required protective equipment and to replace it on presentation of the faulty or defective item.

The person responsible shall identify the appropriate equipment for tasks, which cannot be made safe by any other practicable means. He/she shall present the options available to _____ for decision.

Safe Equipment and Processes

This aspect of the policy statement should outline the company's policy to ensure that tasks are within the competence and capacity of the employees. It is clear that some processes give rise to risks that can be controlled only by adherence to proper procedures. The training provided to workers will identify the areas where care and skill must be exercised.

The statement should also state that it is company policy, when purchasing new equipment, altering existing equipment or changing a system of work, to study such proposed purchases or changes, to ensure insofar as is reasonably practicable, that they are without significant hazard. **Figure 14.6** presents an example of a procurement control policy.

Figure 14.6: Example of a Procurement Control Policy

Chemicals

Before any new chemical is purchased, it must first receive approval from the Health and Safety Department.

Procedure

1. Any employee that requires a new chemical, either for production or as a sample, must first obtain a Material Safety Data Sheet for it.

2. When the Materials Safety Data Sheet arrives, it must be passed to the Health and Safety Officer or his deputy to ascertain whether the chemical is safe to use.

3. The Health and Safety Officer must examine the Material Safety Data Sheet and complete the Chemical Approval Form stating that the chemical is either safe or unsafe to use.

4. Upon receiving approval to use the chemical, the employee may then purchase it.

Equipment

Purchase: For all new equipment purchased at the request of X Ltd's employees, the purchaser is to ensure that the equipment complies with all Safety Standards and has a current CE mark.

Contractors

Before any contractor can be engaged, they must submit a Health and Safety Policy Statement to the Health and Safety Department. All contractors must comply fully with the terms and conditions in the "Contractors' Safety Guide".

Consultation

The safety statement should state that the organisation is committed to meeting its consultation obligation under Section 13 of the Safety Health and Welfare at Work Act, 1989. It should outline consultation arrangements that have been agreed to. If a safety committee is established and working effectively, it can be proposed as part of the consultation process. The appointment of a safety representative should also be referred to. **Figure 14.7** presents an example of a consultation policy.

Figure 14.7: Example of a Consultation Policy

X Ltd. is committed to providing a safe place and a safe system of work. X Ltd. recognises that, to provide these, assistance and co-operation is required from all employees. To keep management informed of all possible problems/suggestions/queries/hazards, a system of consultation has been set up.

System of Consultation

Employees who wish to consult with management in relation to Safety, Health or Welfare must follow the recognised procedure to ensure that any problems are resolved as efficiently and quickly as possible.

Procedure

To consult with management in relation to health, safety and welfare, an employee must, in the first instance, deal with his or her immediate supervisor. The route to follow, for example, within the Manufacturing Department is:

1. Shift Supervisor.

2. Department Supervisor.

If the query cannot be answered within a Department, it should be referred to the following personnel in order of seniority:

1. Health and Safety Officer.

2. Personnel Manager.

3. Departmental Manager.

4. Managing Director.

The Health and Safety representative may also be consulted in relation to safety, health and welfare.

The Health and Safety Statement will be explained in detail to all employees once they commence employment and copies of it will be available to all employees for further reference. Revised copies of the Statement will be kept by:

1. Managing Director.

2. Technical Manager.

3. Finance Manager.

4. Personnel Manager.

5. Quality Manager.

---

6. Purchasing and Materials Manager.

7. Manufacturing Manager.

8. Business Unit Managers.

9. MIS Manager.

10. Health and Safety Officer.

11. Reception.

12. Security.

13. Each Department Supervisor.

Safe Systems of Work

Safe systems of work are concerned with the integration of people, articles and substances in a suitable environment and workplace to produce and maintain an acceptable standard of safety. Consideration should be given to foreseeable emergencies and the provision of adequate rescue facilities.

In order to meet the requirements of the legislation, the following issues must be addressed:

- A layout that allows for safe access to and egress from the working area and plant within, and adequate space between machines and operating plant.

- A correct sequence of operations, with materials and products conveyed mechanically, wherever appropriate, to and from work positions.

- Analysis of tasks, including Job Safety Analysis and the provision of clear job instructions.

- Identification of safe procedures, both routine and emergency, including requirements that:

   ◊ the authorisation for starting and stopping machines is clearly allocated and obvious to all employees.

   ◊ clear instructions should be given to those allowed to lubricate or carry out maintenance work, including the circumstances under which this work may be done.

    ◊   adequate arrangements are made for the removal of materials, components, scrap, trimmings and dirt from plant and the immediate floor area.

    ◊   preventive maintenance schedules incorporate safety checks.

    ◊   there is a firm commitment to cleaning and housekeeping procedures.

- Provision of a safe and healthy working environment, including:

    ◊   illumination levels that prevent glare and sharp contrasts between light and shadow.

    ◊   heating and ventilation systems that avoid extremes of temperature and humidity and which allow circulation of fresh air to all parts of working areas.

    ◊   ambient noise levels kept to within the limits imposed by current legal requirements, otherwise hearing protection may be necessary, and

    ◊   localised exhaust ventilation at workstations where dusts, fumes, gases or vapours are emitted from the work process.

Job Safety Analysis (JSA)

This is a technique that identifies all accident prevention measures appropriate to a particular job or area of work activity, and the behavioural factors that most significantly influence whether these measures are taken. The approach is both diagnostic and descriptive.

This analysis reflects the contribution that should be made by all personnel — managers, supervisors, safety representatives, health and safety specialists, engineers and contractors — in the creation of an overall "safety culture". It is suggested that an integrated approach to accident prevention can be created through analysis, which ensures that all activities and people within an organisation are involved in a co-operative effort. Having recognised the remedial measures necessary, all functions can then become committed to their adoption. This includes design modification, methods improvement and machinery guarding. The training specialist will usually extract the relevant parts from the Job Safety

Analysis for incorporation in the training analysis document. This ensures that subsequent training programmes make appropriate provision for all functions to fulfil their accident prevention roles effectively. If the training analysis has already been prepared, it can often be used as a basis for job safety analysis. **Figure 14.8** lists the types of information to be included in a job safety analysis.

Figure 14.8: Information Included in a Job Safety Analysis

* Job title.
* Department or section.
* Job operations, i.e. a stage-by-stage breakdown of the physical and mental tasks required for the job.
* Machinery and equipment used.
* Materials used, both raw materials and finished products.
* Protection needed, e.g. machinery guarding, personal protective equipment.
* The hazards that may be encountered.
* Degree of risk involved.
* Work organisation, including the responsibility of supervisor and operator, current safety requirements and procedures.
* Specific tasks — Task Analysis splits the job into various stages, e.g. setting up, feeding, controlling, unloading, machine maintenance and housekeeping aspects.

Hazards and Resources

In this section of the safety statement, hazards throughout the organisation are identified and specific strategies are identified to deal with them. The following are some of the more common hazards that may be listed in the statement.

Machinery. Some dangerous parts, like gears, rotating shafts and spindles with projecting keys and setscrews, and pulleys or chains over sprockets, are easy to recognise. Others are not so obvious, such as parts that are only dangerous during cleaning, repairing and testing. **Figure 14.9** suggests some important checkpoints.

Figure 14.9: Checklist of Types of Guards on Machines

Types of Guards

- Fixed Guards — Permanently in position and prevent access to the dangerous parts from all directions.

- Interlocked Guards — Remain in the closed position while machine is in motion.

- Distance Guards — Keeps the operator at a safe distance.

- Automatic Guards — Removes the operator from danger.

- Trip Guards — Stops the machine in case of danger.

Checklist

- Are all the danger parts guarded?

- Are all guards in good condition and properly secured?

- Does the guard prevent the operator, or anyone else, from reaching over or under the guard into dangerous parts?

- Are all guards working properly?

- Are the work-feed openings of guards small enough to prevent the operator from reaching through to the dangerous parts?

- Are the start and stop controls easily accessible, in working order and clearly identifiable?

- Can the machine be positively isolated electrically?

- How often are the guards or safety devices inspected or tested?

Openings. In many factories employees may have to go into vessels, tanks, and other confined spaces where there may be dangerous fumes or a lack of oxygen.

Stacks and Internal Transport. Raw materials, work in progress and finished goods may need to be stacked within the workplace. Specific questions recommended by IBEC include:

- Do the stacks restrict access or visibility?

- Are the stacks bonded to give stability and to prevent collapse?

- Is there a maximum stacking height?

- What is the procedure for dealing with damaged pallets?
- Are all forklift drivers trained and tested?
- The following activities should be prevented:
  ◊ Unauthorised driving of vehicles.
  ◊ Travelling with the load raised.
  ◊ Carrying of passengers.
  ◊ Disregard of speed limits or other work rules.
  ◊ Being used as a crane or means of access unless specially converted.

Hand Tools. Issues to consider include:

- Are the correct tools being used?
- Are the handles secure?
- Are the chisels and punches mushroom-headed? (They should be grounded smooth.)
- Are spanners abused by the use of extension tubes?
- Are knives made from hacksaw blades being used?
- Worn or defective tools should be scrapped.

Physical Structure. Issues to consider include:

- Is there a place for everything, and is everything in its place?
- Are gangways, aisles, passageways and stairs kept clean and free from substances likely to cause a person to slip?
- Is the lighting satisfactory?
- Are handrails provided on stairs?
- What is the system for cleaning spillages of materials or substances?
- Are the floors and stairs in good repair?

Atmosphere. The effect of pollution of the working environment by dust, gas, fumes, and vapour should be considered. IBEC recommends the following questions:

- What potentially harmful substances are used in the work place?

- Are they clearly marked with instructions as to how they should be used, sorted, and disposed of?

- Is the workplace adequately ventilated?

- Are the employees trained in their use?

- What is the system for dealing with an emergency, in relation to these substances?

Fire. The questions that should be posed here include:

- How does one sound the fire alarm?

- How does one use the fire extinguisher?

- How does one escape to a place of safety?

- Are all the extinguishers in their correct position, full and free from obstruction?

- Are all the gangways and staircases that may be used as a means of escape free from obstruction?

- Can every door along the escape route be easily and immediately opened from inside?

- Have fire-resistant or smoke-stopping doors been wedged open?

- Can the fire alarm be heard in all parts of the workplace?

- Has the alarm been tested during the last three months?

Explosives and Highly Flammable Liquids. Many substances, when brought into contact with a source of ignition, will explode. Liquids or fumes from paints, thinners or adhesives may explode or allow the rapid spread of flame. Specific questions that should be asked include:

- What potentially hazardous dusts are used in the workplace?

- What safeguards are used to minimise risk?

- Are the quantities in the workroom kept to a minimum?

- Are the empty containers and contaminated rags, etc. removed immediately from the work place?

- Are there any naked flames or other possible sources of ignition?

- Is smoking prohibited and, if so, is the rule being observed?

Pressure Vessels. Boilers, steam receivers and air receivers connected to a compressor may be pressure vessels. Specific questions that should be asked include:

- Is the safe working pressure marked on it and plainly visible?

- Is there a plainly visible identification mark or number on it?

- Has it been inspected?

- Is it so positioned or fenced as to prevent it being damaged by passing vehicles?

Ladders (and other means of access). The relevant questions here include:

- Is the ladder secured at the top?

- If not, is it firmly fixed at the bottom or secured by a second person?

- Is the ladder in good condition with no missing, cracked or loose rungs?

- Is the ladder varnished and not painted?

- How frequently are the ladders inspected?

Attire. Protective clothing does not prevent accidents, but it can reduce or eliminate the injury. Clothing or equipment can be obtained to protect every part of the body. The wearing of protective clothing is a legal requirement. IBEC recommends the following questions:

- Is the correct equipment available?

- Is it being used where required?

- Does it fit the wearer properly?

- Do new employees have to wait for an issue of protective clothing?

- Is there a system for replacing damaged, worn or lost equipment?

- Are visitors issued with protective equipment?

Cranes. The statistics on accidents demonstrate that many liabilities occur through loads falling from cranes and also from cranes overturning. The following questions should be posed:

- Is the driver authorised to drive the crane?

- Is the safe working load clearly marked?

- Is the crane being overloaded?

- Has the slinger the necessary equipment to sling the load safely?

- Is there a proper system of signals between the slinger and driver?

- Is there anyone working on or near the wheel track of an overhead crane?

- If so, have arrangements been made to prevent any crane coming within 20 feet of the workmen?

- Is anyone working above ground level liable to be struck by an overhead crane?

Lifting Tackle. This includes chains, ropes, slings, hooks, eye bolts and shackles.

- Is the lifting tackle being used correctly?

- Is the safe working load clearly marked?

- Is the equipment being examined every six months?

- Is there a certificate of test showing the safe working load?

Electricity. Electricity is safe, provided the equipment is well made, installed by competent people, properly used and properly maintained. If these basic rules are not followed, electricity can, and does, kill. The issue is dealt with in more detail in **Chapter 17**, but three issues should be considered in the context of the safety statement:

- Signs of damage to apparatus — especially portable equipment.

- Signs of damage to, and exposure of, wires.

- Interference with equipment, damage or otherwise, by un-skilled persons.

Fire and Emergencies

This is a key element of the safety statement and should address the need for a fire and emergency plan, the aims of such a plan and specific fire prevention measures. Broadly the statement should set out the following:

- The delegation of responsibilities for fire prevention and fire-fighting duties to selected members of the staff.

- The nomination of members of staff to carry out certain functions in an emergency.

- The guarantee that members of the staff are aware of fire risks within each section and that they are practised in fire-fighting techniques and evacuation procedures.

The statement should be precise in terms of the overall aims of fire prevention, specifically:

- That fire safety is afforded the same degree of importance as any other management control function.

- To take all reasonable and practicable steps to prevent an outbreak of fire.

- To ensure a safe, effective and orderly response in the event of fire or other emergency.

- To ensure that an alarm is properly raised and all persons are accounted for.

- To ensure that emergency equipment operates properly in the event of fire.

- To ensure an effective use of resources to minimise loss resulting from an emergency.

- To comply with statutory legislation and conditions.

Figure 14.10 presents an example of an emergency procedure.

Figure 14.10: Examples of an Emergency Procedure

Standing Orders for Fire Co-ordination

1. When the alarm sounds, go to reception as quickly as possible.
2. Check the location of the fire.
3. Confirm the location of the fire with the fire team leader.
4. Investigate the presence of a fire in conjunction with the fire team leader. If there is a fire present, ensure that the fire brigade has been called.
5. If the alarm is false:
   ◊ cancel the fire brigade.
   ◊ cancel the evacuation.
6. Co-ordinate with the fire brigade chief as to where the fire is, what is burning, how big the fire is and whether anyone is missing.
7. When the evaluation is complete, mute the firm alarm.
8. If the sprinkler system has been activated, isolate the zone in which the fire has occurred and shut off the pumps once the fire has been completely extinguished.
9. Once the "all clear" has been given, cancel the evacuation, re-set the fire alarm and check the status of the system. Temporarily disconnect any detector and/or break-glass unit that may still be active.

Standing Orders for the Fire Team

1. When the alarm sounds, make safe any equipment you are using.

2. Assemble at reception and await further instructions.

Note: The objective of the fire-fighting team is to protect the health and safety of employees and to minimise damage to property and equipment. If the fire team leader believes that any member of the fire team is in danger due to the fire, he must order an immediate withdrawal from fighting the fire.

Standing Orders for Fire Team Leader

1. When the alarm sounds, make safe any equipment you are using.

2. Proceed to reception as quickly as possible.

3. Confirm with the fire co-ordinator the location of the fire.

4. Check on the status of the fire with the fire co-ordinator.

5. Depending on the existence of a fire, its type and size, one of the following actions should be taken:

    ◊ Small fires: Assemble the fire-fighting team and tackle fire.

    ◊ Large Fires: Assemble the fire-fighting team and tackle the fire, attempting to contain it until the fire brigade arrives.

    ◊ False Alarms: Cancel the fire-fighting team and assist an orderly return to work.

6. In fire conditions, when the local authority fire brigade arrives, the fire chief assumes control of the emergency.

Standing Orders for Supervisors

1. Enforce a disciplined evacuation and roll call.

Standing Orders for Receptionist

1. Remain at the switchboard and operate same unless personal safety is in jeopardy.

2. Call the fire brigade as soon as the fire alarm sounds.

3. Be available to cancel the fire brigade, if requested under the sole authority and direction of the fire co-ordinator.

4. Take notes and be able to give a report with specific times.

Standing Orders for Roll-Call Marshals

1. When alarm sounds, ensure that you have the fire checklist.

2. Check your allocated office/line/department to ensure that all personnel have left the area.

3. Once all personnel have left the area, proceed to the assembly points and undertake the roll call.

4. Report to the fire co-ordinator either that: (a) all personnel are present and correct, or (b) some people are missing and, if possible, where they were last seen.

Notes: (a) Do not hesitate to bring with you anybody who may have useful information when you make your report. (b) Roll-call marshals must know personally all the employees on their checklist.

Standing Orders for All Other Personnel

1. When the alarm sounds, make safe any machine or equipment that you are using.

2. Proceed (a) directly (b) in an orderly way and (c) safely to your nearest exit. Do not run. Do not return to the building or attempt to collect personal possessions.

3. Proceed to your assembly point by the shortest route.

4. Reply "here" when name is called. Do not talk during roll call.

5. Provide the fire marshal with any further information you may have about the fire.

6. Return directly and in an orderly way to your workstation only when you receive authorisation to do so.

Fire Checklist

The fire checklist is printed at the beginning of each shift from the SAP system and distributed to each department.

Fire Drills

X. Ltd. is committed to carrying out fire drills on a regular basis. The drills are seen as necessary for the safety of all employees. The Health and Safety Officer or the Maintenance Supervisor is responsible for carrying out the fire drill. These are to be carried out to meet the defined criteria and to comply with legal requirements.

Criteria of a Fire Drill

Evacuation of the building must take no longer than one and a half minutes only. Fire drill observers must observe the drills at strategic sites throughout the building and report to the Health and Safety Officer or Maintenance Supervisor after the drill.

Notes: (a) Reports on all fire drills will be placed on the Department notice boards. (b) The criterion of less than one minute 30 seconds must be met or the drill must be repeated until it is.

Responsible for Fire Drill

- Health and Safety Officer.
- Deputy Maintenance Supervisor.

Fire Drill Observers

- Fire Team.

Chemical Spills

All chemical spills should be reported to the Department Supervisor/Shift Supervisor and dealt with as laid out in the Material Safety Data Sheet for that chemical. These sheets are available in the Chemical Register located on the perch.

Power/Air Failures

All power and air failures should be reported immediately to the Department Supervisor or Shift Supervisor. During daytime, these occurrences should be reported to the Maintenance Supervisor so that they can be dealt with safely, and during evenings and nights they should be reported to security.

Fire Prevention Aspects

IBEC suggests that the following precautions, as illustrated in **Table 14.2**, should be initiated to control risks.

Fire Protection Aspects

The statement must be precise on five elements of fire protection.

Equipment: Specific issues to be addressed include:

- Location references of fire points and fire boxes should be listed and posted throughout the department.

- All locations should be numbered.

- Adequate stocks of first aid and fire-fighting equipment should be maintained at all times.

- Selected personnel should carry out regular checks of fire equipment and any faults should be rectified.

- Locations of fire equipment should be kept clear and accessible at all times.

Table 14.2: Fire Prevention Precautions

Risk	Precaution
Hot Work Operations	• Introduce safe procedure. • Management authorisations and control.
Electrical Equipment	• Regular checking. • Faults to be remedied. • Portable space heaters unplugged when not in use and after normal working hours.
Rubbish/Waste	• Regular disposal in proper receptacles
Smoking	• No smoking signs posted. • Smoking restricted to specified safe areas. • Ashtrays and sand buckets to be provided. • Non-flammable rubbish containers to be provided.
Cooking	• Restricted to specified safe areas.
Spillages of flammable materials	• Immediate clean-up.
Accumulation of dust	• Regular clean-up procedures. • Plant monitoring to ensure minimum emissions.
Storage of flammable/volatile materials	• Confined to safe storage areas.
Forklift battery re-charging	• Confined to well-ventilated safe areas.

Personnel: Suitable personnel should be selected and trained to: man control functions; forward control functions; maintain and check equipment; ensure effective organisation of fire prevention procedures; and organise fire drills.

Water Supply and Pressure: These include the maintenance of hydrants in proper working order; the clear marking of hydrants and the initiation of flow and pressure tests to ensure adequate hydrant pressure to fight fires.

Alarm: Adequate means of giving warning in the event of a fire will be installed.

Fire Drills: Regular fire drills will be carried out to test the effectiveness of the plan in compliance with statutory requirements.

Hazard Reporting

An important element of hazard management involves the implementation of an effective system of hazard reporting. This can be effectively managed by putting in place a systematic system of hazard reporting. **Figure 14.11** presents an example of a hazard reporting procedure.

Figure 14.11: Example of a Hazard Reporting Procedure

X Ltd. recognises the part that its employees have to play in the reporting of hazards in the workplace. It recognises that, during the employees' work day, they may come into contact with hazards and, therefore, a formal method of identifying and reporting these hazards must exist. The following procedure applies:

Procedure:

1. Any employee who observes a hazard in the workplace should report it immediately to the Shift Supervisor.

2. The Shift Supervisor instructs the employee to fill in a Health, Safety and Welfare Complaint Form, stating clearly what the complaint is, and gives the form to the Department Supervisor.

3. Upon receiving the form, the Department Supervisor signs and dates it to confirm when it was received. The Department Supervisor then assesses the complaint and decides if the solution is within his or her control. If so, the Supervisor fills in what action is to be taken to eliminate the complaint and the date by which the problem will be resolved. The Supervisor gives the Health and Safety Officer a copy of the complaint and proceeds with the specified action. If the solution of the complaint is not within the control of the supervisor, he or she will:

   ◊ Fill in that the form has been passed on to a third party, stating the name of the third party and the completion date for resolution.

   ◊ Pass the original form onto the third party.

   ◊ Keep a copy for his/her own records.

   ◊ Give a copy of the form to the Health and Safety Officer.

   ◊ The third party then carries out whatever action is necessary to resolve the complaint.

   ◊ Upon resolving the complaint, the third party returns the complaint form to the Supervisor.

4. The Department Supervisor then signs the form if the complaint has been satisfactorily resolved and requests the employee who made the complaint to countersign if the employee accepts that the complaint has been resolved.

5. The original form is then passed on to the Health and Safety Officer who checks that the complaint has been satisfactorily resolved.

Note: The Health and Safety Officer in consultation with the Department Supervisor may change the Expected Completion Date depending on the type of complaint.

Department:	Supervisor:
Date:	Time:
Complaint:	
Signed:	
Date received:	Signed:
Action to be taken by Supervisor:	
Expected completion date:	Signed:
Date received:	Signed:
Action to be taken by Third Party:	
Expected completion date:	
	Signed:
Supervisor:	Complaint Resolved Date:
Complainant:	Accepted date:
Health and Safety Officer:	Review Date:

Component Four: Communication, Review and Revision

There should be widespread consultation during the development of the statement. Once the policy has been finalised, it must be effectively communicated to all persons in the organisation, as it is a legal requirement to bring the policy to the attention of all employees. Employers should take a proactive role in its promotion and not just rely on passive communication such as posting copies of the policy on staff notice boards.

Certain key individuals in the organisation will need to receive individual explanation of their responsibility. It may also be necessary to communicate the statement or specific information to persons outside the organisation such as contractors or other persons working in the building. Communication methods will vary from company to company and should be carried out in accordance with tried and tested methods.

Once the statement has been successfully introduced, monitoring must take place to ensure that it is being implemented as planned. Checks should be made to ensure that:

- The statement has reached all levels of the organisation.

- It has been understood by managers and employees.

- Managers are aware of their specific responsibilities under the policy.

- Those responsibilities are being fulfilled.

- Safe working procedures are being followed.

- Other systems of work and procedures introduced under the policy are working.

The policy must be reviewed, at a minimum, yearly. It is important to point out that:

- The review is a more formal affair than monitoring.

- The overall success of the statement should be measured.

- It should be undertaken after an agreed period of time.

- It should be undertaken when there have been significant changes within the company.

- Responsibility for monitoring and reviewing the statement must be assigned to specific individuals.

Figure 14.12 identifies issues that may be considered in the review.

Figure 14.12: Reviewing the Organisation

Reviewing the Organisation — Important Points to Consider

- All those assigned safety responsibilities should be asked to report on any problems in carrying them out.

- It may be that some responsibility will need to be reassigned to a different staff level (managers dealing with trivial matters or employees monitoring things that they have no authority to correct).

- Do those with monitoring responsibilities have the skills to carry out their functions?

- Should those in management have the safety performance tasks for which they are responsible included in their appraisal?

- Are the lines of communication effective — for example, have any matters of concern from the safety committee not been attended to because they have not reached the correct management level?

Reviewing the Arrangements — Important Points to Consider

- Are there any new risk assessments needed for new equipment or processes?

- Are existing assessments adequate, or have there been problems or dangers reported?

- Have accidents/incident reports and first aid treatments identified problem areas that may require the revision of current arrangements? (For example, several reports of strains or foot injuries may indicate poor manual handling procedures; minor hand and forearm cuts or bruises may show inappropriate maintenance methods).

- Have new laws, guidance or standards introduced a requirement for new or amended arrangements?

CHAPTER ROUND UP

- The Safety, Health and Welfare at Work Act, 1989 envisages the safety statement as a fundamental component of the effective management of safety, health and welfare in the workplace.

The safety statement articulates the policies and procedures of the organisation in managing safety and health.

- The contents of the statement are generally prescribed by the legislation and the Health and Safety Authority. However, the statement must reflect the organisational realities and specific characteristics of the workplace. This requires that a generic safety statement will not meet the requirements of the legislation.

- The opening statement indicates management's commitment to achieve the objectives set out in the statement. It will also indicate management's commitment to review the statement in the light of experience. Management must also indicate its willingness to provide the necessary resources to implement the statement and nominate a person with overall responsibility for implementing the statement.

- The safety statement must be based on a systematic, written risk assessment produced by a recognised professional. The organisation is obliged to carry out regular audits and make interim assessments of risks.

- The statement should specify that the company commits itself to dealing with the hazards identified primarily on the basis of their elimination by engineering means. The approach should reflect the norms of the particular industry, the expert advice available and established standards.

- The safety statement should describe in detail the health and safety structure of the organisation through which high safety standards are to be achieved. The statement must emphasise that ultimate responsibility rests with top management. Employee responsibilities must also be identified. Their co-operation is essential to the successful implementation of the statement. A specific element of the statement should consider the role and responsibilities of the supervisor. They represent an important influence on health and safety because they are in immediate control of employees and work processes.

Chapter 15

SAFETY AUDITS, REVIEWS AND ACCIDENT ANALYSIS

INTRODUCTION

The focus of this chapter is on safety auditing and its implications for the management of organisational safety and health. Auditing is an essential component of the safety management process because it provides feedback on performance and enables corrective action to be undertaken. The chapter focuses on the nature and scope of safety auditing; the components of the safety auditing process; the value of safety auditing to the organisation; and the use of accident data and its analysis.

THE NATURE AND SCOPE OF SAFETY AUDITING

A safety audit aims to examine the "total organisation" from a health and safety perspective in order to identify whether it is meeting its safety aims and objectives. It examines hierarchies, safety planning processes, decision-making, delegation, policy-making and implementation, as well as areas such as safety programme planning, implementation, monitoring and evaluation. It also examines all socio-technical systems within safety management and comments on their efficiency and effectiveness.

A safety review, on the other hand, normally examines one part of the audit process such as safety programme evaluation or reviewing current safety procedures, in a particular work area of the organisation.

Safety audits involve a detailed examination of the total organisation and can therefore take a considerable amount of time and resources to complete. If the audit is to be of any value to an organisation, it should be conducted by individuals experienced in safety management systems who are sufficiently divorced from the organisation to be capable of arriving at an objective and unbiased conclusion about safety and health practices.

All control systems within the organisation tend to deteriorate over time or to become obsolete as a result of change. This demands that systems be regularly audited. Health and safety auditing complements the planning and control cycle of the organisation. It aims to provide an independent assessment of the validity and reliability of the safety management planning and control systems. Auditing supports monitoring by providing managers with information on the implementation and effectiveness of safety plans and performance standards. It also provides a check on the reliability, efficiency and effectiveness of the arrangements for safety policy-making, organising, planning, implementing, measuring and reviewing performance. Safety audits need to be comprehensive and examine, over time, all of the components of the health and safety management systems.

Various strategies can be adopted to achieve this objective but they can be divided into two different but complementary approaches. An examination of a "vertical slice" of activities can be undertaken. This involves examining one specific aspect in each of the elements identified. An audit could be made of the policy on eye protection, fire safety or emergency arrangements. This would involve assessing its adequacy relative to the risks and how effectively the organisation, planning, measuring and reviewing processes, secured its implementation. A "horizontal slice" approach can also be adopted. In this case, one particular element of the safety management system is examined in detail. This may involve a detailed examination of the whole process of safety planning. Safety plans are examined to assess their relevance, how they were formulated and whether they are sufficiently specific and realistic to allow for ready implementation and measurement. A "horizontal slice" approach can also be taken in respect of performance standards, examining how they were devised, their relevance to the needs of the organisation and their adequacy.

In practice, a combination of vertical and horizontal slice auditing is necessary to provide a comprehensive picture of how effectively the health and safety system is controlling risks. This may be undertaken either as a single event or as a rolling programme with different aspects, sections or departments examined in turn. It may involve one or a number of persons. A team approach, involving managers, safety representatives and employees may be adopted to widen the nature of involvement and co-operation and help ensure the success of the audit.

It is generally recommended that competent specialists independent of the area or activities being audited should conduct audits. This can be achieved either by using external consultants or by using staff from different sections, departments or sites to audit their colleagues. Organisations may use either their own auditing system or those marketed as proprietary systems or a combination of both.

The HSA in Ireland supports the use of proprietary systems but does not endorse any particular system. Organisations should decide what system, in-house or proprietary, would best meet their needs, taking into account the costs and the potential benefits. In assessing the suitability of proprietary schemes, it should be borne in mind that, because of the variability of organisations, it is unlikely that any one system will suit an organisation perfectly. It will generally be necessary to tailor a system to the particular needs of the organisation. **Figure 15.1** presents the characteristics of effective safety auditing.

Audits generate both qualitative and quantitative data on health and safety performance. Many organisations have tried to provide numerical measures to quantify audit data so that improvements in performance can be readily measured from year to year or month to month. Auditing is a valuable exercise but needs to be supported by sound auditing methodologies that ensure consistency in scoring so that the numerical outputs are valid and reliable. Many organisations do not use numerical systems and rely on a purely qualitative approach.

An audit programme should be prepared to complement other health and safety management activities. Performance standards should be devised for planning and implementing the audit programme and these standards should themselves be monitored. Some organisations have allocated responsibility for health and safety auditing in an attempt to integrate health and safety management into other auditing structures. Audit programmes are only as effective as the staff operating them and depend on the systematic examination and use of the audit results. Unless they are operated with integrity, it is always possible to misuse the system, and so checks and balances need to be built in at various levels to prevent this. Such checks and balances are particularly important at the interpretative review stage.

Figure 15.1: Characteristics of Effective Safety Auditing

- Competent people who are independent of the area or section being audited should carry out audits. This may involve one person, a team of managers, specialists and non-management employees or external consultants. Those with auditing responsibilities will generally require specific training in this task to ensure competence.

- Audit systems are designed to assess safety policy, safety organisation and the acceptance of health and safety responsibilities by line managers and the adequacy of arrangements to ensure control.

- Audits focus on the adequacy of the arrangements to secure the involvement of all employees in the health and safety effort and the adequacy of arrangements to secure the combination of policy and relevant information. They also focus on the adequacy of arrangements to ensure the competence of all employees.

- Safety planning and policy implementation include: overall control and direction of the health and safety programme; standard setting; the allocation of resources to implement standards; the extent of compliance with standards and their effectiveness in risk control; the long-term improvement in the accident and incident performance.

- Safety audits focus on measuring systems in terms of their adequacy and relevance, and reviewing systems and the ability of the organisation to learn from experience and improve safety performance.

SAFETY REVIEWS

Safety reviews are concerned with making judgements about the adequacy of performance and taking decisions about the nature and timing of the actions necessary to remedy deficiencies in safety. Performance standards should be established to identify the responsibilities, timing and systems of reviewing. Supporting performance standards and systems are also necessary to track the implementation of those decisions arising from the review process.

The degree of risk involved and the availability of resources should determine the speed and nature of the response to any situation. The application of risk assessment principles, which we will consider in **Chapter 18**, to decision-making may be useful in identifying risk priorities. The effectiveness of review systems is primarily determined by the competence of those involved, and people responsible for making review decisions should receive specific training in making this type of judgement.

The general aims of a safety review process are:

- To secure the maintenance and development of health and safety policy.

- To secure the maintenance and development of an effective organisation with a positive health and safety culture.

- To secure the maintenance and development of performance standards and reporting systems for controlling both the health and safety systems and specific risks.

The effectiveness of safety review activities is considerably enhanced by clearly establishing who is responsible for implementing the remedial action identified in the review process, and setting deadlines for the completion of remedial action. Reviewing performance is based on information from monitoring activities (including both active and reactive monitoring) and from auditing activities in which an independent assessment is made of the whole safety management system.

Reviewing the results of safety reviews is a continuous process, undertaken at various levels within an organisation. It may include some or all of the following:

- Responses by first line supervisors to remedy the failure to implement performance standards that they observe in the course of routine activities.

- Responses to remedy specific examples of substandard performance identified by reactive monitoring.

- Responses to remedy examples of substandard performance identified as a result of active monitoring.

- Responses to the assessment of plans and objectives whether at individual, departmental, site, group or organisational level.

The reviews undertaken in the first two situations occur randomly and cannot be planned. It is, however, important that review procedures are consistently applied in these situations. The reviews in the latter two situations should arise from planned monitoring activities and should be controlled by appropriate performance standards.

Organisations must decide on the frequency of reviews at each level and the design of review activities should be tailored to measurement activities discussed in **Chapter 14**. Similarly, decisions need to be made on how to review the audit data and integrate it into the general review procedure.

Successful organisations use a number of key performance indicators relating to overall performance and the management of the improvements as the basis for reviews at the highest level. While each organisation needs to develop its own indicators, the safety literature suggests that four indicators should be involved:

- An assessment of the degree of compliance with performance standards.

- An identification of areas where performance standards are absent or inadequate.

- An assessment of the achievement of specific objectives.

- An analysis of accident, ill health and incident data, including analyses of the immediate and underlying causes, trends and common features.

The process of feeding-back information on success and failure into the system is an essential element in motivating employees to improve safety performance. Successful organisations emphasise positive reinforcement and concentrate on encouraging progress on those indicators that demonstrate improvements in risk control.

In addition to making integral assessments of their achievements, organisations may "benchmark" their performance against other organisations. Benchmarking generally takes two forms: comparing accident rates with those of organisations in the same industry that use similar production processes and experience similar risks; and comparing management practices and techniques with those of organisations in any industry, so as to provide a wider perspective and gain new insights on the management of similar problems.

Some organisations now report their health and safety performance in their published annual reports. Public companies are required to do so by law in Ireland. Organisations are prepared, and able, to identify not only the efforts put into health and safety but also the result of such effort in terms of improved health and safety performance and reductions in avoidable costs.

THE COMPONENTS OF SAFETY AUDITING

A safety auditing process generally focuses on four areas: safety policies, safety procedures, safety practices and safety programmes.

Auditing Organisational Safety Policies

It is important that the safety manager has the potential to quickly assess whether company safety policy is adequate in meeting statutory safety obligations. To do this, it is necessary to obtain answers to the following basic questions:

Is the Safety and Health Policy towards Researching Correct?
Specific issues here include:

- **Legal requirements** — those rules and regulations covered by common and statute law, Regulations and other legal requirements.

- **Financial statement of objectives** — organisational and individual.

- **Budgetary provision** — sufficient funds must be available to carry out agreed objectives from predetermined priorities.

- **Staff** — correct people should be deployed on the right tasks and training must be provided and monitored.

- **Organisational structure** — it is important that the hierarchical structure is capable of carrying out its aims and objectives efficiently, effectively and safely. **Figure 15.2** presents key questions that should be posed when assessing the safety organisation.

Is the safety and health policy adequate?

Specific issues here include:

- **The decision-making environment** — safety decisions should be taken efficiently and effectively; they should be communicated to all affected personnel within the organisation; policies, procedures, practice and programmes should be known to all concerned. This aspect should also consider objective-setting and performance-standard criteria.

- **Safety committees** — where appropriate, these should consist of both senior management and safety representatives. If these committees exist, they must have sufficient authority to be effective, otherwise they are just seen as "talking shop". They are no longer a statutory requirement in Ireland. **Figure 15.3** presents a set of questions that should be posed about the safety committee.

- **Management involvement** — senior management should be involved in all levels of the safety management decision-making process and should actively support the work of employees specifically employed on accident prevention and/or reduction work.

Figure 15.2: Questions to be Considered when Auditing the Safety of an Organisation

- Who are the organisation's safety officers?

- Are they competent and are there sufficient officers?

- Do all staff have access to them?

- Are they named in the company safety statement?

- Is there full co-operation between all safety officers, and are they privy to all health and safety and related information?

- If any safety officer has other responsibilities: a) is sufficient time available for health and safety: b) have they been properly trained and are they able to attend refresher training?

- Does the board receive safety reports periodically?

- Are senior management aware of the importance of prompt consideration of safety officers' recommendations?

- Do all managers' job descriptions outline their health and safety responsibilities?

- Have local managers been appointed for branches?

- Do the job descriptions of local managers include their health and safety responsibilities?

- Do safety officers inform the organisation on health and safety training requirements and carry out such training, where appropriate?

- Do safety officers inform the organisation of forthcoming health and safety legislation, which will affect the company?

- Do safety officers act as secretary to the organisation's safety committee?

- Do safety officers ensure compliance with statutory reporting requirements and maintain safety statistics?

- Do safety officers carry out periodic safety inspections?

- Do safety officers investigate accidents in conjunction with nominated colleagues?

- Do safety officers maintain and provide updates for ratification by the board of company safety statement?

- **Trade union liaison** — trade unions have a valuable and necessary contribution to safety management and should be actively encouraged to play their part efficiently and effectively.

- **Liaison with other interested groups** — effective accident reduction and/or prevention is the responsibility of all employees. Therefore the decision-making environment includes co-operation and discussion with all groups with an interest in the safety subject matter.

At this stage, attempts should be made to identify areas where difficulties might be experienced in terms of remedial action.

Figure 15.3: Operation of Safety Committees

- Is some action needed to ensure appropriate consultation with staff on health and safety matters?

Where a safety committee exists:

- Is there a good staff/management balance?

- Are there unfilled vacancies?

- Does the committee meet regularly?

- Are agendas circulated a week before meetings and minutes circulated a week after?

- Do management members delegate attendance to subordinates?

- Are meetings ever postponed or cancelled?

- What, if any, measures are in place to monitor the clear-up rate of concerns raised by the committee?

- Is management regularly appraised of the work and effectiveness of the committee?

Auditing Safety Procedures

This component of the safety auditing process focuses on whether the administrative procedures currently in operation are able to continue to implement organisational policy efficiently and effectively. Key issues to be considered here include:

- **Administrative structures** — these should be designed in such a way that they fully support the health and safety policies, practices, procedures and programmes that are outlined and agreed as the company's safety objectives in the safety statement. Professional staff often have to conform to administrative procedures rather than the other way round.

- **Technical and professional procedures** should be in place to meet the needs of any technical or professional aspects of tasks listed as objectives. These would include maintenance and repair procedures.

- **Communication systems** — all aspects of safety policy, procedures, practice and programmes should be disseminated in a sufficiently clear and concise manner that all employees understand them. Steps should be taken at regular intervals to monitor all aspects of safety communication.

- **Time management** — safety requires time and, therefore, it is important that working procedures allow time for accident reduction and/or prevention measures to be taken at all levels within the organisation.

- **Internal and public relations** — it is important for both staff and people in the local community to be a part of the organisation's safety activities, and procedures should be put in place to cater for this.

- **Recruitment** — recruiting the right person for the right job is essential to the safety management system. Human failure is the cause of a considerable proportion of accidents. Therefore, recruitment must involve appropriate procedures to ensure, as far as possible, that effective staff are recruited and trained.

- **Safety training** — this is an essential part of the safety management system and procedures should be in place to examine current safety training procedures in terms of efficiency and effectiveness, and to ensure that they meet organisational goals and statutory requirements.

- **Supervision** — there are many examples in case law where poor supervision has been identified as a major contributory factor to accidents. Supervisors should be subjected to good strong leadership and should have clearly defined areas of responsibility in terms of authority.

• **Discipline** — the reasons for this, including the appropriate penalties that may form part of the disciplinary procedures within an organisation, should be communicated to, and understood by, everyone.

Figure 15.4 presents some audit questions for safety standards.

Figure 15.4: Organisational Safety Statements: Audit Questions

---

• Has the current safety statement been published in the last two years?

• Is it signed and dated by the managing director?

• Do review procedures exist?

• Have EU-driven regulations been included?

• Does every employee receive a copy?

• Does every employee receive a briefing on the statement?

• Are new employees automatically issued with a copy?

• Do employees understand that breaches of their duties are criminal offences?

• Are the specific duties of key appointment holders and other managers and employees shown?

• If the safety statement is incorporated into an employee handbook, is it given appropriate status?

Auditing Safety Practices

The auditing of safety practices may be based upon historical precedence or upon professional ethos, professional codes of conduct and practice, that directly involve organisational policy and procedure. Questions regarding this focus on the following:

- **Costing and valuation of accidents** — it should be accepted practice that all accidents are costed and that an agreed methodology is employed to meet this aim.

- **Accident investigations** — many organisations in Ireland do not adequately record their accidents or consider the practice of calculating accident costs to be part of normal safety management systems. Such information is essential for decision-making and for deciding on the priority of safety objectives.

- **Data collection** — the practice of systematically collecting accident data is an important part of the safety management process and the information obtained is crucial in calculating safety performance and for making comparisons.

- **Medical examinations** — the practice of requiring employees to undertake regular detailed medical examinations is an important feature of the safety management process and is a requirement of the safety audit process.

- **Welfare** — this requires an enthusiastic commitment by management, if it is to contribute effectively to health and safety practice in the workplace.

- **Hazard and risk assessment** — the practice of hazard and risk quantification and/or qualification should be encouraged at all levels, and safety systems should be in place to facilitate this. Included in this would be areas where accidents have been known to occur, where dangerous occurrences have taken place or where evidence exists of the potential to cause injury and/or ill health.

- **Accident analysis** — companies should systematically analyse all accidents, however small, in order to identify the contributory factors that led to the event. This will allow more efficient and effective counter-measures to be considered.

- **Equipment inspections** — the practice of regularly inspecting equipment must form an integral part of the safety management process. These examinations must be carried out in accordance with guidelines laid down by manufacturers or other competent personnel, and conducted by professionally qualified persons. Records must be maintained and an appropriate maintenance and repair procedure must be in place.

- **Professional codes of practice** — these are issued from time to time by a range of bodies, including the Health and Safety Authority.

Auditing Safety Programmes

In terms of auditing safety programmes, the safety audit will examine past remedial strategies for efficiency and effectiveness using the four basic elements of the safety mix. These are:

- **Enforcement** — it is essential that laws, rules, regulations etc. are available, and they should be used in such as way as to complement other programmes being considered.

- **Engineering** — engineering design, manufacture, equipment and machinery inspections and maintenance are all essential features of safety programmes and, as such, must form part of the safety audit. Research demonstrates that a programme of safety engineering used in isolation is not sufficient to reduce or prevent accidents from occurring. A blend of socio-technical features used with other aspects of the safety mix has been found to be more effective in accident-reduction strategies.

- **Environment** — the working environment must be kept as safe and healthy as is reasonably practicable and, therefore, must form an integral part of the safety audit.

- **Education** — education refers to safety education as a proactive means of developing skill, knowledge and safe behaviour. Safety training is a more reactive and readily used tool by organisations. Publicity programmes are included under education and, therefore, safety education, training and publicity programmes would normally be subjected to audit. **Figure 15.5** presents audit questions for health and safety training.

Figure 15.5: Health and Safety Training: Auditing the Organisation

- Does the organisation comply with its responsibilities as outlined in the Safety, Health and Welfare at Work Act, 1989?

- Does the organisation have documentary records to prove this?

- Who organises health and safety training for the organisation?

- Who carries out the training?

- Is there a formal written induction procedure?

- Does the procedure include a substantial health and safety element?

- Are there regular checks to the induction programme, and do new employees sign to confirm receipt of the training?

- What are the arrangements for refresher/repeat training?

- What special health and safety training do managers receive?

- What arrangements exist to upgrade the present health and safety training to cover the additional requirements imposed by new legislation?

- Does the company safety policy make reference to safety training?

All policies, programmes, procedures and practices should form the basis of the audit if the aim of the safety audit or review is to improve organisational efficiency and effectiveness. Safety audit objectives ultimately test an organisation's performance in terms of accident reduction and/or prevention and keeping risk at a minimum, while keeping the health and safety of the workforce at a maximum. **Table 15.1** summarises the main elements of a safety audit.

Table 15.1: Safety Audit: A Set of Audit Questions

Documentation and Communication	Rating (1-5)
1. Are managers aware of all health and safety legislation applying to their workplace?	
2. Is this legislation available to management and employees?	
3. Has management, with a view to ensuring compliance, studied all Approved Codes of Practice, HSA Codes of Practice and internal codes of practice?	
4. Does the existing Statement of Health and Safety Policy meet current conditions in the workplace?	
5. Is there a named manager with overall responsibility for health and safety?	
6. Are the "organisation and arrangements" to implement the Health and Safety Policy still adequate?	
7. Have the hazards and precautions necessary on the part of staff and other persons been identified and recorded?	
8. Are individual responsibilities for health and safety clearly detailed in the Statement?	
9. Do all job descriptions adequately describe individual health and safety responsibilities and accountabilities?	
10. Do written safe systems exist for all potentially hazardous operations?	
11. Is Permit-to-Work documentation available?	
12. Has a suitable and sufficient assessment of the risks to staff and other persons been made, recorded and brought to the attention of staff and other persons? Have other risk assessments in regard to the following been made, recorded and brought to the attention of staff and other persons: ◊ substances hazardous to health? ◊ risks to hearing? ◊ work equipment? ◊ personal protective equipment? ◊ manual handling operations?	
13. Is the fire certificate available and up-to-date?	
14. Is there a record of inspections of the means of escape in the event of fire, fire appliances, fire alarms, warning notices, fire and smoke-detection equipment?	

15. Is there a record of inspections and maintenance of work equipment, including guards and safety devices?

16. Are all examination and test certificates available, e.g. lifting appliances and pressure systems?

17. Are all necessary licences available, e.g. to store petroleum spirit?

18. Are workplace health and safety rules and procedures available, promoted and enforced?

19. Have these rules and procedures been documented in a way that is comprehensible to staff and others, e.g. Health and Safety Handbook?

20. Are disciplinary procedures for unsafe behaviour clearly documented and known to staff and others?

21. Is a formally written emergency procedure available?

22. Is documentation available for the recording of injuries, near-misses, damage-only accidents, diseases and dangerous occurrences?

23. Are health and safety training records maintained?

24. Are there documented procedures for regulating the activities of contractors, visitors and other persons working on the site?

25. Is hazard reporting documentation available to staff and other persons?

26. Is there a documented planned maintenance system?

Health and Safety Systems

1. Have competent persons been appointed to co-ordinate health and safety measures within the organisation?

2. Have these persons been adequately trained on the basis of identified and assessed risks?

3. Are the role, function, responsibility and accountability of competent persons clearly identified?

4. Are there arrangements for specific forms of safety monitoring, e.g. safety inspections, safety sampling?

5. Is a system in operation for measuring and monitoring individual managers' performance on health and safety issues?

6. Are systems established for the formal investigation of accidents, ill health, near-misses and dangerous occurrences?

7. Do investigation procedures produce results that can be used to prevent future incidents?

8. Are the causes of accidents, ill health, near-misses and dangerous occurrences analysed in terms of failure of established safe systems of work?

9. Is there a hazard reporting system in operation?

10. Is there a system for controlling damage to structural items, machinery, vehicles, etc. in operation?

11. Is the system for joint consultation with trade union safety representatives and staff effective?

12. Is the role, constitution and objectives of the Health and Safety Committees clearly identified?

13. Are there procedures for appointing or electing committee members and trade union safety representatives?

14. Are the capabilities of employees with regard to health and safety taken into account when entrusting them with tasks?

15. Is the provision of first aid arrangements adequate?

16. Are first-aid personnel adequately trained and retrained?

17. Do staff know the procedures covering sickness absence?

18. Is there a procedure for controlling sickness absence?

19. Are managers aware of the current sickness absence rate?

20. Do current arrangements ensure that health and safety implications are considered at the design stage of projects?

21. Is there a formally established annual health and safety budget?

Prevention and Control Procedures

1. Are formal inspections of machinery, plant, hand tools, access equipment, electrical equipment, storage equipment, warning systems, first-aid boxes, resuscitation equipment, welfare amenity areas, etc. undertaken?

2. Are machinery guards and safety devices examined on a regular basis?

3. Is a Permit-to-Work system operated when there is a high degree of foreseeable risk?

4. Are fire and emergency procedures practised on a regular basis?

5. Where specific fire hazards have been identified, are they catered for in the current fire protection arrangements?

6. Are all items of fire protection equipment and alarms tested,

examined and maintained on a regular basis?

7. Are all fire exits and escape routes marked, kept free from obstruction and operational?

8. Are all fire appliances correctly labelled, sited and maintained?

9. Is a planned maintenance system in operation?

10. Are the requirements of cleaning schedules monitored?

11. Is housekeeping of a high standard, e.g. material storage, waste disposal, removal of spillages?

12. Are all gangways, stairways, fire exits, access and egress points to and from the workplace maintained and kept clear?

13. Is environmental monitoring of temperature, lighting, ventilation, humidity, radiation, noise and vibration undertaken on a regular basis?

14. Is health surveillance of persons exposed to assessed health risks undertaken on a regular basis?

15. Is monitoring of personal exposure to assessed health risks undertaken on a regular basis?

16. Are local exhaust ventilation systems examined, tested and maintained on a regular basis?

17. Are arrangements for the storage and handling of substances hazardous to health adequate?

18. Are all substances hazardous to health identified and correctly labelled, including transfer containers?

19. Is the appropriate personal protective equipment available?

20. Is the personal protective equipment worn or used by staff consistently when exposed to risks?

21. Are storage facilities provided for items of personal protective equipment?

22. Are welfare amenity provisions, i.e. sanitation, hand washing, showers and clothing storage arrangements, adequate?

23. Do welfare amenity provisions promote appropriate levels of personal hygiene?

Information, Instruction, Training and Supervision

1. Do manufacturers and suppliers of articles and substances provide the information for use at work and is it adequate?

2. Do employees and other persons have access to this information?

3. Is the means of promoting health and safety adequate?

4. Is effective use made of safety propaganda, e.g. posters?

5. Do current safety signs meet the requirements of the Safety Signs Regulations, (1980)?

6. Are safety signs adequate in terms of the assessed risks?

7. Are fire instructions prominently displayed?

8. Are hazard warning systems adequate?

9. Are the individual training needs of staff and other persons assessed on a regular basis?

10. Is staff health and safety training undertaken:
    ◊   At the induction stage?
    ◊   On their being exposed to new risks because of:
         ●   transfer or change in responsibilities?
         ●   the introduction of new work equipment or a change regarding existing work equipment?
         ●   the introduction of new technology?
         ●   the introduction of a new system of work or change in existing system of work?

11. Is the above training:
    ◊   Repeated periodically?
    ◊   Adapted to take account of new or changed risks?
    ◊   Carried out during working hours?

12. Is specific training carried out regularly for first-aid staff, fork-lift drivers, crane drivers and others exposed to specific risks?

13. Are selected staff trained in the correct use of fire appliances?

OVERALL ASSESSMENT

Are you satisfied that your organisation is as safe and healthy as you can reasonably make it, or that you know what action must be taken to achieve that state?

ANALYSING ACCIDENT DATA

An essential component of the safety auditing process is the requirement to obtain accident, incidence and frequency data and make decisions based on these statistics. This data is a basis to measure safety performance over a period of time and it allows the organisation to benchmark performance with externally published data. Five accident measures can be utilised:

Incident Rate

$$\frac{\text{Total number of injuries in a period}}{\text{Number of persons employed during the same period}} \times 100,000$$

The incident rate is a crude method of calculating the rate per 100,000 employees. It does not make any allowances for variations in part-time employment or overtime work.

Frequency Rate

$$\frac{\text{Total number of injuries during the period}}{\text{Total number of man-hours worked during the period}} \times 1,000,000$$

The accident frequency rate calculates accident frequency per million hours work. This statistic allows accident data to be used for comparison purposes. It uses the hours worked rather than the number of employees and, therefore, avoids distortions, which may arise from the differences between full-time and part-time employees.

Severity Rate

$$\frac{\text{Total number of days lost}}{\text{Total number of man-hours worked}} \times 1,000$$

This statistic is preferred by many specialists, who believe it is a better statistic for company accident trends between departments, organisations and industries.

Mean Duration Rate

$$\frac{\text{Total number of days lost}}{\text{Total number of accidents}}$$

This statistic allows for the calculation of a ratio between the number of days lost in relation to the number of man-hours worked during the same period.

Duration Rate

$$\frac{\text{Number of man - hours worked}}{\text{Total number of accidents}}$$

This statistic expresses the number of man-hours in relation to the number of accidents or injuries in the same period.

Amis and Booth (1991) pose questions about the significance and relevance of accident statistics as a true measure of health and safety performance. They highlight eight deficiencies of the use of accident statistics:

- They measure failure rather than success.

- They are not suitable for staff performance appraisal purposes.

- They are often subject to random fluctuations.

- They reflect the success or otherwise of safety measures adopted in the past.

- They do not measure the incidence of occupational disease where there is a prolonged latent period.

- They measure injury severity but not the potential seriousness of the accident.

- They may not report injuries accurately.

- They are of little use in assessing the future risk of high consequence, low probability accidents.

ACCIDENT INVESTIGATION

The investigation of the direct and indirect causes of accidents is a reactive element of the safety management process. There are very important reasons, however, for the effective and thorough investigation of accidents. Some of the more important reasons suggested in the safety literature include the following:

- On purely humanitarian basis, no one wishes to see people killed or injured.

- The accident may have resulted from a breach of statute or Regulations by the organisation, the accident victim, the manufacturer and/or suppliers of articles and substances used at work, or other persons, e.g. contractors, with the possibility of civil proceedings being instituted by the injured party against the employer and other persons.

- The accident may be reportable to the HSA.

- The accident may result in lost production.

- From a management perspective, a serious accident, particularly a fatal one, can have a long-term detrimental effect on the morale of the workforce and management/worker relations.

- There may be damage to plant and equipment, resulting in the need for repair or replacement, with possible delays in replacement.

- In order to prevent a recurrence of this accident, there will be in most cases a need for immediate remedial action.

Apart from the direct and indirect losses associated with all forms of incident, not just those resulting in injury, there are legal reasons for investigating accidents to identify the direct and indirect causes and to select strategies for preventing recurrences. Above all, the purpose of accident investigation is not primarily to apportion blame or fault, although these may eventually emerge as a result of the investigation.

What Accidents should be Investigated?

There is a case for investigating all accidents and, indeed, all "near-misses". A near-miss, for the purpose of accident investigation, is defined as "an unplanned and unforeseeable event that could have resulted, but did not result, in human injury, property damage or other form of loss". However, it may be impracticable to investigate every accident, and the following factors should be considered in deciding which accidents should be investigated as a priority:

- The type of accident, e.g. falls from a height, chemical handling, machinery-related.

- The form and severity of injury, or the potential for serious injury and/or damage.

- Whether the accident indicates the continuation of a particular trend in the organisation's accident experience.

- The extent of involvement of articles and substances used at work.

- The possibility of a breach of the legislation.

- Whether the injury or occurrence is, by law, notifiable and reportable to the HSA.

- Whether the accident should be reported to the organisation's insurance company as it could result in a claim being submitted.

Accident Investigation Procedures

The following procedure is one that would meet the requirements of the Health and Safety Authority in Ireland:

- Establish the facts as quickly and completely as possible with regard to:

    a) the general environment.

    b) the particular plant, machinery, practice or system of work involved.

    c) the sequence of events leading to the accident.

- Use a camera to take photographs of the accident scene, prior to any clearing-up that may follow the accident.

- Draw sketches and take measurements with a view to producing a scale drawing of the events leading up to the accident.

- List the names of all witnesses, i.e. those who saw, heard, felt or smelt anything; interviewing them thoroughly, if necessary in the presence of a third party, and take full statements. In certain cases, it may be necessary to formally caution witnesses, prior to making a statement. Do not prompt or lead witnesses.

- Evaluate the facts, and individual witnesses' versions of them, as to accuracy, reliability and relevance.

- Endeavour on the basis of relevant facts to arrive at conclusions as to the causes of the accident.

- Examine closely any contradictory evidence. Every accident occurs within the context of a work system. Consider the people involved in terms of their ages, training, experience and level of supervision, and the nature of the work, e.g. routine, sporadic or incidental.

- In certain cases it may be necessary for plant and equipment, such as lifting appliances, machinery and vehicles to be examined by a specialist, e.g. a consultant engineer.

- Produce a report for the responsible manager emphasising the causes and remedies to prevent a recurrence, including any changes necessary.

- In complex and serious cases, consider the establishment of an investigating committee comprising managers, supervisors, technical specialists and trade union safety representatives.

The Outcome of Accident Investigation

Whether the investigation of an accident is undertaken by an individual, e.g. health and safety specialist, or by a special committee, it is necessary, once the causes have been identified, to submit recommendations to management with a view to preventing a recurrence. The organisation of feedback on the causes of accidents is important in large organisations, especially those that operate more than one site or premises. An effective investigation should result in one or more of the following recommendations being made:

- The issue of specific instructions by management covering, for instance, systems of work, the need for more effective guarding of machinery or safe manual handling procedures.

- The establishment of a working party or committee to undertake further investigation, perhaps in conjunction with members of the safety committee and/or representatives.

- The presentation and issue of specific codes of practice or guidance notes dealing with the procedures necessary to minimise a particular risk, e.g. the use of a permit-to-work system.

- The identification of specific training needs for groups of individuals, e.g. managers, foremen, supervisors, machinery operators, drivers, and the implementation of a training programme designed to meet these needs.

- The formal analysis of the job or system in question, perhaps using job safety analysis techniques, to identify skill, knowledge and safety components on the job.

- Identification of the need for further information relating to articles and substances used at work, e.g. work equipment, chemical substances.

- Identification of the need for better environmental control, e.g. noise reduction at source or improved lighting.

- General employee involvement in health and safety issues, e.g. the establishment of a health and safety committee.

- Identification of the specific responsibilities of groups with regard to safe working practices.

An effective system of monitoring should be implemented to ensure that the lessons that have been learned from the accident are put into practice or incorporated in future systems of work, and that procedures and operating systems have been produced for all grades of staff.

THE COST OF ACCIDENTS AT WORK

Accident costs can be direct or indirect in nature.

The Direct Costs

Direct costs, sometimes referred to as "insured costs", are largely concerned with an organisation's liabilities as an employer and occupier of premises. Direct costs are covered by premiums paid to an insurance company to provide cover against claims made by an injured party. Premiums paid are determined, to some extent, by the claims history of the organisation and the risks involved in the business activities.

Other direct costs of accidents are claims by insured persons and users of products manufactured by the company, which are settled either in or out of a court, together with fines imposed by the courts for breaches of health and safety legislation. Substantial legal defence costs may also be incorporated in this category.

The Indirect Costs

These are many and varied and are often difficult to predict. Some indirect costs may be included, and thus hidden, in other costs, e.g. labour costs, production and administration costs. It is common for indirect costs to be ignored, owing to the difficulty experienced in separating them from other costs. Some indirect costs, however, are simple to quantify. These are as follows:

- **Treatment costs**: First aid, transport to hospital, hospital charges, other costs, e.g. local doctors, consultants.

- **Lost time costs**: Lost time of injured person, supervisor, first aider and others involved.

- **Production costs**: Lost production, extra staff payments to meet production targets, damage to plant, vehicles, raw materials and finished products.

- **Training and supervision costs**: Training for replacement and existing labour force, extra supervision costs.

- **Investigation costs**: A number of people may be involved in the investigation of an accident or incident — management, safety representatives, safety adviser, etc. Investigation costs should be based on the total hours involved by all concerned.

- **Miscellaneous costs**: *Ex gratia* payments, perhaps to a widow/widower, replacement costs of personal items belonging to the injured person, incidental costs incurred by witnesses, etc.

- **Costs to the country**: These are difficult to quantify but can be enormous if surgery and a prolonged stay in hospital results from the accident.

- **Costs to the injured person**: Loss of earnings, loss of total earning capacity, legal costs in pursuing injury claims, possible legal costs in defending a prosecution for "unsafe behaviour" at work.

CHAPTER ROUND-UP

* The safety audit seeks to examine the total organisation from a health and safety perspective in order to identify whether it is meeting its safety aims and objectives. It examines structures, safety planning processes, decision-making delegation of responsibilities, safety policy making and implementation. Safety audits involve a detailed examination of all aspects of safety and, therefore, can take a considerable amount of time and resources to complete.

* Safety reviews normally examine any one part of the audit process and are concerned with making judgements about the adequacy of performance and taking decisions about the nature and timing of actions necessary to remedy deficiencies in health and safety. Safety reviews contribute to the development of health and safety policy and help secure the maintenance and development of effective safety organisation and culture.

* The safety auditing process generally emphasises four key areas: safety policies, procedures, practices and programmes. These must form the basis of an effective audit. Safety audits ultimately list an organisation's performance in terms of accident reduction, and of keeping risk at a minimum.

* An essential component of the safety auditing process is the analysis of accident, incident and frequency rates. This data can provide a means of measuring safety performance over a period of time and allow the organisation to benchmark its performance with externally published data. Five measures can be effectively used: incident rate, frequency rate, severity rate, mean duration rate and duration rate. Statistics are not without their limitations in that they measure failure rather than success, they can be subject to random fluctuations and they do not measure the incidence of occupational disease where there is a prolonged latent period.

* The investigation of the direct and indirect causes of accidents is a reactive strategy in safety management. The accident investigation procedure should establish the facts as quickly as possible and in sufficient detail to enable corrective action.

Chapter 16

SPECIAL ISSUES IN HEALTH AND SAFETY MANAGEMENT

INTRODUCTION

This chapter considers a number of specific elements of safety management. These issues are supported by legislative provisions and require specialist procedures to implement them in organisations. The chapter focuses on six important issues:

- The management of the workplace and work equipment.

- The management of fire.

- Manual handling policies, systems and procedures.

- Mechanical handling.

- The handling of dangerous substances.

- Electrical safety.

THE WORKPLACE AND WORK EQUIPMENT

This section briefly examines the issues involved in ensuring the safety of workplace equipment. The important considerations when carrying out housekeeping audits are considered first, followed by an overview of the methods used to safeguard machinery and tools.

Housekeeping Audits

The term "housekeeping" in the health and safety context refers to everyday procedures designed to keep work areas clean and free from danger. Although many housekeeping duties appear unimportant, and are often forgotten, they play an important role in maintaining a safe system of work. Poor housekeeping can have catastrophic effects, and pose unnecessary danger such as the build-up of flammable dusts and rubbish. More frequently, in organisations that ignore housekeeping, this oversight can result in simple accidents, such as trips and falls, that could easily have been avoided.

To ensure that housekeeping is not forgotten, it must become part of every employee's daily work routine. Employees should be responsible for cleaning their own workstation at the end of their shifts, and for keeping their work area tidy during work. In addition, procedures should be in place to clean up other areas, e.g. passages, floors, exits, etc. No items should be incorrectly stored on the floor, and spills should be mopped up immediately. To avoid fire risk, all bins should be emptied frequently and care must be taken with smokers' materials. Specialist consideration must be given to the need to maintain fixtures and fittings, which preserve the ergonomic climate of the work area, such as lighting and temperature systems. **Table 16.1** presents an example of a housekeeping rating form.

Table 16.1: Housekeeping Rating Form

Area _____ Date Inspected _____ Inspector _____

Instructions: Circle the appropriate score under the Item Rating opposite the item being evaluated. Add ratings for your total score.

Definition	Item Ratings						
	No Credit	Very Poor	Poor	Fair	Good	Exc.	Score
A place is in order when there are no unnecessary things about and when all necessary things are in their proper places.							
Machinery and Equipment							
A. Must be clean and free of unnecessary material or hangings.	0	.5	1	1.5	2	3	
B. Must be free of unnecessary dripping of oil or grease.	0	1	2	3	4	5	
C. Must have proper guards provided and be in good condition.	0	1.5	2.5	3.5	5	7	
Stocks and Material							
A. Must be properly piled and arranged.	0	1.5	3	4.5	6	8	
B. Must be loaded safely and in an orderly fashion in pans, cars and trucks.	0	1.5	1.5	3.5	5	7	

Tools						
A. Must be properly stored.	0	1	2	3	4.5	6
B. Must be free of oil and grease when stored.	0	.5	1	1.5	2	3
C. Must be in safe working condition.	0	1	2	3	4.5	6
Aisles						
A. Must be provided for work positions, fire extinguishers, fire blankets and stretcher cases.	0	1	2	3	4.5	6
B. Must be safe and free of obstructions.	0	1	2	3	4.5	6
C. Must be clearly marked.	0	.5	1	1.5	2	3
Floors						
A. Must have surfaces safe and suitable for work.	0	1	2	3	4.5	6
B. Must be clean, dry and free of refuse, unnecessary material, oil and grease.	0	1	2	3	4.5	6
C. Must have an adequate number of receptacles for refuse.	0	5	1	1.5	2	3
Buildings/Facilities						
A. Must have walls and windows that are reasonably clean for operations in that area and free of unnecessary hangings.	0	.5	1	1.5	2	3
B. Must have lighting systems that are maintained in a clean and efficient manner.	0	.5	1	1.5	2	3
C. Must have stairs that are clean, free of materials, well-lit, provided with adequate hand rails and treads in good condition.	0	1	2	3	4	5
D. Must have platforms that are clean, free of unnecessary materials and well-lit.	0	.5	1	2	3	4
Grounds						
A. Must be in good order, free of refuse and unnecessary materials.	0	2	4	6	8	10

Work Equipment, Machinery and Hand Tools

A machine is a device consisting of fixed and moving parts, which applies power to carry out a particular task or set of tasks. The parts of a machine can be classified as operational and non-operational. Operational parts carry out the desired functions of the machine, e.g. the drill bit in a drill or the blade in a saw.

Non-operational parts carry either motion or power to the operational parts, and are often subdivided into parts, which form the prime mover, and those that form the transmission mechanism. The prime mover provides mechanical energy, e.g. a motor, and the transmission transfers motion to the operational parts, e.g. gears.

Machinery and hand tools pose the following safety hazards:

- Individuals may come into contact with the equipment, or become trapped between the equipment and another surface, resulting in burns, lacerations or crush injuries.

- Individuals may be struck by or become entangled in the motion of the equipment, with limbs, clothing and hair being at the greatest risk.

- Individuals may be struck by parts ejected from equipment, such as pieces of metal from broken machine parts.

- Individuals may be struck by material ejected by the equipment, such as chips of the material being processed.

Particular dangers are posed by the unexpected start-up or movement of a machine, mechanical failure, spillages or slippery floor surfaces near the machine, and operators reaching into the machine to feed in materials or to remove trapped objects. Examples of machines that are commonly involved in accidents include drills, grinders, power presses, milling machines, guillotines, lathes, saws and printing presses.

Hand Tools

The misuse or poor maintenance of hand tools can result in serious injuries such as blinding, amputations of fingers, or deep cuts that could sever arteries. Regular inspections and maintenance must be carried out, to ensure that handles and heads are secure, that chips, cracks and other signs of metal fatigue are not present, and that tools are free of oil, dirt and grease. Similarly, care must be taken to store hand tools properly, both to preserve them and to avoid trips and falls.

FIRE SYSTEMS AND FIRE PROCEDURES

The installation of effective fire safety systems and procedures is a fundamental part of managing the risks faced by a business. A failure to do so not only poses a danger to human life, but may also prove financially disastrous for a company, due to the risk of property damage and the threat of extensive legal costs. This section outlines the essential elements required to carry out effective fire safety management, and includes an overview of fire regulations applicable in Ireland. As the potential risk of fire and the extent of its damage are dependent upon a large number of variables, it is impossible to draw up an ideal fire safety management system to suit all premises. However, it is possible to highlight the important principles of fire safety that are relevant to most situations, and therefore, this section is sub-divided into an examination of the nature of fire, fire prevention mechanisms, and fire protection.

The Effects of Fire on the Building

Apart from cosmetic and aesthetic damage, which are themselves important losses for any hotel, the principal damage from fire to such a building is structural. This is due to heat, which causes expansion, deformation, melting, cracking and structural failure, rendering the building no longer able to perform its function. The thermal expansions and consequent strains on the building structure change the stresses at all joints and corners and, since common building materials are not normally elastic at the temperature reached in fires, they may become permanently deformed and so weakened that demolition and reconstruction is necessary.

The Building in the Fire

It is well known in fire engineering that a small, low-intensity fire can become a high-intensity inferno in minutes, if not seconds. The design and decoration of a building affects the fire in such a way as to cause what is known as a flashover, a phenomenon that has been at the heart of numerous high-publicity fire disasters (Rasbash, 1991; Thomas et al., 1980). Flashover occurs when the heat and products of combustion from a fire are trapped within the vicinity of the fire by the surrounding walls and surfaces, and the hot smoke and room boundaries radiate heat back to the fire, thereby enhancing fire development. When the various surfaces within the enclosed space reach about 600°C, they spontaneously burst into flame. Even if a flashover does not occur, there is still a degree of fire enhancement and the fire becomes worse than if it were outdoors, where the heat and smoke is able to escape. The importance of flashover for the building manager is that the achievement of a maximum burning rate occurs so quickly that guests and staff are entirely unprepared for the speed of fire spread, and in the time taken to compose oneself before jumping to safety, a person can be engulfed in flames.

Appropriate interior design and decoration of buildings are therefore crucial in that their potential for impacting on the fire can be significant. The physiological effects of fire on people can be distinguished as those due to heat and those due to smoke.

Heat Effects

Human beings operate within a few degrees of 37° C/98° F. To cope with temperature excesses of a few degrees, the body can lose heat by evaporation of hot breath and sweat, and also by expanding blood capillaries near the skin to divert hot blood flow from major organs to the surface. Higher temperatures increase the possibilities of heat exhaustion (loss of water and salt) and heat stroke where the body cannot adequately control its temperature. Extreme heat causes damage to tissues as burns and scalds (wet burns). Such damage is characterised by percentage area and depth (superficial, intermediate or deep). Deep severe burns involve destruction of nerves or numbness, and may result in cracked, melted and possibly charred skin.

Smoke will affect the senses and (chemically) the physiology. Chemically, smoke contains irritants, toxins, carcinogens and little oxygen. Lack of oxygen causes asphyxia and rapid unconsciousness/death. Carbon monoxide is a toxin that replaces oxygen in the blood and thus causes loss of consciousness and asphyxia. Other toxins can collect around vital organs and interfere with their function. Since they are very difficult to expel, such toxins may stay with victims for years. Some substances actively react with the body and can irritate or worse. Carcinogens destroy cells (cancer causing) and although not an immediate concern, they are present in most fires and are significant to long-term health.

Accumulation of smoke in a building reduces visibility and can render obstacles along an escape route, or even the fire itself, invisible. Additionally, because of its buoyant nature, hot smoke can rapidly spread upwards, reducing visibility even further, and given the height of hotels and the use of atria in many modern premises, the problems of swiftly channelled smoke towards the top floors must be understood. The sight of smoke thickening in the top of an atrium or in the corridors or stairwells can be very disconcerting to guests, confusing and disorientating them and, unless clear guidance and instructions are given, death and injury may result.

There is little agreement as to the long-term combined effects of the mixtures of substances found in smoke. These will vary for every person but a general classification of the percentage of victims, with a given level of injury for given exposure is often thought to follow a vulnerability curve.

Individual Response of People to Fire

In simplest terms, the response of someone to a fire can be characterised by the time required to act. The evacuation time for someone in a hotel on fire is the time taken from the first detection of the fire to the time taken for the last guest/staff member to reach a place of safety, and may be divided into three parts:

- The **delay** time that occurs between the occurrence of the first flames and the time the person becomes aware of the fire because of smell of smoke, sounding of an alarm, etc.

- The **pre-movement** time between the guest hearing the alarm and beginning to leave the building. During this stage, the guest may investigate, warn others, collect belongings, etc.

- The **minimum** time to physically move to an exit.

There will also be a time after fire ignition, when conditions along the possible escape route become untenable. The evacuation time of hotel patrons must be less than this, if they are to survive. Chow and Kong (1993) studied the environment in a hotel during a fire and concluded that a time may be predicted. The fire resistance of the building (the time for which it must continue to function structurally) must be sufficiently long to allow safe egress of guests and staff, and safe access and operation of fire fighters. An hour or half-hour is a common order of magnitude for fire resistance, compared to minutes for the evacuation of people.

The time required from the beginning of a fire to the sounding of an alarm and for ceiling-mounted sprinkler activation is reported in Alpert (1972) and, for modern systems, will be in the order of seconds. However, if the alarms and detectors are absent or malfunctioning, the only warning is likely to be an encounter with the fire, its products or other guests/staff. Such undesirable occurrences must of course be avoided and it is therefore a responsibility of management to ensure that a robust and effective warning system is operational at all times.

It is now commonly accepted that pre-movement time between the first sounding of an alarm and the beginning of evacuation may be the largest single component of the total evacuation time.

Feinberg and Johnson (1999) discovered that a differential rate of dying was not found between patrons and employees in a night club fire, contradicting the argument that those familiar with the fire environment would know their evacuation route and not be forced into split-second choices resulting in panic. Similarly, Canter (1999) reported that, in the Woolworth's fire in 1979, it was observed that people remained in the restaurant area to finish their cups of tea despite the obvious fire raging within the building. People do not die in fire because of panic, but because of lack of panic, and cites the example of two customers walking into a shop, selecting goods, and queuing up at the counter to pay when the centre floor shelving was clearly ablaze after vandals had attempted to cause a diversion by setting fire to the fixtures in order to commit theft.

The pre-movement time will depend on such factors as perceived danger and alertness in relation to the fire. Given this, it is the responsibility of hotel managers to appreciate that, as Canter (1999) has argued, people have their own scripts, are locked into their agendas and routines, and will require firm appropriate instructions by an accepted authority figure in the event of a fire. The implications for hotel staff training are substantial in this respect.

Psychologically, physiologically and physically, people will perform differently in the event of fire, and become more or less vulnerable as a result. Vulnerability can be interpreted in this context as the inability to respond effectively and, in examining the evacuation performance of mixed ability populations, Rubadiri et al. (1997) introduced an evacuation performance index (EPI) that allows for individual disabilities in calculating the movement times. Since it includes considerations such as obstacles along the route and any advantages such as slopes for disabled access, the EPI is a potentially useful tool for all those involved in the design and/or management of fire safety.

Fire Hazards

The majority of fire hazards can be grouped into one of two categories: ignition sources and fuel sources. Common examples of both are listed in **Table 16.2**.

In practice, probably the most effective way of identifying the hazards is to obtain a plan of the premises (or to draw up a basic plan, if one is not already available) so that each area can then be visited in turn. Any hazards identified, along with any defects identified in the fire controls present (or the absence of necessary fire controls), should be noted. Outdoor areas and roof spaces, as well as rooms, should be considered and a note should be made of the work activities that take place in each of the areas visited.

Fire Prevention

Fire prevention measures are aimed at minimising the risk of fire outbreak. Many fires are caused by carelessness in facility design, everyday operations, or by malicious intent. Effective management can help prevent this, by considering fire risks when designing facilities and security systems, and by creating a fire safety culture among employees through training and motivation.

Table 16.2: Fire Hazards

Ignition Sources	Fuel Sources
• Matches and cigarettes. • Electrical installation or equipment. • Heating appliances, for example stoves, boilers, portable heaters. • Flame or sparks from work activities such as welding, cutting and soldering. • Machinery, for example as a result of overheating, hot surfaces, inadequate maintenance or production of sparks. • Contractors' operations (contractors may not possess the same degree of fire safety awareness as company employees). • Cooking equipment, usually as a result of inattention. • Ignition sources introduced during maintenance operations or refurbishment of the premises. • Arson (deliberate ignition).	• Large quantities of combustible materials such as paper, plastic, rubber, cardboard and various packaging materials. • Highly flammable gases, for example, cylinders of liquefied petroleum gas. • Carpets, curtains and furniture. • Flammable liquids, for example paints, thinners, solvents, adhesives, petroleum based products. • Dust. • The structure of the rooms or corridors, for example flammable surface finishes (such as certain paints, or synthetic coverings like polystyrene tiles), surfaces that are smoke-producing, and areas where the internal construction is comprised largely of flammable materials such as hardboard, chipboard, plywood and plastics. • Any fuel sources introduced during maintenance operations or refurbishment of the premises.
Oxygen can be a hazard when it is present in the air at levels higher than normal. Also, some "oxidising" chemicals can provide oxygen in a fire situation that can increase the ferocity of the fire.	

Educating employees in fire safety issues helps to convey an understanding of the risks involved and can be a powerful motivator in developing a fire safety culture. It also aids the training of employees to act and react appropriately in the event of fire. All employees need to receive some form of fire safety training as part of their induction programme, as any member of staff may cause, or be the first to discover, a fire. In addition to this, particular attention should be given to the more detailed training needs of supervisors, those working with hazardous substances and those with special responsibilities such as fire wardens or members of an occupational fire brigade. Vigilance by staff at all times is possibly the most effective means of reducing the risk of fire in any business.

Apart from the human element of fire prevention, there are many practical steps to be taken to prevent the outbreak of fire. Machinery and industrial processes should "design out" ignition risks and provision should be made for the proper handling and containment of volatile substances. A classic example in Ireland of a failure to do this was the cause of the accident at the Hickson PharmaChem Ltd at Ringaskiddy, Co. Cork, in August 1993. A major accident involving a series of explosions and a subsequent large-scale fire resulted from the poor design of a chemical reactor, which became incapable of controlling the industrial process that it was carrying out. The company was later prosecuted by the Health and Safety Authority for breach of European Communities legislation and was convicted and fined.

Other fire prevention methods include the installation of appropriate security systems, such as intruder alarms, security patrols, lighting, controlled access, etc., all of which reduce the threat of arson. Ensuring that electrical systems are fitted, checked and maintained to standard diminishes the problem of electrical faults, a common cause of fires. Placing restrictions on smoking in dangerous areas and providing adequate smoking rooms and ashtrays helps to remove another frequent cause of fire. Finally, choosing fire-resistant materials for furnishings and fittings, together with good housekeeping, goes a long way to lowering the danger of fire outbreak. **Table 16.3** presents a range of fire prevention methods.

Table 16.3: Fire Prevention Methods

Fire hazard	Prevention methods
1. Ignition Sources	
Matches and cigarettes	• Prohibit smoking in areas used infrequently, areas where large amounts of combustible materials are stored or where flammable liquids or gases, etc., are present. Clearly mark such areas with appropriate signs. • If safe smoking areas are available, provide clearly visible signs in the areas to state, for example, "do not put cigarettes out in bins – extinguish cigarettes before leaving the area". Provide suitable ashtrays.
Electrical installation or equipment	• Ensure fixed electrical installation complies with the latest edition of the IEE Wiring Regulations. • Ensure all electrical installation and maintenance work is carried out by competent electricians. • Ensure that electrical fuses are of the correct rating (and consider provision of protective devices such as RCDs). • Implement an appropriate maintenance schedule for portable electrical equipment. • Avoid the use of multi-point adapters. • Instruct staff in the safe use of portable electrical equipment, how to spot defects and where defects should be reported.
Heating appliances (stoves, boilers, portable heaters, etc.)	• Use fixed heating installation rather than portable equipment, where possible. • If portable heaters are provided, ensure they stand on a non-combustible surface and are properly guarded. • Keep combustible materials at a safe distance. • Ensure appliances are installed by a competent person(s) and properly maintained.
Flames and sparks from work processes such as welding and cutting	• Replace or alter work processes to one with a reduced potential for ignition, where possible. • Implement a "hot work" permit-to-work system. • Keep combustible materials at a safe distance.
Machinery	• Ensure good air-circulation around machines. • Keep combustible materials at a safe distance. • Provide adequate maintenance.

Fire hazard	Prevention methods
Contractors' operations	• Ensure that fire safety operations form a part of the contract. • Ensure contractors receive all necessary fire safety information. • Where necessary, draw up procedures to cover such matters as smoking, security, temporary electrical installations and hazardous processes, for example, cutting, welding, flammable substances or combustible materials, etc.
Cooking equipment	• Ensure grease filters and flues are regularly cleaned and kept in a good state of repair. • Exercise care in using deep-fat fryers, frying pans etc. Appropriate instruction and training should be provided for staff.
2. Fuel Sources	
• Large quantities of combustible materials • Highly flammable gases • Carpets, curtains, furniture • Flammable liquids • Dust	• Room structure, for example room structures comprised of flammable materials or with flammable surface finishes • Replace flammable substances and materials with less flammable alternatives where practical, for example, substitution of a flammable solvent with a water-based alternative. • Reduce the stock of such materials, where possible. • Provide suitable storage areas. Build fire-resistant stores or enclosures away from ignition sources for particularly hazardous substances, such as flammable liquids or plastic foams. • Remove or treat flammable surface finishes to slow the rate of flame spread across surface.
3. Oxygen	The risks presented by oxygen can be reduced by ensuring that leaks from oxygen sources (e.g., oxygen cylinders) are prevented, and that such sources are located in well-ventilated areas. Suitable storage and maintenance are required, along with adequate training for employees involved in using such equipment. Suitable storage conditions are also required for oxidising chemicals, for example, away from flammable materials and ignition sources.

Fire hazard	Prevention methods
4. Arson	• Good security, for example: ◊ Controlled access to the premises and to areas of high fire risk (such as storage areas and unmanned areas), particularly at night. ◊ Perimeter fencing, security patrols, external lighting (for use at night), intruder alarms, surveillance cameras.Encouragement of staff to report anything suspicious. ◊ Vetting of staff during recruitment or selection. • Good housekeeping, so that access to waste and other fuel sources is denied to the potential arsonist. Secure (possibly locked) storage may be required. Waste stored outside should be kept away from the main building. • Provision of sprinklers and fire detection systems.

Fire Protection

As no fire safety management system can totally eliminate the risk of fire, steps need to be taken to cope in the event of an outbreak. Fire protection mechanisms are those that prevent damage to persons or property during a fire, and include the following:

• Fire containment mechanisms.

• Fire detection and extinguishing mechanisms.

• Smoke control mechanisms.

• Adequate means of escape.

• Planned procedures in the event of a fire.

As fire spreads through conduction, convection and radiation, the key to preventing fire growth lies in inhibiting heat transfer through good building design and construction, using heat-resistant materials. Compartmentalisation of buildings by using fire-resistant walls and floors is an excellent method, especially if used in conjunction with fire-resistant lining materials. Active fire detection and extinguishing mechanisms such as cooling sprinkler systems and portable extinguishers can also be employed.

In addition to heat, fire often produces many potentially harmful by-products such as smoke and toxic gases (an example being hydrogen cyanide from burning wool and silk). Once again, good building design plays an essential role in preventing damage, along with appropriate smoke detection and ventilation systems to warn occupants and reduce the risk of inhalation.

Safe routes must be provided for persons to exit a building from any point within it, to a pre-arranged place of safety, without any form of outside assistance. These routes must be chosen at the design stage of a facility, and should preferably leave individuals with a choice of routes to prevent their escape from becoming cut off. The routes should be clearly signposted with explicit exit signs, well-lit, well-ventilated, and protected with fire-resistant materials. Exit doors should open easily in the direction of escape, and automatically fasten after escape to prevent fanning the fire.

The dangers posed by the outbreak of a fire will depend on a number of local factors, including the extent of the fire, and the likelihood of further spread to neighbouring areas. The appropriate course of action to be taken will rest on these circumstances, but it is vital to draw up a procedure that can be adapted to cope with such an event. The procedure should contain instructions to be given to every employee on how to react during the fire, and should revolve around three areas:

- Raising the alarm and notifying the fire authorities.

- The immediate fire attack.

- The safe evacuation of the premises.

Raising the Alarm

Often the most effective way of ensuring the proper notification of both occupants of the premises and the fire authorities that a fire has occurred is to bring into operation a control centre. Upon discovery of a fire, the control centre can be alerted, and depending on the severity of the outbreak, a subsequent signal can be given to occupants to stand by or evacuate the premises. This should be done in conjunction with the summoning of the occupational and/or public fire brigades. Usually the most appropriate location for such a control centre is the telephone switchboard. Provision should also be made to have persons instruct the public fire brigade on vital information such as approach entrances, the location of hydrants, and any volatile substances that may be under threat from the fire.

Attacking the Fire

Provided that there is no significant personal danger, a fire should be attacked immediately upon discovery. Naturally, all fires should be reported, but circumstances will dictate the priority of raising the alarm over attempting to extinguish the fire. Often, if more than one person discovers the fire, these two steps can be taken simultaneously. Those not involved in fighting the fire should evacuate the area so as not to create confusion or put themselves at risk. The aspect of vital importance in attempting to extinguish a fire is to use the correct apparatus and method for doing so. The standard classification of fires is presented in **Figure 16.1**.

Figure 16.1: Standard Classification of Fires

- **Class A** — fires involving solids, such as wood, fabrics, paper.
- **Class B** — fires involving liquids, liquifiable solids, and electrical fires.
- **Class C** — fires involving gases.
- **Class D** — fires involving metals.

The evacuation of the premises can be safely carried out only if a well-designed plan is in place, and each occupant has received instructions and is therefore familiar with escape procedures and routes. Responsibility for co-ordinating the evacuation, carrying out roll calls and searching the building for unaccounted-for persons should be given to appropriate supervisors, and their roles clearly understood by all. Periodic fire drills are a must to iron out any potential difficulties, and to ensure that all employees are familiar with the procedure.

Table 16.4 presents some guidelines on fire alarms and fire detectors.

Table 16.4: Guidelines on Fire Alarms and Fire Detectors

Fire Detectors

The purpose of fire detection equipment is to ensure that a building's occupants are given an early warning in the event of a fire.

The main types of fire detectors are:

- Smoke detectors:
  - ◊ Ionisation and optical types exist.
  - ◊ Only suitable for buildings with relatively clean atmospheres.
  - ◊ Sensitive, give a fast response and hence early warning.
  - ◊ Particularly useful in protecting relatively small areas containing electrical equipment.
  - ◊ False alarms can be a problem.
- Heat detectors:
  - ◊ Generally give a slower response than smoke detectors.
  - ◊ Suitable for most buildings, and may be used where dirty atmospheres preclude the use of smoke detectors.
  - ◊ Also useful where a fire is likely to result in large heat output rather than smoke production, for example with flammable liquids.
- Flame detectors:
  - ◊ Infra-red and ultra-violet types exist.
  - ◊ Often used to back up heat or smoke detectors in tall compartments.
  - ◊ Most effective in situations where a fire is likely to result in quick production of flames.

Once activated, the fire detector will either initiate an alarm or a combined alarm and extinguisher system, such as sprinklers.

Fire alarms

Fire alarms may be activated automatically (by detectors) or manually (for example, by breaking glass, pressing a button, using a public address system, etc). The following information is relevant to the use of alarms generally:

- The sound level of an alarm signal should be not less than 65 dB(A), (or 5 dB(A) above any background noise where this is louder). The signal should be clearly audible in all parts of the workplace.
- Call points should be positioned on escape routes, 1.4m above floor level; the maximum distance a person must travel to reach a call point should not exceed 30m.

- "Staged" alarm systems may be used, in order to evacuate areas of highest risk first. An "evacuation" signal is sounded in the area affected by the fire, and an "alert" signal is sounded elsewhere. Fire authority approval should be obtained before installing such a system.

- It may be appropriate to use a public address system rather than sounders, for example where a phased evacuation is required and in buildings where large numbers of members of the public are present such as night-clubs and cinemas.

- Ideally, the alarm system should be such that a signal is transmitted to a remote manned centre (usually the alarm company's central station) so that the fire brigade can be alerted.

MANUAL HANDLING ISSUES

The statistical evidence available on accidents in Ireland demonstrates that manual handling is responsible for approximately 30 per cent of injuries. Such injuries are extremely costly to employers, not just in terms of man-hours lost or compensation demands, but often also in increased employers' liability insurance premiums.

The Legal Considerations

The most important legal considerations for employers to bear in mind regarding manual handling are set out in the Safety, Health and Welfare at Work Act, 1989 and the Safety Health and Welfare at Work Regulations, 1993 and 2001. The former places a duty on an employer to ensure a safe system of work, including a duty to provide information, instruction, training and supervision. It is important for employers to keep written records when carrying out these duties, as such evidence to show that an employee has received appropriate training, etc. on manual handling is an important defence for an employer, should the case go to court. The latter Regulations put into force the EC Directive on Minimum Health and Safety requirements for the handling of loads (1990), and can be broken down into four major areas: steps to be taken to avoid manual handling; the risk-reduction rule; ergonomics and load characteristics; and information to employees.

Employers are required to take organisational measures to avoid the need for manual handling, or attempt to provide alternative means such as mechanical equipment. If manual handling is unavoidable, then the employer must take steps to reduce the risk of injury to employees. Methods to do this include:

- Taking account of the ergonomics and load characteristics of items that employees are expected to carry.

- Providing proper training about safe handling techniques.

- Providing information about the risk involved along with essential information about the loads to be carried.

Typical medical problems associated with poor manual handling can be divided into internal and external injuries. By and large, external injuries tend to be less serious, consisting mainly of cuts, bruises, lacerations and crush injuries. Internal injuries include muscle and ligament tears, hernias, damage to knee, ankle, elbow and shoulder joints and, most commonly, slipped discs or other back injuries.

Movement: The Structure and Function of the Body

The human body is the product of millions of years of evolution but has changed little. Children born today are the same, and have the same physical attributes, as their prehistoric ancestors. Man is the same but has created a new world with a different environment and living conditions from his ancestors. While the changes have been to man's benefit, they have created problems. The body is structured to be down on all fours with the two front limbs providing support for the upper trunk. Man has never really adapted to being upright. The failure of a muscle stretching from the front of the lower spine to the front of the thigh (the ileo psoas muscle) to elongate properly to its full length would seem to have resulted in a lower back curve which is more pronounced in western society. The low back curve in people of primitive tribes such as the Aborigines is less marked than that of Europeans and they do not seem to suffer from back pain extensively. Primitive people are also extremely mobile and flexible because of their lifestyle. They also carry weight upon the head and have distinctively graceful carriage.

The skeleton of a human being shows that the bones of the lower limbs are strong and long. They give attachment to the strongest muscles and have few joints. The spinal column has many bones (or vertebrae) separated by discs that allow movement. Strong strap-like structures called ligaments link the bones together.

Two sections of the spinal column are free of side protection — the neck, or cervical spine, and the lower back, or lumbar spine. These two segments are most vulnerable to damage. They each curve backwards. The lumbar spine supports the weight of the head and trunk above it as well as any weight that is carried in the arms.

When we stand erect, our spine is not straight. It is "S" shaped. The back is strongest and most comfortable, when that curve is minimised. The spine is very strong and, when properly loaded, it will hold weight of up to one tonne. This is far in excess of anyone would be required to lift in any work situation. What is important, however, is the interpretation and understanding of correct loading posture. The position of the disc (material which separates the vertebrae) is the key issue. A straight back is one in which the disc surfaces are parallel, i.e., the disc is not compressed into a wedge shape. We instinctively shift into this position when we put one foot up on a step. This has the effect of relieving compression force on the lumbar facet joints (small joints on either side of the spine). In this position, all the weight is transmitted through the spinal discs, which are structured to withstand compression. Recent research indicates that when pressure is applied evenly and directly, the lumbar discs withstand up to one tonne of pressure before rupturing.

A prolapsed or "slipped" disc happens when a wedge disc is subjected to compression. The soft jelly-like centre of the disc bulges through the outer rim like a tomato that is squashed until the pulp breaks through the skin.

The spinal cord links the brain with the rest of the body and carries messages through a complicated nervous system. If the spinal cord, or its nerves, is damaged, pain results. The spinal cord runs down through the spine towards the back of the vertebrae.

Small joints on either side of the spine (the facet joints) direct movement but they are not structured to bear weight. If posture is poor, these joints are put into a weight-bearing position. Serious damage can occur if poor posture, or a poor work position, becomes a habit. Standing in an upright position puts weight on these joints and is not recommended as a work practice. A high stool or footrest would allow an employee opportunity to change position frequently.

The Safety, Health and Welfare at Work (General Application) Regulations, 1993 include a section that deals specifically with manual handling. It places a duty on the employer to avoid manual handling where possible (by providing lifts, hoists, trolleys). Where manual handling is unavoidable, the employer must carry out a risk assessment and implement risk reduction, and employees must receive training in relation to the risks of manual handling and the correct procedure for manual handling.

The Role of Movement

We can consider the spine as being composed of three regions, which have different characteristics in relation to movements.

In the neck or cervical spine, the facet joint or the joints, which guide movement, are positioned at a 45-degree angle to the transverse plane. This allows a wide range of movement, i.e., forward bending, backward bending, side bending and rotation.

In the thoracic spine, or rib cage area, the facet orientation is a 60-degree angle to the transverse plane and a 20-degree angle to the frontal plane, allowing side bending, rotation and some forward and backward bending.

In the lumbar spine, the facets are at a 90-degree angle to the transverse plane and a 45-degree angle to the frontal plane. This allows forward and backward bending, and side bending, but minimal rotation. The lumbar spine cannot absorb twisting movement.

Corlett has formulated 25 principles of workplace design that he presents in descending order of importance. These are shown in **Figure 16.2**.

Figure 16.2: Corlett's Principles of Workplace Design

1. The worker should be able to maintain an upright and forward posture during work.

2. Where vision is a requirement of the task, the necessary work points must be adequately visible with the head and trunk upright or with just the head inclined slightly forward.

3. All work activities should permit the worker to adopt several different, but equally safe, postures without reducing capability to do the work.

4. Work should be arranged, where possible, so that it may be done at the worker's choice in either a seated or standing position. When seated, the worker should be able to use the backrest of the chair at will, without necessitating a change of movement.

5. The weight of the body, when standing, should be carried equally on both feet and foot pedals designed accordingly.

6. Work should not be performed consistently at or above the level of the heart; even the occasional performance where force is exerted above heart level should be avoided. Where light handwork must be performed above heart level, rests for the upper arms are a requirement.

7. Work activities should be performed with the joints at about the mid-point of their range of movements. This applies particularly to the head, trunk and upper limbs.

8. Where muscular force has to be exerted, it should be by the largest appropriate muscle groups available and in a direction co-linear with the limbs concerned.

9. Where force has to be exerted repeatedly, it should be possible to exert it with either of the arms, or either of the legs, without adjustment to the equipment.

10. Momentum should be employed to assist the worker wherever possible, and it should be reduced to a minimum if it must be overcome by muscular effort.

11. Continuous curved motions are preferable to straight-line motions involving sudden and sharp changes in direction.

12. Ballistic movements are faster, easier and more accurate than restricted or "controlled" movements.

13. Both hands should preferably begin their micro motions simultaneously and finish at the same instant.

14. Both hands should not be idle at the same instant, except during rest periods.

15. Motion of arms should be in opposite and symmetrical directions, instead of in the same direction, and should be made simultaneously.

16. To reduce fatigue, motions should be confined to the lowest possible classification as listed below, the least tiring and most economical being shown first:

   ◊ finger motions.

   ◊ finger and wrist movements.

   ◊ finger, wrist and lower arm motions.

   ◊ finger, wrist, lower and upper arm motions.

   ◊ wrist, lower and upper arm and body motions.

17. Rest pauses should allow rest from all loads experienced at work, including environmental and information loads, and be proportional to the length of work period between successive rest periods.

18. Two or more tools should be combined wherever possible.

19. Gravity feed containers should be used to deliver the material as close to the point of assembly or use as possible. This delivery point should be near the height of the point of use, to eliminate any lighting or change in direction when carrying the parts.

20. Ejectors should be used to remove the finish part.

21. Use "drop delivery", whereby the operator may deliver the finished article, by releasing it in the position in which it was completed, without moving to dispose of it.

22. All materials and tools should be located within the "normal" reach work areas.

23. Consideration should always be given to the transfer of work from the hands to the feet, or other parts of the body.

24. Tools and materials should be so located as to permit a proper sequence of micro motions. The part required at the beginning of the cycle should be next to the point of release of the finished piece from the former cycle.

25. Sequence of motions should be arranged to build rhythm automatically into the operation.

Damaging Movement

A twisting movement with the spine upright is harmless. By contrast, a movement that combines forward bending and side bending of the trunk at the same time is damaging, and should not be confused with a twist. It can be difficult to grasp the difference, but a simple rule of thumb is to consider the direction in which the feet and shoulders are pointing while the trunk is in a forward position. If they are not pointing in the same direction, then the operative is in trouble. A force applied, e.g., a weight lifted in this position, can have serious consequences on the performance of the lumbar spine.

Combining forward and side bending allows force to be applied to the spine in a most vulnerable position, i.e., the greatest force is directed towards the weaker corner. If a job requires an employee to move in this fashion, it is incorrectly designed.

Safer Work Design for Movement

- Raising the work height decreases the forward bending of the trunk and reduces strain.

- Organising work to reduce or eliminate over-reaching allows the body to work in a better posture thus eliminating strain and fatigue.

- Since the upright and standing position is not one of choice for work, it is less damaging if a good posture can be maintained, with the different components of the spine balanced upon one another.

The spinal curves, as seen in the upright stances, are necessary for balance in free standing. Studies undertaken within the past ten years indicate that the spinal column should not be loaded in the upright or erect position.

In general terms, the full range of spinal movement extends from a forward stretch, e.g., lying on the floor with knees bent to chest and head on knees, to a backward stretch, e.g., kneeling on the floor with head thrust backward. Twisting movement happens in the thoracic spine and full range would allow the trunk to twist so that the shoulders come into parallel with the wall at right angles to a sitting position. Full range of body movement can easily be maintained and is crucial to physical health and safety at work.

The human body is designed for movement, with speed and precision being important factors. It is not the aim of safety legislation to eliminate movement or manual handling altogether. Instead, it seeks to assess and reduce the risk of injury and arrange work so that the safest movement is employed at all times.

It is very important to carry out a simple analysis of what movement is taking place in the trunk for any given task. A twisting movement involves the thoracic spine and cannot take place in the lower back. Yet it is often the case to incorrectly attribute an injury of the lower back to a twisting movement. Injury of the lower back most frequently results from what may appear to be a twisting movement, but is, in reality, a combination of two bending movements, each in a different direction. It is essential to learn to distinguish between the two. **Table 16.5** presents guidelines on appropriate manual handling operations.

Assessing Operations Involving Carrying

The guideline figures for assessing figures involving carrying are the same assuming the load is held against the body and carried no further than 10 metres without rest. The figures may need to be reduced where these criteria are not met. Where loads can be carried securely on the shoulder, without first being lifted, the guideline figures can be used in circumstances where loads are carried further than 10 metres.

Assessing Operations Involving Pushing and Pulling

The guideline figures for assessing operations involving pushing and pulling are:

- For starting and stopping the load: approximately 25Kg (around 250 Newtons) maximum force for men; approximately 16Kg (around 160 Newtons) maximum force for women.

- For keeping the load in motion; approximately 10Kg (around 100 Newtons) maximum force for men; approximately 7Kg (around 70 Newtons) maximum force for women.

If the force is not applied with the hands between knuckle and shoulder height, the figures may need to be reduced. A spring gauge is a useful tool for assessing the forces required to move a load.

Table 16.5: Guidelines for Lifting and Lowering

Lifting or lowering between:	Load held close to body (kg)	Load held away from body (kg)
Shoulder height/full height	10	5
Elbow / shoulder	20	10
Knuckle / elbow	25	15
Mid lower leg / knuckle	20	10
Below mid lower leg	10	5

Notes:

- The figures assume that the load is compact, stable and easy to grasp, and that there are no adverse working conditions.

- Where the hands pass through more than one height range, the smallest weight figure should be used.

- Twisting: this increases the risk and will normally mean the operation should be avoided or fully assessed. However, if the operation is carried out infrequently (approx <30 times per hour), the figures above can be used for a preliminary assessment, but should be reduced by 10% where the shoulders twist through 45 degrees in relation to the feet, and 20% where the twist is 90 degrees.

- Frequent lifting and lowering: The figures should be reduced where operations are carried out more frequently than 30 times per hour. As a guide, they should be reduced by:

  - 30% where the operation is repeated once or twice per minute
  - 50% where the operation is repeated around 5-8 times per minute
  - 80% where the operation is repeated more than 12 times per minute

Note: The guideline figures relate only to men. For women, all the figures should be reduced by approximately one-third.

Assessing Operations Involving Seated Handling

For assessing operations for seated handling, guideline figures of 5Kg (for men) and 3Kg (for women) apply, but only for lifting between lap and shoulder height while seated correctly. Where handling above or below this area is unavoidable, a more detailed assessment should be made.

A Policy on Manual Handling

It is generally recommended that an organisation should implement a manual handling policy. Newell (1992), suggests that such a policy should cover the following issues:

- **Policy statement:** This is an expression of the policy that the organisation will follow for manual handling activities. The chief executive must make it clear that this is an important area.

- **Manual handling standards:** A set of guidelines should be established covering the manual handling activities in the organisation. These standards should be written to give guidance to people regarding the method of performing the task in the safest way.

- **Purchasing controls:** This is a very important element in a management strategy since a major causal factor in manual handling injuries is the size, weight, shape and packaging of materials. Purchase of appropriate mechanical handling aids is also important.

- **Engineering controls:** Clearly it is better that manual handling jobs are designed out of the workplace, where possible, and there should be a commitment to this effect. Engineering staff may need training to achieve this objective.

- **Selection of personnel:** The policy should also cover the careful selection of personnel required to carry out manual handling and staff involved in recruitment should be aware of the physical requirements of the jobs involved.

- **Accident/incident investigation:** As with all accidents, it is critical that all accidents and incidents involving manual handling are fully investigated.

- **Training:** Training should be provided by a suitably qualified person and should match the requirements of the job.

Table 16.6 focuses on four issues in respect of manual handling and suggests that all four need to be considered in order to effectively reduce manual handling problems in the workplace. **Table 16.7** presents a summary of research findings on manual handling.

Table 16.6: Manual Handling: Risk Assessment

Problems to Look for When Making an Assessment	Ways of Reducing the Risk of Injury
The tasks: Do they involve: • Holding loads away from trunk? • Twisting, stooping or reaching upwards? • Large vertical movement? • Long carrying distances? • Strenuous pushing or pulling? • Unpredictable movement of loads? • Repetitive handling? • Insufficient rest or recovery from a process?	Can you: • Improve workplace layout to improve efficiency? • Reduce the amount of twisting and stooping? • Avoid lifting from floor level or above shoulder height? • Cut carrying distances? • Avoid repetitive handling? • Vary the work, allowing one set of muscles to rest while another is used?
The loads: Are they: • Heavy, bulky or unwieldy? • Difficult to grasp? • Unstable or unpredictable? • Intrinsically harmful e.g., sharp or hot?	Can you make them: • Lighter or less bulky? • Easier to grasp? • More stable? • Less damaging to hold: Have you asked suppliers to help?
The work environment: Are there: • Constraints on posture? • Poor floors? • Variations in levels? • Hot/cold/humid conditions? • Strong air movements? • Poor lighting conditions? • Restrictions on movement or posture from clothes or personal protective equipment?	Can you: • Remove obstructions to free movement? • Provide better flooring? • Avoid steps and steep ramps? • Prevent extremes of hot and cold? • Improve lighting? • Consider less restrictive clothing or personal protective equipment?
Individual capacity: Does the job: • Require unusual capability? • Endanger those with a health problem? • Endanger pregnant women? • Call for special information or training?	Can you: • Take better care of the physically weak or pregnant? • Give your employees more information, e.g., about the range of tasks they are likely to face? • Provide training?

Table 16.7: Manual Handling — Summary of Research Findings

Actions and Posture

- *The risk of injury increases as the load is held further away from the front of the body:* Holding a load at arms' length imposes about five times the strain experience when holding the same load very close to the body. Picking up a load further away from the body can mean that the handling of the object is not controlled. Accurately placing the load further away from the body will tire the muscles holding the load, due to the need for more careful control over its movement.

- *The risk of injury increases the higher the load is above shoulder height:* To reach above shoulder height means the back is arched, and arms are acting as long levers. The load is more difficult to control. Lowering from this level to a level below mid-thigh height can require a change of grip.

- *The risk of injury increases the closer the load is to the ground:* Bending forward to pick up loads from a low level creates strain, particularly on the lower back.

- *The risk of injury increases with the degree of body twist:* The back is least able to take the stress caused by excessive twisting in repeated movements or prolonged posture. The combination of twisting and bending forward to handle a load represents significant risk.

- *The risk of injury increases with the degree of sideways bending to handle a load:* Lifting and carrying loads in one hand places more stress on the side of the body.

- *The risk of injury increases with distance the load is carried:* Carrying a load for an excessive distance increases muscle fatigue, particularly in the arms. This can affect an individual's ability to carry out other handling activities afterwards.

- *The risk of injury increases as the amount of force required to push and pull becomes greater:* Initial forces to move an object are greater and involve higher risk than those required to keep an object moving. Pushing and pulling across the front of the body puts a twisting strain on the body that can lead to an increased risk of injury.

- *The risk of injury increases with the amount of force used:* Sudden or jerky movements can place unexpected loads on backs that are not prepared. For example, when a gardener jerks a heavy bag of potting mix or fertilizer on to a shoulder, or when a cleaner pulls a stuck vacuum cleaner cord and it comes away suddenly.

Characteristics of the Load

- *The risk of injury increases as the weight of a load increases:* Evaluating the risk of weight of the object needs to take into account:
  - ◊ How long the load is handled: and

◊   How often the load is handled.

As a guide, the risk of back injury increases when loads over 16kg are handled from a standing position. As weight increases from 16kg to 55 kg, the percentage of healthy adults who can safely lift, lower or carry decreases. Generally, no person should be required to lift, lower or carry loads more than they think they are capable of moving.

- *The risk of injury increases as the size of the load becomes larger:* The shape of the load can affect the way it can be held. For example, the risk of injury will be greater if a load has to be lifted from the ground and is wider than the distance between the lifter's knees. When a load's width (measured across the body) is more than 50cm, there is an increased risk. When any dimensions are more than 75cm, a greater risk is incurred. This risk is higher again, if two dimensions are more than 75cm. A large load may also block the view, when carried, and increase the chance of a person tripping.

- *The risk of injury increases with the lack of safe handholds on a load:* Loads become more difficult to grip when they are smooth, slippery, greasy or wet. Extra grip strength will be needed to hold a load. This will be tiring for the person, and will increase the chance of the load being dropped. The absence of handholds due to awkward shape, or handholds in a difficult position, will affect a person's ability to hold the load.

- *The risk of injury increases with the level of instability and unpredictability:* Loads with shifting contents – e.g. drums half-full of liquids – make control of the load more difficult, and lead to sudden additional body stresses for which the person may not be fully prepared. A load where one side or one part is heavier than others will cause uneven muscular strain. This will be worse if the heavier part cannot be carried close to the body.

- *The risk of injury increases with the sharpness or roughness of the load and with hot or cold surface temperatures:* These factors may cause injury – e.g. cuts or burns arising from the external state of the load. They may also impair grip and discourage good posture.

- *The risk of injury increases in relation to the unpredictable actions of the person or animal being handled:* Handling persons who cannot assist, are unable to bear weight, or are uncooperative, will increase the risk of injury. Live animals being lifted or restrained may suddenly move or pull away, placing extra stress on the back.

The Work Environment

- *The risk of injury increases in relation to space constraints in handling:* For space constraint to be a risk, it needs to impose a restriction on a person's handling ability. Restricted head-room will promote a stooping posture, obstructions may increase the need for twisting or leaning, and narrow gangways will hinder manoeuvring of bulky loads.

- *The risk of injury increase with greater degrees of floor slipperiness or un-evenness:* Uneven or slippery floors increase the likelihood of slips, trips or falls. They may also hinder smooth movement and create additional unpredictability. Uneven floor surfaces can hinder the safe use of trolleys.

- *The risk of injury increase with greater differences in floor level:* The presence of steps or steep slopes adds to the difficulty of movement when handling loads, particularly when the load obscures a person's view. Carrying a load up or down a ladder will be difficult due to the need to have a proper hold on the ladder.

- *The risk of injury increase with higher temperatures and humidity, colder temperatures or windy conditions:* Higher temperature and humidity increase the total physical load on the body, which leads to more rapid fatigue. Perspiration on the hands may reduce gripping ability. Cold, windy conditions, particularly in the first part of the work period, may prevent muscles being properly warmed up. Handling roof-sheeting in cold windy conditions increases the risk of injury.

- *The risk of injury increases with lower levels of light or higher levels of glare:* Low levels of light or high contrast between areas of bright light and deep shadows can aggravate tripping hazards. Concentration on the tasks may be reduced.

Employee Characteristics

- *The risk of injury increases for persons aged below 18 years:* Young workers under the age of 18 are at greater risk than adult workers because they are still developing physically and their spine and other joints are more easily damaged. Loads over 16kg represent significant risk to young workers.

- *The risk of injury increases as pregnancy progresses:* Hormonal changes can affect ligaments, increasing susceptibility to injury. Postural problems may increase as the pregnancy progresses. Difficulty in getting a load close to the body can be a particular problem. Care should also be taken for women who may handle loads following a return to work during the three months after childbirth.

- *The risk of injury increases with decreased physical ability:* Employees returning to work after injury may not be able to perform at their normal level of work. Specific disabilities and illnesses – for example, scoliosis and osteoarthritis – though not necessarily work-related, may affect a person's ability in manual handling. Staff returning from an extended absence may not be as fit for physical work. Occasional heavy manual handling may place extra demands on staff, who normally carry out lighter tasks, like office work.

- *The risk of injury may increase where a greater degree of special skills, capabilities and/or knowledge is required:* Some manual handling activities – e.g., patient handling – require very specific skills and knowledge to perform.

- *The risk of injury may increase from the use of PPE and some types of clothing:* Tight clothing that restricts movement will adversely affect manual handling technique. Where personal protective equipment must be worn, its effect on injury risk should be considered. For example, gloves may reduce ability to grip loads firmly; the weight of gas cylinders used with breathing apparatus will increase the stresses of the body.

Task Redesign

The whole thrust of the EU Directive on Manual Handling is on the identification of hazards from such tasks and the assessment of risks. Where manual handling cannot be avoided, the employer must take measures to remove or reduce the risk. The Directive establishes a strategy for dealing with manual handling problems:

- Manual handling operations should be avoided where possible.

- Manual handling operations that cannot be avoided must be assessed.

- Actions to eliminate or reduce the risks must be taken by the employer.

The tasks that remain should then be assessed from an ergonomics perspective and redesigned if possible. **Figure 16.3** presents the principles of task redesign.

Figure 16.3: Principles of Task Redesign

A. Reduce bending motions
Eliminate the need to bend by:
- using lift tables, work dispensers and similar mechanical aids.
- raising the work level to an appropriate height.
- lowering the worker.
- providing all material at work level.
- keeping materials at work level (e.g., do not lower to the floor anything that must be lifted later).

B. Reduce twisting motions
Eliminate the need to twist by:
- providing all materials and tools in front of the worker.
- using conveyors, chutes, slides or turntables to change.

direction of material flow.
- providing adjustable swivel chairs for seated workers.
- providing sufficient workspace for the whole body to turn.
- improving layout of work areas.

C. Reduce reaching out motions
Eliminate the need to reach by:
- providing tools and machine controls close to the worker to eliminate horizontal reaches over 16 inches.
- placing materials, workplaces and other heavy objects as near to the worker as possible.
- reducing the size of cartons or pallets being loaded and allowing the worker to walk around them.
- reducing the size of the object being handled.
- allowing the object to be kept close to the body.

Reduce Object Weights/Forces

A. Reduce lifting and lowering forces
1. Eliminate the need to lift or lower manually by:
   - using lift tables, lift trucks, cranes, hoists, balances, drum and barrel dampers, elevating conveyors, and similar aids.
   - raising the work level.
   - lowering the operator.
   - using gravity dumps and chutes.

2. Reduce the weight of the object by:
   - reducing the size of the object.
   - reducing the capacity of containers.
   - reducing the weight of the container itself.
   - reducing the load in the container (administrative control).
   - reducing the number of objects lifted or lowered at one time (administrative controls).

3. Increase the weight of the object so that it must be handled mechanically by:
   - using the unit-load concept (such as bins or containers, preferably with fold-down sides, rather than smaller totes and boxes).
   - using palletised loads.

4. Reduce the hand distance by:
   - changing the shape of the object.
   - providing grips or handles.
   - providing better access to object.
   - improving layout of work areas.

B. Reduce Pushing and Pulling Force

1. Eliminate the need to push or pull by:
   - using powered conveyors.
   - using powered trucks.
   - using slides and chutes.

2. Reduce the required force by:
   - reducing the weight of the load.
   - using non-powered conveyors, air bearings, ball-caster tables, monorails and similar aids.
   - using four-wheel hand-trucks and dollies with large diameter casters and good bearings.
   - providing good maintenance of floor surfaces, hand-trucks etc.
   - treating surfaces to reduce friction.
   - using air cylinder pushers or pullers.

3. Reduce the distance of push or pull by:
   - improving layout of work areas.
   - relocating production or storage areas.

C. Reducing Carrying Forces

1. Eliminate the need to carry by converting to pushing or pulling:
   - using conveyors, air bearings, ball-caster tables, monorails, slides, chutes and similar aids.
   - using lift trucks, two-hand trucks, four-wheel hand-trucks, dollies and similar aids.

2. Reduce the weight of the objects by:
   - reducing the size of the object (specify size to suppliers).
   - reducing the capacity of containers.
   - reducing the weight of the container itself.
   - reducing the load in the container (administrative control).
   - reducing the number of objects lifted or lowered at one time (administrative control).

3. Reducing the distance by:
   - improving layout of work area.
   - relocating production or storage areas.

Figure 16.4: Manual Handling: Reducing the Risk of Injury

Risk Factors	Corrective Action

Excessive lifting and lowering distances, poor posture	*Modify the task layout, e.g.* • store loads at optimum waist height.
Poor handling techniques	*Promote better use of the body* (e.g., using legs rather than back muscles, holding load close to body), e.g., • change task layout. • change equipment used. • provide information and training.
Fixed postures, frequent or prolonged physical effort, insufficient rest or recovery periods.	*Job redesign, e.g.,* • minimise need for fixed postures. • reduce frequency of lifts (particularly where risk factors associated with the load exist). • introduce flexible breaks or (preferably) job rotation in order to prevent onset of muscular fatigue.
Seated handling (this is a risk factor because the seated handler is more prone to injury)	*Address relevant ergonomic issues, e.g.,* • provide adjustable seat height (to ensure work surface is in a comfortable position). • provide swivel seat (to reduce the need to twist)
Various, e.g., load is heavy, unstable, difficult to grasp, etc.	*Introduce team handling:* • primarily where the operation is unsafe for one person. • caution is required in recommending this option – problems can arise such as lack of space and insufficient handholds for team members.

Various, e.g., load is heavy, slippery, dirty, etc.	*Provide personal protective equipment (PPE) e.g.,* • gloves. • safety footwear. • overalls and aprons. Note: PPE must be suitable for its intended use, well maintained and readily accessible.
Modifying the Load	
Heavy load	*Make the load lighter, e.g.,* • break it down into smaller units. • discuss with suppliers the possibility of having goods delivered in lighter containers.
Bulky or awkward load	*Bring centre of gravity closer to handler's body, e.g.,* • make load smaller and less bulky. • ensure handlers keep heaviest side towards them (where weight distribution is uneven).
Load is difficult to grasp	*Make load easier to grasp, e.g.,* • fit a handle or handgrips. • use handling aids.
Load is unstable or contents likely to shift	*Increase stability,* e.g., • use packaging that will prevent objects moving around. • transport liquids in full or empty containers only. **Note:** "Live" loads, such as animals or people, can be particularly risky and specialist advice may be needed.

Specific hazards present, e.g., the load is hot, cold, sharp, dirty, etc.	*Introduce appropriate control measures,* e.g., • use an insulated container for hot or cold objects. • provide suitable gloves where there may be sharp edges. • clean the load.
Altering the Work Environment	
Space constraints	*Remove space constraints, e.g.,* • relocate machinery or equipment to remove constrictions. • aim to ensure that the load is delivered to a point from which it can be moved without lack of space causing problems.
Uneven or slippery floor	*Improve floor conditions, e.g.,* • provide a flat surface where possible. • maintain the floor in a safe condition – aim to prevent spillages and remove them should they occur. • fix down carpet edges, maintain good housekeeping. • consider providing a slip-resistant floor surface.
Changes in work level whilst handling load	*Avoid changes in work level, e.g.,* • modify the route taken by handlers to avoid carrying the load up or down ladders. *and if the route cannot be avoided:* • consider provision of appropriate handling aids (e.g., a chute or conveyor) rather than a ladder. • install a gentle slope to replace steps (for wheeled equipment).

Temperature extremes or inadequate ventilation	*Provide additional heating, cooling or ventilation, or relocate the operation to a more suitable area.*
Poor lighting conditions	*Improve the quality of lighting, e.g.,* • provide additional lighting. • avoid the need for handlers to travel through poorly lit areas or from areas of bright light into dimly lit areas.
Assessing Individual Capability	
The operation could put at risk handlers who have pre-existing health problems	*Make provision for the needs of such employees, e.g.,* • use pre-employment screening to identify employees who have a history of back injury or other relevant health problems. • assign light duties to employees returning after a period of illness.
The operation could put at risk women who may be pregnant (or their babies)	*Make provision for such employees, e.g.,* • re-assess the manual handling operation with a view to further reducing the risk to women who are pregnant or have recently given birth. • allow more frequent rest breaks. • provide lighter duties temporarily. • consult the woman's GP on whether it is safe for her to continue in manual handling work. • provide handling aids.
Handlers must be trained to perform the operation safely	*Provide appropriate information and training.*

MECHANICAL HANDLING

Whenever possible, mechanical handling should be used in preference to manual handling. The wide range of devices available to assist handling is far too extensive to cover in detail, so this section outlines the safety issues surrounding the main forms of mechanical handling. The categories of devices covered here are:

Conveyors

The most common types of conveyors are:

- **Belt conveyors** — Used to transfer packages or loose materials over long distances.

- **Roller conveyors** — Used for the movement of unit loads.

- **Chain conveyors** — Used to suspend objects requiring transfer, e.g. cars in a car assembly.

- **Slat conveyors** — Used for the transfer of boxed or stacked goods.

- **Screw conveyors** — Used for the transfer of loose solids over short distances.

The hazards associated with conveyors include:

- Traps between moving parts of the conveyor.

- Traps between moving and fixed parts of the conveyor.

- Traps in the drive mechanism.

- Traps in the transfer point between conveyors.

- Dangers from sharp edges and worn conveyor parts.

Safety precautions to be taken include fixed and interlocking guards, suitable side rails, and appropriate lubrication to prevent excess wear and sharp edges. Emergency stop mechanisms should be provided, such as trip wires or stop buttons. However, stop buttons should not be used as a substitute for guards.

Elevators

Elevators may be fixed or mobile, and may be of a bucket or bar type. The main hazards associated with them are overloading, trapping caused by inappropriate speed during usage, and dust explosions where loose materials are being carried. Adequate fireproofing of elevator heads must be in place where dust explosions are likely, e.g. in milling operations.

Internal Trucks

Internal trucks to assist handling may be pedestrian-operated or power-driven. The simplest of these are manually-operated stacking trucks, and power-operated stackers. Forklift trucks are commonly used in goods handling because of their mobility, versatility and variety of attachments available. Hazards associated with internal truck operations are presented in **Figure 16.5**.

To provide safe operating conditions for internal trucks, the following should be considered:

- Appropriate floor materials and good housekeeping to remove obstacles.

- Designated space for manoeuvres such as turning and passing.

- Stacking systems that allow safe manoeuvres to be performed.

- Adequate lighting and visibility for operators.

- Restricted access to loading areas.

- Proper training, instruction and supervision of operators.

- Operators should be carefully selected to ensure they are physically fit and also have an aptitude for forklift driving.

- Pedestrians should be segregated from forklift areas.

- There should be mirrors at blind corners and the workplace as a whole should be well-lit and illuminated.

- Forklifts should be capable of carrying out the tasks required of them and the proper attachments for special operators should be available.

- The safe working load should be prominently displayed.

- A standard procedure should be laid down for any accidents or near-misses.

- Forklifts should have regular preventative maintenance and must be kept in safe working conditions.

- Train supervisors in the safe operation of forklifts to enable them to recognise unsafe practices.

Figure 16.5: Hazards Associated with Internal Truck Operations

---

- Overloading can result in breakages, overturning, collisions, and falling objects.

- Excess speed, sudden braking, shifting loads, unsuitable floor surfaces or hitting obstructions can cause overturning and collisions.

- Overhead or floor obstructions such as pipes, cables, and other fixtures pose hazards as they are beyond the visibility of the driver.

- Shifting loads can occur if goods are not properly restrained.

- Mechanical failure of the truck may also result in an accident.

- Some trucks are battery-operated and there is a risk of fire and explosion if they are recharged incorrectly.

DANGEROUS SUBSTANCES

When discussing the handling of dangerous substances, it is important to make a distinction between "hazard" and "risk". In this context, hazard refers to the inherent propensity of a substance to damage health. The term risk, however, refers to the probability of a substance actually causing such damage. For instance, butane gas is hazardous in that it is flammable in air at normal pressure, and so can be classed as a dangerous substance. However, when properly piped, the risk to health posed by butane is minimal, and therefore it can be safely used in a variety of everyday applications.

Dangerous substances are, therefore, those that have a high inherent propensity to cause damage to health, but the risk posed depends on how the substance is handled. They are usually classified according to the effect of their chemical properties on employees. They may have adverse consequences on health in two main ways; firstly, by direct toxic effects upon entry to the body, or secondly, indirectly as the result of a chemical reaction external to the body — for instance an explosion. Often the extent of the damage caused will depend on the form that the substance takes, e.g. dusts, fumes, liquids, etc. Classification usually takes into account the likely damage, and whether a substance is:

- Explosive.
- Oxidising.
- Flammable.
- Extremely/highly flammable.
- Toxic or very toxic.
- Harmful.
- Corrosive.
- Sensitising.
- Carcinogenic.
- Mutagenic.
- Teratogenic.
- Dangerous for the environment.

EU legislation on the classification, packaging and labelling of dangerous substances takes into account both physio-chemical and toxicological properties of substances, and contains seven hazard categories with specific symbols which are outlined in **Figure 16.6** below.

Figure 16.6: Hazard Categories

Physio-Chemical	Toxicological
• Explosive.	• Toxic.
• Oxidising.	• Harmful.
• Extremely/highly flammable.	• Irritant.
• Corrosive.	

Article 3/91/155/EP states that anyone putting a dangerous substance on the market must supply the user with a safety data sheet free of charge. This sheet must contain the following information.

Identification of Substance/Preparation

The full name, address, telephone number and emergency telephone number of the manufacturer/importer/distributor must be given. In Ireland, it is important that Irish telephone codes are provided. Where the Irish operation is a branch plant of a globally-dispersed transnational company and all material is simply shipped through another subsidiary operation or from head office, this must be made clear. Workers sometimes complain that material arrives in unmarked containers with no information because it is, in effect, being moved within a productive process, a process that nevertheless just happens to be spread across two or more continents. It may also be the case that the relatively small Irish operation does not directly employ any specially-trained personnel, at managerial or any other level, who would either have, or fully understand, the information required, as all major operational decisions are taken elsewhere. These regulations now eliminate such hurdles.

Composition/Information on Ingredients

The information should "enable the recipient to identify readily the risks associated with the substance or preparation". It should list known hazards and threshold limit values (TLVs), where these are known. The difficulty for the untrained eye may be to abstract such information from a mass of less relevant or crucial data. There may, therefore, be a case for "customising" Safety Data Sheets for the workplace user, presenting them in a simplified and easy-to-follow form and concentrating simply on that information that is most relevant to the user. Such data should be available at the point of use and operatives should receive any necessary instruction or training in recognition and how to respond to first aid or other emergencies.

Hazards Identification

Warning signs or phrases should accompany the dangerous substance at all times. A common complaint is that, while full detail may be provided in stores, on the factory floor, in a laboratory or in the work situation, the substance may be broken down into smaller, unmarked containers for convenient use or be a part of the productive process. In these situations, workers would not necessarily have any indication as to what they were working with. This practice must change and effective labelling should accompany use.

First Aid Measures

The regulations state that first aid information must be "easily understood by victim, bystander or first aider". Symptoms and effects should be clearly summarised, including the possibility of any delayed effects. It is important that the first aid measures are incorporated into the general first aid training programme of the employment. While the Red Cross, Civil Defence or similar bodies provide excellent first aid training programmes, such courses will not necessarily relate completely to the first aid treatment requirements of certain chemical or biological agents. Certain agents, for example, may require specific antidotes to neutralise an inhaled lung content or to act in a general palliative way. The following questions would then arise:

• Are such antidotes available within the employment?

• Are extra supplies of such material given to the local hospital?

• Are the local hospital, company doctor and ambulance crew given the Safety Data Sheet, or its first aid elements, to enable them to know precisely what they may be dealing with?

• Who is responsible for co-ordinating such policy within the employment at general and/or departmental/shift levels?

- Are such persons named in the Safety Statement?

- Does the Safety Committee (where one exists) regularly review first aid practices, supplies and training in the light of Safety Data Sheet information?

Fire-Fighting Measures

Similar concerns arise when considering fire-fighting measures:

- Does the company have suitable extinguishing materials?

- Are there any special exposure hazards?

- Will fire fighters require any special personal protective equipment or breathing apparatus?

- Who is responsible for training company-based fire-fighting personnel or liasing with local fire brigade units?

- Is this person, and their duties, written into the Safety Statement?

Accidental Release Measures

- What personal precautions may be necessary in the event of an accidental release?

- Is the appropriate/necessary equipment readily available?

- Who raises the alarm within the employment and, through the emergency services, to the local inhabitants?

It is worth remembering that Section 7 of the Safety, Health and Welfare at Work Act, 1989, obliges employers to conduct their business in such a way that "persons not in (their) employment who may be affected thereby are not exposed to risk".

The Regulations prescribe particular "clearing-up" methods that might include the use of absorbent materials such as sand, kieselguhr, acid binder, universal binder and sawdust, with additional measures listed to reduce gas/fume/vapour emission. Special indicators might include warning phrases such as "never use with" or "neutralise with". All such matters should be included within the Safety Statement.

Handling and Storage

Careful consideration must be given to handling and storage. Are storage areas adequately ventilated? Are temperature and humidity controlled? Are measures taken to avoid or control the generation of aerosols or dust? Are incompatible materials isolated from each other? What happens as long-stored materials decompose? The Safety Statement should identify those managing handling and storage, and policy should be monitored and reviewed through the Safety Committee.

SAFE USE OF CHEMICALS

A chemical accident or incident has the potential to affect many people, not only the operator, nearby workers and others on site, but also members of the public. The results of some incidents such as Bhopal have been of huge proportions and were catastrophic. Bhopal caused much human suffering and loss of life and the image of the parent company, Union Carbide, was severely damaged.

All chemicals can be handled safely, even the most toxic and flammable substances. If mishandled, the risk of damage to health can be great. Typically, people are told only what the chemical is used for and how to use it on the job. Rarely are they told how to use the product safely. There are a number of problems associated with the safe use of chemicals:

- In general, the label is rarely read — unless perhaps it is an unfamiliar substance. Through familiarity, the users often think they know everything necessary about the substance.

- People often ignore or underestimate the risks associated with the substances that they are used to handling.

- Even when the symbols are recognised as indicating a hazardous chemical, the precise information is not read and understood.

- The difference between the various terms used — toxic, corrosive, irritant, etc., is not appreciated.

- The Risk and Safety Phase is not known and the terminology is not readily understood.

- The safeguards suggested are seen as unrealistic, for example: "Don't inhale aerosols" is regarded as being totally unrealistic.

- There are many inherent factors that have to be overcome when attempting to introduce procedures for the safe use of chemicals. Among these are:

  ◊ They are difficult to detect — the vapours are heavier than air and sink to the floor where they may not be seen or smelled.

  ◊ They are highly explosive — sparks, flame, hot surfaces or static electricity can ignite them.

  ◊ They are affected by temperature change — if containers are overfilled, a temperature rise can result in leakage from the build-up of pressure.

  ◊ They are subject to flashback — fires and explosions often occur when spreading vapours ignite and spread fire back to the flammable liquid.

The most important property that influences the fire hazard of a flammable liquid is its flashpoint. The flash point is the lowest temperature at which a flammable liquid gives off sufficient flammable vapour to cause ignition on the application of an external source of flame near its surface.

Figure 16.7 presents a summary of symbols for labelling dangerous chemicals.

Chemical Toxicity

The toxicity of a substance is its ability to cause harmful effects. These effects can strike a single cell, a group of cells, an organ system, or the entire body. A toxic effect may be visible damage, or a decrease in performance or function measurable only by a test. All chemicals can cause harm. When only a very large amount of the chemical can cause damage, the chemical is considered to be relatively non-toxic. When a small amount can be harmful, the chemical is considered toxic.

Figure 16.7: EU Danger Symbols for Labelling Dangerous Chemicals

Symbol	What it Means	Precautions (General)
	Can cause irritation to skin, eyes or breathing system if inhaled. (Non-corrosive).	Wear protective clothing to avoid contact with skin and eyes. Provide good ventilation or use protective facemask.
	May cause limited health risks if it is inhaled, swallowed or penetrates the skin.	Wear protective clothing to avoid contact with skin and eyes. Provide good ventilation or use protective facemask. Do not eat, drink or smoke. Wash hands after use.
	Can cause chemical burns to skin and eyes. (May also be corrosive to certain metals).	Wear protective clothing to avoid contact with skin and eyes and clothing.
	May cause serious or extremely serious health risks or death, if inhaled, swallowed or penetrates the skin.	Use exhaust ventilation system or full breathing apparatus to prevent exposure to dusts, vapours, etc. Wear protective clothing. Do not eat, drink or smoke. Wash hands thoroughly after use.
	A liquid, having a flash point between 21 deg. and 44 deg. C. Highly flammable gas, or solid; or a liquid with flashpoint below 21° C; extremely flammable liquid with flashpoint below 0° C and boiling point below or equal to 35° C.	Keep away from sources of ignition. Do not smoke. Keep away from sources of ignition. Do not smoke. Store in a secure place. Keep container tightly closed.
	Produces heat on reaction with other materials and creates a fire risk in contact with flammable or combustible materials.	Store away from other materials. Always observe recommendations for storage and use. Keep container tightly closed.
	May explode if subject to heat, shocks or friction.	Store away from other materials. Always observe recommendations for storage and use.

Source: CIS/ILO.

The toxicity of a substance depends on its chemical structure, the extent to which the substance is absorbed by the body, and the body's ability to detoxify the substance (change it into less toxic substances) and eliminate it from the body. Issues include:

- **Toxicity**: how much of the substance is required to cause harm.

- **Route of exposure**: how the substance enters the body.

- **Dose**: how much enters the body.

- **Duration**: the length of time exposed to the substance.

- **Reaction and interaction**: concurrent exposure to other substances.

- **Sensitivity**: how one body reacts to the substance in comparison with other people.

Some chemicals are hazardous because of the risk of fire or explosion. These are important dangers, but are considered to be safety, rather than toxic, hazards. The factors of a toxic hazard are more fully explained below.

The most important factor in toxicity is the chemical structure of a substance — what it is made of, what atoms and molecules it contains and how they are arranged. Substances with similar structures often cause similar health problems. However, slight differences in chemical structure can lead to large differences in the type of health effect produced. For example, silica in one form (amorphous) has little effect on health, and is allowed to be present in the workplace at relatively high levels. After it is heated, however, it turns into another form of silica (crystalline) that causes serious lung damage, and is allowed to be present only at very low levels (200 times lower than amorphous silica).

The effects of toxic substances may appear immediately or soon after exposure, or they may take years to appear. *Acute* exposure is a single exposure or a few exposures. Acute effects are those that occur following acute exposures. Acute effects can occur immediately, or be delayed and occur days or weeks after exposure. *Chronic* exposure is repeated exposure that occurs over months and years. Chronic effects are those that occur following chronic exposure, and so are always delayed.

Figure 16.8: Chemicals Entering the Body: Different Routes

Inhalation

The most common type of exposure occurs when a substance is inhaled into the lungs. The lungs consist of branching airways (called bronchi) with clusters of tiny air sacs (called alveoli) at the ends. The alveoli absorb oxygen and other chemicals into the bloodstream. Some chemicals are irritants and cause nose or throat irritation, they may also cause discomfort, coughing or chest pain when they are inhaled. Others may be inhaled without triggering such warning symptoms but they can still be dangerous. Sometimes a chemical is present in the air as small particles (dust or mist). Some of these particles, depending on their size, may be deposited in the bronchi and/or alveoli. Many of them may be coughed out, but others may stay in the lungs and may cause lung damage. Some particles may dissolve and be absorbed into the bloodstream, and have effects elsewhere in the body.

Skin Contact

The skin is a protective barrier that helps keep foreign chemicals out of the body. However, some chemicals can easily pass through the skin and enter the bloodstream. If the skin is cut or cracked, chemicals can penetrate the skin more easily. Also some caustic substances, such as strong acids and alkalis, can chemically burn the skin. Others can irritate the skin. Many chemicals, particularly organic solvents, dissolve the oils in the skin, leaving it dry, cracked, and susceptible to infection and absorption of other chemicals.

Eye contact

Some chemicals may burn or irritate the eye. Occasionally, they may be absorbed through the eye and enter the bloodstream. Chemicals easily harm the eyes, so any eye contact with chemicals should be considered as a serious accident.

Ingestion

The least common source of exposure in the workplace is swallowing chemicals. Chemicals can be ingested if they are left on hands, clothing or beard, or accidentally contaminate food, drinks or cigarettes. Chemicals present in the workplace as dust, for example, metal dusts such as lead or cadmium, are easily ingested.

A toxic chemical may cause acute effects, chronic effects or both. For example, if solvents are inhaled on the job, acute effects such as headaches and dizziness may be experienced, but disappear by at the end of the day. Over months, chronic effects may begin to develop such as liver and kidney damage. The delay between the beginning of exposure and the appearance of disease caused by that exposure is called the *latency* period. Some chronic effects caused by chemicals, such as cancer, have very long latency periods. Cancer has been known to develop up to 40 years after a worker's exposure to a cancer-causing chemical.

The length of the latency period for chronic effects makes it difficult to establish the cause-and-effect relationship between the exposure and the illness. Since chronic diseases develop gradually, one may have the disease for some time before it is detected. It is, therefore, important that each employee and their physician are aware of the chronic effects, which might be caused by the substances used on the job.

Figure 16.9: The Differences Between Acute and Chronic Effects

Acute	Chronic
• Occurs immediately or soon after exposure (short latency).	• Occurs over time (long latency).
• Often involves a high exposure (large dose) over a short period.	• Often involves low exposures (small doses) over a long period.
• Often reversible after exposure stops.	• Many effects are not reversible.
• Can be minor or severe. For example, a small amount of ammonia can cause throat or eye irritation; larger amounts can be serious or even fatal.	• Chronic effects are still unknown for many chemicals. For example, most chemicals have not been tested for effects on reproductive system.
• Relationship between chemical exposure and symptoms is generally, although not always, obvious.	• It may be difficult to establish the relationship between chemical exposure and illness because of the long time delay or latency period.
• Knowledge often bases on human exposure.	• Knowledge often based on animal studies.

Properties of Hazardous Chemicals

The properties and hazards associated with corrosive, flammable and explosive chemicals are now considered. **Figure 16.10** presents a summary of hazardous substances.

Corrosive Chemicals

Acids such as sulphuric and hydrofluoric, and alkalis such as caustic soda and caustic potash, can cause burns, irritate the skin, damage the eyes and affect the respiratory system. Direct contact with corrosive chemicals can cause destruction of the skin, the surface mucous membranes of the body and their underlying tissues. Eyes are particularly vulnerable to corrosive materials.

Figure 16.10: Categorising Hazardous Substances

Category	Symbol
Explosive This is a solid, liquid, pasty or gelatinous substance and preparation which may react producing heat (exothermically) without oxygen evolving gases, that may explode if subjected to heat, shock, friction or any ignition source. For example, Nitro-glycerine. Risk Phase R3 – extreme risk of explosion by shock, friction, fire or other sources of ignition.	E
Oxidising Oxidising agents contain large amounts of available oxygen which is easily released especially when heated, and will cause combustible materials to burn with other materials such as flammables. They will react generating heat and causing ignition. For example, Hydrogen Peroxide. Risk Phase R8 – contact with combustible material may cause fire.	O
Extremely Flammable Liquid substances and preparations having an extremely low flash-point and a low boiling point. These substances are flammable on contact with air at ambient temperatures and pressure. For example, Hydrogen. Risk Phase R12 – extremely flammable.	F+

Highly Flammable Substances and preparations: 1) Which become hot and catch fire on contact with air at ambient temperature. 2) Solid substances and preparations, which may readily catch fire after brief contact with an ignition source, 3) Liquid substances having a very low flashpoint. 4) Which, in contact with water or damp air, evolve highly flammable gases in dangerous quantities. For example, Dimethylcarbonate. Risk Phase R11 – highly flammable.	F
Flammable Liquid substances having a low flash-point.	
Very Toxic Substances, which in very low quantities cause death, acute or chronic damage to the health when inhaled, swallowed or absorbed via the skin. For example, Fluroacetic acid. Risk Phase R28 – very toxic if swallowed.	T+
Toxic Substances, which in low quantities cause death, acute or chronic damage to health when, inhaled, swallowed or absorbed via the skin. For example, Fumarin. Risk Phase R25 –48 – toxic if swallowed, danger of serious damage to health if swallowed.	T
Harmful Substances which may cause death, acute or chronic damage to health when inhaled, swallowed or absorbed via the skin. For example, 1,1,2 Trichlorethane Risk Phase R20/21/22 – harmful by contact by inhalation/skin/swallowed.	Xn
Corrosive Substances, which may on contact with living tissue destroy them. For example, Sulphuric acid. Risk Phase R35 – causes severe burns.	C
Irritant Non corrosive substances which through immediate, prolonged or repeated contact with the skin of mucous membrane, may cause inflammation. For example, Valinamide. Risk Phase R36–43 – irritating to eye, respiratory system, skin, irreversible effects, sensitisation.	Xi

Sensitisers Substances, which are capable of producing an allergic reaction on inhalation on skin penetration, such, that further exposure, will result in characteristic adverse health effects.	Sen
Carcinogenic Substances and preparations which, if they are inhaled, ingested or if they penetrate the skin, may induce cancer or increase its incidence. *Category 1* – substances known to be carcinogenic to man. Risk Phase R45 – may cause cancer. *Category 2* – substances that should be regarded as carcinogenic to man on the basis of animal studies and other investigations. *Category 3* – substances, which cause concern for man, owing to possible carcinogenic effects. Risk Phase R40 – possible risk of irreversible effects. An example for carcinogen is asbestos. Risk Phase R45-R48/23 – may cause cancer, serious damage to health by prolonged exposure. Toxic by inhalation.	T Xn Xn
Mutagenic Substances or preparations which, if inhaled, ingested or penetrate the skin, may induce inheritable genetic defects or increase their incidence. *Category 1* – substances known to be carcinogenic to man. Risk Phase R46 – may cause genetic damage. *Category 2* – substances which should be regarded as mutagenic to man on the basis of animal and other studies. *Category 3* – substances which cause concern to man, owing to possible mutagenic effects. Risk Phase R40 – possible risk of irreversible effects.	T Xn Xn
Toxic for Reproduction Substances which, if inhaled, ingested or penetrate the skin may produce or increase the incidence of non-hereditary adverse effects in children or an impairment of reproductive functions or capacity.	T
Dangerous to the Environment Substances which, on enter to the environment, would present immediate or delayed damage for one of more components of the environment.	N

Flammable Chemicals

A definition of flammable is that which easily ignites and is capable of burning with great rapidity. They are liquids that release vapours that travel unseen into the atmosphere of the workplace and are easily ignited or exploded. Ignition can be caused by: heat alone, working near an open flame, build up of static electricity leading to a spark. They are commonly used as fuel, e.g. petrol; cleaning agents, e.g. toluene; solvents, e.g. acetone; and raw materials for other products, e.g. vinyl acetate. The precautions necessary are designed to prevent the accidental inhalation of the vapours by people and the accidental ignition or explosion of the material. In view of the hazards, non-flammable and non-toxic materials should be used wherever possible.

Highly flammable liquids are used as solvents in adhesives and other materials. They are extremely dangerous if handled improperly. Their vapours can be flammable and explosive. A solvent is a liquid that has the power to dissolve a substance. Water is a common example. In industry, organic liquids are often used as solvents and these are mainly hydrocarbons (compounds containing hydrogen and carbon). They are used as degreasing agents and are constituents of paint and paint strippers, glues, adhesives, etc.

All organic solvents are volatile, i.e. they release vapours and, besides being flammable, may be toxic. Also they are heavier and can build up in confined spaces to exclude oxygen. They will settle at floor level, which is important when considering ventilation. They tend to be flammable and will float on water. Examples are trichlorethylene, carbon tetrachloride, benzene, toluene and trichloroethane. Besides being volatile, they also cause dermatitis by removing natural oils from the skin, and may damage the central nervous system, liver and kidneys. Other dangerous substances, hazardous to health, include isocyanates, which are used in insulating foams, paints, varnishes and adhesives. They irritate the respiratory tract and can lead to asthma. Spraying foam containing isocyanate is a most hazardous operation.

Polychlorinated Biphenyls (PCBs) — Toxic Fluid

PCBs were used in electrical transformers and capacitors and are still used in refrigeration and heating equipment. Their vapours are toxic and, if PCBs are involved in fires, highly toxic by-products are released.

Inhalation or absorption through the skin can cause impaired judgement and dizziness followed by confusion, sleepiness and unconsciousness and various long-term effects may follow. Other symptoms are irritation of the respiratory tract and headache. The inhalation risk is greatest when solvents are used in confined spaces. To prevent damage to health due to inhalation, the following precautions are necessary: adequate ventilation including forced ventilation if necessary; forced extraction; use of breathing apparatus; enclosure; wet methods of work; food hygiene practices including no smoking; avoiding contact; personal protective clothing and equipment and permits-to-work.

Fire Hazards

Flammable liquid fires can result in injury or death and monetary losses. Although accidental fires are usually caused by carelessness, there are some chemical reactions that can produce sufficient heat to start a fire. The use of flammable liquids is the biggest potential risk in causing fires. Flammable liquids pose some special problems because of the vapours they form. Neglecting to use proper containers can be dangerous and failing to report suspicious odours can lead to fires. Precautions should include procedures to prevent the above occurrences by persuasion and training.

Explosive Chemicals

Explosion may be caused by the sudden release and vaporisation of a highly flammable liquid in a confined space in the presence of air; chemicals being inherently unstable and exploding without warning; or unstable and exploding as a result of degradation. For many materials, their chemical activity is greatly increased when they are finely-powdered, and in this form can give rise to a dust explosion.

Storage of Chemicals

The following guidelines are recommended for storing chemicals:

- Stores should be dry, well ventilated and secure and surrounded by a barrier or boundary sufficient to contain a leak. Chemicals should be kept away from direct heat and sunlight.

- Warning signs, e.g. "Flammable Chemical", "No Smoking", "No Naked Lights" should be displayed.

- Supervision should be by a competent trained person.

- Bulk storage drums should be earthed, stored upright and have a pressure relief valve.

- A drip tray should be in place to catch any spillages when liquid is drawn off.

- Approved non-spill containers (not glass or plastic) with flame arresters should be used for small amounts of liquid and only enough for a one-day work supply on site be drawn off. If possible, draw off in the open air. Unused amounts should be returned to the storage area at the end of the day.

- Containers should be kept closed when not in use.

- Containers should be inspected regularly for excessive wear, e.g. corrosion or leaks. If leaks occur, they should be reported to the supervisor immediately, the contents transferred to another container and the spill cleaned up with dry sand.

- Bulk storage areas should have automatic fire-extinguishing systems, safe light fixtures, fire-resistant walls and doors, good ventilation, clear warning signs ("Hazard", "No Smoking", etc.) and should be secure.

- Chemicals that can react with one another should be kept apart.

- Storage cabinets near work areas should be of approved construction and be earthed.

- First aid equipment, including an eye wash bottle, should always be available in the vicinity of the store.

There are stringent statutory storage regulations covering explosives, which must be stored in separate locked buildings away from the workplace. The following precautions apply:

- Only the minimum amount needed for the job should be used.

- Good ventilation is essential.

- Personnel should be trained in safe use of chemicals.

- No smoking (or ignition sources) should be allowed in the area.

- Operations should be carried out as distant as possible from other personnel.

- Fire safety equipment should be available.

- Protective clothing should be worn.

- Spills should be cleaned up promptly.

Wastes

Flammable wastes should be disposed of promptly. Used liquids should be kept in safety containers equipped with vents and earth wires, rags, paper, etc. kept in approved metal containers. The contents of these containers should be safely disposed of each day. Protective clothing should be worn when handling chemicals, such as safety goggles to protect eyes from splashes; long sleeves and trousers to protect skin from possible toxic effects; gloves and barrier creams to protect the hands from chemical irritation and safety shoes to give a more secure footing and protect the feet. Finally, if a fire occurs, water should not be used to extinguish the flames. Dry powder or foam should be used. Sand or a fire blanket can be used for small fires. Employees should be trained in the use of fire-fighting equipment.

Gases

The majority of gases and vapours have a toxic effect and inhalation usually results in rapid absorption into the blood stream. Others may have the effect of displacing or reducing the amount of oxygen available in the air, producing a situation where there is no "air" to breath. Examples in everyday use in industry include acetylene, oxygen and liquid petroleum gas (LPG) — propane, butane or a mixture of both.

Acetylene has a distinctive garlic-like smell. Fire and explosion hazards are similar to those of propane. However, it is lighter than air and less likely to collect in ducts and drains. Acetylene can decompose spontaneously when stored under pressure. For this reason, it is dissolved in acetone contained in a porous mass within the cylinder.

Oxygen has no smell. It is non-toxic and will not burn but supports and accelerates combustion. Materials not normally considered combustible may be ignited by sparks in oxygen-rich atmospheres. Oxygen leaks create conditions where substances not normally flammable will become highly combustible.

Liquid Petroleum Gases are used as a source of power for heating offices, canteens, etc., and for cooking. The gas is also used as a fuel for burning metal, welding, melting bitumen and lead, and for flame torches. At normal temperatures and pressures, LPG is a gas but is supplied as a liquid under pressure. When this pressure is reduced, e.g. the control valve is opened, the liquid starts to boil and gas is evolved: 1 litre of liquid will provide about 250 litres of gas. Butane has a much lower vapour pressure than propane (it is less volatile) and propane is used more frequently in construction. LPG is not toxic but can produce a narcotic effect leading to asphyxiation if sufficient air is displaced. If LPG-fuelled heaters are used in confined spaces, the occupants can, if adequate ventilation is not provided, suffer unconsciousness and death through depletion of oxygen. Propane and butane can cause drowsiness. Recommended exposure limits for butane are, long-term: 600 ppm (8 hour TWA) and short-term: 750 ppm (10min TWA). There is also the danger of asphyxiation when LPG is burned to provide heating, lighting, cooking, etc., unless there is adequate ventilation, as not only will the atmosphere become oxygen-deficient but toxic products of combustion will be formed.

It has a distinctive fish-like smell and will ignite and burn instantly from a spark or piece of hot metal. It is heavier than air and will collect in ducts, drains etc. Because of its rapid vaporisation, LPG can cause severe frost burns if in contact with the skin. Precautions that should be taken with compressed gases include:

- All cylinders may leak, so ventilation is essential.

- Cylinders should be strapped upright to minimise leaks.

- Regulators should not be mixed.

- Broken hoses should not be used.

- Flashback arrestors must be fitted between the cylinder and the equipment when using a flammable gas.

- Transport should be on trolleys.

Operators should be aware that flammable gas cylinders have a left-hand thread and should always treat cylinders with respect, as the energy equivalent in some cylinders is similar to a high-explosive shell.

Cylinders

Where cylinders are stored, the area should be at ground level and readily accessible to facilitate the prompt removal of cylinders in case of emergency. Wherever possible, storage areas should be in the open air, protected from unauthorised access by a fence at least 2m high. There should be sufficient shelter to prevent cylinders being exposed to extremes of weather. The floor should be paved or compacted level and with a suitable hard standing provided for the delivery and dispatch of cylinders. The area should be kept clear of all-flammable material, weeds and rubbish; there should be no adjacent drains or cellars and permanent notices stating "Highly Flammable" should be prominently displayed adjacent to each entry point. Notices prohibiting smoking and naked lights should also be posted. Cylinders, whether full or "empty", must be stored valve uppermost.

Good practice in handling, loading and unloading will minimise the risk of accidental gas leakage and consequently the major hazard, fire. A damaged or leaking valve can have serious and dangerous consequences and a crumpled base ring cannot hold a cylinder upright.

Cylinders, valves, connections, piping and hoses should be inspected regularly for leaks. Leaks may be detected by a characteristic smell, by the sound of escaping gas, by condensation or frost around the area of the leak or by brushing soapy water over the suspect area or valve and looking for bubbles.

Sourcing of Ignition and Permits-to-Work

The following must be excluded from hazardous areas where LPG is present:

- Smoking and the use of matches and lighters.

- Welding, cutting and blow lamps.

- Abrasive wheels and discs.

- Heating appliances such as space-heating equipment, electric fires, bitumen boilers, asphalt cauldrons.

- Steel tools — use non-spark alloy tools.

- Rubbish burning.

- Mechanically-propelled vehicles.

- Unprotected electric equipment.

Where it is necessary to work in or adjacent to an area where LPG is stored in either cylinder or bulk form, a permit-to-work system must be established if the operation is to proceed safely. The person carrying out the work covered by the permit must be instructed as to the necessary precautions to be taken, and a written handover procedure should be adopted. The permit should:

- Present the necessary information clearly and unambiguously.

- Specify the date and time of commencement and expiry.

- Specify precisely the area or item of plant on which work is to be carried out and detail the safety precautions.

The person issuing the permit should be satisfied that all the specified action has been taken. An example is given in **Figure 16.11**.

Figure 16.11: Sample Permit-to-Work Document

Permit-to-work for confined spaces	Signature	Position	Time/Date
Plant/area to be entered			
Work to be done			
Area removed from service			
Plant isolation Type			
Cleaning and purging to be carried out			
Testing:			
Flammable materials			
Toxic materials			
Oxygen levels			

I certify that the plant is safe to enter and the above particulars are correct

Mark safety equipment required:

        Goggles ☐   Gloves ☐ Breathing apparatus ☐   Revival appliance ☐
       Safety harness ☐   Lifeline ☐   Fire extinguisher ☐   First Aid ☐

Acceptance of Certificate			
Completion of work			
Request for extension			
Permit cancelled			
Plant returned to service			

Figure 16.12: Other Gases Found in the Workplace

Carbon Monoxide (CO) — a toxic gas: Carbon monoxide is a product of combustion, e.g. from engines of site vehicles, it is particularly hazardous in confined spaces.

Hazard: Carbon monoxide poisoning. The symptoms are drowsiness, vomiting, unconsciousness and may lead to death.

Carbon Dioxide (CO_2) — Gas: Again a product of combustion, which can build-up on confined spaces. Compressed CO_2 may be used in purging pipelines and tanks.

Hazard: Unconsciousness.

Hydrogen Sulphide (H_2S) — Highly toxic and flammable. H_2S is found in tunnels, mines, sewers or deep excavations. It can be recognised as the smell of rotten eggs but olfactory fatigue can increase the danger of exposure. In low concentrations, the eyes, nose and throat become irritated and headaches and dizziness occur. Exposure to high concentrations can lead to death.

Methane (CH4) Gas — Highly flammable and explosive. Methane is the principal component of natural gas. There is a danger of build-up in sewers and in excavations.

Arsine — damages red blood cells. Can be fatal. Used as nerve gas in World War 1. Lung damage occurs.

Chlorine — an irritant that may affect the lungs causing bronchitis and breathing difficulties.

Hydrochloric Acid — similar properties to chlorine.

Nitrogen Oxide — causes lung irritation. Occurs in engine exhaust.

Phosgene — Arises from burning of chlorinated hydrocarbons. Causes lung irritation.

Employees may be exposed to gases, including carbon monoxide and nitrous fumes from vehicles and machinery. These gases are dangerous in confined spaces, such as tunnels, manholes, basements, etc. Oil mist from the exhausts of pneumatic tools can also build up in confined spaces and cause nausea. Inhalation of some fumes, e.g. copper, tin, magnesium and calcium may cause an influenza-like illness. **Figure 16.12** lists other gases found in the workplace.

Strategies to Deal with Toxic Substances

- **Knowledge:** Everyone who works with toxic substances should know the names, toxicity and other hazards of the substances they use. Employers are required by law to provide this information, along with training in how to use toxic substances safely. A worker may obtain information about a chemical's composition, physical characteristics, and toxicity from the Material Safety Data Sheet (MSDS). Under law, manufacturers are required to supply the MSDS for products that contain certain toxic substances. Employers obtain the MSDS when they purchase the product and must make the MSDS available to employees. Unfortunately, the precise chemical composition is often proprietary (trade secret) information and the toxicity information on an MSDS may be incomplete and unreliable. NIFAST can help in the interpretation of the information on an MSDS.

- **Engineering Controls:** Limiting exposure at the source is the preferred way to protect workers. The types of engineering controls, in order of effectiveness, are:

  ◊ **Substitution** is using a less hazardous substance. But before choosing a substitute, carefully consider its physical and health hazards. For example, mineral spirits (Stoddard Solvent) is less of a health hazard than perchloroethylene for dry cleaning, but is more of a fire hazard and an air pollutant.

  ◊ **Process or equipment enclosure** is the isolation of the source of exposure, often through automation. This completely eliminates the routine exposure of workers. For example, handling of radioactive materials is often done by mechanical arms or robots.

  ◊ **Local exhaust ventilation** is a hood or intake at or over the source of exposure to capture or draw contaminated air from its source before it spreads into the room and the breathing zone.

  ◊ **General or dilution ventilation** is continual replacement and circulation of fresh air sufficient to keep concentrations of toxic substances diluted below hazardous levels. However, concentrations will be highest near the source, and overexposure may occur in this area. If the diluted air is not well mixed throughout the room, air pockets of high concentrations may exist.

- **Personal Protective Equipment:** The following devices should be used only when engineering controls are not possible or are not sufficient to reduce exposure:

  ◊ **Respiratory protective equipment** consists of devices that cover the mouth and nose to prevent substances in the air from being inhaled. A respirator is effective only when used as part of a comprehensive program established by the employer, which includes measurement of concentrations of all hazardous substances, selection of the proper respirator, training the worker in its proper use, fitting of the respirator to the worker, maintenance, and replacement of parts when necessary.

  ◊ **Protective clothing** includes gloves, aprons, goggles, boots, face shields, and any other materials worn as protection, and should be made of material designed to resist penetration by the particular chemical being used. The manufacturer of the protective clothing usually can provide some information regarding the substances that are effectively blocked.

  ◊ **Barrier creams** are used to coat the skin and prevent chemicals from reaching it. They may be helpful when the type of work prevents the use of gloves. However, barrier creams are *not* recommended as substitutes for gloves. General skin creams and lotions (such as moisturising lotion) are *not* barrier creams.

ELECTRICAL SAFETY

The study of electricity and its properties is a complex topic. Electricity is a useful and safe energy source if a number of basic precautions are taken. The simplest rule with electricity is to respect it, and not to interfere with any aspect of it, which one is not qualified to deal with. Treated carelessly, electricity can cause serious injury and, if it flows through vital organs of the body such as the heart, even death. Fortunately, even where electrical accidents do occur, serious injury and fatalities are rare, but nevertheless, burns at the point of contact can result in unpleasant injuries. **Figure 16.13** presents a set of general questions to pose in respect of electrical safety.

Figure 16.13: An Electrical Safety Checklist

- Are all plugs, sockets and fittings obtained from a reputable manufacturer and sufficiently robust for business use?

- Are fuses, circuit breakers and other devices correctly rated for the circuit they protect?

- Are covers to electrical dangers kept close and, where possible, locked?

- Are main switches readily accessible and clearly marked?

- Does everyone know how to use them in an emergency?

- Are electrical installations checked periodically and repairs carried out by a competent electrician?

- Is all portable apparatus listed so that it can be regularly inspected and its condition recorded?

- Is all suspect or faulty equipment taken out of use, put in a secure place and labelled 'do not use'?

- Have the special maintenance requirements of waterproof or explosion-protected equipment been recorded and someone made responsible for them?

- Has someone been made responsible for checking the test button on residual current circuit breakers?

- Are all tools and power sockets switched off before being plugged in?

- Are all appliances unplugged before cleaning or maintenance commences?

- Are there written and understood procedures for undertaking work on electrical systems and equipment, on the basis that danger is removed by disconnection of the electricity supply?

- Do these procedures specify the requirements for the necessary safe systems of work, including the arrangements to ensure that the isolation is secure?

- Is there a clear management policy setting out the justified circumstances when live working is permitted?

- When live working is justified and is carried out, are there properly documented work procedures to prevent injury?

- Do the procedures for live work specify the requirements for the necessary safe systems of work, including the provision and use of specialist equipment such as insulated tools, rubber gloves, rubber mats and screening material?

- Do those staff required to undertake electrical work first receive appropriate training, whether for work on de-energised or on live systems?

- Do staff receive refresher or additional training when required?

- Are checks undertaken on a regular basis to confirm the competency of staff engaged on electrical work, and which is appropriate to the type of electrical system and work to be undertaken?

- Are records kept of all training and assessments?

- Are staff given adequate instructions for all work, including information on relevant hazards and precautions to be undertaken?

- During the course of work, do staff receive adequate supervision?

- Do the managers in control understand their duties under the regulations?

Electrical Hazards

Electricity is one of the most commonly encountered hazards in any facility. Under normal conditions, the inherent safety features of the electrical utilisation equipment afford protection from shock. Nonetheless, accidental contact with electricity can cause serious injury or death. Most electrical systems establish a voltage reference point by connecting a portion of the system to an earth ground. Because these systems use conductors that have voltages with respect to ground, a shock hazard exists for workers who are in contact with the earth and exposed to the conductors. If people come in contact with a "live" (ungrounded) conductor while they are in contact with the ground, they become part of the circuit and current passes through their bodies.

Figure 16.14: The Effects of Electric Shock on Men and Women

	Current, mA					
	Direct Current		*Alternating Current*			
			60 Hz		10kHz	
	Men	Women	Men	Women	Men	Women
Slight sensation on hand	1	0.6	0.4	0.3	7	5
Perception threshold, median	6.2	3.5	1.1	0.7	12	8
Shock- not painful and no loss of muscular control	9	6	1.8	1.2	17	11
Painful shock – let go threshold, median	62	41	9	6	55	37
Painful shock – let go threshold, median	76	51	16	10.5	75	50
Painful and severe shock – breathing difficulty, muscular control lost by 99.5%	90	60	23	15	94	63
Possible ventricular fibrillation:						
Three second shocks	500	500	100	100		
			165/%T	165/%T		
	50b	50b	13.6 b	13.6b		

Source: The Deleterious Effects of Electric Shock, Charles F. Dalziel, p.24. Presented at a meeting of experts on electrical accidents and related matters, sponsored by the International Labour Office, World Health Office and International Electrotechnical Commission, Geneva, Switzerland, October 23-31, 1961. Reproduced by Berkeley Lab, California, with permission of the author. Energy in joules(watt·seconds)

The effects of electric current on the human body depend on:

- Contact and internal resistance of the body.

- The current's pathway through the body determined by contact location and internal body chemistry.

- Duration of contact.

- Environmental conditions affecting the body's contact resistance.

The most damaging route of electricity is through the chest cavity or brain. Fatal ventricular fibrillation of the heart (stopping the rhythmic pumping action) can be initiated by a current flow of as little as several milliamperes. Nearly instantaneous fatalities can result from either direct paralysis of the respiratory system, failure of rhythmic pumping action, or immediate heart stoppage. Severe injuries, such as deep internal burns, can occur even if the current does not pass through the vital organs or nerve centre.

Burns

Burns suffered in electrical accidents are of three basic types: electrical burns, arc burns and thermal contact burns. In electrical burns, tissue damage (whether skin deep or deeper) occurs because the body is unable to dissipate the heat from the current flow. Typically, electrical burns are slow to heal. Arc burns are caused by electric arcs and are similar to heat burns from high-temperature sources. Temperatures generated by electric arcs can melt nearby material, vaporise metal in close vicinity, and burn flesh and ignite clothing at distances surfaces of overheated electric conductors.

Delayed Effects

Damage to the internal tissues may not be apparent immediately after contact with the current. Delayed internal tissue swelling and irritation are possible. Prompt medical attention can help minimise these effects and avoid death or long-term injury.

Other Hazards

Voltage sources that do not have dangerous current capabilities may not pose serious shock or burn hazards in themselves and therefore are often treated in a casual manner. However, they are frequently used adjacent to lethal circuits, and even a minor shock could cause a worker to rebound into a lethal circuit. Such an involuntary reaction may also result in bruises, bone fractures, and even death from collisions or falls. Electricity poses other hazards. An arc is often created when a short circuit occurs or current flow is interrupted. If the current involved is strong enough, these arcs can cause injury or start a fire. Fires can also be started by overheated equipment or by conductors that carry too much current. Extremely high energy arcs can cause an explosion that sends fragmented metal flying in all directions. Even low-energy arcs can cause violent explosive or combustible atmospheres.

Electric Shock

In the electrical installation where the neutral connection is commonly used, there is always a chance for current to flow from the live conductor to earth and therefore back to the current source. Usually current that flows to earth is caused by some type of defect and is termed an earth fault current.

Earth fault currents can be dangerous and even fatal, depending on the magnitude and the surrounding environment. Dangers and fatalities due to earth fault current include fire as a result of materials being ignited and humans or animals being killed by electric shock. There is nothing that can prevent an earth fault from occurring, but quick disconnection should be possible if a suitable apparatus is installed.

The degree of danger of electric shock depends on the voltage of the current and the time for which the current flows. So a low current for a long duration can be just as dangerous as a high current for a relatively short period. Of course voltage has to be present in order to produce the current through the resistance of the body.

Table 16.8 presents a summary of issues related to managing electrical safety.

***Table 16.8: Managing Electrical Safety — Implementation
Issues in Organisations***

It is company policy to follow the fundamental principles of safety described below. Implementation of these principles increases the safety of employees who work with or around electrical equipment.

- **Practice proper housekeeping and cleanliness.** Poor housekeeping is a major factor in many accidents. A cluttered area is likely to be both unsafe and inefficient. Every employee is responsible for keeping a clean area, and every supervisor is responsible for ensuring that his or her areas of responsibility remain clean.

- **Identify hazards and anticipate problems.** Think through what might go wrong and the consequences of that action. Do not hesitate to discuss any situation or question with your supervisor and co-workers.

- **Resist "hurry-up" pressure.** Programme pressures should not cause you to by-pass thoughtful consideration and planned procedures.

- **Design for safety.** Consider safety to be an integral part of the design process. Protective devices, warning signs, and administrative procedures are supplements to good design — not a substitute for it. Engineering controls are always preferable to administrative controls. Completed designs should include provisions for safe maintenance.

- **Maintain for safety.** Good maintenance is essential to safe operations. Maintenance procedures and schedules for servicing and maintaining equipment and facilities, including documentation of repairs, removals, replacements, and disposals, should be established.

- **Document for work.** An up-to-date set of documentation adequate for operation, maintenance, testing and safety should be available to anyone working on potentially hazardous equipment. Keep drawings and prints up to date. Dispose of obsolete drawings and be certain that active file drawings have the latest corrections. All facilities drawings are to be archived with the records analyst and control specialist.

- **Have designs reviewed.** All systems and modifications to systems performing a safety function or controlling a potentially hazardous operation must be reviewed and approved at the level of project engineer or above.

- **Have designs and operation verified.** All systems performing safety functions or controlling a potentially hazardous operation must be validated by actual test procedures before being placed in service, at least once a year, and anytime the system is suspected of malfunction. Both the procedures and actual tests must be documented.

- **Test equipment safety.** Conduct tests with the electrical equipment de-energised, or, if the equipment cannot be de-energised, with reduced hazard.

- **Know emergency procedures.** All persons working in areas of high hazard (high-voltage power supplies, capacitor banks, etc) must be trained in emergency response procedures, including cardiopulmonary resuscitation (CPR) certification.

- **Beware of the wet areas.** While working with liquids (e.g., washing, mopping and spraying), exercise extra care to avoid contact with electrical outlets or devices. Cover electrical openings if liquids can penetrate them. If the openings cannot be covered, the power must be disconnected and locked.

- **Use electrical devices only as intended.** Electrical devices may not be modified beyond the intent of their design. Electrical equipment is only safe when used according to its intended purpose. Some examples of misuse of electrical equipment are:
  1. Pulling out a plug by the cord rather than by the plug.
  2. Inserting wires or objects other than a standard plug into a receptacle outlet.
  3. Constructing homemade extension cords from standard junction boxes and receptacles (a "radar box").
  4. Deforming a contact to enable it to fit a receptacle for which it was not intended.

- **Always consider electrical equipment energised unless positively proven otherwise.** When working on electrical equipment, treat the equipment as live until it is tested, locked, tagged, shorted and/or grounded, as appropriate.

- **Re-set circuit breakers only after the problem has been corrected.** When a circuit breaker or other overcurrent device trips, it is usually due to an overload or fault condition on the line. Repeated attempts to re-energise the breaker under these conditions may cause the breaker to explode. Do not attempt to re-set a circuit breaker unless the problem has first been identified and corrected or isolated.

An electric shock affects the nervous system and can cause muscular contraction, including the inability to relax, thus increasing the period of contact and the possibility of serious consequences. If the current passes through the heart, it disrupts its pumping action and, death is almost certain. This is called fibrillation of the heart. A shock that in itself might not be serious may cause a reaction that results in loss of balance and a subsequent fall, which could have serious results.

Shock is usually caused by the passage of current through the body to earth, one part of the body touching a live conductor and another part being in contact with earth; for example, by standing on the ground or touching metalwork connected to earth. It is possible to get a shock from a three-phase system by parts of the body coming into contact with two phases without being in contact with an earth, but this is comparatively rare. A shock from Direct Current has less muscular contraction effect than Alternating Current, the tendency being to cause the victim violently to withdraw from contact if possible, so that the period of contact is usually short.

Extensive research conducted by scientists such as Professor Dr. Beigelmeier of Austria demonstrates that human body resistance varies with different parts of the body, whether the person is alive or dead and if the conditions are wet or dry. IEC 479, which is an international report published by the International Electromechanical Commission, describes the time/current zones of the effects of 50/60Hz voltage and current on human body. Briefly the physical effect of shock intensifies as follows:

- Threshold of perception about 1mA average.

- The "no let go" values — women 10mA, men 16.5mA.

- Ventricular fibrillation usually occurs above 50mA.

Shock between live conductors is largely confined to electrical staff when carrying out maintenance and testing, and there is no positive means available for its prevention. The only safeguard is close control of safety procedures and the responsibility and training of competent people authorised for such work. Work in situations where inadvertent contact with live metal, including those instances where it may be necessary to re-engage exploded electrical equipment for observation of its performance, should be permitted only when a second person is present to effect a rescue in cases of emergency. It is recommended never to work on live equipment. The occasion should never arise on a construction site.

Electrical shock to earth is the most frequent cause of electrocution to the ordinary user of electricity as only one contact with live metal or earth is necessary to complete the circuit. Electric shock is more associated with portable apparatus than fixed parts of installation. Fortunately, this hazard can now be almost totally eliminated by the use of highly sensitive residual current devices (RCDs) and low voltage supply.

Protection by RCDs

Residual current devices (RCDs) previously known as earth leakage circuit breakers (ELCBs) give protection to humans and livestock against the dangers of electrocution from direct or indirect contact. They also provide safeguards against fire risks by automatically detecting earth leakage currents.

Recommendations for the use of RCDs are primarily aimed at providing protection against electric shock due to indirect contact. In particular, their use is preferred where shock protection by overcurrent devices, such as fuses, is impracticable due to high values of earth-loop impedance preventing compliance with disconnection time as specified in the National Rules for Electrical Installations. For construction sites, the disconnection time should be halved. Safe design of an electrical installation is based on the criteria that the touch voltage should not exceed 50V but this value should be halved to 25V for construction sites.

An RCD operates by constantly ensuring that the phase current entering a circuit is the same as the neutral (or other phase current) leaving the circuit. Under normal circumstances, these should be equal. In the event of an imbalance due to leakage to earth, the RCD will trip.

Earth leakage circuit breakers were introduced in Ireland in 1972 as a legal requirement for industrial locations including construction sites and, in all other premises built since 1980, the Electro-Technical Council of Ireland wiring rules require that RCDs be installed to protect all socket outlets. The RCD should be a high-sensitivity type with an operating current not exceeding 30mA and installed at the distribution board in order to protect electrically-operated appliances that are used outdoors with such devices. Through the use of residual current devices of low sensitivity, there has been a marked decline in accidents attributable to portable and transportable apparatus.

Portable and Transportable Apparatus

Portable apparatus, due to the nature of its handling, has been a source of electric shock and electrocution in recent times but, with the introduction of the residual current devices and the legal requirements of low-voltage supply for certain locations, the danger has been greatly reduced. Since 1974 specific Regulations dealing with portable, transportable apparatus and low voltage supply have been introduced to Ireland. Before discussing the requirements, and to avoid confusion, the following definitions are given:

- **Portable apparatus** includes "all hand-held apparatus required to be moved while working and which is designed so that it can be moved while it is working" e.g. drills, sanders, polishers, grinders, vibrators, paint sprayers, etc.

- **Transportable apparatus** means an apparatus that, because of its design and purpose, is moved from time to time between the periods during which it is working. This would include festoon lighting, flood lighting on portable stands, conveyors, pumps, compressors, small mixers, and mobile cranes.

In damp or confined situations, on building operations and on works of engineering construction, legislation requires that all portable and transportable apparatus with electric motors of up to and including 2 HP should be operated at a voltage not exceeding 125 volts AC. Portable, hand-held lamps must be operated at a voltage not exceeding 25 volts AC or 50 volts DC.

The supply of electricity to portable or transportable apparatus and portable hand lamps should be obtained from a double-wound-type transformer with the centre point of the secondary or low-voltage winding tapped and brought out for permanent connection to earth. This gives a voltage to earth of 62.5 volts for portable and transportable apparatus, and 12.5 volts for portable hand lamps. The practice in Ireland is to use 110 volts, which gives 55 volts to earth.

All hand-held apparatus should be provided with a switching-off device that must form part of the apparatus. In addition, every portable hand lamp should be provided with a properly insulated holder and a substantial guard, enclosing the bulb of the lamp.

Portable and transportable apparatus rated above 2 HP or 2 KVA may be operated at a voltage above 125 volts alternating current (AC) but the circuit should be protected by a residual current device (RCD) with an operating current of 30mA. The RCD should be in a fixed position and not fitted to the apparatus in use. It is best housed at the supply end and should be a totally enclosed type to withstand the environmental conditions. These circuit breakers afford added protection and do not, in any way, replace the earthing neutralising system or site earth.

It is strongly recommended that where portable tools are returned to stores or workshops on completion of each job, they should be examined and tested before reissue. Examination should be carried out to ensure that the connections of the equipment at the terminals and plug top are secure. Special attention should be given to the cord grip or bridge used to prevent mechanical pull or load on flexible cable, at the point of entry to the apparatus or plug top.

Types of Safety

Table 16.9 presents a summary of the distribution voltages allowed under the Electricity Regulations.

Table 16.9: Distribution Voltages under Electricity Regulations

Fixed, portable and transportable apparatus (above 2HP or 2 KVA)	380/220 volts three or single phase
Installation in site building	220 volts single phase
Semi-permanent flood lighting	220 volts single phase
Portable and transportable apparatus (under 2HP or 2 KVA)	110 volts three or single phase
Site lighting (festoon lighting, portable and transportable floodlighting)	110 volts single phase
Portable hand lamps	25 volt single phase

Distribution Systems

The use of modular site distribution systems is recommended for larger construction sites. The system has the following advantages:

- Flexible in application for repeated use on contract work, which allows easy substitution of components for specific duty as, may be required from site to site.

- Acceptable for transport and storage.

- Robust in construction to resist damage.

- May be used on an expansive site or a high-rise building.

The function of each unit in the system is:

- SIU (main distribution unit) — to take supply from SIU through an incoming switch (fused and connected to a busbar system). Outgoing circuits (three-phase and neutral or single-phase and neutral) are connected to the busbar through moulded-case circuit-breakers.

- TU (transformer unit: 380-110V: 3-phase) — to transform voltage within the range quoted. It is a three-phase, double-wound transformer with a star-connected secondary winding. Its socket-outlets are switched through miniature circuit-breakers.

- TU (transformer unit: 220-110V: 1-phase) — to transform voltage within the range quoted. It is a single-phased, double-wound transformer with a centre tap secondary winding. Its socket outlets are switched through miniature circuit-breakers.

- OU (outlet unit: 110V) — to provide additional socket outlets, protected by miniature circuit breakers, to extend the range of the TU to which it is connected by flexible cable and plug.

- EOU (extension outlet unit: 110V) — to extend the range of the OU by providing two-socket outlets. It is connected to the OU by flexible cables and plug.

The cost of these units may be prohibitive for the smaller and medium-sized builders. These separate items could be amalgamated into a single unit. The use of miniature circuit breakers (MCBs) has the advantage that they may be easily switched on when the fault has cleared. However, it is essential that the MCBs have a back-up protection of a fuse of a suitable type.

Flexible Cables

Probably the most vulnerable piece of electrical apparatus is the flexible cable, especially when used as a trailing cable to supply a portable or transportable apparatus. In view of the prevalence of this hazard, the use of metallic covering to protect flexible cables is necessary where the voltage exceeds 125AC. In addition, all flexible cables used for supplying portable or transportable apparatus, except for 110-volts double-insulated type, must include an earthing conductor of a cross sectional area of not less than that of the largest current carrying conductor in the cable.

Flexible cables must be connected to the apparatus by efficient permanent joints or by a properly constructed connector and arranged so that tension in the cable cannot be transmitted through the conductors to the terminal at either end. Metallic covering on flexible cables must be securely attached to the apparatus.

Every electrical joint and connection must be of proper construction as regards conductance, insulation, mechanical strength and protection. The use of tape joints is not allowed and a proper male/female connection must be used for flexible cables and extensions.

Plugs, Socket Outlets and Couplers

Industrial plugs and sockets based on BS 4343 1968 and CEE are recommended for use on construction sites. The internationally standardised system is suitable for all DC and AC voltages up to 750V. Non-interchangeability between different voltages is achieved by means of a keyway in the socket shroud and a corresponding key on the plug connection with different positioning of the insert in the housing. These are given as relative position of earth socket tube to keyway making use of hour positions (**Table 16.10**).

Table 16.10: Types of Plugs, Socket Outlets and Couplers

Volts	Phase	Ampere	Position of Pins	Colour	Hour Position "H"
380	3	16/32	5	Red	6
380	3	62/122	6	Red	6
220	1	16/32	3	Blue	6
110	3	16/32	4	Yellow	4
110	1	16/32		Yellow	4

If these types of plugs, socket outlets and couplers are used by the main and sub-contractor, electrical apparatus used anywhere in the country will fit the distribution system provided by the main contractor. The colour code also gives easy identification of the various voltage supplies and improves the safety factor.

The lesson to be learned from this is that all contact with live electrical conductors should be avoided. The basis of electrical safety is to protect against such contact either through providing direct protection in the form of adequate insulation, and indirect protection by providing earthing for any parts that might become charged should the basic insulation fail. Another safety mechanism is to reduce the voltage used in the circuit, in order to reduce the corresponding risk in the event of a shock, but this is often impracticable in many industrial applications.

Proper electrical installation involves ensuring the effective insulation of all circuits, the use of safe switches to prevent the flow of current when not required, and the use of appropriate socket outlets and plugs to allow the safe extension of circuitry to mobile appliances. The use of fuses and circuit breakers (trip switches) is essential to ensure the safety of appliances, should an overload of current occur. Most large fixed electrical appliances are fitted with their own circuits and overload protection mechanisms, but the fuses in the plug attached to a mobile appliance must be checked to ensure they are of a suitable value.

Due to the flexibility of portable appliances, they are common causes of shocks and burns. Their mobility often results in unnoticed wear and tear, causing defects in the cables or insulating covers. Some appliances such as saws and lawnmowers run the added risk of causing a short circuit through cutting their own cables, and appliances used on construction sites pose specific dangers because of the often rugged working conditions. Using reduced voltage systems or double-insulated tools can help diminish the effects of these problems.

In order to use all electrical appliances safely, the list of basic rules outlined in **Figure 16.15** should be observed.

Figure 16.15: Electrical Appliance Safety

- Electrical systems and appliances should be designed and constructed to fit the intended use, and conform to desired international standards.

- They must be adapted to suit the specific environment in which they are to be used, e.g. special fireproofing systems may be required for electrical circuits which are used in environments with a high risk of combustion.

- They must be installed by experts to corresponding standards.

- They must be used for the purpose intended, as alternative uses may result in damage to component parts, causing shock or fire.

- The user must be supplied with all the information relevant to the safe operation of the appliance.

- Proper training, instruction and supervision should be provided to operators to ensure competent use of appliances.

- Regular inspections and maintenance of equipment must be carried out, and records kept of such.

- All inspection and maintenance work should be carried out by qualified persons, or under supervision of a qualified person.

- All such work should be guided by written procedures, justifying the work to be done, and the methods used to do it.

- Employees carrying out such work should receive and use proper insulating protective equipment such as gloves, platforms, mats, etc.

CHAPTER ROUND-UP

* Housekeeping is an important component of safety management within the workplace. It refers to everyday activities designed to keep work areas clean and free from dangers. These duties play an important role in maintaining safe systems of work. Poor housekeeping, on the other hand, can pose unnecessary dangers such as the build-up of rubbish and waste. To be effective, housekeeping, must become part of every employee's daily work routine. Regular audits of housekeeping should be conducted to assess housekeeping performance.

* Another component of effective workplace safety management is the proper maintenance of work equipment, machinery and hand tools. Machines and handtools pose many safety hazards including situations where employees come into contact with machines, where they come into contact with equipment or where they are struck by parts ejected from equipment.

* The installation of effective fire safety systems and procedures is a fundamental aspect of risk management. Fire safety management begins with an understanding of the physics and chemistry of fire and any fire prevention measures should be aimed at minimising the risk of fire outbreak. Many fires are caused by carelessness, resulting in faulty design, everyday operations and malicious intent. Educating employees on fire safety issues helps to convey an understanding of the risks involved and can be a powerful motivator in developing a fire safety culture.

* The statistical evidence on accidents in Ireland demonstrates that manual handling is responsible for approximately 30% of injuries. It is recommended that an organisation should implement a manual handling policy. This policy should cover issues such as manual handling standards, purchasing controls, engineering controls, the selection of personnel, accident/incident investigations and training. Whenever possible, mechanical handling should be used in preference to manual handling. A wide range of devices exist to assist handling.

- Dangerous substances have a high inherent propensity to cause damage to health but the risk posed depends on how the substance is handled. Substances are usually classified according to the effect of their chemical properties on employees. They can have adverse consequences on health in terms of direct toxic effects or indirectly as a result of a chemical reaction external to the body.

- Electricity is a useful and safe energy source but, treated carelessly, electricity can cause injury and even death if it flows through vital organs of the body. Specific legislation and standards are now in place to facilitate organisations in implementing effective procedures to minimise the risks from electricity.

Chapter 17

MANAGING THE ENVIRONMENT: SYSTEMS, AUDITS AND WASTE MINIMISATION

INTRODUCTION

Since the early 1970s environmental protection and management of the environment have become a priority. This is primarily due to the realisation that consumption of natural resources and indiscriminate dumping of waste materials, by commercial organisations, into the environment is having effects at local and global levels, some of which may be irreversible. Traditional methods of environmental protection primarily involved command and control systems, including a variety of laws covering all aspects of the environment. Since 1973, the EU has enacted over 450 separate pieces of environmental legislation. The areas covered include air, water, soil, waste management, environmental impact assessment and conservation of nature. This legislation, together with scientific evidence demonstrating the continuing deterioration of the environment and an increased public awareness, has helped ensure that environmental issues are now a priority on the business agenda.

Because many aspects of an organisation's activities impinge on the environment, it is necessary to ensure co-ordination and management of the organisation's environmental management system. The system should ensure that, through operating procedures, records, documentation and management action, adverse environmental effects are prevented at source.

This chapter sketches the background to the emergence of environmentalism and describes the evaluation and components of environmental management systems that may be implemented by organisations. It also details how these systems have come to form the basis of environmental management standards at Irish, European and global levels.

THE EMERGENCE OF ENVIRONMENTALISM

The past two decades have witnessed the emergence of the environmental movement as a powerful force with major economic and organisational implications. Business organisations are significantly impeded by environmentalism. There is, in general, a greater concern about conserving natural resources, and using less environment-polluting technologies and more environmentally-safe and -friendly products.

Concern for the environment has been highlighted by widespread publicity given to ecological crises caused by acid rain, air pollution, the greenhouse effect, ozone depletion, hazardous wastes and major industrial disasters such as the Bhopal disaster, the Chernobyl nuclear accident and the Exxon Valdez oil spill. In Europe, Green political parties have made impressive showings in national elections with the result that many mainstream parties have added environmental protection to their political agendas. Legislation and policy, at EU level, has forced European companies to deal increasingly with environmental protection, worker health and industrial safety issues. Pollutant and hazardous industries such as those involved in the production of motor vehicles, chemicals, petroleum, nuclear power and hazardous waste management, to name a few, have been affected by a large volume of new laws and regulations.

The environmental impulse, as understood by many European companies, is not limited to narrow demands for environmental awareness. It has a broader scope covering issues of industrial safety, environmental protection, natural resource conservation, protection of human health and the management of technological risks. **Figure 17.1** summarises the scope of these activities.

It is argued that environmental management issues must be dealt with at operating and strategic levels within organisations. At the operational level, the issue is to develop operational policies and procedures, provide adequate training, establish standards and monitor and reward performance. The need to comply with relevant Regulations and provide necessary information to regulating agencies is also an issue at an operational level. At the lating agencies is also an issue at an operational level. At the strategic level, the issue is to develop appropriate policies and formulate an overall environmental management strategy. This should focus on the development of safe technologies and developing corporate-wide capabilities for dealing with crises and ensuring that top management monitors environmental performance.

Figure 17.1: The Scope of Environmentalism

Industrial Safety: Focuses on making plants, warehouses and other industrial protection systems safe for workers and the public. Important concern involves making choices about safety technologies and the formulation and implementation of safety policies and procedures.

Environmental Protection: Focuses on the reduction of environmentally-harmful emissions and effluents from industrial facilities. Gives consideration to the design and implementation of conservation measures that enable reduced use of non-renewable environmental resources.

Waste Management: Focuses on the identification and reduction of hazardous waste sites and programmes for the reduction of waste generation.

Employee Health: Focuses on implementing policies and programmes aimed at ensuring healthy working conditions, compliance with health and safety regulations and the monitoring of health hazards.

Product Safety: Focuses on programmes for ensuring safety over the life of a product and disposal of used products and packaging.

Industrial Security: Focuses on programmes to ensure security of company assets and loss-minimisation programmes.

Risk, Liability and Insurance Management: Focuses on programmes aimed at minimising technological and environmental risks and the minimisation of corporate liability for product injuries, technological hazards and hazardous waste sites.

Crises Management: Focuses on programmes aimed at preventing incidents that could trigger corporate crises and developing systems to deal with such crises.

It is also argued that a step towards environmentalism requires a change in values. Smith (1994) suggests that many corporate values are undermining the spirit of environmentalism. He suggests that the value of individualism stand in contrast to the environmentalists' notion of communitarianism or the idea of humans as part of a larger community. Likewise, the cultural values of consumerism contrasts with the consumption-for-survival ethic of environmentalism. Environmentalism believes in the absolute right of nature to exist and prosper independent of its benefits for humans. Therefore it is not sufficient to understand environmentalist values. Companies must accommodate them by modifying their existing corporate cultures. Such efforts require education initiatives and investment in products and technologies that are more environmentally friendly.

THE BUSINESS CASE FOR ENVIRONMENTAL MANAGEMENT

There is some debate about the return to organisations that adopt green policies. An Earthscan Report entitled *The Link between Company Environmental and Management Performance* asserts that it does pay to be green.

The Earthscan Report is based on a comparative two-stage analysis of the financial performance of 50 green companies. At stage one of the analysis, the financial performance of each green company was compared to the financial performance of a number on non-green companies of a similar profile. At the second stage of the analysis, each green company was compared to the best financial performer from the non-green sample.

The results from the study suggest that there is a positive link between environmental and financial performance. At the stage one analysis, over two-thirds of the green companies performed better than their non-green comparators. At the stage two analysis, when the green companies were compared with best financial performers from the non-green comparators, the Earthscan Report states that they performed "as well".

Financial Analysis

The Earthscan Report examines the results of companies in a number of sectors — electrical/electronic equipment, engineering, healthcare, support services, food retailers, paper/packaging/printing, general retailers, building materials — and examines the return on capital employed and on equity. The results shown in **Table 17.1** are the average outcome over the years (1992) to (1996).

Table 17.1: Comparative Results of Return on Capital and Equity, Green and Non-Green Companies

	Green	**Non-green**
Stage One		
Return on capital employed	24.96%	14.38%
Return on equity	13.66%	8.6%
Stage Two		
Return on capital employed	24.92%	24.69%
Return on equity	19.29%	22.05%

The Earthscan Report argues that companies with an environmental management system may find that their external financing is positively affected. It is suggested that the "cost of capital may be lowered, insurance premiums reduced and share price improved".

Some commentators suggest that "it is not easy to prove that investments in environmental risk management is wise". Reinhart (2000) focuses on how environmental management can be justified by differentiating products and by what he terms "managing your competitors" — working together with competitors on regulatory control — he looks at internal cost reduction. He cites the example of how Inter-Continental Hotels have saved $300,000 a year by replacing small bottles of shampoo with bulk dispensers. He encourages companies to audit their insurance policies and risk management systems. He argues the case for integrating environmental management into "overall risk management approaches". This will offer "better decisions over the long run".

APPROACHES TO ENVIRONMENTAL MANAGEMENT

Scannell (1995) suggests that countries can adopt six options in terms of managing the physical environment:

- Formulate policies that promote the protection of the environment.

- Draw up environmental management plans.

- Use criminal sanctions against those who fail to comply with legal requirements.

- Use civil sanctions such as injunctions or damages.

- Introduce a system of prior authorisation requirements.

- Develop and implement environmental standards.

Environmental Policies

The formulation of environmental policies is viewed as an essential component of effective environmental management. Clearly defined policies and parameters for institutions, companies and individuals provide the framework within which environmental strategies can be implemented. Until 1989, Ireland had no national policy on the environment, with the result that environmental measures were taken in a piecemeal fashion. The situation has improved somewhat since then, although many areas still lack clear policy guidelines.

There has also been a failure to integrate environmental policies into other sectoral policies, with the result that many problems of an environmental nature have emerged, e.g. smoke levels in major cities, because of grants for solid fuel fires, the use of open fireplaces and farming methods which lead to pollution. It is argued that many of these problems would not have arisen had clear policies on the environment been articulated at national level. The existence of such policies would make the ground rules clear and provide a framework for debate.

Environmental Management Plans

Management plans are viewed as an effective environmental management strategy. They can set out the conditions under which activities, that have environmental consequences, can be managed and protected. Like policies, they provide a framework and guidelines for decision-makers and give a sense of security to developers and environmental protection organisations.

There is a limited degree of statutory provision in Ireland for making environmental plans. Local authorities are required to draw up land-use management plans, water quality management plans, waste management plans and plans for dangerous waste. They are also required to formulate air quality management plans and the Minister for State at the Department of Finance has the power to designate land as a refuge for a particular species of flora. Scannell (1995) highlights that the use of such plans is limited in Ireland.

Criminal Sanctions

Many statutory initiatives on the environment provide for the imposition of criminal sanctions, in the form of fines and/or imprisonment, for breach or failure to comply with these provisions. In general, a large maximum fine is provided for in the legislation and these fines may, in some cases, be paid to the local authority rather than going directly to the Exchequer. There is now a tendency to impose obligations on the directors and senior management of companies. This is viewed as an effective way of obtaining commitment to environmental issues from senior management.

Civil Sanctions

Contemporary environmental legislation provides for a range of civil law remedies to any individual who wishes to enforce environmental legislation. It is possible for an individual, whether or not they have a personal interest in the issue, to sue in order to enforce planning, water pollution and air pollution controls. Such a trend is based on the view that it provides a powerful incentive to individuals to enforce environmental controls and take responsibility for managing the environment.

Prior Authorisation Requirements

Scannell (1995) defines a prior authorisation as any form of permission, licence or permit, which may be obtained from a statutory authority before certain activities can be initiated. These activities must have potential to affect the environment. Prior authorisation is now required under EU and Irish law for a wide range of private and public sector activities. These include planning permission, licences for the discharge of trade and sewage effluents and the disposal of wastes on land and at sea. The effectiveness of prior authorisation arrangements is contingent upon the existence of accurate data on the state of the environment, which may be affected by the proposed activity.

ENVIRONMENTAL AUDITING

Environmental Management Systems are a progression from Environmental Auditing, which began in the US in the 1970s. It was used as an internal management tool, to measure an organisation's performance, initially in the health and safety area, and subsequently in the environmental area for legal compliance and conformity to the company's environmental policy. The oil and chemical industries were particularly environmentally-sensitive, and were the first companies to adopt Environmental Auditing procedures. Examples of such audits include:

- Legal compliance audits.

- Waste minimisation audits.

- Water use audits.

- Product audits.

- Policy compliance audits.

- Liability audits.

- Environmental management audits.

Environmental management systems may be monitored by an environmental audit. The Environmental Protection Agency Act, 1992 defines such an audit as:

> ... a management tool comprising a systematic, documented, periodic and objective evaluation of how well the organisation, management and equipment are performing with the aim of helping to safeguard the environment by facilitating management control of environmental practices,

and assessing compliance with company policies, which would include meeting regulatory requirement.

The ISO/SAGE definition of environmental auditing is:

A systematic process of objectively obtaining and evaluating evidence to determine the reliability of an assertion with regard to environmental aspects of activities, events and conditions, as to how they measure to established criteria, and communicating the results to the client.

However, audits alone are inadequate.

Audits and reviews cannot provide all organisations with the assurance that its performance not only meets, but will continue to meet, legislative and policy requirements.

To be effective, they need to be conducted within a structured management system, integrated with overall management activity and address all aspects of the environment. Audits are restricted to past and current environmental performance, whereas Environmental Management Systems set objects and targets for continuous improvement in environmental performance.

Formulating Environment Management Policies

It is generally accepted as good practice to formulate a policy statement on the environment.

The policy statement must be signed by top management and will represent the organisation's formal undertaking to protect the environment. Environmental policy is defined as:

... a formal public statement by top management of the intention and principles of action of the organisation regarding its environmental performance, giving rise to its objectives and targets.

The review, therefore, is an essential first step to the formulation of an environmental policy.

The principles state the following:

As a public relations or communications tool the policy must encapsulate and transmit to the outside world (investors, shareholders and the public) the organisation's aspirations; as a management tool it must set directions for managers and employees, provide the framework within which environmental systems are developed and lay down a basis for performance assessment at corporate and departmental levels.

The policy must be relevant to the organisation's activities; be understood; be publicly available; and be regularly updated.

Top management commitment is fundamental to the success of the policy and the policy should be binding on all employees. It should encompass sustainability as far as is economically practicable with reuse and recycling and waste minimisation as examples of good sustainable practice. Attainable targets together with a commitment to continual improvement should become part of the company's business strategy, which should also extend to transport policy and to suppliers. Finally, a procedure document should be prepared explaining how the policy is to be implemented.

Some of the general issues that should be included in a policy statement, are:

- A commitment to sustainable development.

- A commitment that current environmental standards will be exceeded.

- Cradle-to-grave environmental assessment.

- Waste and energy minimisation, production and use.

- Safe waste disposal.

- Involvement of suppliers and contractors in improving environmental performance.

- Involvement of the local community.

- Adoption of an environmentally sound transport policy.

- Assessment of environment impact of all activities through audits.

- Preservation of natural habitat and encouraging conservation schemes.

- Acceptance of liability for environmental damage.

- Assistance in developing solutions to environmental problems.

Figure 17.2: An Example of an Environmental Management Policy

It is the policy of X Limited to ensure that our business practices protect the welfare of our employees and the community in which we operate. We recognise that excellence in environmental performance is consistent with X's corporate objectives and is essential to our continued business success.

X Limited has asserted the following principles to implement this policy for its site operations:

- Ensure that the environmental impact of our operations are documented and that appropriate programmes are implemented to minimise the impacts, ensure that environmental programmes are maintained and reviewed and the environmental performance standards are an integral part of the site's planning and decision-making process.

- Comply with all applicable environmental legislation and corporate requirements and develop relationships with our environmental regulators, our contractors and the local community as our site develops.

- Design and construct our facilities and operations to minimise and monitor our environmental impact, especially in the areas of waste generation, pollution control and energy use.

- Communicate this policy to and foster environmental responsibility among our employees; provide appropriate training where necessary, and encourage employee initiative and involvement with our environmental programmes.

- Be open and responsible to the environmental expectations and concerns of our employees, government agencies and the public by providing relevant information about our environmental policy and the environmental impacts of our operations.

- Regard sound environmental management as an integral part of our total quality commitment and apply the principles and practice of continuous improvement accordingly.

- Ensure that suppliers are aware of our Environmental Management Policy and encourage them to adopt similar policies.

ENVIRONMENTAL STANDARDS AND SYSTEMS: ISO 14001

Environmental standards and systems are designed to prevent the harmful effects that pollution of the environment by companies can have on people and the natural environment. Such standards can be fixed by legislation or may be set out in the form of international standards. The general purpose of an international environmental standard is to provide assistance to organisations implementing or improving its approach to managing the environment.

An Environment Management System (EMS) provides order and consistency for organisations to address environmental concerns through the allocation of resources, assignment of responsibilities, and ongoing evaluation of practices, procedures and processes.

International Standard ISO 14001 considers the elements of and EMS and provides practical advice on implementing or enhancing such a system. It also provides organisations with advice on how to effectively initiate, improve or sustain an environmental management system. Such a system is essential to an organisation's ability to anticipate and meet its environmental objectives and to ensure ongoing compliance with national and/or international requirements.

Environmental management is an integral part of an organisation's overall management system. The design of an EMS is considered an ongoing and interactive process. The structure, responsibilities, practices, procedures, processes and resources of implementing environmental policies, objectives and targets can be coordinated with existing efforts in other areas (e.g., operations, finance, quality, occupational health and safety). It is generally argued that many economic benefits can be obtained from implementing an environmental management system. These benefits are:

- Compliance with regulatory requirements, where relevant.

- Protecting the environment for future generations.

- Assuring customers of commitment to demonstrate environmental management.

- Satisfying investor criteria and improving access to capital.

- Obtaining insurance at reasonable cost.

- Enhancing image and market share.

- Meeting vendor certification criteria.

- Improving cost control.

- Reducing incidents that result in liability.

- Demonstrating reasonable care.

- Conserving input materials and energy.

- Facilitating the attainment of permits and authorisations.

- Fostering development and sharing environmental solutions.

- Improving industry-government relations.

The ISO 14001 Standard

This International Standard provides guidance on the development and implementation of environmental management systems and principles and their co-ordination with other management systems. The standard is considered applicable to any organisation, regardless of size or age.

An environmental management system as specified in ISO 14001 will subscribe to the following principles.

Commitment and Policy

To ensure success, an early step in developing or improving an EMS involves obtaining commitment from the top management of the organisation to improve the environmental management of its activities, products or services. The on-going commitment and leadership of the top management are crucial.

An important first step in securing commitment and formulating policy is the preparation of an initial environment review. This initial review will cover the following:

- Identification of legislative and regulatory requirements.

- Identification of environmental aspects of its activities, products or services in order to determine those that have, or can have, significant environmental impacts and liabilities.

- Evaluation of performance compared with relevant internal criteria, external standards, Regulations, codes of practice and sets of principles and guidelines.

- Existing environmental management practices and procedures.

- Identification of the existing policies and procedures dealing with procurement and contracting activities.

- Feedback from the investigation of previous incidents of non-compliance.

- The views of interested parties.

- Functions or activities of other organisational systems that can enable or impede environmental performance.

Following the environmental review, the organisation must prepare a written environmental policy statement that incorporates the organisation's commitment to environmental protection, describes its policy objectives and targets, and identifies the senior manager with responsibility for environmental protection.

An environmental policy establishes an overall sense of direction and sets the principles of action for an organisation. It sets the goals regarding the level of environmental responsibility and performance required of the organisation, against which all subsequent actions will be judged.

The responsibility for setting environmental policy normally rests with the organisation's top management. The organisation's management is responsible for implementing the policy and for providing input to the formulation and modification of the policy. The following are examples of issues included in the policy:

- Does the organisation have an environmental policy that is relevant to its activities, products and services?

- Does the policy reflect the organisation's values and guiding principles?

- Has top management approved the environmental policy and has someone been identified and given the authority to oversee and implement the policy?

- Does the policy guide the setting of environmental objectives and targets?

- Does the policy guide the organisation towards monitoring appropriate technology and management practices?

- What commitments are embodied in the environmental policy, for example, support for continual improvement, support for the prevention of pollution, monitoring, meeting or exceeding legal requirements and consideration of the expectations of interested parties?

- Does the policy provide a commitment that current environmental standards will be exceeded?

- Does the policy provide for the involvement of the local community?

- Does the policy provide for the involvement of the suppliers and contractors in improving environmental performance?

Planning

The planning of an effective environmental management system will consider the following issues.

Environmental Aspects and Impacts

An organisation's policy, objectives and targets should be based on knowledge about the environmental aspects and significant environmental impacts associated with its activities, products or services. This can ensure that the significant environmental impacts associated with these aspects are taken into account in setting the environmental objectives.

Legal and Other Requirements

The organisation should establish and maintain procedures to identify, have access to and understand all legal and other requirements to which it subscribes, that directly relate to the environment.

Internal Performance Criteria

Internal priorities and criteria should be developed and implemented where external standards do not meet the needs of the organisation or are non-existent. Internal and external criteria will facilitate the development of objectives and targets.

Environmental Objectives and Targets

Objectives should be established to meet the organisational environmental policy. These objectives represent the overall goals for environmental policy. Targets can then be set to achieve these objectives within a specified timeframe. These targets should be specific and measurable and assigned to specific individuals so that ownership is defined.

Environmental Management Programme

Within a general planning framework, an organisation should establish an environmental management programme that addresses its environmental objectives. The environmental plans should integrate into an organisation's strategic plan.

Implementation

In order to achieve its environmental objectives, an organisation should focus and align its people, systems, strategy, resources and structure. The following issues should be considered:

- **Resources:** The appropriate human, physical and financial resources essential to the implementation of an organisation's environmental policies and the achievement of its objectives, should be defined and made available.

- **Alignment and Integration:** To manage environmental concerns effectively, the EMS elements should be designed or revised so that they are effectively aligned and integrated with the existing management system.

- **Accountability and Responsibility:** Responsibility for the overall effectiveness of the EMS system should be assigned to a function and/or person with sufficient authority, competence and resources.

- **Awareness and Motivation:** Top management should play a major role in building awareness and motivating employees by explaining the organisation's environmental values and communicating its commitment to the environmental policy.

- **Knowledge, Skills and Training:** The knowledge and shills necessary to achieve environmental objectives should be identified. These should be considered in personnel selection, recruitment, training, development and ongoing education.

- **Communication and Reporting:** Communication includes establishing processes to report internally and in some cases externally (regulatory bodies, corporate HQs, general public etc). Furthermore, the results of EMS monitoring, auditing and management reviews should be communicated to those within the organisation who are responsible for performance.

- **EMS documentation:** Operational processes and procedures should be defined and properly documented and updated as necessary. Effective EMS documentation supports employee awareness of what is required to achieve environmental objectives.

- **Operational Control:** Effect implementation is facilitated through establishing and maintaining operational procedures and controls. These tools enable the organisation to monitor its environmental policy, objectives and targets.

- **Emergency Preparation and Response:** Emergency plans and procedures should be established to ensure that the organisation can make an appropriate response to unexpected or accidental incidents so that damage to the environment and loss in general is minimised.

Measurement and Evaluation

An important principle underpinning the standard is that an organisation should measure, monitor and evaluate its environmental performance. Specific issues here include the following:

- **Measuring Ongoing Performance:** An effective system of measurement of results. This includes compliance with relevant environmental legislation and regulations.

- **Corrective and Preventive Action:** The results of monitoring and audits should result in appropriate corrective action.

- **Audits:** Audits should be conducted on a periodic basis to determine whether the system conforms to planned arrangements and is properly implemented and maintained. They are usually carried out by internal/external auditors, selected by an organisation.

- **Continual Improvement:** The concept of continual improvement is central to an environmental management system. These improvements are facilitated through performance, evaluation, feedback and corrective action.

WASTE REDUCTION AND ENERGY CONSERVATION

There is a general consensus that waste minimisation makes good sense because waste in all its forms reduces profitability. There is, however, a common perceptive that waste minimisation and energy conservation involve expensive technology and apply to heavy industries only. However, it is quite feasible for organisations to take significant steps without incurring significant costs. It is recommended that a waste minimisation and energy conservation programme is incorporated into the business strategy. Below is a set of questions an organisation should consider when devising such a programme.

- Does my business have an environmental policy, which is clearly defined?

- Am I aware of where I may be causing environmental damage?

- Do I generate waste solvents?

- Where do I dispose of them?

- Do I supply a product, which is contained in packaging?

- What type of packaging is it?

- What happens to it once the product is used?

An effective waste-minimisation strategy should be based on three principles:

- **Reduce:** Aim for a reduction in the amount of raw materials and resources used and therefore reduce the amount of waste generated. It is generally argued that prevention is better than cure.

- **Reuse:** This means getting more than a single use out of disposable material or switching to a reusable material.

- **Recycle:** It is generally accepted that recycling of paper, glass, metals, plastics and solvents reduces the amount of disposal and disposal costs.

FORMULATING WASTE MANAGEMENT POLICIES

Waste management should form part of the safety statement. The statement should ideally specify the policy of the organisation in respect of how it deals with waste. Its content will depend on the type of organisation and the waste involved. Some examples of waste include the following:

- Building waste from construction work etc. will require the use of a skip or similar container and removal to a landfill site. No hazardous waste should be placed in the skip. Hazardous is defined as material that, if it were supplied in a labelled container, would have one of the dangerous substances labels on it as required by the Classification, Packaging, Labelling and Notification of Dangerous Substances Regulations and the equivalent preparations regulations – so this applies to organic solvents and similar materials not likely to be found in the office environment except when building work is undertaken.

- Hazardous waste, such as large numbers of fluorescent tubes, should be segregated and safely held until collected by a specialist waste contractor.

- Medical waste arising from the treatment of a medical condition such as diabetes should be segregated with sharps such as syringes in a yellow sharps bin and other waste in a yellow clinical waste bag. The person suffering from that condition should be able to obtain appropriate supplies but, if there are problems, suppliers of other hygiene products will be able to assist. Arrangements may then be made with the local authority or a specialist waste contractor for periodic collection.

- Asbestos arising from the removal of pipework insulation and similar building structural work should be dealt with only by competent contractors, sealed in appropriately labelled containers and disposed of to a licensed site. This is a legal requirement under the Asbestos Regulations.

Some of the points that may be included in the policy include:

- The organisation will seek to minimise the creation of waste by avoiding unnecessary wastage of materials and recycling materials that cannot be directly reused as far as practicable.

- All staff are required to comply with this policy by minimising waste creation and co-operating actively with the recycling programme. Where waste is created, it shall be safely placed in appropriate storage receptacles, care being taken not to overload the storage.

- Managers shall take care to provide suitable waste receptacles, and ensure that arrangements are made for their collection/emptying at a suitable frequency.

- Cleaners and other staff responsible for collecting waste shall avoid handling over-filled bags, etc. to minimise the risk of a manual handling injury.

- Waste collection points (disposal and recycling) shall be the responsibility of (named manager such as Premises Manager) and kept in a clean, accessible condition with due regard to fire protection and a suitable container (such a covered skip, wheely bin etc).

- All waste, for recycling or disposal, shall be collected by either local authority-employed refuse collectors or by authorised waste carriers.

Waste recycling programmes include:

- Collecting paper waste arising from computer printouts, photocopying, shredded secure documents, etc. This material is collected by a recycling firm, which uses the paper to produce clean new products. The waste originators receive a fee for the waste.

- The providers of plastic cups (for water dispensers, coffee machines, etc) provide a receptacle for the cups, which are periodically collected and recycled.

- Some suppliers collect and refill laser printer toner cartridges.

Elements of an Organisation's Waste Minimisation Programme

The Organisation's Waste

Before embarking on a waste minimisation programme, it is important to establish a waste profile by determining the following information:

- The type of waste generated?

- The quantity of the waste generated?

- What media are affected by waste (air, water, land)?

- Characteristics of waste (toxicity, concentration)?

- Are waste streams mixed?

- Where does waste come from?

- Are waste materials valuable in a process after treatment?

Commitment and Involvement of Staff

A successful waste minimisation strategy needs staff involvement and management commitment. Unless responsibility for waste minimisation and energy conservation is allocated to key people throughout the company, each will expect everyone else to take responsibility, and progress will be hard and slow.

It may be an idea to appoint a team of officers who are responsible for co-ordinating their department's ongoing programme. They should involve all of the workforce, meet regularly with other officers to plan strategy, share ideas and review progress.

Setting Targets

It is important to set targets that are measurable and meaningful, and priority should be set for fast results. Categories for action can be established:

- Immediate actions, where the benefit or result will be achieved in the short term.

- Immediate action for longer-term results

- Future actions.

Segregation of Waste Streams

Segregation of waste streams can help improve waste recovery and reduce the amount of waste for disposal, as can be seen from the following example.

A manufacturer of chipboard products bonds a laminate to the bare board using an adhesive, then cuts, shapes and bonds the board into the product. After bonding, the adhesive is cleaned from the rollers using detergent/water but the dried adhesive is removed with methylene chloride. The combined washings were collected for disposal. Changes in landfill management practices meant that waste could no longer be disposed of by landfill and had to be incinerated at ten times the cost. The operating procedures were modified to segregate the water and methylene chloride. This reduced the volume sent for incineration by 80 per cent.

Technology Transfer

Initial investment in technology for waste reduction has a definite payback period. Once this is achieved, the money is spent on transferring the same technology to another company (sister company). This scheme is self-perpetuating and requires small investment, while covering a large number of businesses over time.

Waste Data Bank

All companies that create waste and those that buy waste log into the system in order to ascertain whether use can be made of waste. For example, a company that generates a large amount of metal waste may be identified by a user of metal waste and a business deal established to purchase and remove this waste from the site.

Figure 17.3: Ways of Reducing Energy Use and Waste

Heating, Cooling and Ventilation

- When replacing windows, replace with double-glazing rather than single-glazing.

- Lag areas where heat can escape (e.g. above ceiling on top floor of building).

- See if the thermostat can be lowered by a few degrees.

- Ensure that doors and windows are kept closed if heating or air conditioning is on.

- Ensure that vents, radiators, etc. are not blocked.

- Where possible, open windows instead of turning on fans or air conditioning.

- When the area is empty, ensure that all fans and other equipment are turned off.

Lighting

- Ensure that natural light is taken advantage of by placing work stations near to its source.

- Keep light-bulbs/fixtures clean, ensure regular dusting.

- Select the most energy-efficient options when replacing lighting systems and equipment.

- Always turn off lights when not needed.

Equipment

- Ensure only essential use of equipment. Can photocopying needs be reduced? Can the stairs be used instead of the lift?

- Ensure that all equipment is switched off when not in use.

- Ensure that all problems, sparking, overheating, etc. are reported and repaired as soon as possible.

- Ensure that energy-efficient equipment is purchased (equipment with power-saver buttons).

- Maintain and repair equipment rather than replacing it.

- Consider parts that can be reused — refillable toner cartridge, re-inked printer ribbons.

- Rent, instead of buying, rarely used equipment.

- Sell or donate items no longer in use (old typewriters, etc.).

Transport

- Cycle or walk where possible, use public transport or car pool.

- Where possible, cut down on business travel and use the phone or fax where possible.

- Urge customers to take merchandise with them.

- Shorten delivery schedules.

- Turn off engines when delivering (loading, unloading).

- Minimise choke use, accelerate slowly, keep speed down.

Water

- All leaks should be reported.

- Water should not be allowed to run unnecessarily.

- Do not use toilets as ashtrays or waste bins.

- Use a mop to clean instead of a hose.

Paper/Packaging etc.

- Using the phone or electronic mail can save paper. Circulation memos should be sent instead of individual copies.

- Try to ensure that less of everything, from office supplies to cleaning materials, is used.

- Use scrap paper for notes, etc.

- Reuse envelopes for internal mail.

- Make double-sided photocopies.

- Write replies directly on internal memos.

- Cover old addresses with new labels for re-posting.

- Reuse all infill materials (bubble wrap, beads, etc.).

- Ask if other departments have a use for packaging materials.

- Avoid using disposables. For example, clean up harmless spills with rags or sponges, not paper towels.

- Choose items in refillable containers — cleaning materials, lubricants, bottled water, etc.

- Avoid products that use batteries for power (if you must, use rechargeable batteries).

- Select high-quality products for better quality and longer use.

Recycling

- The following materials can be recycled: paper, cardboard, metals (tin and aluminium), glass, certain plastics, including polystyrene cups, cloths and clothing, oil and rubber, solvents.

- Always use separate skips or bins for each recyclable material (if there are not separate containers).

- Make sure each item is put into the correct container.

- Do not dispose of other waste in recycling containers.

- Try to use products that can be recycled or are made from recycled materials.

- Select products with little or no packaging. If that is not possible, check that the packaging materials can be used or recycled — or are made of recycled materials.

- Research the use of recycled products as raw materials.

- It is worth finding out about recycling schemes, and encourage your organisation to take part in them.

Waste Storage

- Different types of waste should be held in separate containers and general waste never mixed with hazardous waste.

- Paper containers should not be used to store waste. Containing waste securely means using a container that does not leak and is "animal-proof".

- Lids should always be replaced securely.

- Waste should never be disposed of into the water supply or onto the ground, since even small amounts can contaminate.

- It should be part of everybody's daily routine to keep their work area neat and tidy, and ensure that all spills are cleaned up promptly.

CHAPTER ROUND-UP

- The issue of managing the environment now comes within the remit of many health and safety departments. This is based on the belief that many of the organisation's activities impinge on the environment. It is therefore necessary to ensure co-ordination and management of the organisation's environmental system. This system should help to ensure that, through operating procedures, records, documentation and managing action, adverse effects are prevented at source.

- An environmental approach to health and safety includes issues such as individual safety, environmental protection, waste management, employee health, product safety and risk liability, and insurance management. The primary impetus for an environmental approach comes from the EU.

- Countries that have adopted an environmental agenda adopt a range of measures in their efforts to manage the external environment. These include the formulation of policies that promote the protection of the environment, the production of environmental plans, criminal sanctions, civil sanctions such as injunctions and damages, and the development and implementation of environmental standards. Each option has its associated strengths and weaknesses.

- A key component of an environmental approach relates to the auditing of the environmental performance of organisations. This is achieved through the implementation of environmental management systems. Such a system is part of an overall management system, which includes the organisational structure, responsibilities, practices, procedures, processes and resources, and how they facilitate the implementation of environmental policy.

- Environmental management systems are generally monitored using an environmental audit. An environmental audit is a systematic process of objectively obtaining and evaluating evidence to determine the reliability of environmental systems and how they measure up to established criteria. To be effective, they need to be conducted within a structured management system, be integrated with overall management activities, and address all aspects of the environment.

- There is a general consensus that waste management makes good sense. There is a common misconception, however, that waste minimisation and energy conservation involve expensive technology and apply to heavy industry only. However, they should be part of any business activity.

PART FOUR

RISK MANAGEMENT

Chapter 18

A RISK MANAGEMENT APPROACH: CONCEPTS AND PROCESSES

INTRODUCTION

This chapter focuses on risk management and its contribution to the management of health and safety management. The emphasis has shifted in the last 20 years away from a traditional, injury prevention approach to health and safety, to one emphasising prediction and control of all forms of risk and loss. This is now generally termed "risk management" and is the concern of this and the next chapter. This chapter considers the following aspects of risk management:

- The nature and scope of risk management.

- Risk management terminology.

- The nature of risk and categories of risk.

- Risk management principles and philosophy.

- The risk management process.

- Appropriate risk management techniques.

- Strategies for dealing with different types of risks.

THE SCOPE AND PHILOSOPHY OF RISK MANAGEMENT

Risk management is a developing discipline, which originated in the US. There is an ongoing debate as to its nature and the tasks that a risk manager may carry out. Many commentators are of the view that the risk manager should be involved in pure risk only, but others acknowledge that risk management should extend beyond this limited perspective.

Cox and Tait (1991) suggest that risk management should consider issues of equity and fairness in the distribution of risks and benefits. This involves considerations of ethical, as well as political, measures for technology development and the environment. Kloman (1990) advocates that risk should be examined holistically and suggests that risk management is a combination and interaction of an understanding of hazards and business risk.

The traditional view of risk management is that it is a function within a business in the same way as marketing, purchasing and finance. Few companies employ somebody with the title of risk manager and there is considerable diversity in the perception of the risk management function, ranging from dealing purely with insurance to a situation where it handles all types of risk.

Risk management should be considered a process, rather than a function of the business, the primary task of which is to establish the nature of all risks that a business is likely to face. This information can be used when the organisation is considering its strategic position in the marketplace and formulating objectives and strategies. This suggests that risk management can assist top management in making strategic decisions.

Stranks (1995) suggests four ways in which risk management can be defined:

1. The minimisation of the adverse affects of pure and speculative risks within a business.

2. The identification, measurement and control of the risks that threaten a business.

3. The identification and evaluation of risk and the identification of the best financial solution.

4. A set of techniques for coping with the effects of change.

Risk management therefore is based on the assumption that, as the investment in safety management measures increases, the accident rate decreases, though this risk cannot be reduced to zero. However, an organisation with a strong commitment to health and safety that makes the appropriate investment will minimise the risk of accident and loss.

There are six principles that underpin contemporary risk management:

1. Accident prevention is an essential part of good management and of good workmanship.

2. Management and workers must co-operate wholeheartedly in securing freedom from accidents.

3. Top management must take the lead in organising safety in the workplace.

4. There must be a definite and known safety policy in each workplace.

5. The organisation and resources necessary to carry out the policy must exist.

6. The best available knowledge and methods must be applied.

Dickson (1989) suggests that risk management is concerned with the identification, analysis and economic control of risks that threaten the assets or earning capacity of the organisation. Valsamakis et al. (1992) argue that this definition is significantly oriented towards a general management function and offer an alternative definition as follows:

> Risk management is a managerial function aimed at protecting the organisation, its people, assets and profits, against the adverse consequences of pure risk and more particularly aimed at reducing the severity and variability of losses.

Risk management in general aims at producing savings in insurance premiums by first defining and then minimising industrial risk. The role of risk management is therefore threefold:

• To consider the impact of certain risky events on the performance of the organisation.

• To devise alternative strategies for controlling these risks and/or their impact on the organisation.

- To relate these alternative strategies to the general decision framework used by the organisation.

There is, however, a debate concerning the reasons for the emergence of risk management. Valsamakis et al. (1992) suggest four reasons:

1. Increased automation, the use of new technology and the discovery of new processes, chemicals, etc. have resulted in risks becoming more sophisticated. These new developments present potential new risks to the organisation.

2. There is also an increasing concentration of risks. This concentration of risk manifests itself in the size of new buildings, manufacturing plants and organisations and changing individual values.

3. There is evidence to suggest that the public is more safety-conscious and more aware of risks. Kloman (1990) has formulated the term "entitlement", to describe a situation where individuals who suffer injury refuse to accept personal accountability and instead turn to others, and particularly the state, as a source for compensation.

4. There is evidence to suggest a steady decline in the use of insurance as a risk-financing technique. Valsamakis et al. (1992) suggest that such a trend requires that risk control and risk financing be interrelated activities and that a trade-off is necessary between risk retained and self-funded and risk insured.

RISK MANAGEMENT TERMINOLOGY

Risk management has a unique set of terminology underpinning its activities. We will consider a number of these issues here.

An Accident

For risk management purposes, an accident can be defined as:

> ... some concrete happening which intervenes or obtrudes itself upon the normal course of employment. It has the ordinary everyday meaning of an unlooked-for mishap or an

untoward event, which is not expected or designed by the victim.

This definition refers to an event occurring to an employee that was an unlooked-for mishap, having a degree of unexpectedness about it. It would seem to be somewhat narrow, because it is only concerned with accidents resulting in injury to employees. An appropriate accident definition should have two distinct components: a description of the causes and a description of the effects.

Causes may include unexpectedness or unplanned events, multi-causality and sequence of events; while the effects may cover injury, disease, damage, near-miss and loss. The following definition is considered more appropriate in a risk management context:

> An accident is an unexpected, unplanned event in a sequence of events, which occurs through a combination of causes; it results in physical harm (injury or disease) to an individual, damage to property, a near-miss, a loss or any combination of these effects.

This definition gives recognition of a wider range of accidents than those resulting in injury.

Peril and Hazard

Mehr (1986) defines a peril as the cause of a loss. Others have defined it as the source of a loss, which is now the preferred view. Examples of perils include fire, earthquakes, storms, etc. A hazard is defined as the environment surrounding the loss. Mehr argues that behind every peril is a hazard. Valsamakis et al. (1992) makes a distinction between physical and moral hazards. The former relates to the material or physical aspects of the environment whereas the latter is concerned with the personal dimension.

The risk from a substance is the likelihood that it will cause harm in the actual circumstances of use. This will depend on the hazard presented by the substance, how it is used, how it is controlled, and who is exposed to how much for how long. Risk should be thought of in terms of "chance-taking". What are the odds — the probability — of an accident occurring? Risk can be taken after careful consideration, or out of ignorance. The result can be fortuitous or disastrous, or anything in between.

The link between "hazard" and "risk" is important. Poor control can create substantial risk even from a substance with low hazard. But with proper controls, the risk of being harmed by even the most hazardous substance is greatly reduced.

A Risk

There are many definitions of the term "risk" to be found in the literature on risk management, primarily because of the multiplicity of perspectives adopted. Examples of common definitions include the following:

- Risk as uncertainty of loss where the degree of uncertainty is not necessarily measurable (Denenberg et al., 1974).

- Risk as concerned with the uncertainty of the occurrence of economic loss (Green and Serbein, 1983).

- Risk as a condition in which loss(es) is (are) possible (Athearn and Pritchett, 1984).

- Risk implies the possibility of uncertainty and, therefore, the degree of uncertainty surrounding an event determines the extent of the risk involved (Valsamakis et al., 1992).

The degree of risk is dependent on the variability rather than the probability value surrounding an event or its outcome. Valsamakis et al. (1992) argue that there exists uncertainty concerning whether an event or occurrence will take place and where it does what the financial outcome of that event will be.

DIFFERENT CONCEPTIONS OF RISK

Risk can be understood in terms of a conceptual chain, where at one end is the engineering view and the other a societal view. Conventionally, risk is viewed at the engineering end of this concept chain. Engineers and technologists consider risk as the probability of a hazard occurring. It is a concept that measures the possibility of something going wrong and consists of a number of between 0 and 1, with both ends of the scale representing certainty of an event either occurring (usually 1) or not occurring (usually 0). A distinction is made between a hazard and a risk, the former something that facilitates the occurrence of a loss-causing event while risk measures the probability of that event occurring. At the societal end of the chain, risk is generally perceived as a function of fairness, and includes considerations such as trust, liability, distribution and content (Rayner and Cantor, 1987). Issues of probability are rarely considered at all. Between these extremes lies a range of risk concepts that represent an uncomfortable mixture of probabilistic and fairness issues, all of which are properly considered aspects of the term "risk" as used in ordinary language. Psychologists take the view that people can be placed on a scale relating to their attitudes towards risk. Individuals may be risk-averse — they will take all necessary steps to avoid risk; risk-neutral — they do not have an attitude towards risk; or risk-loving — they are keen to take risks.

In conducting risk assessment, risk is commonly conceived of as the quantification of the expected loss. Economists consider this an extremely narrow conception, which denies access to economically interesting risk-related problems, such as that of risk aversion and its consequences. The use of expected loss implies risk-neutral behaviour and does not allow for the idea of risk aversity. Economists view risk from the point of view of allocation. They understand it as the product of probability and the extent of damage. All possible uncertain situations can, in the view of economists, be considered risk issues. Generally, economists assume that economic man is risk-averse whereas the general public views risk as a distributive problem. There is, therefore, a question of how the concepts of economists in relation to the nature of risk and those of the layperson can be compared. There is also some difficulty with the idea that compensation for risk is always possible.

The presumption made by economists that an individual is risk-averse in making decisions is considered simplistic. Psychologists demonstrate that individuals may be risk-neutral or risk-averse (Greenford, 1991). In situations of uncertainty, lay people often use heuristic strategies to assess probabilities. Evidence demonstrates that lay people do a good job of assessing the extent of damage. Their estimates have a high correlation with the assessment of experts and/or with actual data. However, lay people tend to overestimate low probabilities and underestimate high ones. There is, likewise, evidence suggesting that the number of potential victims also affect the lay person's view of risk.

In behavioural terms, the lay person tends to evaluate gains differently from losses. In those cases where there are certain gains, they seem to prefer this choice. Framing of the choice seems to be very important in decision-making under risk (Jungermann, et al., 1988).

Insurers tend to view risk as the possibility of an untoward event occurring that can affect the subject matter of their insurance policies. Risk denotes the uncertainty of loss regarding outcomes that follow from a given state of affairs. Sometimes insurers refer to the thing insured as "the risk". According to Knights and Vurdubakis (1993), risk owes its status as the self-evident object of insurance, to the relationship it is presumed to have with reality whose occurrence it objectively presents. This approach defines risks, and makes insurance appear as a simple pragmatic response to the objective risks residing in the external world. Insurance, together with its calculation techniques, is a particular way of breaking down, reconstructing and rearranging certain elements of reality. According to Ewald (in Knights and Vurdubakis, 1993), there is no class of events that is naturally insurable, yet everything can be a risk insofar as the type of event in question can be processed in accordance with the principles of insurance. The insurance industry is continuously elaborating on the concept of risk and causes certain familiar events such as death and illness to be viewed in a new light. It replaces their arbitrariness with a sense of consistency and objectivity. Death or misadventure is seen to threaten an individual, but insurance and its actuarial technique turns risk into a threat to a population, thus bringing more certainty into the lives of society (Knights and Vurdubakis, 1993).

Financiers and bankers consider risk in terms of statistical concepts such as the variance or standard deviation. Thus risk is measured using statistical concepts. Financiers are concerned with losses arising from interest rates, foreign exchange rates, and commodity prices and have developed a variety of tools, known as derivatives, to deal with these risks. They take a similar position to economists by assuming that all individuals are rational and risk-averse.

Douglas (1992), a social anthropologist, suggests that risk has come to mean danger. Society refers to risk in terms of the danger to, for example, children in families or the danger of being affected by a chemical factory. Beck (1992) likewise argues that society has become more concerned with the distribution of risk than with the distribution of wealth. Douglas suggests that society construct its own view of what is dangerous. She points to the need for various societies in the event of bad things happening, to appeal to or blame the Gods.

Behavioural approaches to risk concentrate on how attitudes and beliefs influence subjective assessment of risks. Individuals have a perception, rather than an objective external view, of risk (Knights and Vurdubakis, 1993). An individual's view of risk is affected by a number of factors. Controllability of the risk being run is one such factor. If the risk is considered to be outside the control of the individual, it will be assessed as a greater risk than an event within the individual's control. A second distinction is made between risk faced voluntarily and risk faced involuntarily. The former is perceived as less risky than the latter, or less concern is shown about its extent. Other factors that affect an individual's perception of risk are geographical and temporal distance: the further away in time or space, the smaller the risk.

MacCrimmon and Wehrung (1986) suggest an alternative perspective. They conclude that risk consists of three elements: (a) a potential loss, (b) a chance of loss, and (c) an exposure to loss. Without these three elements there can be no risk. Risk implies loss so there must be the potential for loss, there must be a chance of loss as opposed to a certainty of loss or no loss.

Risk also has a political dimension. Evidence of this can be seen by considering the BSE scare in the UK and Europe. The public has accepted that BSE is dangerous and does not take any cognisance of the rational calls to science being made by governments. This gives credence to the view that society has its own view of risk despite what the experts and governments say.

Risk, therefore, is viewed by different professions and societies through different lenses. The meaning of risk can be considered to be on a continuum ranging from the narrow definition of the probability of an event occurring to being a function of fair and equitable considerations in society. These societal considerations focus on factors such as liability distribution, trust and consent. Risk, therefore, needs to be understood in terms of the mutual interdependency of culture, politics, moral and mathematical calculations (Knights and Vurdubakis, 1993).

Risk is socially constructed. Each society or culture decides what risks are and how they are to be perceived. If risk is constructed by society, this means that organisational and societal culture is an important concern of risk managers if risk is to be managed.

CATEGORIES OF RISK

Pure Risk

Pure risk can be defined as the occurrence of an undesired event from which the sufferer cannot profit. Thus the risk of a fire occurring in a building is considered pure risk. It is assumed that, in normal circumstances, the owner can only suffer a loss following the occurrence. Insurance specialists and risk managers have claimed this type of risk as their own.

Speculative Risk

Speculative risk is in opposition to pure risk in that, should the event occur, there is the possibility of making a profit. A distinction thus can be made between risks that a business manager handles and those allocated to a risk manager. Because it is difficult to distinguish between the two types of risk, the distinction is not useful in practice. In fact, some commentators have suggested that the distinction between pure and speculative risk should be dispensed with.

Dynamic and Static Risk

A distinction is made between dynamic and static risk. Dynamic risk refers to the uncertainties that occur as a result of ever-changing society, the environment and consumer demands; while static risk covers those that exist despite these changes. Examples of static risk include storms, hurricanes, fire and flood. As knowledge of the environment grows, so-called dynamic risks can affect static risks. Consequently, there is little merit in distinguishing between the two.

Objective and Subjective Risk

Another distinction is made between objective and subjective risk. Objective risk refers to the statistical measure of the degree of variation from the expected. According to the law of large numbers, the variation in the proportion of actual outcomes from expected outcomes will decrease as the number of events increases, until risk (that is, the variation) becomes zero. This statistical tool is very useful in risk management. Subjective risk, in contrast, occurs when an individual perceives the possibility of a particular adverse event occurring. This perception depends upon the risk profile of the individual providing the assessment.

Financial and Physical Risk

The risks that businesses face can be divided into financial and physical risks. In some instances, financial and physical risks overlap. Financial risk is loss arising out of financial transactions such as investments, foreign exchange and other similar types of dealings. Physical risk involves eventualities whereby loss or damage could occur to property or to persons. This chapter focuses on physical risk.

THE RISK MANAGEMENT PROCESS

The risk management process involves the identification, evaluation and control of risks within the organisation (**Figure 18.1**).

Objective Setting

Risk management objectives should be formulated in accordance with the organisation's characteristics, mission and objectives. The objectives should be specific, measurable and attainable. They should indicate clearly what is to be done in risk management terms, how it is to be done and the timescale for attainment. It is advisable to draw up a policy statement that contains the risk management objectives and the strategies that the organisation will use to attain them.

Figure 18.1: The Risk Management Process

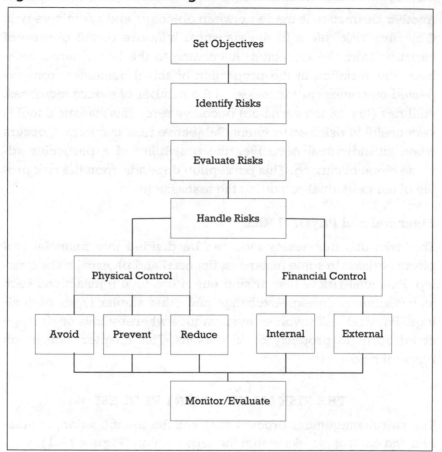

Risk Identification

The second step in a risk management approach is the identification of risk. The identification of sources of risk can be conceptualised on a macro or micro level. A macro-identification is directed at discovering risks that are normally dealt with by insurance. It considers risks that give rise to the loss of or damage to assets, any consequential losses, losses suffered to personnel and pure financial loss.

The principal focus of macro-identification is to provide the organisation with protection as far as possible, from the negative financial consequences of loss arising from major risk sources. In considering a macro-identification, the most common method is an insurance review. This review will focus on uninsured perils as well as perils for which no insurance is available, or it may be available but at a very high rate of premium. Other methods include the production of organisational and flow charts and the analysis of financial statements.

Micro-risk identification involves a process of discovering those risks, which do not affect insurance cover. Micro-identification focuses on identifying special perils within main peril classes. A number of methods can be utilised to carry out this activity. These will be considered in the next section.

Irish law dictates that systematic risk identification must consider the following issues:

- Identify all the hazards associated with the operation, and evaluate the risks arising from those hazards, taking into account current legal requirements.

- Record the significant findings if more than five persons are employed, even if they are in different locations.

- Identify any employee or group of employees who are especially at risk.

- Identify others who may be especially at risk, e.g. visitors, contractors, members of the public.

- Evaluate existing controls, stating whether or not they are satisfactory and, if not, what action should be taken.

- Evaluate the need for information, instruction, training and supervision.

- Assess and record the probability or likelihood of an accident occurring as a result of uncontrolled risk, including the "worst case" likely outcome.

- Record any circumstances arising from the assessment where serious and imminent danger could arise.

- Provide an action plan for implementation of additional controls, in order of priority, and with a realistic time scale.

Figure 18.2 presents the statutory requirements relevant to the conduct of a risk assessment.

Figure 18.2: Risk Assessment: The Legal Responsibilities Checklist

SHWW Act, 1989 and General Application Regulations	
Have we, as required by s12 of the SHWW Act, (1989) identified the hazards of the workplace and assessed the risks?	Yes/No
Have we, as required by the Reg 10 of the General Application Regulations (SI 44/93) assessed that risk in writing and have we decided on protective measures to be taken and PPE (if necessary) to be used?	Yes/No
Are we in possession of a written risk assessment?	Yes/No
The published guidance states that the purpose of risk assessment is to identify measures to be taken to comply with requirements and prohibitions imposed by statutory provisions. Does the risk assessment identify the risks of our workplace and identify other statutory risk assessment provisions we should consider?	Yes/No
In carrying out the risk assessment, have we consulted our workers?	Yes/No
Who should carry out the risk assessment?	Employer/self-employed
What risks should be assessed?	Those to which employees, self-employed or third parties may be exposed.
When should the risk assessment be carried out?	Whenever new plant equipment or new work practices are introduced, in the light of staff changes and always subject to regular review. It should also be carried out if new regulations are adopted.
Should the risk assessment be recorded?	Yes

How long should it be kept?	The ever-present possibility of litigation suggests until the possibility of legal action has expired. For machinery risks this might be three years from date of last accident. For health risks this might be for the normal life expectancy of workers plus some years.
Have we, as required under the General Principles of Prevention (see Reg 5(1) first schedule (b)) evaluated unavoidable risks?	Yes/No
Do we have a system, as required by Reg 5(b), which ensures that we periodically evaluate risks, including those related to choice of work equipment, use of substances, fitting out of workplace?	Yes/No
Does our system for assessing the risks show, as required by Reg 22(a) that when we use PPE there are no other means available to avoid the risk?	Yes/No
Has our risk assessment, as required by Reg 22(b), taken account of the risks the PPE may present?	Yes/No
Has our risk assessment, as required by Reg 23(a&b) taken account of the risks the PPE may present?	Yes/No
Has our assessment of manual handling risks, having concluded that manual handling cannot be avoided, had regard to characteristics of the load, working environment and physical effort, as defined in Schedule 8 of SI 44/93 and individual risk factors – employee unsuited to task, wearing unsuitable clothing, lack of knowledge/training – specified in Schedule 9?	Yes/No
Does our analysis of VDUs, as required by Reg 31, show that the use of VDU equipment is not, as specified in Schedule 10, a source of risk?	Yes/No
Does the risk assessment indicate other Regulations apply? If so, specify which Regulations.	Yes/No

Asbestos Regulations	
Have we made an assessment of the risk of exposure to dust from asbestos, as required by Reg 9 (S1 34/89)?	Yes/No
Does the risk assessment identify the type of asbestos and establish steps to prevent or minimise exposure?	Yes/No
Have we in place a system to carry out a revised assessment, if it is necessitated by a material change or a reason to believe the original assessment is incorrect?	Yes/No
In carrying out this risk assessment, have we consulted workers/workers representatives?	Yes/No
Biological Agents Regulations	
Have we assessed the risk of possible exposure to biological agents (S1 146/94)?	Yes/No
Does the assessment indicate possible exposure?	Yes/No
If yes, have we taken preventative measures?	Yes/No
Carcinogen Regulations	
Have we assessed risk of possible exposure to carcinogens (S1 80/93, Reg 4[b])?	Yes/No
Do we review the assessment regularly and when there is a major change in conditions of work (Reg 4c)?	Yes/No
If assessment indicates possible exposure, have we taken preventative measures?	Yes/No
Construction Regulations	
Has the project supervisor, at the design stage, carried out an assessment as to whether the work will involve particular risks specified (Reg 4 (1,a,iii & sch 11))?	Yes/No
Ionising Radiation Regulations	
Is there a possibility that our workers may be exposed to ionising radiation and, if so, have we carried out an assessment, acceptable to the Radiological Protection Institute (S1 125/2000, Reg 9[2])?	Yes/No

Lead Regulations	
Have we carried out a risk assessment to assess the risk that a worker might absorb lead (S1 219/88, Reg 4[1]) , and, when doing so, have we checked schedule 1, S1 219/88?	Yes/No
Have we consulted workers/workers representatives (S1 219/88, Reg 4[4])?	Yes/No
Does the assessment reveal concentrations that require preventative actions?	Yes/No
Have we taken preventative action?	Yes/No
Noise Regulations	
Have we assessed noise levels (S1 157/90, Reg 4[1])?	Yes/No
If so, have we taken necessary preventative action?	Yes/No
Have we recorded the assessment (we must keep records for three years) (S1 157, Reg 4[6])?	Yes/No
Pregnant Employees Regulations	
Have we assessed the specific risks that women who are pregnant or breastfeeding may be exposed to (S1 218/2000, Reg 4) (see HSA guide)?	Yes/No
If there are risks, have we offered other work?	Yes/No
Working Time	
Have we carried out a risk assessment of the hazards to which night workers are exposed (S1 485/98, Reg 5[1])?	Yes/No
Young Persons	
Do we employ young persons – aged under 18?	Yes/No
Before we employ a young person we must carry out a risk assessment and, if there is a major change in the place of work, we must review risk assessment (S1 504[3b]). Have we done so?	Yes/No
Have we assessed the risks arising from their lack of experience, absence of awareness of risk, lack of maturity, risks from biological/physical/chemical agents or the process of work (S1 504/98, Reg 39[a] and schedule Part 11)?	Yes/No
Before we employ the young person, are we satisfied the risk is not one that prevents us from employing him/her (S1 504, Reg 3[d])?	Yes/No

Byrne (1994) suggests nine risk principles that form the basis of EU and Irish legislation and that guide any risk assessment approach.

1. The organisation should aim at risk avoidance, where possible.

2. All unavoidable risks should be systematically evaluated.

3. Risks should be dealt with at the source rather than later.

4. Work systems should be designed to meet the needs of the individual.

5. The organisation should implement a policy of replacing the dangerous with the non-dangerous or the less dangerous.

6. Priority should be given to collective protection measures over individual protection measures.

7. Safety policies should take account of technology, work organisation, work conditions, social factors and the general work environment.

8. There should be a policy of continually adapting to technical progress, technical standards and technological developments, which enhance safe working conditions.

9. Systematic training and instruction should be provided to employees at all levels within the organisation.

Risk identification and assessment is an ongoing process. Where there are significant changes in the workplace, in processes or activities, or on the introduction of a new process, a new risk assessment must be undertaken. It is recommended that a risk assessment should be periodically reviewed and updated. An effective system of monitoring will need to be implemented.

A number of techniques are available to identify hazards. These are summarised in **Figure 18.3**.

Useful information on checking performance against control standards can also be obtained reactively from accident and ill-health investigations, the investigation of damage to plant, equipment and vehicles and the investigation of "near-miss" situations.

The frequency of review depends upon the level of risk in the operation, and should normally be at least every ten years. Furthermore, if a serious accident occurs in the organisation, or elsewhere but is possible in the organisation, and where a check on the risk assessment shows no assessment or a gap in assessment procedures, then a review is necessary. **Figure 18.4** presents an example of a completed hazard worksheet.

Figure 18.3: Some Appropriate Methods for Hazard Identification

Visual Inspections (Walk-through Surveys)

This is an ideal way of identifying hazards before they have turned into accidents. This is the most proactive method. Walk-through Surveys of the whole of the business activity enable the manager to gain a much better picture of how safety is being managed within the organisation. Consideration should be given to undertaking the Walk-through Survey before any risk assessment programme is put into place. A well conducted survey will:

- Allow the manager to view the organisation globally.
- Identify what good controls are already in place.
- Identify any failings in the system.
- Identify the attitude towards safety.
- Identify housekeeping standards.

The premises themselves need to be reviewed against the requirements to provide a safe place of work. Access routes, signage, emergency lighting and general lighting, condition of floors and traffic routes, all of these and more require checking by a walk-through of each area. Specific modules dealing with particular aspects of health and safety give more detailed checklists on what to look for in each area.

Each item of equipment should be reviewed on three counts:

- Is the equipment safe to use, satisfactorily labelled, electrically insulated and capable of isolation, electrically checked periodically, stable and properly positioned?
- Is the equipment subject to routine maintenance and checking?
- Are there specified staff authorised to use the equipment, and are staff informed of the risks and aware of any precautions to be taken, including those in the event of a foreseeable contingency?

Specific modules dealing with particular equipment give more detailed checklists on what to look for in each area.

Visual Inspections of Work Activities

Risk assessments can be carried out in general terms as a "desk exercise". The information collated may then form a "generic assessment" that applies in general to all work activities of that type. However, it is necessary to check the local arrangements for the immediate environment, the knowledge and skill of staff, other activities undertaken in the vicinity – these and others may affect the degree and nature of the risk and hence the precautions to be taken. Visual inspections of work areas are best undertaken after a review of what is occurring and of what is expected to be found during a survey.

Job Safety Analysis

In order to evaluate the hazards and precautions associated with any job, there is a set of simple questions to be answered:

Question 1: What are the tasks which, when followed in sequence, permit the job to be done?

Question 2: What harm could arise to the worker carrying out these tasks?

Question 3: What precautions, including training, already have been taken to protect against the specified harms?

This process of breaking a job down into component parts enables the effective review of current arrangements and facilitates the addition of new ones to make the work as safe as possible. With tasks that are complicated and include a high hazard component, it prevents more minor risks passing unnoticed until someone is injured.

Accident Research

The best health and safety management system, based upon high quality risk assessments, may result in failures. Sometimes the failures are the results of events occurring that the original evaluation of risks had not foreseen, on other occasions staff will act unsafely out of ignorance or because of other motivations (speed, bravado) against the established rules. Whatever the reason for the accident, an investigation is useful if it generates information to prevent a recurrence. No organisation is perfect, but learning from experience, rather than repeating mistakes, is vital. The research into accidents highlights that, for every serious accident, there are many minor ones and even more "near misses", where no person was harmed. The extent to which these last provide an early warning of what may go seriously wrong in the future should not be underestimated.

Feedback from Employees

When staff are engaged in a task, particularly one that they carry out many times over a period, they become genuine experts at that task. This does not mean that they will always automatically be aware of the hazards and risks associated with their work, but it is important that their knowledge and skill are utilised rather than under-estimated when it comes to risk assessment. There are many occasions on which the operator of a machine or a maintenance fitter in a plantroom has a far greater understanding of the risks to be assessed and controlled than a manager or other person reviewing the work for a few minutes. Good organisations actively encourage feedback from their staff, on the work itself and the hazards intrinsic to it, and on the precautions to be adopted to control the resultant risks. Inviting comments from staff and encouraging participation in the risk management process, is also a way of motivating people to take the precautions seriously.

Figure 18. 4: Example of a Completed Hazard Worksheet

SECTION: ACTIVITY:		WORKPLACE:			ASSESSOR:	
Hazard Identification	Risk Assessment	Affects	Control Measures	List additional controls required	Responsible person to implement controls	Date to implement
List hazard which you expect to result in harm	What's the risk under normal conditions in your workplace?	List groups of people who might be harmed	What, if any, existing control measures are in place?			
Electrical appliances	Electrocution, fire, trips and falls	Employees, customers, visitors, cleaners	All leads properly secured and routed to prevent trips and falls. ELCB protection provided. Regular checks	Annual check on electrics by qualified electrician	Hotel Manager / Maintenance Manager	Additional controls implemented immediately
Manual handling	Back injury, hand injury, foot injury and sprains/strains	All staff but particularly bar and housekeeping and porters	All staff trained in manual handling. Staff lifting heavy loads provided with safety shoes, e.g. keg handling. Mechanical aids include push trucks, etc.	Provide protective gloves, review stacking of kegs	Supervisors / Hotel Manager	Additional controls implemented by (Date)

Risk Evaluation

The risk evaluation stage provides the foundation for planning, organising and managing risk. Risk evaluation involves a process of quantifying risks and determining their possible impact on the organisation. Risk evaluation has two important components:

- The evaluation of loss frequency and loss severity. This analysis will provide measures of expected average loss and maximum possible loss. This evaluation is a continuous process.

- An analysis of the financial strengths of the organisation. This involves an assessment of the organisation's risk retention capacity and is designed to determine what the impact of a given risk might be, relative to the financial strength of the firm.

Loss Dimensions

A major consideration in risk management is the determination of the size or quantum of a possible loss. Several measures have been developed in order to facilitate this process:

- **Maximum foreseeable loss (MFL)**: The maximum foreseeable loss is defined as the value of the largest possible loss from a single event that is reasonably foreseeable under the most adverse conditions.

- **Estimated maximum loss (EML)**: The estimated maximum loss is defined as a reasonable estimated loss size from a single event, given that the control measures are not capable of totally performing the task of loss containment or loss reduction. EML is a measure of loss and is usually smaller than the MFL.

- **Normal loss expectancy (NLE)**: This is defined as the average loss that could result from a single event, assuming that all risk control measures operate as expected.

- **Loss frequency**: This is a measure of the number of events that occur in a defined interval. It may relate to the frequency of industrial accidents per hundred hours worked, etc.

- **Loss probability**: This is defined as the relative frequency with which an event occurs, as the number of observations tend towards infinity. Relative frequency is defined as the proportion of time an event takes place and the frequency with which it takes place in the long run relative to its probability.

Figure 18.5 presents an example of a risk assessment framework.

Figure 18.5: Risk Assessment Framework

Consequence of Hazard	Frequency	Risk
Serious	High	Serious
	Medium	Medium/Serious
	Low	Medium
Significant	High	Serious
	Medium	Medium
	Low	Low
Minor	High	Medium
	Medium	Medium/Low
	Low	Low

Method: Each hazard is considered and a judgement made whether the worse consequences are:

• Serious — death or serious disease/permanent disability;

• Significant — broken bones, deep lacerations;

• Minor — minor injury or short-term ill health.

The second column expresses the frequency, which considers the number of similar hazards — for example, machines operating, and the duration of the risk (how often the machine is used).

A safety specialist can undertake qualitative assessment. However, in more complex work situations, a more detailed quantitative assessment is required and a professional, such as a risk assessor, should execute this.

The simplest form of numerical assessment involves assigning a numerical scale, say from 1-5, for the likelihood where 1 denotes most unlikely and 5 denotes almost certain. Another similar scale is used to express the consequence where 1 is a trivial injury and 5 is death. The risk number is the product of the two quantities, i.e.

25 as a maximum. While some systems have scales with up to nine points, it becomes increasingly difficult to allocate scale numbers.

More complex methods, capable of giving more reliable information, involve setting up numerical scales to quantify maximum probable loss (MPL), frequency of exposure (FE), number of persons at risk (NP) and probability of exposure (PE). The product of these gives the hazard risk rating (HRR):

$$HRR = MPL \times FE \times NP \times PE$$

There is no system that is uniformly applicable. The best system for a workplace is one that works and can be understood and readily applied. It is beneficial to use the same rating system throughout a site/process so that relative comparisons in the degree of risk can be determined. This will help prioritise remedial actions to address unacceptable risks.

Another method for estimating the risk involves quantifying:

1. The probability of exposure to the hazard.

2. The frequency of exposure to the hazard.

3. The number of persons at risk.

4. The maximum probable loss.

Numerical values are assigned to a descriptive phase relating to the above factors, these values being weighted where relevant. Such tables of values and descriptive phrases are given below, though each organisation should select tables of values and phrases to suit their own needs. **Table 18.1** illustrates the method:

Table 18.1: Example of Risk Estimation Methods

Values and Descriptive Phrases	
0 Impossible:	Cannot happen under any circumstances.
1 Unlikely:	Though conceivable.
2 Possible:	But unusual.
5 Even chance:	Could happen.
8 Probable:	Not surprised.
10 Likely:	Only to be expected.
15 Certain:	No doubt.

Probability of Exposure to/Contact with Hazard (PE)	
0.1	Infrequently.
0.2	Annually.
1.0	Monthly.
1.5	Weekly.
2.5	Daily.
4	Hourly.
5	Constantly.

Frequency of Exposure to Hazard (FE)	
15	Fatality.
8	Loss of 2 limbs/eyes or serious illness (permanent).
4	Loss of 1 limb/eye or serious illness (temporary).
2	Break — major bone or minor illness (permanent).
1	Break — minor bone or minor illness (temporary).
0.5	Lacerating/mild ill health effect.
0.1	Scratch/bruise.

Note: Damage losses (e.g., based on cost) can also be included above.

Maximum Probable Loss (MPL)	
1	1-2 Persons.
2	3-7 Persons.
4	8-15 Persons.
8	16-50 Persons.
12	More than 50 Persons.

Action Timetable

Risk	HRN	Action Timetable
Acceptable risk	0 – 1	Accept risk/consider action.
Very low risk	1 – 5	Action within one year.
Low risk	5 - 10	Action within three months.
Significant risk	10 – 50	Action within one month.
High risk	50 – 100	Action within one week.

Very high risk	100 – 500	Action within one day.
Extreme risk	500 – 1000	Immediate action.
Unacceptable risk	Over 1000	Stop the activity.

Number of Persons at Risk (NP)

How we use these four factors to arrive at a notional hazard rating depends partly on the numbers chosen and partly on the weightings assigned. The above tables have numbers and weightings selected to give a hazard rating number (HRN) from the product of all four values:

$$\text{(HRN)} = \text{PE} \times \text{FE} \times \text{MPL} \times \text{NP}$$

An action table is then arranged to reflect the importance of the risk and the action required. Using the system is relatively simple once all involved in it are agreed upon the values assigned in the tables and the action priorities selected. Here are some examples:

- Four employees are exposed to a hazard weekly. Because of the nature of the activity, it is possible but unusual that contact will occur. If it does, the maximum probable loss would be amputation of two limbs of one employee. The Hazard Rating Number would be:

$$\text{HRN} = \text{PE} \times \text{FE} \times \text{MPL} \times \text{NP} = 2 \times 1.5 \times 8 \times 2 = 48$$

From the action table, it can be determined that some action should be taken within a month to reduce the risk.

- A hairdresser faces an even chance of sustaining a cut during the working day.

$$\text{HRN} = 5 \times 5 \times 0.1 \times 1 = 2.5$$

Action required within a year. The only effective solution here is to reduce the probability of contact with sharp edges.

- The ventilation system fitted to a paint spray booth cannot cope with the larger jobs that occur four or five times a day. This results in highly flammable vapours escaping into the workshop where 12 other persons work. There are a number of ignition sources in this workshop.

$$\text{HRN} = 8 \times 4 \times 15 \times 4 = 1920$$

Action — stop the hazardous activity until appropriate measures are taken to reduce the risk.

One of the advantages of using a risk assessment methodology is that it can assist in selection, by directing attention to one or more of four areas where appropriate actions can be taken. These four areas are as follows:

- Reduce probability of contact (PE).

- Reduce frequency of exposure (FE).

- Reduce the maximum probable loss (MPL).

- Reduce the numbers at risk (NP).

Reducing any or all of these values will reduce the HRN and the best solution is likely to be the combination of measures that reduces HRN to the lowest value. If PE, by itself, can be reduced to a value of zero, the risk is eliminated, as HRN also reduces to zero. In reality, achievement of a zero probability of contact is unlikely as even the best safeguards fail on occasions. If, however, backup safeguards, fail-to-safety devices, etc. are used, PE may be reduced to almost zero.

Note that this approach to elimination of the risk by reducing PE supports the notion of engineering revision as the first choice of remedy. The next measure that will provide a reduction in risk is exposure frequency reduction. This may be achieved through exposure, design or process change, etc.

Reducing the MPL largely relies on two general methods, the first of which is to reduce the amount of energy involved in the hazard when exposure occurs and the second is to provide energy-absorbing barriers between the persons and the hazard such as personal protective equipment.

Reducing HRN by limiting numbers at risk is perhaps the least valuable method; however, it would be of benefit in conjunction with any of the other measures.

Not all hazards are easily identified or assessed and may require the application of special analytical techniques by a safety specialist or risk management consultant. The methods include: Job Safety Analysis (JSA), Failure Modes and Effects Analysis (FMEA), Fault Tree Analysis (FTA) and Hazards and Operability Studies (HAZOPS). Some of these methods will be considered in the next section.

An outcome of the risk assessment process may be the identification of hazards where the level of risk is unacceptable. Where this is the case, the risk must be controlled to an acceptable level or, where possible, eliminated.

Irish law requires that, as far as is reasonably practicable, management must eliminate or control the risk in question. However, if a risk is likely only to result in a minor injury very infrequently, and would cost a considerable sum of money to eliminate the problem, that risk may be deemed acceptable. If the potential outcome is death or serious injury, and the probability is likely, the risk must be eliminated or satisfactorily controlled, whatever the cost. In some circumstances, work must be stopped until the danger is removed. This law is of little value in making a judgement call on what is acceptable or unacceptable.

The following are the main control measures listed, in decreasing order of their use by an organisation:

- **Elimination of the Hazard:** achieved by stopping the operation, changing the machines, changing the process, installing physical barriers, guards or interlocks that prevent operators from coming in contact with the hazard. Consider the use of robotics, but note that they also have associated hazards.

- **Substitution:** of safer chemicals in place of more hazardous ones. Devise more effective guards. Change to low voltage electricity, pneumatic or hydraulic power.

- **Housekeeping:** a place for everything and everything in its place. Avoid trips and falls.

- **Isolation:** enclose the operator or the operation.

- **Environmental Control:** suitable lighting and heating. The accident rate is lowest around 20/21°C.

- **Ventilation:** hazardous chemicals, fumes or fibres should, as far as possible, be contained as close as possible to the source, e.g., fumehood/cabinet; otherwise use local extraction at source. General ventilation/dilution is often a suitable means of control for less hazardous materials. But it is necessary to remember that, emissions will have to be released to the environment at some point. However, it may be necessary to install some form of abatement system e.g., filters, scrubbers.

- **Safety Awareness:** increase safety awareness by notices, posters, slogans, training and education activities.

- **Training and Supervision:** consider if more training or re-training may reduce the risk. Are work manuals clear and precise? Are emergency procedures concisely stated and capable of being exercised? Is the supervision suitable and adequate?

- **Personal Protective Equipment (PPE):** must be regarded as the last resort when all the other strategies are not a practical reality. PPE is rarely more than 90 per cent effective.

Figure 18.6: An Example of Control Strategies

Main Types of Risk	Managing the Risk
Cutting Injuries or Amputation From knives and dangerous equipment	• Employ safe practices. For example, always cut or chip on a board, never in the hand. • Do not leave knives in sinks. Store knives in suitable racks or sheaths. • Make sure dangerous machines, such as slicers, mixers and food processors are suitably located, securely fixed and adequately guarded. • Site the equipment so that the operator cannot be accidentally bumped/distracted. Display warning notices alongside machines to remind operators and others of the dangers they pose. • Maintain equipment in good condition.
Burns and Scalds From cooking appliances, utensils and boiling water.	• Do not top up deep-fat fryers with oil from large containers. • Lower food into the fat slowly. • Provide suitable gloves and aprons for dishwashing and use only special oven cloths for removing hot items from the oven. • Use long-handled baskets for deep sinks. • Never leave cooking pots so that the handles project over the stove edge. • Keep face clear when opening lids on bain maries and saucepans. Never reach across hot containers, saucepans, etc.

Main Types of Risk	Managing the Risk
Fire Risks From electrical faults in wiring, lights and equipment, burning fat and grease, flare-ups in cooking appliances and smoking.	• Do not overfill or leave deep-fat fryers unattended. • Do not leave ovens and ranges unattended. • Ensure that thermostats are working. • Ensure adequate fire fighting equipment is available, e.g., fire blankets. • Clean microwave ovens on a daily basis. • Ensure that all means of escape are properly maintained and kept free from obstruction, unlocked and easy to open. • Ensure electrical systems are checked regularly and faults reported and repaired immediately. • Do not overload electrical systems by using adaptors.
Slips, Trips and Falls Uneven, slippery or obstructed floor surfaces and trailing cables may lead to accidents and injury.	• Provide adequate lighting and sufficient room. • Train staff in safe working practice, e.g., never carry hot food over the head of a customer, be aware of handbags, etc. • Establish a one-way system in and out of the kitchen. • Provide mops so that spills can be cleaned up immediately. • Provide safe access equipment for reaching heights. • Avoid trailing cables.
Cleaning Substances used for cleaning sinks, toilets and floors and for washing dishes are potentially dangerous chemicals and may cause dermatitis and chemical burns.	• Use the safest possible cleaning agents and instruct staff how to use chemicals safely. • Obtain information on all substances used in the premises from manufacturers' hazard data sheets. • Train staff and provide appropriate protective clothing.

Main Types of Risk	Managing the Risk
Maintenance People have lost their lives, others have suffered injuries as a result of accidents during maintenance work, e.g., window cleaning, changing light bulbs, painting, etc., or lift and equipment maintenance.	• Do not overlook routine cleaning and maintenance work when considering health and safety. Develop safe systems of work for employees. • Ensure there is nothing on the premises, which could pose a risk to the health and safety of contractors.

Risk Control/Evaluation

Having identified the risks and evaluated their possible impacts, the next step is to attempt to minimise those risks through the implementation of a physical risk management programme. Valsamakis et al. (1992) define risk control as any activity the organisation adopts that is aimed at preventing losses, or minimising the consequences of losses that may arise from the pure risks facing the organisation. They view risk control as a pervasive activity not limited to the prevention of losses, which are viewed as inevitable. Risk control is based on five important philosophical principles:

• The identification and application of management principles to the control of risk.

• The recognition, on the part of the organisation, that risk exposure and associated losses should be systematically and deliberately assessed.

• A desire to engage in loss prevention.

• A recognition that the risk control process is an on-going one.

• The belief that risk control is an activity that requires integration with other activities within the organisation.

SELECTING RISK IDENTIFICATION TECHNIQUES

Different methods or techniques of risk identification can be used in a variety of circumstances. No one method can effectively deal with all types of organisations or firms and the task, therefore, is to choose a method or combination of methods best suited to the organisation, undertaking the risk audit. It is important to understand that the identification of risk should be carried out on a consultative basis. No one individual has sufficient knowledge of all processes to effectively recognise all possible hazards. Consequently, it is prudent for risk management specialists to consult with operators, supervisors and management on the factory floor. A committee should be formed, to meet on a regular basis, with the individual responsible for risk management acting as chairperson.

The process of risk identification is known as a risk audit and the person co-ordinating and executing the audit should be the risk manager or the person responsible for the management of risk. In carrying out the risk audit the cost of the exercise must be considered.

Risk Inspection

Risk inspection involves a physical inspection and is a commonly-used method. It allows the safety/risk specialist to view the site/plant at first hand and facilitates contact with employees who may have important information concerning risks and hazards in the workplace. It is, however, very time-consuming and its overall effectiveness is determined by the skill and expertise of the safety/risk specialist carrying it out. The focus of a risk inspection is primarily on physical observations, whereas the problems may have a systems source.

A physical inspection is the best means of acquiring information. Viewing the site assists the risk manager in visualising the dangers that can arise. Making an appearance at a site also makes the risk manager more visible. Risk inspection is costly in terms of both money and time. The risk manager must attend all company sites and spend time with supervisors, employees and manager in order to become familiar with operations.

Questionnaire Studies

Although the best method of acquiring information on risk is to visit the premises, there are other means of obtaining the required data. One method is to construct a questionnaire. Questionnaires may be drafted in a variety of ways. The golden rule is to make the questionnaire short, simple and suitable for the persons to whom it is to be sent. A questionnaire is a cheap and simple way of obtaining risk information and allows for comparisons. In addition, questionnaires can usually be adjusted to take into account changes that have occurred. Because somebody completes the questionnaire other than the person who designed it, the responses may be deliberately or accidentally inaccurate. There is also always the problem of ambiguity. The person completing the form may misunderstand a question or understand it in a different way from the person designing it; consequently, the answers will be unsuitable. Another difficulty concerns the completion of the form. Many managers or supervisors are very busy and the completion of a questionnaire will be low on their priority list. In view of this, the risk manager must motivate the respondents to return the completed questionnaire as soon as possible.

Organisational Charts

Organisational charts provide the risk manager with an overview of the organisation. They assist in ascertaining the nature of the organisation and reveal possible interconnections. An organisational chart of the whole corporation should be formulated as well as charts for individual companies showing how they operate.

Flow Charts

Another tool that may be used to assist the risk manager is a flow chart. This depicts the flow of material in any system that has an input and an output. In order to construct the flow chart, the risk manager must obtain full details of how the system operates from start to finish. This will mean consultation with persons familiar with the system.

Hazard And Operability Studies (HAZOP)

The previous methods of identifying risk dealt with the subject on a broad scale. Hazard and operability studies break down the identification process into manageable parts. This method has been used extensively in the chemical industry and is suitable for hazardous operations. Before commencing the HAZOP study, the operation or plant is broken down into its component parts and each is examined extensively in order to identify the dangers associated with it. HAZOP studies address four main questions:

- The intention of the part examined.

- Deviations from the declared intention.

- Causes of the deviations.

- Consequences of the deviations.

The first step involves the selection of the section or part of the plant to be studied. This can be done by using a flow chart of the process under consideration. Once this has been completed, the purpose of the part being examined is ascertained. The question to be asked is: what does this section of the process do? At this stage, assistance of the production manager and/or engineers may be required. In fact, it would be better to carry out a HAZOP study with a team consisting of engineers, chemists and other relevant professionals. After establishing the purpose of the section being studied, the analyst must then decide what property or aspect of the process should be considered. This process continues throughout the plant.

Once the intention of the process is established, all possible deviations from that intention must be listed. This is an important step and, again, participation of a team will be extremely helpful. In order to structure the investigation, guide words (see **Figure 18.7**) are applied to each section being studied.

Figure 18.7: Guide Words used in HAZOP Studies

Guide Words	Meaning	Comments
No or not	There is a complete negation of the intention.	No part of the intentions achieved, i.e. nothing works.
More/less	There is an increase or decrease in the quantity of the property.	The part works but it is producing more or less of its product.
As well as	There is a qualitative increase in the property.	The intention is achieved but something else is being achieved as well.
Part of	There is a qualitative decrease in the property.	Only part of the intention is achieved and part not.
Reverse	The logical opposite of the intention.	The process is reversed, the machine pushes instead of pulls.
Other than	The complete substitution of the intention.	No part of the original intention is achieved and something else is substituted.

Once the causes of the deviations have been listed, the next step is to consider what could cause the deviations. Again, teamwork is essential in establishing all of the causes for the deviations.

The next step involves listing the results of the various deviations. This may give rise to a number of possible actions that must be considered in order to reduce the identified hazards. A different form should be used for each part or aspect of the process being studied.

The advantages of a HAZOP study are that it is very thorough and there is very little likelihood of any large risk being overlooked. It ensures that each part of a complicated system is considered and the possible dangers identified. This would be extremely difficult without a systematic approach. This system is a far more concentrated approach than the others mentioned above, which are more sweeping than the HAZOP method.

The main disadvantage is that it is time-consuming and expensive to operate. A team is usually required to carry out the HAZOP study efficiently and these are usually highly-paid employees of the organisation.

Fault Trees

Fault trees provide a way of quantitatively analysing the possible risks that could occur. The previous methods are essentially qualitative in nature: they do not include a way in which the danger can be quantified and measured against other hazards. Using a fault tree will overcome this problem.

A fault tree is a diagrammatic representation of all of the events that may give rise to some major events. It answers the question "How can a defect occur?". A logical network is created from the major event through the possible causes that lead up to, or could lead up to, the disaster shown as the "head event".

The only consideration relates to whether there is the probability of a failure or no failure, as a part failure is considered to be a failure. The tree commences with the "head event", the consequence under consideration. An example is the loss of an eye by an employee using a grinder or from the explosion of a tank. This leads down to a primary event, which is caused by a characteristic of the component itself, such as a rise in pressure in a tank or boiler or the drying of a grinding stone or the overheating of a plug due to faulty connection. This leads to a secondary event, which is initiated by an external source such as a power failure or misuse of a machine. The final event, known as the "basic event", is a possible initiating cause or causes and is found at the bottom of the tree. This is usually indicated by a circle and indicates that no further causes exist or can be traced. **Figure 18.8** provides an example of a fault tree.

Figure 18.8: A Fault Tree for an Eye Injury to a Driller

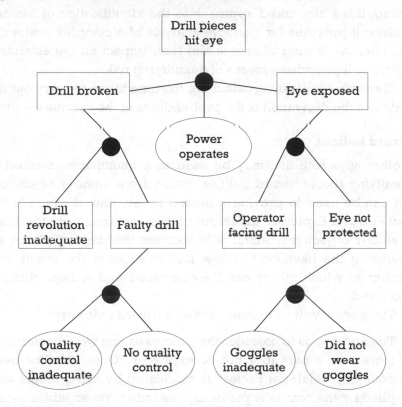

Two logical operators, AND and OR gates are used to define the relationships between the branches of the tree. AND gates indicate that both or all the events must occur before the head event can happen while OR indicates only one of the subsidiary events needs to operate before the head event can occur.

A major benefit of the fault tree is that it can provide a means of calculating the minimum number of combinations of events that can bring about the main event, as well as listing all of the ways in which it can come about. Knowing the minimum number of ways the head event could come about allows us to ascertain which set of events is most likely, which has the greatest impact on the head event and where changes in the system would be most effective. The minimum number of ways a head event can occur is called the set of minimum cut sets and the cut set is the group of events or primary sources of failure that can bring about the head event.

Other advantages of using fault tree analysis include the following: it is a structured approach to the identification of hazards or risks; it provides for a simple analysis of a complex system; it facilitates the tracing of causes and their impact on the establishment; and it provides a means of quantifying risk.

The main disadvantages include the time taken to carry out the study and the derivation of the probabilities of the various events.

Hazard Indices

Another approach that may be used as a quantitative method of identifying risk is hazard indices. There are a number of sources that can be used to provide a hazard index, one of which is the Dow Fire and Explosion Index. All of these sources have the same or similar objectives, which is to express the degree of risk by measuring the likelihood of loss and to express the result as a number to which others can be compared and annual changes monitored.

The steps involved in constructing a hazard index are:

- The first step is to consider the processes that would contribute more than others to a fire or explosion. Once this has been done, the "Material Factor" is calculated by using tables supplied by the company providing the index. These tables measure the intensity of energy released from certain named chemicals or substances that may be used in the process. This "Material Factor" is a measure of the hazard faced in using certain chemicals.

- The hazards connected to the materials used in the process are then considered. These are divided into two categories:

  ◊ General process hazards, which could increase the magnitude of the loss; and

  ◊ Special process hazards, which are known to contribute to incidents that increase the probability of fire or explosion.

- A loading or penalty is applied for each hazard discovered. This penalty is laid down by the index, as is the particular hazard.

- Once the general and special factors have been calculated, they are multiplied together to provide the unit hazard factor.

- The unit hazard factor is then multiplied by the material factor to produce the fire and explosion index.

- It is possible to find two processes with the same unit hazard factor, but this does not mean that they represent the same hazard, as different materials may be used. The Dow Fire and Explosion Index overcomes this by supplying a table that relates the unit hazard factor to the material factor. This table consists of two axes, the vertical measuring the overall effect of a fire or explosion on a scale of 0 to 1. By comparing the unit hazard factor with the material factor, the damage factor can be ascertained. This will show the appropriate level of destruction that could occur if a fire or explosion were to happen.

- The fire and explosion factor can be used to obtain an approximation of an area of exposure — that is, the area that is likely to be affected by a fire or explosion.

- The damage factor represents the probable extent of any fire; so, if the value of property within the area is ascertained, an approximation of the amount of risks can be gained.

- Credit is given for effective features in the plant such as sprinklers, emergency shutdown systems, etc.

The object of hazard indices, therefore, is to provide an understanding of the maximum amount at risk in any process as well as the estimated area of exposure.

The Human Error Role Probability Technique (THERP)

THERP is a technique that can be used to predict the potential for human error in a work activity. It evaluates in quantitative terms the contribution of the human error component in the development of an incident. It uses human behaviour as the basis for the evaluation process. It adopts the concept of a basic error rate, which it assumes to be relatively consistent between tasks requiring similar human performance efforts. The methodology employed in THERP consists of four elements: selecting the system failure; identifying all of the behavioural elements; estimating the probability of human error; and calculating the probabilities as to which human error will produce the accident/incident or system failure. Once the probable errors are identified, it is then possible to implement specific corrective actions in order to eliminate or reduce the likelihood of error.

Probabilistic Risk Assessment (PRA)

A probabilistic risk assessment consists of five stages:

1. **Identification of undesired events**. This stage involves the use of HAZOP studies that are carried out at the conceptual design, the detailed design and operational stages of a system.

2. **The likelihood of undesired events**. This stage involves an estimation of the probability of the undesired events occurring. It is possible to establish probabilities mathematically based upon the probable failure rates of individual components of the system.

3. **Consequences of undesired event occurring**. Initially, a hazard analysis is undertaken that informs the analyst of the magnitude of the potential problem and its potential for harm to people, plant, processes and the public. A risk analysis can then examine the actual consequences or worst possible case considerations and express them mathematically.

4. **Is the risk of the event occurring significant?** The outcome of stage 3 is a number, which expresses the risk in individual and/or societal terms. Individual risk is the probability of death to a group of people. A social risk is usually expressed as a fatal accident frequency rate.

5. **Taking control action**. If the calculated risk figure is above accepted limits, some form of corrective action is necessary.

Management Oversight and Risk-free Tree (MORT)

MORT is defined as a systematic approach to the management of risk in an organisation. It is based on four philosophical principles:

- Management takes risks of many kinds including cost, production, quality of environment and health and safety risks.

- Risks in one area affect operation in other areas.

- Risks should be made explicit where possible and the organisation should know the potential consequences of these risks.

- Risk management techniques should be adaptable enough to suit a wide range of situations.

The MORT process utilises four analytical techniques.

Change Analyses

This is based on the Kepner-Tegoe method of rational decision-analysis. The method works by comparing a problem-free situation with a problem (in this case, an accident) situation. The objective is to isolate cause-and-effect relationships. The method is useful when the decision-maker needs to find the answer quickly, or in situations where the cause is obscure or where generally, well-behaved personnel deviate from normal good behaviour.

Energy Trees and Barrier Analysis (ETBA)

This technique is based on the idea that some form of energy is necessary in order to accomplish tasks. However, uncontrolled energy flow, in the absence of adequate barriers, may result in accidents. The aim is to answer the question of what happened in the accident situation.

MORT Tree Analysis

This is a more complex method combining principles from the field of management and safety, using fault methodology. The technique operates by organising 1,500 basic causes leading to 98 generic problems. This allows the investigator to discover what happened and why. It considers both specific control factors and management systems factors as potential contributors to the accident. Human resources, procedures and hardware are analysed separately and then together as key system elements.

Positive Tree Design

This method operates from the stance that the proper sequence of events needed to accomplish an objective should be set out. This allows the analyst to identify where the accident deviated from the correct sequence.

MORT places significant emphasis on management oversight as a contributory factor to accidents at work. The system, if properly implemented, can lead to a reduction in such oversights. It can help to determine the order of risks and allow them to be dealt with appropriately. It also facilitates the best allocation of resources to prevent and reduce the number and severity of adverse incidents and accidents.

It is unlikely that one particular technique or method of identification will suffice. The general advice is to utilise a number of methods in order to ensure that the identification process is complete. Some methods may be more suitable for certain industries than others. The identification process can be considerably enhanced by a process of consulting with key individuals within the organisation, including line managers and employees at operator level. Risk identification is an on-going process and cannot be regarded as an isolated exercise.

SELECTING A RISK MANAGEMENT APPROACH

The risk management tools to be used in a particular situation depend on the characteristics of the situation and the risk being dealt with. Each loss-producing event is different and needs to be considered separately by the risk manager. The decision will also depend on their appropriateness and comparative cost. Generally speaking, risk can be considered in terms of the relative frequency and severity of possible losses. From this generalisation, risk can be classified into four classes, which are depicted in the matrix shown in **Figure 18.9**. This matrix can be used as a starting point for considering which risk management tool should be used.

Figure 18.9: Matrix of Risk Management Approaches

Frequency

	High	Low
High	Avoid Control	Insure
Low	Control Finance Internally	Finance Internally

Severity

High Frequency, High Severity Losses

If the probability of loss is high and the pecuniary implications arising from the occurrence severe, taking into account the firm's financial position, the activity having these risk characteristics should be avoided or loss control measures effected in order to reduce the risk to manageable proportions. This risk will be costly to insure and also the firm will not be able to retain the loss itself and, therefore, the risk should be avoided.

High Frequency and Low Severity

In the event of an activity producing frequent losses of low severity, provision should be made for retention because insurance will be comparatively expensive. In order to reduce the amount of the losses, a loss control programme should be implemented. Because the losses are of high frequency, the firm should be able to predict and make provision for them in the budget. If the possible losses are of a low severity, the organisation should be able to pay for them out of its earnings, provided its cash flow is large enough to deal with them. If not, the organisation can consider building up a fund to pay for the losses.

High Severity and Low Frequency

High severity and low frequency losses should be relatively inexpensive to insure. As insurers deal with a large number of risks, they are able to calculate the future possible losses with greater accuracy than the individual risk-bearer and, therefore, the amount to be set aside to meet these losses can be calculated by the insurer with greater precision. This reduces the cost of risk, that is to say, the cost of uncertainty. When calculating expected losses, provision should be made for the reality that these calculations may not be accurate. Therefore, the greater the number of exposures, the more accurate the expected loss calculation and the less the provision for contingencies.

Although frequency is low, the severity of a possible loss is high and may exceed the amount a firm can afford. This is another reason why insurance should be maintained for this type of loss.

Low Frequency and Low Severity

This is best dealt with by retention. If the loss should occur, the cost will be easily absorbed as part of normal operating expenses and included in the budget. In making the decision concerning the retention of risk, the basic rules of risk management must be borne in mind.

Do Not Risk More than You Can Afford

If the expected or maximum possible loss is large enough to threaten the existence of the organisation or the attainment of its objectives, insurance should be used to provide finance in the event of such a loss occurring. The establishing of this upper limit is difficult to calculate and will depend on a number of factors such as:

- The net worth of the enterprise.

- The enterprise's cash flow.

- Its liquid reserves.

- Availability of funds from the outside.

The objective of this exercise is to ascertain the maximum amount a firm can bear without becoming bankrupt or the achievement of its objectives being hindered. If the organisation's cash flow is not sufficient to meet losses and there are no liquid reserves or a possibility of obtaining funds from outside, the question of insuring all possible losses should be seriously considered.

Consider the Odds

In considering how the organisation should handle risk, the risk manager must bear in mind the probability of a loss occurring. This involves ascertaining the relative frequency of losses over a number of years. Insurance is cheapest when the probability of loss is low. This is because the premium charged by the insurer has to take into account the value of claims it will have to pay in the future. If claims are frequent, the insurer can calculate, with some element of certainty, the value of expected losses and charge a premium for this amount plus a percentage for expenses and profits. If the frequency is low, it is difficult for both the risk manager and the insurer to calculate the future possible losses although it is known that the number will be small. In view of this, the premium may be relatively cheaper than the expected losses, and the risk manager will be certain that, in the event of the unexpected occurring, the firm will be capable of financing it.

Don't Risk a Lot for a Little

It is pointless deciding to retain a risk if the savings made are small compared with the possible loss. Some of these issues will be considered in the next chapter on loss control.

CHAPTER ROUNDUP

- Recent times have witnessed a movement away from the traditional injury approach to health and safety, to an approach, which focuses on predicting and controlling all forms of loss within the organisations. This approach has become known as risk management. Risk can be conceptualised on a continuum, where at one end is the engineering view and at the other society's concept of risk. Engineers and technologists consider risk as the possibility of something going wrong. In societal terms, it is viewed as a function of fairness, trust, liability, distribution and content, and the issue of probability is given little consideration.

- Different classifications of risk have been developed. Pure risk is defined as the occurrence of an undesired event from which the sufferer cannot profit. Speculative risk does allow for the possibility of making a profit. Dynamic risks refer to uncertainties, which occur as a result of ever-changing society. Static risks are those that occur despite changes in society. Objective risk refers to the statistical measures of the degree of variation from the expected, whereas subjective risk occurs when an individual perceives the possibility of a particular adverse event occurring.

- The risk management process consists of a number of steps including the setting of objectives, the identification and evaluation of risk, the selection of risk handling devices and the implementation of monitoring of risk plan/strategy.

- A wide range of macro and micro risk identification techniques exist for use in a risk management approach. This is generally viewed as the most important component of the risk management process because, if risks are not discovered, they cannot be dealt with. Risks can only be controlled once identified. Identification techniques include risk inspections, check lists, organisational charts, flow charts, hazard operability studies and fault trees.

Chapter 19

RISK MANAGEMENT: HANDLING RISK, LOSS CONTROL AND FINANCING RISK

INTRODUCTION

This chapter considers ways in which an organisation can manage risk. It is divided into two sections, loss control and the financing of risk. Loss control is defined as a strategy used by the organisation to reduce the probability of an untoward event occurring or prevent it occurring at all. The term can also be used in the sense of controlling the loss after the event occurs. The financing of risk involves making provision should a loss occur. It is a strategy of providing for the financial impact of loss and includes insurance and the self-financing of risk.

This chapter considers the following issues:

- General approaches to loss control and theories of loss control.

- The principles of total loss control.

- Stages of the total loss control process.

- Alternative risk control strategies that may be used by organisations.

- The nature and scope of risk financing.

- The monitoring of an organisation's risk management strategy.

APPROACHES TO LOSS CONTROL

Loss control involves the identification of the source or cause of loss and the initiation of steps to eliminate or reduce its effects. The basis of loss control is the identification of all unplanned events, whether or not they lead to personal injury, as undesirable, and warranting management and staff action to minimise them. The aim of a loss control programme is to correct and prevent all unsafe acts and conditions, which in turn benefit quality and efficiency. Denenberg et al. (1974) suggests a number of general approaches.

Engineering Approach

The engineering approach aims to control the physical aspects of the risk situation. Risk is generally managed from an engineering perspective and uses the knowledge of the physical sciences to prevent loss-producing events occurring and to minimise any loss that does occur. An engineering approach is usually the first to be considered and implemented by organisations.

Human or Behavioural Approach

The human or behavioural approach is based on the premise that losses are caused in part by physical factors, but the most important causes are generally human fault-related or, at least, can be traced to the actions of humans. Therefore, the prevention of losses should focus on remedying employees' faults or difficulties with the work environment. The basis of the human or behavioural approach is found in the work of Heinrich (1950), who formulated three basic conclusions:

- Eighty-eight per cent of all accidents are primarily the result of the unsafe actions of employees.

- The causes of major accidents are the same as those for minor accidents.

- Indirect losses from industrial accidents amount to four times the direct losses.

Safety Systems Approach

The safety systems approach represents a variant of an engineering approach. Stranks (1994a) defines this approach as the identification and correction of hazards from the concept stage of a product through to design and operation. It places an emphasis on the identification of possible causes of losses before they occur. It requires the use of advanced techniques to identify possible costs.

Education Approach

An education approach advocates that, for risk management to be implemented successfully, there must be an understanding of and commitment to the concept, philosophy and policies that underpin risk management. This understanding and commitment must originate at the top level of management and consist of education, training and communication activities. An education approach must extend beyond established training and awareness programmes and include custom-designed training materials.

An Enforcement Approach

With an enforcement approach there is a basic assumption that human beings are fallible and prone to forgetfulness and other weaknesses. This requires that prevention measures be used carefully and consistently. This process can be achieved only through the use of legislation and codes of practice. Enforcement is, however, best viewed as a continuum: at one end is a deliberate policy laid down by top management specifying its desire to enforce risk control strategies, whereas at the other end is a reliance on the use of legislation and penalties to achieve results. **Figure 19.1** presents the key principles of loss control management.

Figure 19.1: Principles of Loss Control Management

> **Safety** can be defined as "anything done to avoid or reduce accident loss" (injury, ill health, damage, or interruption).
>
> **Safety Management** can be defined as "applying management principles to safety"(see the principles listed below).
>
> **Safety Management System** can be defined as a systematic approach to managing safety, i.e. who is supposed to do what, when, where and how.
>
> If accidents are the problems, what are the management solutions? Perhaps the following?

Principle of the Critical Few (Pareto): 80% of results (accidents) are usually due to 20% of the causes, so it is essential that we assess the risk involved that is the probable frequency and probable severity of recurrences.

Principle of Future Characteristics: the future will be the same as the past, unless things change, but . . .

Principle of Resistance to Change: sweeping changes cause resentment unless spread over time (eat the elephant in hand, bite-size portions) and unless certain other criteria are also met, as follows . . .

Principle of Communication: those affected must be told about the background, the need for change and, above all, the desired outcomes of the proposed changes; as well as clearly who is required to do what, how, when and where . . .

Principle of Participation: they must be involved in decision-making process (help build solutions), using effective consultation mechanisms; e.g. employees involved in determining their own safety rules are more likely to comply . . .

Principle of Recognition: especially when positive efforts are commended (as well as disciplinary action); unless employees are motivated to perform safely they are unlikely to comply, especially if there is a benefit to working unsafely!!

Principle of Reciprocated Interest: "What's in it for me?" If no perceived benefit, then no co-operation!

Principle of Point of Control: the minimum capacity for change occurs at the coal-face: While senior managers must lead and control, and employees must comply, the critical area for effectiveness is at supervisor level.

Principle of Definition: A logical decision can be made only if the real problem is first defined.

Principle of reporting to the highest authority: The higher the level to which loss control managers report, the more management co-operation they receive.

Principle of multiple causes: A loss is seldom, if ever, the result of a single cause.

Principles of management results: A loss control manager tends to secure most effective results through and with others by planning, organising, leading and controlling.

THEORIES OF LOSS CONTROL

The Chain Concept

A chain concept suggests that loss control can be considered in terms of a chain of events leading to the final occurrence. The steps to be taken in instituting a loss control programme can be considered at each link. These links are:

- **Source of Loss**: At this stage, the source of loss can be controlled. Before a building is constructed, the risk manager can consider, together with fire and safety experts, precautions that should be incorporated into the building. For example, fire walls can be installed or sprinklers can be placed in store rooms, access and egress can be planned in the light of safety, and so on. In the case of employee safety, each person entering an organisation can be given training in safety and in the philosophy of the organisation concerning health and safety. New drivers may have to undergo regular driving tests to ensure that they are up to standard.

- **Reduction of Hazards**: Continuous inspection and reduction of hazards, once the loss exposure comes into existence, should be a feature of any risk management programme. Driving tests for all drivers on an annual basis may be implemented, buildings and other assets may be inspected regularly to ensure that there are no increasing dangers, and so on.

- **Minimisation of Loss**: At this link in the chain, control can be exercised by minimising the loss once the untoward event has occurred. A burglar alarm may alert the police, once thieves have entered the premises and reduce the amount of time available to them to steal goods. Sprinklers may be installed to reduce loss from a fire. An efficient first aid service in the organisation may reduce the extent of the possible injury suffered as a result of an accident.

- **Salvage**: Loss control may be effected through effective salvage operations, once the untoward event has occurred. Carpets damaged by water can be professionally dried and cleaned. Rehabilitation of injured employees may reduce the damages that may be awarded due to an accident.

Risk control methods should be applied early and dealt with at source. In the Irish Stardust disaster, for example, the risk of loss occurring could have been considered at the design stage when the building was converted to use as a club. Instead of flammable carpet tiles being placed on the walls, other non-combustible material could have been used. The seats, which were highly inflammable and led to the quick spread of the fire, could have been designed to be flame-resistant.

The Stardust disaster also illustrated the dangers of failing to maintain the safety features of a building used for entertainment purposes. In this case, emergency exits were provided but some were locked and others blocked.

Haddon's Energy Transfer Approach

Another approach to loss control is represented by Haddon's (1972) energy transfer theory. Haddon is of the view that accidents generally occur because of the sudden, unplanned release of energy such as by hurricanes, fire, lighting and vehicles. According to Haddon, there are ten ways in which these sudden release of energy can be handled and these are shown in **Figure 19.2**.

Haddon's theory focuses on the way in which a common energy or force that could cause an accident can be handled. It can be applied regardless of the type of untoward event being considered: whether it be fire, embezzlement, personal injury or theft, this approach can be implemented to attempt to overcome its effects. The methods, or strategies, as Haddon calls them, need not be used independently but as many as possible can be implemented in order to reduce the possibility of a loss-producing event.

Figure 19.2: Handling the Sudden Release of Energy

	Strategy	Illustration
1.	Prevent marshalling of energy in the first place.	Prevent workers climbing to high places from which they may fall.
2.	Balance the amount of energy which is marshalled from which accidents may result.	Reduce the number of workers permitted to climb to high places.
3.	Prevent the release of energy which has built up.	Build guard rails to prevent falls from high places.
4.	Slow down the release of energy.	Reduce the height at which employees must work; slow down the rate at which explosives are permitted to burn.
5.	Separate, in space or time, the energy which is released from the object susceptible to injury.	Prohibit entry to blasting areas during blasting periods.
6.	Place a physical barrier between energy source and the object susceptible to injury.	Require workers to use safety helmets, safety shoes, or eyeglasses.
7.	Modify the contact surface by rounding or softening edges.	Design cars with padded dashes; build toys without sharp edges.
8.	Strengthen the object against damage by energy release.	Require fireproof building construction. Workers to be vaccinated.
9.	Mitigate the damage which has not been prevented by the above eight measures.	Use fire alarm, sprinkler, and storm-warning systems, and emergency medical care facilities.
10.	Use rehabilitation and restorative techniques where damage occurs.	Retrain injured workmen with permanent disability.

Hoyos and Zimolong's Behavioural Approach

Hoyos and Zimolong (1988) suggest that risk conditions can be controlled and improved in a number of ways. These are summarised in **Figure 19.3**.

Figure 19.3: Applying Behavioural Concepts to Manage Loss

Ergonomic Design

- Optimising the physical work environment such as illumination, vibration, heat, noise, toxic material control;

- Design of tools, machinery, equipment, workplaces and man-machine interfaces.

Organisational Factors

- Improving organisational attitudes and goals with respect to safety performance such as safety policy formulation, monitoring safety performance, supervisory attitudes, and practices concerning safety and the communication of safety information.

- Allocation, sequencing and scheduling of task work and shift cycles.

Personal Factors

- Physiological and psychological conditions such as vision, audition, information processing, skill level, expertise, motor performance.

- Person/environment fit: safety motivation, level of training and practice, safe/unsafe performance, workload, types and levels of stress.

STAGES OF THE LOSS CONTROL PROCESS

Loss control is generally implemented as a long-term intervention. Generally, most programmes tend to have five stages:

Injury Prevention

This stage is concerned with the humanitarian and legal aspects of employee safety and employers' compensation costs. It normally incorporates features such as machinery safety, cleaning and housekeeping procedures, health and safety training at all levels, personal protective equipment, joint consultation (safety representatives and safety committees), the promulgation of safety rules, regulations and disciplinary procedures, and safety propaganda.

Damage Control

This component of the programme addresses the control of accidents that cause damage to property and plant, and that might conceivably cause injury. Essential elements of this stage are damage reporting, recording and costing.

Total Accident Control

This stage of loss control is directed at the prevention of all accidents resulting in personal injury and/or property damage. Three steps towards total accident control are incorporated, namely: spot-checking systems, reporting and control centres and health and safety audits.

Business Interruption

This stage entails the incorporation into the programme of controls over all situations and influences, which downgrade the system and result in business interruption, e.g. fire prevention, security procedures, health and hygiene monitoring, pollution prevention, product liability procedures. Business interruption can result in lost money (e.g. operating expenses), lost time (e.g. cost of idle labour and equipment), reduced production and lost sales, perhaps through delays in delivery. Product liability claims are an increasing cost being borne by many manufacturers.

Total Loss Control

This stage is concerned with the control of all insured and uninsured costs arising from any incidents that downgrade the system. It includes aspects associated with "business interruption" and identifies the possible tools and methods of measurement.

To develop a loss control programme usually requires statistical data to associate the general argument with evidence of actual losses to the organisations. The costs that are identified will fall under two main headings – insured and uninsured losses. The HSA suggests that, if almost every accident is investigated, uninsured losses can be shown to cost many times more than those insured – they liken it to the tip of an iceberg with most of the mass hidden underwater. The costs include management time, lost production, loss of customer goodwill and general reputation. In contrast, a loss control programme that reduces accidents generates many diffuse benefits including heightened staff morale, lower staff turnover, better public relations, increased productivity and reduction in operating costs.

Total loss control is a management programme that seeks to eliminate as many of these losses as possible and, in consequence, protects staff and others from the effects of accident and poor working environments.

SELECTING RISK CONTROL STRATEGIES

Risk control may be classified into four main areas: risk avoidance, risk retention, risk transfer and risk reduction. **Figure 19.4** presents a flow chart of questions to be considered when assessing organisational controls.

Risk Avoidance

This strategy involves a conscious decision on the part of the organisation to avoid completely a particular risk by discontinuing the operation producing the risk. It presupposes that the risk has been identified and evaluated. For example, a decision may be made, subject to employees' agreement, to pay all wages by cheque or credit transfer, thus obviating the need to have large amounts of cash on the premises and the inherent risk of a wages snatch. Another example of a risk-avoidance strategy — from the health and safety field — would be the decision to replace a hazardous chemical by one with less or no risk potential.

Figure 19.4 : Assessing an Organisation's Current Controls

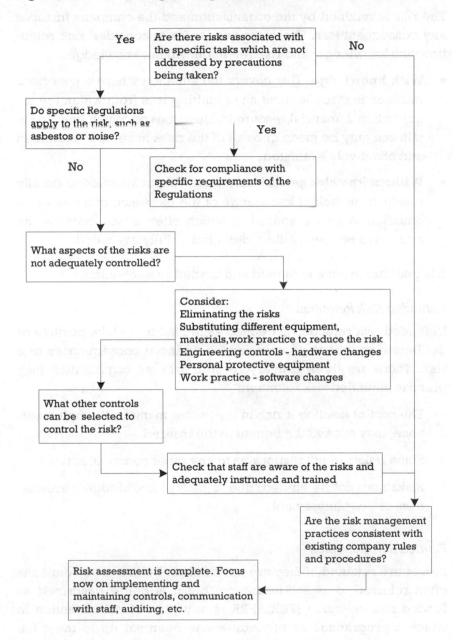

Risk Retention

The risk is retained by the organisation and the company finances any consequent loss. There are two issues to consider: risk retention with knowledge; and risk retention without knowledge.

- **With knowledge**: This covers the situation where a conscious decision is made to meet any resulting loss from within the organisation's financial resources. Decisions on which risks to retain can only be made once all of the risks have been identified and effectively evaluated.

- **Without knowledge**: Risk retention without knowledge usually results from lack of knowledge of the existence of a risk or an omission to insure against it, which often arises because the risks have not been either identified or fully evaluated.

It is possible to have unfunded and funded risk retention:

Unfunded Risk Retention

Unfunded risk retention is defined as the failure to take positive or deliberate actions to provide for the financial consequences of a risk. There are three primary reasons why an organisation may practise unfunded risk retention:

- The cost of treating a risk in a positive manner, through insurance, may exceed the benefit to the insured.

- Some risks are not responsive to any other course of action.

- Risks may not be funded, due to lack of knowledge, carelessness or poor judgement.

Funded Risk Retention

Losses are retained, if they are not insured. Deliberate retention is often referred to as self-insurance, but it is better described as funded risk retention (FRR). FRR is any plan of risk retention in which a programme or procedure has been set up to meet the negative consequences of a financed loss. Such a strategy is adopted for two reasons:

- It may not be possible to transfer the risk fully through insurance.

- It may be less expensive than other transfer techniques.

Figure 19.5 presents some of the considerations in developing a risk retention programme.

Figure 19.5: Considerations in Developing a Risk Retention Programme

---

- What risk financing techniques are available to the risk bearer?

- What types of risks does the firm face in terms of insurable and uninsurable risks?

- What are the statistical properties of the risk exposure retained?

- Retain risks that display high loss frequency with a potential for relatively low severity.

- Carry out a clear evaluation of a risk retention strategy *vis-à-vis* alternative risk financing techniques.

- Give careful consideration to the choice of an appropriate fund retention vehicle.

- What are the tax implications of a risk retention strategy?

Risk Transfer

Risk transfer refers to the legal assignment of the costs of certain potential losses from one party to another. The most common way of effecting such a transfer is by insurance. Under an insurance policy, the insurer (insurance company) undertakes to compensate the insured (organisation) against losses resulting from the occurrence of an event, specified in the insurance policy (e.g. fire, accident, etc.). The introduction of clauses into agreements whereby another party accepts responsibility for the costs of a particular loss is an alternative risk transfer strategy.

Risk Reduction

The principles of risk reduction rely on the reduction of risk within the organisation by the implementation of a loss control programme, whose basic aim is to protect the company's assets from wastage caused by accidental loss. Risk reduction involves the collection of data on as many loss-producing incidents as possible, the collation of all areas where losses arise from the above incidents, and the formulation of future strategies with the aim of reducing loss.

RISK FINANCING STRATEGIES

There are two primary methods of providing for the financing of a loss: insurance and retention of the loss. Other methods include making provision for loans and passing the loss on to somebody else by means of a contract.

Insurance

The most common method of providing for post-loss financing is by purchasing insurance. This is carried out either by approaching an insurance company or by making use of insurance brokers or agents.

The insurance market is divided into three main sections: the life market, which deals with long-term insurance; the general market, which deals with short-term insurance; and the health insurance market. Brokers or insurance agents may act in all or one aspect of the insurance market and set themselves up as specialists in the particular area of insurance in which they are operating. The well-known international brokers such as Bowrings, Minets and Sedgwicks, operate in all three markets.

The market sells insurance in various forms to cover a variety of risks faced by a business. A contemporary trend is to supply insurance in a packaged form, whereby all business perils are covered under one policy. Large organisations may purchase policies specifically drawn up to cover particular risks.

The general insurance market deals with all short-term insurance. Sometimes this market is called "non-life", because it generally deals with property, pecuniary and liability insurance. Unfortunately, this term is not quite accurate because the market also provides personal accident insurance, which covers death arising out of an accident. A better classification is short-term insurance.

Property Insurance

A number of insurance policies are sold by the insurance market that provide cover in the event of a loss occurring from a particular peril. Some of the perils covered by the insurance market include:

Fire

Property faces the risk of fire and insurers generally provide fire policies to cover such a risk. The premium is generally based on: the value of the property at risk, the nature of the industry and the state of the fire precautions implemented by the owner of the property. Insurers will generally cover buildings and contents.

The policy usually covers not only fire, but also explosion from domestic boilers, lightning and thunderbolt. It can be extended by means of a special perils extension to cover storm, loss or damage caused by water, earthquake, riot, strike and malicious damage, explosion, impact by vehicles, aircraft, spontaneous combustion and sprinkler leakage.

Theft

Insurance companies will provide cover for goods stolen from premises occupied by the insured, provided there has been forcible and violent entry or exit from the premises. This policy does not generally include cover for loss of money or theft by members of staff or theft resulting from collusion with employees. Occasionally a small amount of cover may be provided for money stolen, as well as for property belonging to employees, if it is not insured elsewhere.

Money policies provide cover for loss of money held in a locked safe while the premises are closed for business, money in transit or while in the insured premises, when open for business. There are generally different limits for these types of losses: the highest for money kept in a locked safe and the lowest for money on the premises, not in a locked safe and stolen during working hours. This limit may be increased in the event of an armed robbery. Some money policies provide personal accident cover for employees.

Fidelity guarantee policies provide cover in the event of money or stock being stolen by employees. Some companies provide blanket cover for this risk whilst others will grant cover only to named employees or listed jobs such as accountant, cashier, and the like.

Glass

Policies are provided by insurers to cover the breakage of plate glass windows or plate glass in the shop or factory. This will generally include cover for sign writing and fixtures and fittings in the window damaged by the breaking glass.

Engineering

Policies provide cover in the event of a breakdown of a machine including an extension to cover for loss of profits arising from the breakdown. In order to obtain compensation from insurers, the breakdown must be fortuitous. Computers are often included under this type of cover or under a separate computer policy. The computer policies generally extend to include the cost of recovery of data and other extraneous expenses that may arise from computer breakdown. Some insurers provide cover for computer abuse such as fraud, viruses and other factors that could affect the operation of the computer system.

Transit

Policies cover goods while in transit from the insured's factory to anywhere in the world. The organisation should ensure that the goods being transported are at the organisation's risk. It is possible to pass ownership of the goods to the purchaser from the time they leave the organisation's premises and to have delivery made at the purchaser's risk. This will pass on to the person receiving them the risk of loss occurring to the goods. This is usually effected by means of a contract and the organisation could check the contract of sale to ascertain whether it contains any conditions that would affect risk.

Motor

The most common form of insurance is that covering motor vehicles. All motor vehicles on the roads have to carry at least third party insurance. Third party insurance provides cover in the event of a driver negligently injuring another person, be it a pedestrian or someone in another vehicle. It also covers the property of that third person.

The second type of cover, slightly more expensive, is third party, fire and theft. This policy provides cover for loss or damage to the insured vehicle in respect of fire or theft. Thus, if a vehicle is stolen and returned damaged, the cost of repair will be covered.

The final type of motor insurance policy is a comprehensive one. The basic cover includes third party liability insurance for persons outside the vehicle as well as inside and also damages to the vehicle itself. Although the policy is called a comprehensive policy, there are a number of exclusions that need to be examined to ascertain the precise nature of the cover provided.

Motor policies may be issued on an individual basis for each vehicle or on a fleet basis. The latter requires that all registration numbers of the insured vehicles are supplied or, in some cases, blanket cover may be provided to cover any vehicle in the fleet. The latter would normally be granted only for very large fleets and is expensive.

Liability Insurance

Liability insurance is an extremely important component of the risk manager's consideration of risk. The main categories of liability insurance are:

- **General Liability:** General liability represents the liability an organisation owes to members of the public. It does not cover liability to employees or arising out of products sold or advice given.

- **Product Liability:** Product liability represents the liability that may arise out of goods sold and supplied by an industry. It does not cover damage to the goods themselves but only loss or damage caused by the use of the product.

- **Employers' Liability:** Employers' liability policies cover the liability an employer has towards an employee while acting in the course of employment. Employers' liability insurance was considered in **Chapter 5**.

- **Professional Liability:** Professional liability covers the legal liability, which may arise while an individual, or organisation is involved in giving advice as a member of a profession. Examples include advice given by doctors, accountants or brokers. In the case of each of these policies, claims are paid if the insured is legally liable to a third party, and in no other case.

- **Product Guarantee:** Technically speaking, product guarantee is not a liability policy because it guarantees the product that is being supplied. Insurers are sometimes prepared to offer this class of insurance.

- **Product Recall:** Product recall insurance covers the cost of recalling a product in the event of its being defective. This is quite an expensive form of insurance in Ireland.

- **Personnel:** The most common form of policy covering personnel is the personal accident policy. This can be sold to individuals or groups and covers the insured in the event of injury or death caused by an accident. Normally a lump sum is paid to the injured person or their estate although cover can provide for regular payments. The policy normally covers death, loss of limb, deafness, loss of an eye or other permanent disability. It can be extended to cover temporary total disablement (TTD) or temporary partial disablement (TPD) as well as medical expenses arising out of an accident.

Loans as a Method of Risk Financing

If insurance is not purchased, there are other ways of providing an income in the event of a loss. It can be done by providing for a loan from a financial institution to be made available in the event of an untoward occurrence. In this case, arrangements would have to be made for a bank to provide immediate cash in the event of a large fire or other occurrences where any delay could have severe consequences for the business. It is not a very common way of providing for losses, but it is possible.

Managing Risk Using Contracts

Another way of transferring liability is by means of a contract. In business contracts an exception clause can be included in the contract whereby one of the parties is relieved of any liability or responsibility for loss or damage. This would effectively ensure that, however loss or damage was caused, the party benefiting from the exclusion clause would not suffer loss. A clause could be placed in a contract setting out where risk of loss lies. This is quite common. For example, a contract may state that, in the event of building works being carried out, the contractor will be responsible for all buildings on site until they have been officially handed over following the completion of an engineer's certificate; after that, they become the risk of the principal or purchaser.

Another type of clause is an indemnity clause whereby one party is obliged to indemnify the other. In this case, if a loss occurs, the person to be indemnified is entitled to claim the extent of their loss. Indemnity clauses are most common in the building and transport industries.

MANAGING LOSS CONTROL STRATEGIES

All loss control strategies must be managed to ensure that they are working effectively. Management controls can be strategic or operational in focus.

Strategic Controls

There are four basic types of strategic control available to the organisation:

Premises Control

Loss control strategies are based on certain assumed or predicted conditions, called planning premises. Premises control is designed to check systematically and continuously whether the premises set out during the planning and implementation process are still valid.

Premises are generally concerned with two types of factors: environmental and industry. The first concerns those factors over which the organisation has no control: weather patterns, new technology, inflation, Regulations, political disturbances, and new laws. Management can gauge the likelihood of changes in weather patterns but is unable to control them, and they should therefore be monitored. Industry factors are those that affect the operation of a particular industry and will vary from industry to industry.

It may be difficult for management to track all premises upon which its loss control strategies are based; consequently, only the most important ones are usually monitored.

Implementation Control

Implementation control is designed to ascertain whether the overall loss control strategy should be changed in the light of unfolding events. The two basic types of implementation control are monitoring strategic thrusts and milestone reviews.

- **Monitoring Strategic Thrusts:** In pursuing the organisation's objectives, new projects are implemented to accomplish the overall strategy. These thrusts will assist the risk manager and top management in deciding whether any further changes need to be made to the organisation's loss control strategy to reduce risks.

- **Milestone Reviews:** In attempting to achieve the organisation's goals and objectives, management may have identified critical milestones that could occur over the period of implementation. Once the milestone is reached, a review of the organisation's progress should be considered. This review will usually involve a full-scale reassessment of the risk control strategy and a decision as to the advisability of continuing with the present strategy or refocusing it. Risk management should consider at the milestone stage whether there has been a change in the risks faced by the organisation and whether these affect the loss control strategies that have been adopted.

Strategic Surveillance

Strategic surveillance is designed to monitor a broad range of events inside and outside the organisation that are likely to undermine the loss control strategy. Information sources should be monitored on a regular basis so that information concerning unanticipated events can be discovered and acted upon.

Special Alert Control

Special alert control ensures that, in the case of a sudden unexpected event, the organisation's risk management strategies can be assessed. For example, on the occurrence of a war, the risk manager should immediately review the risks that the firm is facing. Does the organisation own any property in the danger area? Is any of its property making its way on board ships in the war area? Are any of the employees of the organisation engaged in work in the area, etc.?

It may be necessary to develop a crisis team to deal with disasters that may occur. This team can immediately put into effect any disaster or contingency plans, or consider the action that needs to be taken to reduce the amount of loss.

Operational Controls

Risk management operates at the operational level and therefore operational controls should be maintained. These systems guide, monitor and evaluate the progress made towards meeting the short-term risk management objectives. There are three types of operational control systems that can be used by the organisation:

- **Budgets:** A budgetary system is simply a plan whereby available resources are allocated. It assists management to co-ordinate operations and facilitates the control of performance by managers. The risk manager will usually be mandated to budget for the resources required during the year as well as for the expenditures that may occur. The risk manager will generally have a capital budget that deals with the purchase of items such as sprinklers, new safety equipment, etc. The extent of the risk manager's budget will depend on the objectives and strategies of the organisation.

- **Schedules:** Timing is sometimes an important factor and scheduling is purely a way of ensuring that each loss control activity is timed correctly.

- **Key Success Factors:** A useful way of ensuring that the organisation's risk management strategy is on target is to identify performance areas that are key to the total risk management strategy. A strategy to reduce insurance premiums, for example, would have as a key success factor the reduction of employers' liability claims. The achievement of key success factors is a prerequisite to attaining the overall objectives. Therefore, with appropriate monitoring there is more likelihood of success.

MONITORING PERFORMANCE

Once a loss control strategy has been set up and performance standards drawn up, the performance must be monitored and deviations evaluated. Information concerning the progress of the loss control strategy must be obtained so that deviations can be identified and the cause of the deviation established and managed.

At evaluation stage, risk management is concerned with comparing progress to date with expected progress. Of particular interest to the manager monitoring the performance, therefore, is the current situation because it provides a basis for future action. Before any action is taken, an acceptable level of deviation must occur. So, in order to allow for flexibility, the risk manager must agree a level or degree of deviation that can be allowed before any action is necessary. The standards set are also not necessarily accurate: they are based on historical figures and, therefore, are an educated guess as to what may happen in the future. If there has been an increase in accidents, the risk manager should ensure that this is a significant deviation from the expected before establishing the underlying cause.

A useful concept is the use of a trigger point in monitoring, especially when dealing with key factors. A trigger point is a level of deviation of a key indicator or figure that is identified as a major threat or opportunity by the organisation. When this point is reached, management is immediately alerted and action can be taken.

It is also useful to develop contingency plans so that, in the event of a disaster or other "triggering" event, management knows exactly what to do. For example, if a company keeps all of its records on computer or carries out many of its transactions using information technology, plans should be established to deal with the consequences of system failure. Arrangements could be made to hire another computer. In the event of a large fire, the risk manager should have plans in place to reduce the loss by knowing of alternative premises if the insured's factory is destroyed.

Corrective action can take a variety of forms. Plans may have to be changed, new staff hired, the retraining of existing staff, and so on. The rationale for monitoring progress is to ensure that all changes that may occur are taken into account in the loss control strategy.

MOTIVATION TO MANAGE RISK

Once objectives have been established, they must be operationalised. Staff in all areas must be motivated to follow the recommendations put forward to handle risk and minimise loss. This can be done by using both positive reinforcement and sanctions. The former should be given the primary emphasis and the latter used only in extreme circumstances.

The manager responsible for risk management could be rewarded by reference to achievements in risk control. If the objectives are attained or exceeded, a lump sum could be payable, or possibly a reduction in salary or other sanction could be imposed for poor performance.

Reward systems should be based on the control of both long-term and short-term strategies, and not solely on the latter, as happens in many organisations. There often is a tendency to consider end-of-the-year balance sheet figures on which to base the reward system, which can lead to short-term thinking rather than the integration of long-term and short-term objectives. An effective system should provide rewards that control and evaluate potential future performance as well as the results of the previous year.

CHAPTER ROUNDUP

- The effective handling of risk is an important component of a health and safety management system. It consists of two important activities, loss control and the financing of risk. Loss control is a method used by organisations to reduce the probability of an untoward event occurring or to prevent it occurring at all. Financing risk is making provision should a loss occur. It is a method of providing for the financial impact of loss and includes insurance and self-financing of risk.

- Loss control can be considered as a chain of events leading to the final occurrence. The steps to be taken in instituting a loss control programme can be considered at each link. These links are sources of loss, reduction of hazards, the minimisation of loss and salvage. Risk control methods should be applied early and dealt with at source.

- There are two dominant philosophies of loss control. One concentrates on human factors, whereas the other focuses on mechanical factors. The former approach places emphasis on staff training, the implementation of safety rules and the development of a safety culture. The mechanical approach emphasises good lighting, the installation of guards, effective housekeeping and sound-proofing equipment.

- There are two primary ways to finance a loss — insurance or retention of the loss. There are other methods such as making provision for loans and passing the risk on to somebody else by means of a contract.

- Risk management strategy needs to be effectively managed. Once such as system is put in place it is not the end of the process. The risk manager must monitor the strategy to ensure that its objectives are achieved. The types of controls utilised may be strategic or operational in focus.

PART FIVE

OCCUPATIONAL HEALTH AND HYGIENE

Chapter 20

OCCUPATIONAL HEALTH AND HYGIENE: THE PRINCIPLES

INTRODUCTION

This chapter considers the broad but related areas of occupational health and hygiene. These are functions that have gained in importance in recent years primarily due to the emergence of issues such as HIV/AIDS, substance abuse and occupational stress. The chapter focuses on the following issues:

- The nature and scope of the occupational health and hygiene function.

- The different typologies of occupational diseases.

- The nature of physical, biological and ergonomic hazards and their implications for organisations.

- The different hygiene strategies that can be implemented by an organisation.

THE NATURE OF OCCUPATIONAL HEALTH AND HYGIENE

Occupational health is concerned with the promotion and preservation of employee health at work, covering all aspects of work and the working environment. This broad aim requires a blend of expertise drawn from various disciplines (medicine, toxicology, physiology, psychology, ergonomics, etc.) and effective management to ensure the well being of employees.

Research conducted by the Institute of Personnel and Development (IPD, 1996) in the UK, which included Irish companies, revealed that employers that organised and implemented occupational health and 'wellness' programmes incurred annual employment costs of between €1,693 and €3,695 less per employee than employers who did not. This suggests that consideration of health and welfare issues has quantifiable benefits for organisations. Irish health and safety law requires employers to provide a safe and healthy work environment. However, it is not legislative requirements alone that place concern for health issues high on the agenda. Changing social attitudes and employee expectations also significantly influences the importance of such issues. Better-educated and informed employees expect employers to consider new research and changing lifestyles and have these reflected in positive occupational health and welfare policies and practices.

The International Labour Organisation broadly defines occupational health as:

> Occupational health should aim at: the promotion and maintenance of the highest degree of physical, mental and social well-being of workers in all occupations; the prevention among workers of departures from health caused by their working conditions; the protection of workers in their employment from risks resulting from factors adverse to health; the placing and maintenance of the worker in an occupational environment adapted to his/her physiological and psychological ability and, to summarise: the adaptation of work to man and of each man/woman to his/her job.

As with any area of health, a distinction can be made in occupational health between dimensions of prevention and cure. Occupational hygiene, on the other hand, involves attempts to recognise, understand, anticipate and control hazards arising from work and the workplace, and is therefore the preventative aspect. Occupational medicine (or occupational pathology) deals with health problems caused by poorly controlled work hazards, and is, therefore, the cure aspect. The role of the modern occupational health specialist is frequently limited to occupational hygiene, along with the more simplistic areas of occupational medicine such as routine health monitoring and first aid. This occurs because of the high cost and complexity of facilities required to treat those with serious occupational diseases, which usually can be effectively treated only by external medical institutions.

Controlling Health Risks

Occupational health gives specific emphasis to the control of health risks. The distinctive features of health risks include:

- Ill health often results not from immediate injury but from complex biological processes such as the repair of repeated damage (irritant dermatitis), immune responses (asthma), or abnormal cell behaviour (cancers). There is individual variation in response.

- These processes may take place over a long period (e.g. asbestos-related diseases). Hence hazards may become apparent only after many people have been put at risk. Cases of disease may continue for decades after exposure has been controlled.

- The same disease may have both occupational and non-occupational causes (e.g. asthma, back pain, lung cancer). The link with an occupation can sometimes be established, but confirmation of an occupational cause usually comes from studies comparing frequency of disease in exposed and non-exposed groups.

- Exposure to disease risks is not always apparent. Measurement of risk factors is often required. The probability of disease occurring often depends on the level of exposure over a long period. The severity of many diseases, but not all (e.g. cancers), also depends on the level of exposure.

These characteristics have major implications for health risk control:

- The complexity of many health risks means that the identification of health hazards and health risk assessment will generally require greater input of appropriate in-house or external consultant expertise than that required for many safety assessments.

- The assessment of health risks often requires the measurement of exposure, calling for specific monitoring and assessment techniques and the competence to use them.

- While health risks arising from the use of substances can be controlled by physical control measures, systems of work and personal protective equipment, the operation of which can be measured, confirmation of the adequacy of control will often require measurements of the working environment to check that exposures are within pre-set limits. Sometimes surveillance of those at risk, to detect excessive uptake of a substance (biological monitoring) or early signs of harm (health surveillance), may also be necessary. These techniques require occupational hygiene and clinical skills and individual results will need to be handled within a framework of medical confidentiality.

Occupational Health Activities in Organisations

Occupational health includes the study of all factors relating to work, working methods, conditions of work and the working environment that may cause diseases, injuries or deviation from health, including maladjustment to work, for instance, chemical and physical hazards such as intoxication from inhaled dusts, fumes, gas or vapours, silicosis from inhaled quartz dust, skin diseases from irritating substances, or deafness from noise; mechanical risks involving machinery; and physical and mental strain from heavy or monotonous work, high speed or long working hours. Furthermore, poor human relations at work may cause or contribute to maladjustment, with different nervous symptoms. This part of occupational health deals with the health protection of the worker against hazards or other unhealthy factors at work or in the working environment.

However, occupational health means not only health protection but also health promotion, a concept that includes everything that can promote the health and working capacity of the worker, such as preventative measures against communicable diseases, improvement of nutrition and general mental health.

Occupational health is sometimes divided into different specialities related to different kinds of problems and different types of applied scientific methods: occupational physiology deals with physiological reactions to factors at work, such as heavy work and heat stress and the study of different kinds of fatigue; occupational psychology deals with the psychological and mental demands of the job and how to evaluate the mental capacity of different individuals in order to achieve a proper placement from the health point of view. In relation to the influence of physiological and psychological factors upon the individual at work, a new field has developed: ergonomics, which is the applied science of adjusting work to people, in the light of their anatomy, physiology and psychology. Occupational pathology or occupational medicine deals with occupational diseases caused by chemical factors.

THE ROLE OF THE OCCUPATIONAL HEALTH DEPARTMENT

The traditional role of the occupational health specialist developed as a result of the rapid advances in medicine (particularly in bacteriology) during the late 19th century. At that time, it was believed that most diseases could be attributed to one specific cause. Thus the occupational health specialist's role was to safeguard workers from injuries or diseases arising directly from a specific cause at work or in the working environment. However, subsequent medical research has shown that health problems are very often caused by a combination of many separate factors. In light of this knowledge, the role of the occupational health specialist has widened, to consider the influence of occupational hazards on non-occupational diseases that would normally be the domain of public health specialists. Furthermore, well-documented industrial catastrophes since the 1950s (such as Three Mile Island, Bhopal and Chernobyl), along with the increasing emphasis on green issues, have highlighted the important link between workplace hazards and public health, forcing occupational health practitioners to become more fully aware of the effects that their workplace has on the health of those who are not workers. The modern occupational health specialist is becoming more and more involved in the environmental management of the organisation, especially at the design stage of facilities and work systems.

The typical occupational health department of today consists of an occupational health nurse, an occupational health physician, an occupational hygienist, a health and safety specialist, and a trained first aider. **Figure 20.1** summarises the main activities of the occupational health department, many of which revolve around the surveillance of the employee and their environment. Subsequent data analyses aid the understanding and control of workplace hazards, and safe work methods can be identified, promoted and monitored.

Figure 20.1: Main Activities of the Occupational Health Department

Safety Measures: Avoidance of potential risk through environmental surveillance, to aid identification of hazards affecting both workers and the public, and implementation of effective control mechanism.

Health Surveillance

- *Primary monitoring* — concentrates on those with an existing health condition and may point to a previously unforeseen hazard.

- *Secondary monitoring* — concentrates on monitoring the effects of known hazards.

- *Monitoring for non-occupational diseases* — to detect early signs of occupational conditions that may prevent the worker from fulfilling work duties, e.g. cancer screening programmes.

- *Supervision of vulnerable groups* — keeping a close eye on groups especially at risk, e.g. the disabled, the aged, those with a history of long health-related absences.

- *Recruitment screening* — to match recruits to jobs by ensuring they possess the right physical and mental capabilities for tasks.

- *Maintaining Health Records* — to assist both occupational and public health staff in the provision of health care; to provide data for epidemiological studies; to aid monitoring and decision making.

- *Liaise with external health specialists* — to ensure that procedures are in place to deal with health concerns beyond the scope of the occupational health department.

Treatment Services

- *First Aid* — to deal with any emergency situations

- *Specialist Treatment* — organisations may have specialist treatment services for common conditions, although cost often necessitates external treatment services.

Health Promotion

- *Health education programmes* — to advance healthier lifestyles among workers, and to promote an understanding of and engagement in safe work practices.

- *Counselling* — may take the form of advice on specific physiological health conditions, or counselling on a range of personal, social and emotional problems.

- *Welfare amenities* — provision of sanitary and other facilities such as washing and showering areas, nurseries, kitchens, canteens, rest rooms etc.

Occupational health is a rapidly expanding area, with greater public awareness of health issues and ever-expanding technologies creating new demands on organisations to provide better standards of care. This focus on moulding rapidly expanding technologies into safer work systems has spawned an ever-increasing number of specialities within occupational health, bringing together knowledge from disciplines as obscure as meteorology and biotechnology. The day-to-day priorities of occupational health specialist are, of course, usually organisational and industry-specific. However, according to Berry (1991), there is a growing acceptance of the need to go beyond this essential, but often limited and retrospective, involvement of the occupational health team, to develop prospective studies involving co-ordination between as many disciplines as possible. Otherwise safety in emergent technologies will have to continually rely on sketchy retrospective data.

This, in turn, presents difficulties, as aspects of judgement become even more important. Experts disagree on "safe" levels of toxicity — for example, the balance between economic viability and acceptable risk are viewed differently by industrialised and developing countries. As we approach a new century where one of the fastest growing fields of technology is genetic engineering, it seems certain that more attention will be focused on the ethics of occupational health, with many issues remaining unresolved.

SOME SPECIFIC AREAS OF OCCUPATIONAL HEALTH

We will briefly examine some activities that fall within the scope of an occupational health function.

Epidemiology

Epidemiology is the method of research used to measure the occurrence of disease in populations. It answers questions like:

- Is the risk of asbestos employees dying of lung cancer greater than the risk of dying of lung cancer in the population generally?

- Have patients with cancer of the sinus (the part of the face that is beside the nose) a greater likelihood of having worked in woodworking factories?

- How many employees in a flourmill develop asthma each year?

These three examples in fact reveal three different ways of conducting epidemiological studies, or "study designs".

Cohort Studies

A cohort was the basic unit of the army in ancient Rome. In epidemiology, it is used to describe a group, such as the employees in a factory. A cohort study starts with a group of employees in a factory, or other workplace, exposed to a particular hazard. After a reasonable period, usually between 10 and 40 years, the occurrence of a particular disease amongst these employees is followed up.

In order to check that the disease is more common amongst these employees it is necessary to have a control group of employees who form a cohort that has not been exposed to the hazard in question. For example, it has been shown that employees exposed to uncontrolled clouds of asbestos in the past have a much greater chance of dying from cancer of the lung than the non-exposed population. This tells us that the excess risk can be minimised or eliminated by controlling the (asbestos), and the disease (lung cancer) is common.

Case Control Studies

"Case" means a case of a particular disease, and again a control group is used. In this type of study, we start with a group of people who have the disease and look for the exposure. In the cohort study, we started with a group of people who had the common exposure (asbestos) and looked for the disease (lung cancer). Here we look at a group of people who have a disease (cancer of the sinus) and look at a control group (usually of the other patients at the hospital, who are similar in every other respect) who do not have cancer of the sinus. We then see whether the experience of having been exposed to clouds of wood dust in woodworking factories is more common among the patients with sinus cancer. This risk can then be minimised by controlling the wood dust. Case control studies are best where the exposure (wood dust) is common but the disease (sinus cancer) is rare.

Descriptive Epidemiology

Here the number of cases of a disease that occur in a particular population of employees is counted. No particular comparison is required; the disease is known to occur in employees exposed to that particular risk and we are just using the head count as a measure of our success in controlling the exposure. For example, flour dust is one of the known causes of occupational asthma; controlling the dust reduces the number of cases of asthma. This head count, without any comparisons, is known as "descriptive epidemiology". It lets us know how well we have protected each individual employee.

Health Surveillance

Health surveillance is any procedure that monitors change in the health of employees. It could just be the keeping of lists of employees employed in a particular process or workplace. Again, however, this does little for the individual employee

The next step in health surveillance is health inspection. A good example of this is the requirement in the chrome plating regulations for the supervisor to check the hands and nostrils of employees involved in chrome plating departments to make sure that they have not got small ulcers caused by exposure to chrome.

An increasingly common form of health surveillance is the health questionnaire. Again, a useful example is to survey employees at risk of asthma. A simple list of questions asks them whether they cough, wheeze or experience breathlessness. In this way, the early signs of asthma resulting from allergy to dust can be detected, and action taken to prevent that employee from further harmful exposure.

Among the best examples of health surveillance are screening tests. A screening test is the use of a particular instrument or technique to detect a deviation from normal, which in turn indicates the early stages of an occupational disease at a stage where it can be prevented. One well-known example is audiometry. An audiogram is a way of measuring a worker's hearing ability at different frequencies (different pitches of sound). Employees who are developing noise-induced hearing loss show a characteristic pattern. Another example of a screening test is lung function testing. This measures whether an employee breathing out a forced breath into a machine has a normal pattern, or is showing early signs of asthma or occupational lung disease.

Last, we come to medical examinations by a doctor. (The screening tests referred to are often carried out by an occupational health nurse). Medical examinations have a limited role in protecting employees from occupational disease. They do have a use, however, in making sure that employees are fit for "critical occupations". They can often tell us whether the control measures in place to reduce the risk of exposure to a specific hazard are adequate. We will deal with this in the section discussing the effects of health on work.

Biological monitoring is one of the most useful forms of health surveillance. It involves measuring the levels of workplace hazardous substances that have been absorbed, so as to monitor the effectiveness of control measures. The most common example is the measurement of the blood lead level of employees who are exposed to lead fumes or dust. Many organic chemicals, or the chemicals into which they are transformed in the body, can be measured in urine specimens. These levels can then be compared with what is generally regarded as a relatively "safe level" known as the "biological limit value".

First Aid

First aid is usually included within the scope of occupational health. It can be defined as:

- Treatment given in an emergency, until further treatment can be given by a doctor or nurse.

- Treatment of minor injuries in situations where the person will not require further treatment from a nurse or doctor.

This means, at one extreme, the use of cardio-pulmonary resuscitation (CPR). CPR is the special technique of combining mouth-to-mouth ventilation with compressions of the breast-bone to keep the heart beating. In this way, a casualty whose heart has stopped can be kept alive until they get to hospital. At the other end of the scale, there is the application of an adhesive dressing to a small cut or scratch.

In carrying out the identification of hazards and assessment of risks, you must identify what first aid cover is required and the extent of cover. The extent of cover will concern first aid equipment and whether a trained occupational first aider is required. All workplaces will require some first aid equipment (mainly dressings). A trained first aider will be required where the assessment identifies situations (toxic chemicals, dangerous tools, isolated workplaces) that indicate such a need, or if a factory had more than 50 employees or an office more than 100 employees.

Occupational first aiders are defined in the regulations as persons who have been trained and certified by a "recognised Occupational First Aid Instructor".

Health Promotion

Health promotion is the improvement of the health of people by any means. The means might be legislative (limiting or banning the availability of cigarettes), health education (encouraging better eating habits), and other initiatives such as the provision of sports facilities. Working populations are ideal for health promotion as rules can be made ("no smoking", "no chips in the canteen"), and groups can easily be assembled for health education talks. Most Health Boards now have health education officers who are delighted to provide talks and resource material for these activities. Resource material is also available from the Health Promotion Unit of the Department of Health.

What relationship has health promotion to occupational health and safety? Employees who are fit have less time off work sick. If they do have to go for minor operations, they will be back to their full duties more quickly. Non-smokers are less likely to get sick and die as early as their smoking colleagues. Educating young employees in sensible drinking habits will mean less time lost through excessive drinking or accidents resulting from employees drinking before, or during, working hours.

Substance Abuse and Rehabilitation

Addiction to drugs and alcohol, but particularly alcohol, is all too common. It can gradually erode an employee's ability to work safely. Under the influence of alcohol, they may injure themselves or their workmates. Many workplaces have arrangements for identifying and counselling employees who are in the early stages of addiction. Some of these programmes include counselling in other areas, such as financial difficulties, and are known as "employee assistance programmes" or EAPs.

Rehabilitation

Rehabilitation is the process by which seriously disabled employeees are retrained for a new occupation that they can carry out despite their disability. The important issue in rehabilitation is to adapt the workplace to suit the employee. Thus, employees returning to work after a heart attack should have their duties modified, and their day shortened, until they have fully recovered. The employee should never be told to go home and stay there until he is fully better. This process of letting sick or injured employees return slowly, by gradual steps, towards their full normal duties is known as re-adaptation.

OCCUPATIONAL DISEASES AND CONDITIONS

Occupational diseases and conditions are those that arise from excessive exposure to workplace hazards. The wide range and complexity of occupational health problems puts a detailed examination beyond the scope of this handbook. Instead, this section briefly examines the more common problems, outlining their causes and symptoms. The simplest form of classification when studying occupational health problems is to group them by cause, using the following headings:

- Physical causes: e.g. heat, light, noise, vibration, radiation, dust, pressure.

- Chemical causes: e.g. acids and alkalis, metals, gases, non-metals.

- Biological causes: e.g. human-borne, animal-borne and plant-borne.

- Ergonomic causes: e.g. friction, pressure, repetitive movement.

- Social causes: psychological strain, isolation.

Some of these causes are looked at more closely in the next chapter on contemporary issues in occupational health, but the remainder of this section outlines occupational diseases and conditions along with their symptoms under each group of causes.

Health hazards may be classified in general terms as:

- Chemical (dusts, fumes, gases, etc.).

- Physical (noise, vibration, temperature, radiation, etc.).

- Ergonomic (back strain, etc.).

- Biological (bacterial, viral, fungal, etc.).

- Lifestyle illnesses (due to diet, alcohol, etc.).

The chemical classification includes the following:

- Toxic chemicals — there are gases, liquids or solids which, if not handled safely, can cause illness or death, e.g. asbestos, solvents, caustic soda, hydrogen chloride gas, pesticides.

- Flammable liquids — which release vapours that can form explosive mixtures with air, e.g. acetone, ether.

Table 20.1: Physical Causes

Cause	Condition	Symptoms
Heat/Microwaves	Heat Cataract	Cataracts of the eyes, resulting in opacity of the lens, with coagulation of protein.
	Heat Stroke	Poor thermoregulation, unconsciousness likely with body temperature of +40°C
	Heat Cramps	Intermittent muscular pain, resolved by drinking salt water
Poor Lighting	Various	Headaches, eyestrain, insomnia, vertigo, poor performance.
Excess Noise	Deafness	Temporary or permanent noise induced hearing loss
Excess Vibration	VWF	Blanching of fingers
	Osteoarthritis	Extreme joint pain
	WBV	Nausea
Radiation	Radiation Sickness	Problems with cell regeneration, genetic defects, cancers, burns, eye problems.
Dust and Fumes	Pneumoconiosis	Lung tissue reactions, alveolar damage
	Silicosis	Lung scarring nodular lesions
	Asbestosis	Lung scarring nodular lesions
Pressure	Decompression Sickness	Itching vertigo, nausea
		Epigastric pain, build up of nitrogen bubbles in blood.

- Dangerous gases — which can be corrosive, flammable, explosive, poisonous or all of these e.g. welding fumes, oxygen, acetylene.

- Explosives — mixtures of compounds that can cause an explosion e.g. degreasing agents.

- Corrosives — which can destroy living tissue and other substances, e.g. vapour of a solvent and air.

- Irritant — can cause inflammation on contact with the skin or eyes, or if inhaled, e.g. adhesives, paint removers.

Table 20.2: Chemical Causes

Cause	Condition	Symptoms
Metals		
Lead	Lead poisoning	Sweetish taste in mouth, anorexia, nausea, vomiting, headache, twitching, mania hallucinations, and death
Mercury	Mercury poisoning	Tremors, drowsiness by day, insomnia by night, paranoia, death
Chromium	Chronic ulceration	Deep ulcer with black edges, dead tissue at base
Non-metals		
Benzene	Benzene poisoning	Euphoria, headache, vomiting, unconsciousness, respiratory failure, death
Hydrocarbons	Various	Dizziness, nausea, headaches, renal and hepatic damage, death
Solvents	Various	Dizziness, headache, blindness, hallucinations, unconsciousness, death
Arsenic	Arsenic poisoning	Nausea, headache, hepatic and renal damage, "typhoid" state, death
Phosphorus	Phosphine poisoning	Abdominal pain, nausea, ataxia, coma, death
Gases		
Carbon Monoxide	Carbon monoxide poisoning	Asphyxiation
Arsine	Arsine poisoning	As with arsenic poisoning

Table 20.3: Ergonomic Causes

Cause	Condition	Symptoms
Muscular action	Cramp	Muscle pain, twitching, fatigue
Dirt, friction and pressure	Injured hand, knee or elbow	Inflammation, infection, presence of pus
Repetitive muscular action	Various RSIs	Inflammation, localised pain, swelling, tenderness, aggravated by movement.

Table 20.4: Biological Causes

Cause	Condition	Symptoms
Animal-borne		
Bacillusan- thracis (found in cattle)	Anthrax	Malignant pustules on exposed surfaces, vertigo, respiratory difficulty, croup, pneumonia, death
Leptospira (found in rats)	Leptospirosis (Weil's Disease)	High fever, rigors, muscular pain, haemorrhages, hepatic damage
Brucella (found in cattle, sheep and pigs)	Brucellosis	Joint pains, headache, fever, back pain, inflammation of heart and vertebrae
Human-borne		
Legionella	Legionnaire's Disease	High fever, chills, muscle pain, delirium, death.
Hepatitis A and B viruses	Viral hepatitis	Muscle pain, headache, nausea, abdominal pain, enlarged liver, death
HIV Virus	AIDS	Breakdown of the immune system
Plant-borne		
Mouldy hay and vegetables	Aspergillosis (Farmers' Lung)	Influenza-like, with fever, joint pain and cough

Response of Body to Hazard

Occupational health hazards are unlike hazards leading to injury, because their effects may not become apparent for years. The symptoms may develop so gradually that the employees ignore them. The symptoms that do occur are often common to many non-occupational diseases, for example, coughs, increased fatigue, loss of appetite, indigestion, etc. and so may not be recognised as being caused by exposure to unhealthy substances on-site. Because of this cause-effect relationship, such diseases are difficult to prove and so compensation is difficult to obtain. In many cases, an employee may not actually develop the disease for two to 30 years after exposure, as occurs with cancer caused by exposure to asbestos, benzene or to radiation.

Damage may be acute and/or chronic. The substances may have the same toxic effect of a single exposure; however, the effect from prolonged or repeated exposure may be quite different.

Acute toxicity is defined as that effect which occurs in short exposure, on single contact, ingestion or inhalation. **Chronic toxicity** is the effect observed when a toxic substance acts on body tissues over a long period of time; days to years. These effects may not be observed until an advanced stage is reached and permanent damage is done. Therefore, the toxic nature of a substance is related to the duration of exposure.

Figure 20.2 outlines a set of factors that influences the impact of toxic substances on the individual.

Figure 20.2: Factors that Influence Effects of Toxic Substances

---

- Mode of entry — commonly, toxic materials contact the skin, eye, respiratory tract, and/or digestive system.

- Physical conditions of recipient — are they already suffering ill health?

- Dosage of substance.

- Duration of exposure.

- Sensitivity — how sensitive is the person to the chemical?

- Combined effects — what other chemicals were part of the exposure?

- Stress — is the recipient under any physical or mental stress during or after the exposure?

Routes of Entry into the Body

There are three routes of entry into the body.

Ingestion (Swallowing)

People rarely deliberately eat/drink the substances they handle. However, even small amounts of some substances transferred from the hands to the mouth from food or cigarettes can cause health problems. Therefore, personal hygiene is very important and smoking during work should be prohibited.

Absorption through the Skin

Skin acts as a protection and also as a selective filter but does not always block the entry of certain hazardous substances. Acids and alkalis spilled on to the skin, first burn through the flesh (corrosive action), then enter the blood stream where they can poison the system (toxic action). Some chemicals react extremely rapidly and penetrates the skin even before they can be washed off.

Some substances will react with the skin and cause irritation leading to a rash or allergy. Some chemicals, e.g. trifluoroacetic acid will burn through the skin. Others like phenol and hydrogen cyanide will be readily absorbed without the person knowing that anything is amiss. Once a chemical passes through the skin it will pass into the blood stream and will be carried throughout the body.

Cuts make entry easier and it is important that all cuts are properly protected. The eye is a particularly sensitive entry route and, therefore, the wearing of properly fitted protective glasses is important when working with hazardous substances.

Inhalation

Inhalation is the breathing-in of vapour, gas, sprays, fumes or mists. This is the most important entry route for substances into the body. Lungs are extremely efficient in getting gases into and out of the body. $10m^3$ of air is breathed in during an eight-hour shift and, therefore, a considerable amount of material (gas, vapour or solid particles) can be inhaled, even if the material is present in very low amounts in the air. As many materials are hazardous to inhale in concentrations that neither smell unpleasant nor cause irritation, e.g. coughing, it might not be realised that permanent harm is occurring. Some substances, e.g. chlorine and ammonia gases, cause local irritation of the airways and lungs, while most solvents can give rise to toxic vapours even at low temperatures.

Insoluble substances (silica, asbestos) tend to remain in the lungs for long periods. They may cause serious local reactions immediately, e.g. lung damage, or the effects may not become apparent for many years. Some materials act directly on the blood. An example is carbon monoxide, which can lead to unconsciousness and ultimately death. If the material dissolves in the blood stream, it may be deposited in the tissues, especially the fatty tissue and may be released over a period of time. The material may affect the kidneys, liver, heart or brain.

In some cases, a whole system may be attacked: for example, benzene affects the blood-forming system and the central nervous system. Some substances attack the nerve ends, while others may affect enzyme systems. One of the peculiarities of toxic effects is that they differ from individual to individual. Furthermore, experimentation is carried out on animals and not on man, so it is extremely difficult to predict long-term effects.

Many toxics reveal their presence by giving sensory warnings, such as pain or smell, and remedial action can be taken immediately. Often however, these senses may not respond for some time (the pain from some acid burns may not be noticed for several hours) or may not respond at all. The facility to smell danger may be lost because the nasal passages become accustomed to particular substances after a period of exposure. This phenomenon is called "olfactory fatigue" and the affected person may not react quickly enough to the presence of certain chemicals, hydrogen sulphide — the smell of rotten eggs — is an example. Because inhalation is very common, preventative measures, such as ventilation and using personal protection, are widely practised.

Toxicology

The science of toxicity is called toxicology. Toxicology is the study of the effects of chemicals on living systems. The toxicity of a substance is one of its properties. Hazard is the capacity of a substance to do harm. Risk is the probability of harm arising. The product of a hazard and the actions of people is the risk. To put it another way, the effect of a chemical on a living system is proportional to the frequency and duration of exposure and the concentration of the chemical. This is called the dose (concentration) response relationship.

To illustrate, sulphuric acid is corrosive and can cause severe burns if it comes into contact with the skin. Yet tons of sulphuric acid are used, transported and stored daily without major hazard. This is because its toxic and dangerous properties are known and understood and proper precautions are taken.

Ill health/damage, therefore, cannot occur without exposure to a certain concentration. So, if the process is designed to minimise exposure and introduces safe handling procedures, e.g. safe systems of work, the hazard will be removed or reduced to an acceptable level.

Unfortunately, the effects of the vast majority of substances in common use are not well known. Each year, thousands of new chemicals are introduced into use, yet their effects on employees who will use them are unknown.

Standards for allowable exposure exist for less than 500 of the toxic chemicals currently in use. These standards are designed to be the maximum concentrations to which employees can be exposed for eight hours per day, every day, without harm. They are based on average exposures of airborne concentrations, which means it is not illegal to be exposed to higher levels at certain times, as long as the average exposure is below the legal limit. This limit is called the threshold limit value or TLV.

In order to determine effects, the chemicals are tested on animals — usually rats — and the dose that causes half of the animals to die is determined and expressed as weight of toxin per kilogram body weight. This dose is called the lethal dose and is written as LD_{50}. Another expression, lethal concentration (LC_{50}), refers to substances that are inhaled such as a gas or vapour and the concentration is expressed as parts per million (PPM).

The dose is expressed per unit of body weight and scaled up to give a figure for humans. A safety factor ranging from 10 to 10,000 is applied to this figure to give the threshold limit value for the substance under examination. There are a number of criticisms of the use of TLVs:

- TLVs are only available for a small number of chemicals, as already stated.

- Safety factors are a matter of individual judgement and may be set too low.

- Employees are often exposed for longer than eight hours.

- Some scientists question the use of scaled-up figures from test animals to humans.

- Some employees are more susceptible than others to certain chemicals.

- People who smoke run a greater risk of damage from chemicals than people who do not.

- The limit values are set for individual chemicals but employees may be exposed to several chemicals at the same time and the combined effects of these chemicals are not known.

- Little information is available on long-term exposure to chemicals. The TLV values relate to acute, i.e. lethal, effects only.

PARTS OF THE BODY SUBJECT TO OCCUPATIONAL DISEASES

The Eye and Nose

The eye is designed to detect light but, like any sensory organ, too much exposure can damage it. In the case of the eye, excessive exposure to laser beams and ultraviolet radiation can cause damage.

Ultraviolet radiation is absorbed by the cornea and causes "arc-eye" in welders who forget to wear eye protection. This is a very painful condition, which fortunately is self-limiting and lasts 24 to 48 hours. It is similar to getting sunburn of the eye.

The nose is used as a heat exchanger, humidifier and filter for air going to the lungs and therefore has a large surface area and rich blood supply. It is particularly prone to ulceration by chromic acid. Hardwood dusts are associated with nasal cancer.

The Ear

Like the eye, the ear can be damaged by high intensity exposure to the physical agent, in this case, noise, which it is designed to detect. Unfortunately, evolution did not design the ear to be exposed to noises over 85 dB(A) for eight hours per day as commonly occurs in the modern industrial environment.

If you have to raise your voice to be heard one metre away, there may be a noise problem at work. The basic rule is to make it quiet, and only when you have done everything in your power to make it quiet, use personal hearing protection. Noise-induced hearing loss first affects frequencies around 6,000 hertz but spares low and very high frequencies. If allowed to develop further, the higher frequencies are affected and a ringing may be present in the ear (tinnitus).

The Lung

The lungs allow oxygen to be taken in to the blood and carbon dioxide to be exhaled — this occurs in small air sacs called alveoli, which have elastic walls. The lungs are supplied by air from the bronchial tree, which consists of the trachea, or windpipe, which divides repeatedly into smaller air packages known as bronchioles until the alveoli are reached.

Tubes such as bronchioles found in the body are variable in diameter because they have small muscles in their walls, which, when contracted, reduce the size of the lumen and hence reduce the amount of air that goes to that part of the lung. This is important in disease such as asthma. The outside of the lung has a lubricating layer called the pleura, which allows the lungs to expand without causing friction against the ribs.

The alveoli have very delicate thin walls that if laid flat would cover the same area as a tennis court and are protected by a system of filters, which prevents dust clogging them up. But, if particles are less than about 10 microns, they can still penetrate as far as the alveoli of the lungs and cause damage there. Fibrous particles are particularly damaging because their shape means they penetrate further drown the bronchial tree, beyond the protective filters, and when they split they often do so along their long axis so getting thinner, but still remaining the same length.

The three important areas of the lung affected by occupational diseases are the air passages, which are constricted in conditions such as occupational asthma and bronchitis; the alveoli, which have their elastic tissue replaced by fibrosis tissue in conditions such as farmers' lung, silicosis and asbestos; and the pleura, where a special cancer called mesothelioma can be caused following asbestos exposure.

Some substances, if they penetrate deep into the alveoli (<10 microns), can result in the body responding by replacing the elastic fibres surrounding the alveoli with fibrous ones that do not allow expansion and contraction and interfere with the exchange of gases between the blood and air sacs. Spores released from fungi that grow in mouldy hay causes "farmers' lung" when hay is distributed and the spore containing dust is inhaled. The effect is not immediate, but six hours after exposure the farmer notices a light fever, often with muscle and joint pains, which gradually improves, often by the next day. However, if he gets repeated exposures, permanent damage may be caused to the lung.

A similar replacement of elastic tissue by fibrous tissue occurs in quarry men exposed to silica present in quartz-containing rock. The silicosis it causes has a very slow onset and results in gradually increased breathlessness over a period of years and also decreases the person's ability to fight off TB.

The Skin

The skin is particularly vulnerable to environmental agents, since it is often the point of first contact. It is a complicated structure, which is responsible for heat regulation and water retention.

The outer layer is known as the epidermis and consists of dry keratin, which is shed once per month, being replaced by more keratin produced in the germinal layer. Beneath the germinal layer is the dermas, which contains sweat glands and hair follicles with associated glands.

Water-soluble chemicals cannot generally penetrate the skin but lipid or fat-soluble chemicals can. It can be the site of occupational disease or a means of entry for agents into the body.

It takes a minimum period of two weeks for an employee to become sensitised and skin patch testing can test this for. Resin-exposure will result in red, itchy flaking with cracks, fissures and vesicles.

Cement employees' dermatitis occurs in bricklayers, carpenters, plasterers and other occupations working on construction sites who become exposed to wet cement. They gradually become sensitised to the chrome in the cement and, in the end, they may well have to abandon their involvement in the construction trades.

Cement dermatitis is due to chrome but chrome occurs in many other situations, including leather tanning, metal plating, etc.

Chrome is a potent sensitiser and anywhere it occurs as a chemical should immediately start red lights flashing (before skin of the employees starts to glow red!). Epoxy-based adhesives, such as those used by floor-tilers in the construction industry or manufacturers of fibreglass products are also patent sensitisers. It is essential to check the label of any new substance used in the workplace and to search the Material Safety Sheets for the word "sensitise" and then to use the appropriate PPE.

Other occupational skin conditions include the following:

- *Burns from Acids and Alkalis:* Alkali burns are most serious as they penetrate deeply and are often painless at first so the employee often does not remove clothing immediately. Treatment involves lots of water and not attempting neutralising it with an opposite (i.e. do not put acid on an alkali burn as you will not get the concentration just right).

- *Phototoxic Dermatitis* occurs when tars and sunlight are both exposed to the skin at the same time. Some plants contain psoralens, which react with sunlight on the skin to cause a severe rash.

- *Contact Urticaria:* this is more severe and occurs in association with shellfish, ammonium persulphate (hairdressers) and platinum salts, antibiotics and occasionally rubber latex. It is potentially life-threatening and the treatment is to give adrenaline.

- *Chlorine:* Exposure to chlorinated hydrocarbons, e.g. polychlorinated biphenyls (PCB) in lubricating or transformer colling coil can result in a condition similar to acne except the blackheads, cysts and milia (white dots) occur around the eyes, upper cheeks and nose. The commonest condition, which occurred to residents around the Seveso plant, which discharged diodins into the environment in the 1970s, was chloracne. Acne can also be caused by pitch, tar and some oils.

- *Callosities* occur at sites of friction, e.g. violinists' neck.

- *Skin Cancer:* Farmers and fishermen exposed to midday sun, and people exposed to unfiltered tungsten lights which give off harmful UV light, can contract skin cancer. Cancer of the scrotum was first noticed due to soot exposure in young boys used to clean out chimneys.

- *Viral Skin Infections:* This is often found in sheep farmers. Warts in butchers and abattoir employees.

Figure 20.3: Causal Agents

Causal Agent	Occupational Group
Epoxy resins	Painters, electronics, aircraft maintenance.
Formaldehyde	Woodworkers, embalmers, mushroom growers.
Acrylic monomers	Printers, dentists.
Rubber accelerators	Tyres and rubber glove manufacturers.
Metals (chromium, nickel, cobalt, platinum)	Cement employees, hairdressers, electronics.
Plants (tulips)	Florists.
Pharmaceuticals (glutaraldehyde, antibiotics)	Vets, nurses.
Dyes	Hairdressers.

The Kidneys and Liver

Kidneys filter out impurities from the blood, whilst the liver is important in detoxifying chemicals, especially fat soluble ones, and is involved in food metabolism. The kidneys filter out most water-soluble industrial impurities if these are absorbed into the blood stream and, if fat-soluble, the liver modifies them to make them more water-soluble or excretes them as bile in the gut.

The kidneys can be damaged by cadmium, mercury and lead, whilst the liver is affected by organic solvents. Hepatitis B and vinyl chloride can cause liver cancer.

A substance called B naphtylamine, which was used in the rubber industry, is an example of a substance that caused bladder cancer because it was concentrated in the urine and caused damage to the bladder before it was excreted.

The Blood

Blood is an important body tissue, composed of red cells, which carry oxygen from the lungs to the tissues and transport food molecules around the body. The red cells are produced by the bone marrow and live for about three months before being replaced, which is why it takes about three months for a person to eliminate lead after heavy exposure. The white cells are much fewer in number and are involved in fighting infections and providing body immunity. They are also involved in abnormal immune responses such as allergies and asthma.

Benzene, such as in high-octane lead-free petrol, and ionising radiation can cause leukaemia (over-production of white cells) where the white cells reproduce excessively, squeezing the red cells from the bone marrow.

The Nervous System

This consists of the brain and peripheral nerves, which carry motor and sensory fibres to the body. Beside the spine, there is the automatic nervous system, which controls the automatic functions such as breathing, sweating, reduction and movement of the gut. Some chemicals affect the nervous system, especially fat-soluble substances, as the nervous tissue is made up of fatty substances.

Organic solvents and lubricants are an example of this, where high-level exposure results in anti-static-like side effects and depression of the higher function of the brain.

Calcium plays an important role in nerve impulses so that any substance that is similar to calcium will interfere with electrical conduction by nerves. Lead is such a substance and advanced cases of lead poisoning are associated with the classical wrist drop, because of loss of power to the nerves supplying the wrist muscles. Mercury affects the central nervous system and can also impact on a person's character and those affected become overly shy or paranoid. Historically, this was first noticed in hat makers who used mercury in curing felt and then licking the rim of the hat in making it, hence the expression "Mad as a Hatter".

SPECIFIC OCCUPATIONAL DISEASES AND ILLNESSES

A list of occupational diseases and illnesses now exist. **Table 20.5** presents the main occupational illnesses and their related occupations. A number of them will be considered in this section.

Table 20.5: Occupational Illnesses and Related Occupations

Illness	Occupation
Musculo-skeletal/RSI	All occupations, both manual and clerical
Trauma	Manual workers
Stress	Teachers, nurses, those who have experienced violence
Headaches/eyestrain	Office employees
Asthma	Industrial workers
Deafness	Industrial and construction workers
Dermatitis	Workers who use chemicals and rough substances
Asbestos-related	Construction workers, industrial workers

Note: This is an indicative, not an exhaustive, list.

Dermatitis

Dermatitis means an inflammation or rash of the skin. A very common example, especially among housewives, is chapping of the hands caused by prolonged immersion in water. The skin becomes itchy and sore and redness appears. Small blisters may open and after a period of time the skin becomes crusty and cracked. Dermatitis is not infectious and most commonly affects the hands, forearms and legs. When the condition is due to contact with substances at work, it is called "occupational" or "industrial dermatitis". It is the commonest cause of occupational disease and accounts for about two-thirds of all prescribed disease at work. Hundreds of days are lost every year and thousands of pounds in compensation are paid out under the Social Welfare Prescribed Disease Benefit Scheme. Because there is so much variation in people's reaction to substances, the number of materials known to cause dermatitis runs into the hundreds. Some of the most common dermatitis-causing substances include:

- Pitch, tar, bitumen, brick

- Stone, plaster, dust

- Cement

- Paint, varnishes, lacquers

- Some woods

- Some epoxy resins

- Acrylic and formaldehyde resins

- Chromate compounds found in primer paint and cements

- Petrol, white spirits, thinners

- Acids

- Alkalis.

Normally healthy skin is designed to be a barrier and so protect the body from harmful substances. It has two layers — the epidermis and the dermas. The outer layer is the epidermis. This consists of a layer of interwoven dead cells, which are constantly being replaced from the living layer or dermas underneath. The dermas contains fatty glands, which secrete a waxy coating onto the skin surface making it waterproof and resistant to chemicals.

If the intact skin is broken by a cut or the fatty covering washed off, chemicals can pass into the dermas and so cause damage. Repeated hand-washing without proper drying, and the use of solvents, will remove this protective layer and leave the skin unprotected against further damage. The commonest type of skin problem is dermatitis caused by chemicals or other substances coming into contact with the skin.

There are two main forms of dermatitis, which look similar but have significant differences in terms of effect:

- **Irritant dermatitis:** In the case of irritant dermatitis, the substance in contact with the skin acts by irritating the skin. The major cause of this irritation is the dose or concentration of the substance on the skin, and frequently, by altering the dose (dose is concentration x time), by dilution or reducing the time of skin exposure, the irritation can be prevented. It usually occurs on the parts of the body in contact with the substance — hands, face, at cuffs of overall, thighs where oily overalls chafe. Common irritants include wet work accompanied by minor skin cuts and grazes, some cutting oils, alkalis/acids. Solvents and de-greasing agents remove the skin's fatty barrier layer and allow for easy penetration of hazardous substances.

- **Allergic or sensitivity dermatitis:** In allergic dermatitis, the substance causes the exposed employee to become sensitised or to develop an allergy. After the initial period when sensitising occurs, which can be after days or years, each time the worker comes into contact with the substance, even in very small amounts, dermatitis will develop. The long-term health consequences and ability to remain at work are quite significant.

Sensitivity dermatitis may not occur the first time the employee comes into contact with the sensitising substance and may not appear for many years. However, once it has occurred, it will re-occur every time the employee comes into contact with the particular substance. The employee may have to be moved to a different job, if available, or leave the industry altogether.

Strimmer's Dermatitis

The introduction of new technologies and work practices is usually associated with an improvement in working conditions, but often-unforeseen health risks can arise as a result. The introduction of nylon-corded motorised strimmers for control of weeds in recent years and the fine weather of 1995 resulted in reports of a new cause of phyto-photo dermatitis — "strimmer's dermatitis" being reported to the HSA's medical service.

This occurs when operators wear only a pair of shorts in sunny weather and sap from certain plants comes in contact with their skin and reacts with sunlight to cause a severe blistering rash. The offending agent is psoralens contained in the sap of the giant hog-weed (near river banks), cow parsley (common in hedge rows) and members of the celery and carrot family. Strimmer's disease is caused by psoralens in the sap of these plants being dispersed by the centrifugal forces for the rotating nylon cord onto an operator's skin. The subsequent reaction with ultraviolet light leads to a severe burning or blistering reaction, often on the legs, and is typically found in linear streaks occurring 1-2 days after exposure. The problem is aggravated by the speed with which small pieces of plant are flung from the rotating strimmer head and can cause abrasions of unexposed skin even if no psoralen sap is present in the plants.

Operators should be aware of the plants that cause this reaction and use only strimmers that have a guard shielding the operator from plant debris, and appropriate skin protection should be worn, especially in sunny weather. With the increased incidence of skin cancer, outdoor summer employees should, in any case, be using skin protection from sunlight.

Preventing Dermatitis

Two strategies can be effectively implemented to prevent dermatitis: maintenance of a healthy intact skin and avoidance of unnecessary contact with substances likely to damage the skin. To ensure that skin is kept healthy, dirty or contaminated skin should be washed thoroughly and dried. There should be sufficient convenient wash-bowls for the workforce. Special skin-cleaning tissues are available for outdoor use. The cleansers and soap used should be strong enough to remove chemicals, yet not so strong as to damage the skin. Solvents such as acetone may clean off oils and grease but they may also clean off the skin's natural fatty protection and increase the risk of skin damage. Barrier creams may afford the skin protection by providing an extra layer through which the harmful substances must penetrate.

If it is necessary to use hazardous substances, employees should be adequately protected. Appropriate well-fitting rubber-type gloves, with airways to prevent sweating, should be provided. A check should be made to ensure the gloves do not allow the particular chemical through. Overalls should be clean and dry with no gap between cuffs and gloves. Oily overalls can themselves irritate the skin.

Dust and Fumes: Related Diseases

All dusts and fumes must be regarded as a health hazard. However, the effects of dust and fume particles in the air is dependent not only on their toxicity, but also on their size, which in turn determines whether they can be drawn into the deep lung spaces or are filtered out in the upper respiratory air passages of the nose. A problem associated with constantly working with fumes, gases and vapours is where the nasal passages become used to the substance in question and, as a result, do not warn the employee of possible danger. This condition is called "olfactory fatigue".

Most damage and toxic effects occur in the deep lung spaces and those particles are deposited there are called "respirable dust". Irrespirable dust, on the other hand, refers to airborne material capable of entering the lungs, but which is filtered out by the respiratory tract. Airborne dusts that do not have identifiable toxic effects are termed "nuisance dusts". Where possible, dust-inhibiting measures, including dampening of floors and surfaces, vacuum-cleaning and exhaust ventilation of power tools should be used. Some materials, particularly metals and metal coatings, may be hazardous, as may dusts from cutting or grinding, or fumes when welding or gas cutting is in operation.

Lung and respiratory disease resulting from dust is called pneumoconiosis, derived from the Greek — "pneumo", meaning lung, "coni", meaning dust, and "osis" meaning reaction. The development of pneumoconiosis depends on the type of dust, the susceptibility of the individual, the duration of exposure and the exposure to other chemicals or cigarette smoke at the same time.

Particle size affects toxicity: the smaller the particle, the further down in the lungs it can go, and the greater the amount of dust that will be retained. The more dust retained, the more severe the resulting illness. Microscopic dust particles may be so small that they behave like air, passing unimpeded through the protective barriers of hair in the upper airways.

Typical dangerous dusts and fumes that may be encountered in industry are presented in **Figure 20.4**.

Figure 20.4: Dangerous Dusts and Fumes found in Industry

Silicosis
Silicosis is a form of pneumoconiosis due to the inhalation of silica dust. The symptoms are similar to asbestos in that breathlessness is the first sign accompanied by coughing. The end result is respiratory disablement. Chest x-rays will reveal the condition.

Hardwood Dust
This occurs during sawing and sanding. Inhalation can cause asthma and severe irritation of the eyes and lungs.

Cadmium (dust and fumes)
Cadmium dust and fumes arise during welding, soldering or heating of cadmium-plated steel. The dust and fumes can lead to poisoning with symptoms of vomiting and shortness of breath. In the long term kidney damage may result.

Lead (dust and fumes)
Exposure can cause lead poisoning. The symptoms may take a long time to appear and may not be detected easily as one of the symptoms is fatigue, which may be attributed to other causes.

Welding and Cutting Fumes
Various types of fumes are involved in welding and cutting certain metals and metal coatings, in particular galvanised sheeting and brass. The symptoms are fever and a flu-like illness.

Mercury
This was the cause of an industrial tragedy in Minimata in Japan, where discarded mercury was found to have been metabolised in the sediment to methyl mercury, which then built up in the food chain. Fish eaten by local people gave rise to a severe illness, birth deformations and death. Used in dentistry, manufacture of scientific instruments, paint, paper and explosives. Chronic poisoning leads to gum bleeding, kidney damage, personality disorders, inability to concentrate and depression. Dermatitis may also occur.

Chromium
Used in dyeing, photography, plating and cement. Causes ulcers of the face and hands.

Manganese
Used to make alloy steel, batteries; causes irritation of the lungs and muscular problems.

Nickel
Used in electroplating. Causes skin and lung irritation.

Vanadium
Used as a catalyst. Causes eye and chest irritation.

Asbestos-Related Illnesses

There are three important types of asbestos — blue, brown and white — and there are two health hazards associated with contact with asbestos:

- A condition called *asbestosis*. This is a reaction of the lung to the presence of asbestos fibres, which cause thickening of the lower lung tissue making breathing difficult. Symptoms develop slowly after exposure and may not appear for many years. Breathing difficulties increase, leading to severe disablement of the lungs. The condition is dose-related and results from prolonged exposure. Early diagnosis is essential and periodic lung x-rays should be carried out. Man-made mineral fibres, e.g. fibreglass, are often used instead of asbestos in insulating boards and lagging. There is no evidence that these fibres cause disease. However, their inhalation should be avoided.

- *Mesothelima* — This results from exposure to blue asbestos. This is a serious form of cancer affecting the lining of the lungs. The symptoms are breathlessness, together with chest pain. Death usually occurs within two years of diagnosis.

Asthma

Occupational asthma has been identified by the HSA as a serious work-related problem in Ireland. It accounted for 65 per cent of all new cases of respiratory diseases reported during the last quarter of 1996. Many cases do not show up in the official statistics because some employers, fearing compensation claims, play down the incidence of workplace asthma. It is described as the fastest-growing occupational disease, leading to the loss of at least a million working days a year and a big rise in compensation cases.

Occupational asthma is reversible airways obstruction caused by a substance at work that acts as a sensitiser. Non-occupational causes of asthma include pets, house-mite dust, food, cold and infections. The muscle in the walls of the airways contracts so making the lumen very narrow and extra thick mucous is excreted into the already narrowed air passages so further slowing the passage of air to the alveoli. The symptoms of occupational asthma are wheezing (like blowing through a narrow whistle), cough or breathlessness or any combination of the three. It often comes on at night-time or whilst at work but improves at weekends or holidays.

A common way of spraying paint in automobile or furniture repair, for example, is to use "two pack paints". For this technology to work, a substance known as isocyanate, or TDI, has to be mixed, at the time of spraying, with other chemicals to finally produce a coat of polyurethane paint on the surface. Spray painters should be warned that this substance can produce asthma and that appropriate PPE (Personal Protective Equipment) must be worn and all appropriate engineering precautions taken.

Many of the solders used typically in electronic factories for assembling components on to printed circuit boards contain a substance known as colophony. This colophon is in fact the resin that those who play the violin use on the bows. It comes originally from pine trees. It is a potential sensitiser and, if employees are exposed to the fumes that come off the colophony, which is used as a 'flux' in the solder, over a period of time, they will become sensitised to it and develop occupational asthma.

Flour and grain, essentially different versions of the same substance, can give rise to occupational asthmas. However, not all flour millers or grain millers develop asthma but some will do so. Again, the key is to keep the dust levels as low as possible by engineering methods.

Work-related asthma is caused by exposure to respiratory sensitisers, substances that, when inhaled, can trigger an irreversible reaction to the respiratory system. Once this sensitisation has taken place, further exposure to even the smallest trace of the substance causes symptoms such as coughing, wheezing and chest tightness. There are several main occupational groups that carry a high risk of occupational asthma. These include employees engaged in spray-painting, manufacturing foam, handling grain in docks, baking, welding, working in sawmills and handling glues and resins. White-collar jobs are not excluded from the list of those at risk, with nurses and hospital employees among those affected. **Table 20.6** presents the types of substances associated with occupational asthma.

Table 20.6: Substances Associated with Occupational Asthma, as Related to Industry Sector

Industry/Trade	Substance
Car sprayers, foam manufacturing	Isocyanates* (R42)
Bakers	Flour grain*
Electronics	Colophony-based soldering flux*
Research technicians	Laboratory animals*
Poultry farmers	Other animals
Carpenters	Wood dusts*
Fibre-glass workers	Phthalic, Maleic, Anhydrides* (R42)
Composting yard workers	Fungi*
Pharmaceutical workers	Antibiotics
Crab processors	Crustaceans and fish
Rubber processors	Ethylene diamine (R42)
Food processing	Azodicarbonamide (R42)
Detergent manufacture	Enzymes*
Refining	Platinum salts* (R42)
Diamond polishing	Cobalt and salts (R42)
Plating	Nickel and salts (R42)
Food processing	Coffee and soya beans
Hairdressing	Persulphate salts (R42)
Textile manufacturing	Reactive dyes, e.g. Triazine (R42)
Furniture makers	Glues and resins
Nursing	Glutaraldhyde

* Occupational prescribed diseases by the Department of Social Welfare

Source: HSA Medical Guidance Notes on Occupational Asthma (1995).

To reduce the incidence of occupational asthma, the UK launched the Breathe Freely Campaign, which aims to raise general awareness of the problem, particularly among small and medium-sized companies. The campaign highlights the substances that cause occupational asthma and reminds employers of their duties to prevent or control employee exposure. The law in Ireland requires employers to protect people in the workplace against health risks from hazardous substances, which include respiratory sensitisers.

PHYSICAL HAZARDS

Vibration

Unwanted vibration (or noise at very low frequencies, 1-8Hz) also poses occupational dangers. The principal problems arise in the form of whole body vibration, vibration-induced white finger (VWF), and upper limb disorders such as osteoarthritis.

Symptoms of whole body vibration include blurred vision, loss of concentration, balance and nausea. As this condition is most common amongst heavy goods vehicle drivers, it can pose a substantial threat to public safety. VWF is found among those using power tools such as pneumatic drills, etc. It results in a tingling and numbness of the fingers, followed by a blanching of the tips of the fingers. Continued exposure leads to severe pain, and, if ignored, extreme cases can lead to gangrene and necrosis. Osteoarthritis induced by vibration occurs most often in the wrist, elbow and shoulder joints.

Employees who handle vibrating tools have been found to have special problems *vis-à-vis*:

- **Injury to the bones**: X-ray of the hands may show small holes due to loss of calcium in the small bones of the wrists.

- **Injury to the soft tissue**: The soft tissue of the hands — the muscles, nerves and connective tissue — may be injured by vibrations. This may result in loss of the use of the hand muscles.

- **Injury to the joints**: The joints of the hands, wrists and elbow may develop osteoarthritis. This type of arthritis results from the wearing-out or degeneration of the cartilage.

- **Injury to the circulation**: This form of vibration injury is quite disabling. The vibration causes injury to the mechanisms that control circulation in the fingers and the damage becomes progressively worse. At first the worker notices that his fingers have become white. When the worker tries to use his fingers, his movements are clumsy and may be painful. The injury may spread to the other fingers, and the whole hand may become involved. This impairment of circulation is aggravated by cold.

As with many industrial exposures, there is also a non-specific, or general, response of the body to vibration. Employees exposed to vibrations become uneasy, fatigued, and irritable and experience vague discomfort. They bring these feelings home with them, which means both they and their families have to pay an emotional price for exposure. Since vibrations are frequently accompanied by noise, all the body responses to noise are occurring at the same time.

Prevention of health hazards arising from vibration depends primarily on proper equipment design. Equipment design should allow for padding and insulation to prevent the transmission of vibrations. Hand tools should be held in a normally comfortable position with a loose grip. Although gloves do little to diminish the transmission of vibration, they help to keep the hands warm and prevent additional injury from cold. Rest periods, short work-days and job rotations decrease a worker's exposure and delay the onset of vibration effects.

Control Techniques

Control techniques to prevent noise-induced hearing loss and conditions caused by unwanted vibration can be prioritised in the following manner:

Reduce at Source

This is the best form of noise control but it is often the most difficult and most expensive. This option is normally left to the manufacturer, so noise levels generated should be checked on specification when purchasing new equipment. However, the engineering design of the machine may be capable of modification, e.g. silencers could be fitted on pneumatic drills or metal washers could be replaced with plastic equivalents.

Reduction along the Transmission Path

This can be done by isolating the noise source, using acoustic barriers or by enclosing the operator in a noise shelter. The use of ear-muffs, plugs, etc. should be as a very last resort. If they must be used, they should be provided to the workforce individually and should not be interchanged. Muffs are considered the best of the protective devices, although they can become uncomfortable, especially if the environment is very warm. If it is necessary to use plugs, they must be inserted properly.

An effective noise control strategy involves:

- Firstly, quantifying the problem in terms of the noise levels and the number of people exposed.

- In the short term, providing personal protective equipment to those exposed to excessive levels and undertake basic noise control procedures e.g. silencers, insulation, rotation of staff, etc.

- In the medium term, reducing noise from existing plant using barriers and enclosures, etc.

- In the long term, replacing plant and equipment with quieter processes and equipment.

Airborne Contaminants

Airborne contaminants are common occupational health hazards. They consist of the following:

- Solid particulate contaminants, such as dusts and fumes.

- Airborne liquid droplets such as mists.

- Toxic and flammable gases and vapours.

The terms listed above are often incorrectly used. In fact, the terms dust and fume refer to differing sizes of solid airborne particles, with dusts being in the range of 1 to 1,000 microns, and fumes being between 0.1 to 1 micron (1,000 microns = 1 millimetre).

The term mist refers to a suspension in air of liquid droplets of a certain size range. The term vapour refers to the gaseous form (or free modular form) of substances that are liquids or solids at room temperature and normal atmospheric pressure. Gases are always in free molecular form under these normal conditions.

Fumes are often erroneously taken to refer to many forms of airborne contaminant, such as solvent vapours. The confusion arises because fumes are usually formed from the rapid condensation of metals that have been vaporised or oxidised.

Health Risks

Contaminants pose a direct risk to health if inhaled, and often also an indirect risk of fire or explosion if a source of ignition is present.

The effects of the inhalation of airborne contaminants may be classified as fibrogenic and toxic. Fibrogenic substances cause harmful changes to lung tissues, resulting in conditions such as asbestosis and silicosis. Toxic effects may be acute, chronic or, in less dangerous cases, simply a nuisance. Unfortunately, because of their excessive presence in industrial processes, and the life-threatening effects that they have, airborne contaminants are associated with high levels of risk.

Respiratory Defences

The body's natural defences against airborne contaminants include the nose, the cilia of the respiratory tract, macrophages and the lymphatic system.

The coarse hair and mucus membrane of the nose filter trap larger particles, which are then expelled by sneezing and blowing the nose. The cilia and respiratory mucus trap finer articles, and use a wave-like motion to carry contaminant back to the pharynx, where they are swallowed or coughed up. Macrophages are special cells found in the alveoli that surround invading particles, covering them with attacking enzymes and carrying them to the cilia for removal from the body. The lymphatic system also acts as a system for removing foreign bodies.

Common Sources of Airborne Contaminants

Many industrial processes produce airborne contaminants, such as those involving the use of powders, asbestos, mineral wool, cement, wood, solvents, welding, painting etc.

Unfortunately, many hazardous airborne contaminants are difficult to identify, and thus may be present in concentrations well above their control limits, without being visible or having immediate physiological effect on employees. It is, therefore, imperative to list all of the raw materials used in the facility, noting their Threshold Limit Values (TLVs). Secondly, the potential exposure of employees to the materials must be assessed, taking into account the following factors:

- Does the way in which materials are handled give rise to airborne contaminants?

- Are new compounds formed in processes, and if so, how hazardous are they?

- How detectable are the potential contaminants?

- Is there evidence of the presence of hazardous contaminants in the area? **Figure 20.5** presents some issues that should be considered when controlling hazardous substances.

Figure 20.5 : The Control of Hazardous Substances

Hazardous substances are not only used or produced in factories. They can be found in offices, shops, hotels, etc. They may be used directly in the workplace like paints and cleaning agents or they may arise from the work process itself in the form of fumes and waste products. Contact with, or exposure to, hazardous substances at work can result in discomfort, pain, time off work and even death, e.g. skin irritation, dermatitis or skin cancer from frequent contact with oils, and injuries to hands and eyes from contact with corrosive liquids. The following checklist will help to understand the steps that must be taken to control the risks from any hazardous substances present in the workplace.	
Step 1	Identify and list all the substances brought into the workplace or used or stored there, that may be hazardous. Normally they will be labelled Toxic, Harmful, Irritant or Corrosive (e.g. detergents, cleaning products, paints, toners, etc.). Also identify all work activities likely to produce or generate hazardous substances.
Step 2	Obtain information on all the hazardous substances from hazard data sheets (available from the manufacturer or supplier). Consider the relevance of the information to the way the substances are used in the workplace i.e. where and how they are used, handled, generated, released, etc. (identify places, e.g. storage areas, painting booths). Find out if substances have occupational exposure limits (OELs).
Step 3	Identify who might be affected (e.g. employees, contractors, public) and to what extent they are likely to be exposed to a hazardous substance and how (e.g. from inhaling the substance, swallowing it or through contact with the skin).

Step 4	If it is reasonably practicable, exposure should be prevented by: • Changing the process or activity so that the hazardous substance is not required or generated, or • Replacing it with a safer alternative, or • Using it in safer form, e.g. pellets instead of powder.
Step 5	If prevention is not practicable, exposure must be adequately controlled by a combination of the following: • Total enclosure of the process. • Partial enclosure and extraction equipment. • General ventilation. • Using systems of work and handling procedures which minimise the chances of spills, leaks, and other escapes of hazardous substances. • The use of personal protective equipment (PPE) such as goggles, gloves and masks (this should never be the first or only form of control).
Step 6	Ensure that control measures remain effective by introducing a regular inspection, testing and maintenance system for plant and equipment (including any PPE).
Step 7	Determine whether it is necessary to monitor employee exposure and provide health and/or medical surveillance.
Step 8	Train and inform the workforce about the risks they may face and the precautions to be taken.
Step 9	Record the assessment, including the control measure introduced (unless the range of products and substances which might cause harm is very limited).

Radiation

The Nature of Radiation

Certain nuclides (isotopes) of elements are unstable, spontaneously changing into other nuclides and emitting energy in the process. This energy is known as radiation, and may be present in two forms — particulate (e.g. alpha and beta particles) or electromagnetic (e.g. gamma rays). The process is known as radioactive decay, and thus a nuclide emitting such energy is said to be radioactive. Although most naturally occurring nuclides are stable, some are radioactive (such as uranium) and other radioactive nuclides can be artificially produced (such as strontium 90 and caesium 137).

Forms of radiation can be differentiated by using the categories of ionising and non-ionising radiation. Ionisation is the process of molecules losing or gaining electrons, and occurs during the course of many chemical processes. Ionising radiation can produce chemical changes by altering the number of electrons in the molecules in which it is resident. Non-ionising radiation, however, is absorbed by the molecules that it is resident upon, with the result that the material affected heats up (e.g. food in a microwave oven). The main types of ionising radiation occurring in industry are alpha, beta, gamma, x-rays, *Brehmsstrahlung* and neutrons. Typical forms of non-ionising radiation are made up of lower wavelength electromagnetic radiation such as ultraviolet, visible, infrared, microwave and radio frequency radiations and electric and magnetic fields.

Biological Effects of Radiation

Biological damage due to radiation can come from both external and internal sources. Examples are x-ray machines and ingested food containing radioactive material. In general, internal sources are more dangerous because of the close proximity to vital organs, and the difficulty of isolating the radiation. The biological effects of ionising and non-ionising radiation differ and therefore suitable control strategies have to be developed for each. The extent of biological damage is dependent upon several factors:

- The nature of the radiation, e.g. alpha particles damage more than x-rays.

- The dose and duration of exposure.

- The location of the tissue affected.

- The sensitivity of the tissue affected.

- The scope of the tissue affected.

- Whether the source is internal or external.

Ionising radiation may affect the chemical balance of DNA molecules, and can cause cell mutation or cell death. Such chemical changes in DNA are often the result of direct ionisation, or due to a reaction with other cell constituents that have been ionised by the radiation. The extent of damage to the organism as a whole depends upon the factors listed above, and ranges from localised tissue damage to possible death of the organism. Damage is often not immediately apparent, often arising only after regeneration of malignant cells. In the case of irradiated reproductive cells, genetic defects may occur in the offspring. An example of such latent damage is the steady growth in cancers among children affected by the Chernobyl disaster, now more than ten years ago.

The various types of radiation have different energies and penetrating powers. Alpha radiation has the least amount of energy and can be stopped by a thin sheet of paper. Beta rays have more penetration ability and need at least a quarter of an inch of aluminium to stop them. Gamma rays, like x-rays, have deep penetration ability and need heavy shielding, such as several inches of lead. X-ray technicians, while taking pictures, stand behind a thick lead shield to avoid exposure to radiation. The penetration ability of x-rays is the reason for this. Finally, neutrons are so penetrating that special, very absorbent materials are necessary for shielding.

Exposure of a small area of the body may result in reddening of the skin. Eye exposure to 200 rem (the unit of radiation measurement) may cause cataracts and exposure to the genitals may lead to infertility. Exposure to 200+ rem leads to nausea, fever, and infection, and may be fatal.

The widespread use of radiography for non-destructive testing has led to cases of excessive exposure of radiographers. The chief causes of radiant accidents are "unsuitable working techniques" and "inadequate training or supervision", both of which can be countered by good management.

Exposure can also occur from the presence of radon, an inert gas that is one of the naturally occurring products of uranium. Traces of uranium are present in many rock formations, but significant levels are likely to occur in some areas. Risks to health from exposure to radon arise mainly from inhalation of its radioactive decay practices. Lung cancer has been observed in miners following radon inhalation. Exposure to radium can lead to tumours and severe anaemia. The long-term effects of exposure to radiation may include skin cancers, leukaemia, hair loss, cataracts and diminished fertility. Therefore, personal protective equipment is necessary if working with or near radioactive materials. Radiation film badges, which measure the absorbed radiation, should be worn at all times.

Non-ionising radiation can also cause biological damage in a number of ways. Ultraviolet radiation can react with oxygen to provide harmful levels of ozone, affecting the eyes, nose and throat. However, the main hazard posed by UV-radiation is direct exposure to the eyes and skin. Because UV-radiation does not penetrate beyond these parts, they are the organs most at risk from industrial process using ultraviolet radiation (e.g. killing bacteria). In recent years, much attention has focused on the causal link between solar UV-rays and skin cancers such as malignant melanoma, but there is little evidence to demonstrate that cancers have been caused by occupational UV-radiation. The effects of UV-radiation on the eyes result in conditions such as snow blindness from solar radiation, and "arc-eye" from intense occupational light sources, e.g. arc welding.

Infrared radiation is emitted when matter is heated, and can cause damage by heating the tissues it is resident upon. This can result in skin burns and cataracts in the eyes. The effects of both UV and infrared radiation can be heightened by hazards such as lasers, which greatly concentrate the radiation, and can transfer large amounts of power to distant targets because of their very low beam convergence. Other forms of electromagnetic radiation such as radio frequency radiations (e.g. microwaves, radar waves) can cause damage by internal heating, and arguably by non-thermal effects as well.

Radiological Protection Strategies

The key principle involved in radiological protection is to ensure that no one receives a dose above the internationally recommended standards. The three basic methods of protection to ensure this entail the use of shielding, distance and time.

- Shielding can be achieved through the use of absorbent materials such as plastics or cement, which seal the radiation source and prevent exposure. For gamma and x-radiation lead and concrete are commonly used, while plastics are best suited to beta radiation as they produce very little *Brehmsstrahlung*.

- Using distance as a protection strategy requires restricted-access areas, barriers and other similar controls to prevent individuals from coming close enough to the radiation source to receive a harmful dose.

- The use of time limits for those working in contaminated areas also allows the control of dosage to pre-determined standards.

Naturally, the appropriate method depends upon the radiation source, and the type of handling procedures involved. High standards of cleanliness and good housekeeping are essential in preventing the spread of radioactive contamination, and must aim at preventing workers from being exposed to internal sources of radiation. The intake of radioactive material into the body through ingestion, inhalation and absorption is avoided by using personal protective materials, and by implementing eating, drinking and smoking bans in contaminated areas. The rapid treatment of breaks in the skin is also important, and those with cuts should not attempt to work with radioactive substances.

Temperature

Cold

Cold is most damaging to health when it is associated with wet conditions as it is difficult to maintain normal body temperatures. Being cold and wet for long periods may increase the likelihood of bronchitis and arthritis.

The effects of cold and wet on employees' health and welfare can be mitigated by three factors — food, clothing and shelter. Where practicable, shelter from the worst of the wind and wet should be provided by screens or sheeting. Accommodation provided during interruption of work owing to bad weather should be used for warming-up and drying-out breaks where employees have become cold, wet and uncomfortable.

The provision of hot drinks and hot meals helps to keep up the body's resistance to cold and restores morale.

The third line of defence against cold and wet is being suitably clad, especially with footwear suitable for the conditions. Young people tend to be careless of health hazards, especially if the effects are not likely to be felt until later in life. But they often respond to someone taking time and trouble to explain to him or her personally some good reasons why they should take more care.

Heat

Whatever the climate, a potential hazard exists when work is carried out in confined spaces, particularly if hot services are operating; similar problems can arise where impermeable protective clothing is worn for asbestos removal, etc. It is important to appreciate that there may be a problem and to be able to recognise symptoms, so that the sufferer does not receive the incorrect treatment.

Common forms of heat stress produce such symptoms as headache, giddiness, fainting or muscle cramps. Sweating results in loss of fluids and salt from the body and danger arises when this is not adequately compensated for by increased intake of salt and fluids. If the body becomes seriously depleted, it can lead to severe muscular cramps.

The harmful effects of heat depend on air temperature, relative humidity, the amount of air movement, and radiant heat. The evaporation of sweat is one of the body's chief cooling devices — when humidity is high, sweat evaporation is inhibited and the body is robbed of this cooling effect. The problem is made greater if there is very little breeze, or very little air movement of any kind, as in a confined space. The hazard exists in hot, humid weather, even if there is no exposure to the sun. Radiant heat from direct sunlight adds the risk of sunburn, to which fair-skinned people are particularly prone. Thermal discomfort arises from a combination of these factors and, if the person feels ill, medical advice should be obtained.

Moving the individual to a cool place, giving fluids and allowing the individual to rest can usually relieve mild cases of heat stress. In more severe cases, it is essential to give salt and a little sugar in addition to fluids, especially when the symptoms include heat cramps, with pain in arms, legs, back or stomach muscles.

The sufferer must be left to rest in a cool place until they have completely recovered and afterwards allowed to work in a cooler situation.

BIOLOGICAL AND MICROBIOLOGICAL HAZARDS

Workers can be exposed to infections through micro-organisms that can give rise to a number of specific conditions, e g ·

- **Tetanus (lock-jaw)** — This is a serious disease resulting from a wound infection. Construction workers are vulnerable when breaking new ground and particularly when working on sites previously used for agriculture. Large, dirty, lacerated wounds are very susceptible, but infection can result from minor pricks or puncture wounds, e.g. treading on a nail. Workers should be encouraged to arrange an appropriate course of immunisation with tetanus toxoid by the employer where company medical facilities exist.

- **Leptospirosis (Weil's Disease)** — Leptospirosis, also known as Leptospiral Jaundice, is a prescribed disease caused by an organism found notably in rats (although similar organisms occur in other animals) and is passed in their urine. Work in any situation where there is likely to be contamination by rat urine, notably in rivers, sewers or in old rat-infested premises, presents a particular risk of infection.

Farmers are particularly exposed to disease sources, including lung problems from hay spores, brucellosis from cattle and anthrax. Exposure to organo-phosphorus dips can lead to muscle twitching, respiratory problems and death, while exposure to pesticides and herbicides can lead to a variety of health problems.

OCCUPATIONAL HYGIENE

The American Industrial Hygiene Association (1992) has defined the discipline of occupational hygiene as follows:

> ... that science and art devoted to the recognition, evaluation and control of those environmental factors and stresses, arising in or from the workplace, which may cause sickness,

impaired health and well-being, or significant discomfort and inefficiency among workers or among the citizens of the community.

Most practitioners of occupational hygiene feel that the above definition does not adequately describe their professional concerns and responsibilities. Recognition represents an after-the-fact concept, which has been superceded by the realisation that initial concern should be regarding the anticipation of potential hazards. Much effort and expense is now expended in the area of experimental toxicology, where potential hazards can be evaluated and preventive measures taken before industrial usage begins.

The concern for the employee alone has been enlarged by a concern for the family of the employee and the community. The experience of beryllium employees and asbestos employees has widened this concept to include the family. Waste disposal has also come within the purview of occupational hygiene. This may concern the disposal of chemical wastes in a landfill operation or the use of uranium mining tailings for backfill around new home construction.

The financial involvement of many industries in a medical fringe-benefit package leads the occupational hygienist into new areas of concern in such widely disparate areas as community water supplies, sewage disposal and the availability and quality of health services. The occupational hygienist is thus seen to be moving towards the role of a manager of environmental affairs.

Specialists have emerged within the field of occupational hygiene. While the traditional role of the generalist still exists and is now identified in a certification movement such as comprehensive practice, there are also specialists in chemistry, engineering, noise, radiation, air pollution and toxicology. Undoubtedly, there will be more specialists emerging in the near future.

The study of exposure to occupational hazards has created a new field, occupational hygiene. This includes methods of measuring occupational hazards such as the concentration of gases and dusts, and the intensity and frequency of noise and vibrations. The techniques of elimination of these hazards are then developed against the background of industrial hygiene surveys. Industrial or occupational hygiene engineering is a new and important part of modern occupational health. The prevention of accidents at work has created a special field — safety — where not only mechanical but also human factors are considered. Occupational psychiatry deals with factors at work, in the physical or mental working environment or in the human relations at work that may cause or contribute to nervous disease or deviations from mental health. It is important to study the early stages of such diseases or maladjustment. Occupational sociology will increase our knowledge concerning man's behaviour at work. Considering the above-mentioned definition of health as "physical, mental and social well being", the social adjustment of the employee to his work and to his workmates must also be included in modern occupational health. Attitudes to work, working conditions, management and workmates are studied by sociologists.

Different occupations present different health problems such as high accident frequency in mines, occupational intoxications in the chemical industry, intoxication from pesticides in agriculture, etc. This will call for different priorities of occupational health services and different preventive measures in different occupations. Health problems were first studied in industries, and industrial health was developed as a speciality. Later, other branches were developed, with specialists, research, monographs, committees; for instance, aviation medicine, agricultural health, health of seafarers, health of workers in the building industry.

OCCUPATIONAL HYGIENE AUDITS

An audit of the workplace is carried out by an industrial hygienist. The first step in this procedure is to carry out an inventory of all substances in use, and identify which are hazardous to health. The hygienist will also examine all health complaints and sickness/absenteeism records. The route of entry into the body will also be examined, i.e. ingestion, absorption through the skin or inhalation.

To carry out the identification process, the hygienist will usually walk through the working area noting potential hazards, for example:

- Are there dusts/fumes/mists in the atmosphere and, if so, are workers wearing suitable masks?

- Is there a noticeable odour of chemicals?

- Are ventilation systems in use and checked frequently?

- Are goggles being worn?

- Are workers wearing gloves when handling chemicals?

- Is the area very noisy?

- Is ionising or non-ionising radiation being used?

- Are biological or ergonomic hazards present?

Having located the hazards, the hygienist will assign a risk value to the various substances and make recommendations for control measures to be implemented.

There are several possible outcomes of an initial walk-through, as shown in **Table 20.7**.

Table 20.7: Outcomes of an Occupational Hygiene Audit

Finding	Action
The risks are insignificant.	None.
Risks are high and not adequately controlled.	Put in place immediate prevention/control measures.
Risks are controlled but could increase in future.	Suggest precautionary control methods.
Risks are uncertain.	Put in place detailed monitoring programme to assess hazards.
Insufficient information available.	Put in place detailed monitoring programme to assess hazards.

The next step is to carry out a survey. A basic survey involves choosing a representative section of the workplace and monitoring it, using recommended techniques. A detailed survey involves taking a statistically representative proportion of all those significantly exposed and monitoring for an entire shift. From the survey, a priority list of areas/substances to be sampled should be drawn up. A starting point would be to identify the individual or group of individuals receiving the most exposure and decide on a sampling strategy to determine the exposure level. What is sampled will depend on the problems identified during the initial walk-through of the site, together with discussions with the workforce and examination of illness/absenteeism records.

Where sampling takes place, risks will also have been determined from the walk-through, and the extent of the hazards identified will determine whether a basic or detailed survey will be required. **Table 20.8** outlines the types of hazards and the possible sampling regimes associated with them.

Table 20.8: Hazard Levels and Sampling Procedures

Type of Hazard	Possible Measurements
Chronic Hazard	• Continuous or average personal samples. • Continuous or average static samples. • Spot readings of contaminant levels at selected positions and times.
Acute Hazard	• Continuous personal monitoring. • Continuous static monitoring. • Frequent spot readings of background contaminant levels at selected positions and times.
Engineering Control	• Continuous static monitoring. • Spot reading of background contamination levels at selected positions and times.
Whether area is safe to enter	• Directing reading instruments.

The most common form of occupational health hazards are dusts, fumes, gases, and vapours. Noise is also a major hazard. Some dusts, e.g. asbestos, may be present in very low concentrations without any indication of their presence. Therefore, the hygienist must know what materials are being used in the workplace. Measurements of airborne contaminants consist of two operations: sampling and analysis.

Sampling Methods

There are two ways of assessing occupational exposure:

- **Static/area sampling**: The measuring devices are located at one or more fixed points around the site.

- **Personal sampling**: Carried out by means of a portable device attached near the operator's breathing zone (usually the lapel, ear, etc.). The nature of the hazard will determine the type of sampling, which should be used.

Because of the length of exposure, as well as the concentration, it is important that three possible time scales are used with each of the two sampling procedures:

- **Spot or grab sample**: This is once-off sample or reading taken at a specific time, e.g. 4.00 p.m. Grab samples are used for gases only and not for dusts. Grab samples are of limited value and should be used only as a rough guide.

- **Average samples**: Readings are taken over definite time periods. Concentration-versus-time plots will give an average picture of exposure levels.

- **Continuous sampling**: As the technique implies, the concentration is recorded at all times during the shift. This would be used when a detailed survey of exposure levels is necessary. Direct reading instruments are used by the hygienist for continuous sampling.

If the hazard is acute and has a short-term exposure standard, then measurements over 10 to 15 minutes are appropriate; however, if the hazard is chronic, then measurements over a full eight-hour shift may be necessary.

Instruments Used in Measuring Exposure Levels

The occupational hygienist will use a variety of instruments to measure exposure levels. For example, to determine levels of gases, tubes called stain detector tubes are used. The technique is similar to that used in the breathalyser test for alcohol. A sealed glass tube contains a particular chemical known to react with the substance to be tested. The seal is broken, a hand pump attached and a known volume of contaminated air is drawn through the tube. The chemical in the tube undergoes a colour change or stain that is compared to the calibrated (PPM) mark on the tube. This concentration can then be read off directly. There are more than 200 different tubes available, each designed for a particular gas or vapour. Stain detector tubes have several advantages in that measurement is immediate and the technique is easy to use. However, they have three major limitations:

- Interference may occur from other chemicals in the workplace. For example, xylene will interfere with toluene measurement.

- The accuracy rate can be ±25 per cent.

- They do not measure contamination over an eight-hour day.

Tubes containing absorbent materials are also available, e.g. charcoal or silica, which will absorb the contamination to be measured, the concentration of which can be determined in a laboratory. These tubes are often used for personal sampling.

Static/Area Sampling

Static/area sampling is carried out if it is required to measure contamination levels at different steps in a process, at different periods throughout the shift (peak levels) or if a reading of a fast-acting chemical is required. There are two means of doing this:

- Long-term stain detector tubes can be used, attached to a pump that draws air through the tube at a predetermined constant rate. At the end of the sampling period, the amount of contaminant can be read off on the tube and the average level of contamination calculated.

- Direct monitoring: There is a wide range of instruments capable of detecting contaminants in air, based on different physical principles of detection. A quantitative analysis is made and a readout of levels displayed on an ammeter. For example, portable gas analysers use the fact that many gas and vapours will absorb infra-red radiation and the amount absorbed is directly proportional to the concentration of contaminant. The analyser takes a sample of air, the contaminant interrupts the infra-red beam and gives a readout of the result.

The instrument must be calibrated for the particular chemical to be measured. For dust measurements, the amount of scattering that dust causes to a light beam is a measure of concentration and particle size. Mists are usually collected on filters and analysed chemically. Examples of determinations using instruments are:

- **Oxygen**: Before entering into confined spaces, it is advisable to check oxygen levels and portable analysers with long leads are available for this purpose.

- **Humidity**: Hygrometers are used to measure vapour in air (humidity) to ensure thermal comfort. Humidity is expressed as relative humidity and quoted as a percentage (%).

Personal Sampling

The best and most accurate means of detecting exposure levels to individuals is by attaching appropriate samplers to the individual worker and measuring the amount of contaminant to which the individual is exposed. They are usually attached to the worker's lapel and are positioned to ensure that the flow of contaminant is trapped as it passes over the sampler.

Passive monitors may be used. These are similar to radiation badges worn by hospital workers who may be exposed to radiation. They operate by diffusion. Each gas or vapour diffuses, at a rate particular to the contaminant being tested, across a membrane and is absorbed on to charcoal. The diffusion rate is proportional to the concentration of gaseous contaminant. Validation, by comparison with another known technique, is necessary when using passive monitors because workplace conditions can affect the results.

Air is drawn through at a known flow rate (usually two litres per minute) by a small pump and the contaminant passes over a preweighted filter. For nuisance dusts with a TLV of $10mg/m^3$ (the highest value allowed, the filter is usually of fibreglass and is weighted. The increase in weight and the volume of air sampled can be converted to an airborne concentration in $10mg/m^3$.

For toxic dusts that have relatively low TLVs, lead (0.15mg/m^3) or calcium (0.05mg/m^3), special membrane filters are used and these are dissolved in acid after sampling and analysed using laboratory instruments to give a figure for the type and content of metal or metals present.

For asbestos, the concentration is expressed as fibres/cc. In this case, the membrane filter is mounted on a glass slide, dissolved in an organic solvent and the number of fibres counted under a microscope. To compare with the known TLV level, which is based on an exposure level of eight hours, the rest is converted to reflect the time the worker may not have been exposed, e.g., meals, working in another area, etc.

Assume an average exposure over five hours of 14mg/m^3 and three hours with no exposure. The average concentration then over eight hours is:

$$\frac{5\times14}{8}+\frac{1\times3}{8}=8.75+0.375=9.125\,\text{mg/m}^3$$

The value is then compared to an established standard in order to recommend the appropriate control strategy. Often employees are exposed to mixtures of chemicals, which may increase the hazard, and where this is the case the individual TLVs should be added together. It should be noted that physical factors such as heat, high humidity, etc. place added environmental stress on the body and may increase the toxic effect of a substance. For substances considered hazardous as a result of ingestion or absorption, biological tests may be necessary, e.g., blood and urine sampling and analysis. The EU Lead Regulations (S.I. 2109, 1988) specify the frequency of monitoring for both airborne lead and blood lead and also specify actions depending on the levels determined.

In order to assess the damage potential of a particular substance, the amount present must be measured and the value compared to a safe level of standard, usually a TLV value. TLV concentration units are expressed in milligrams of contaminant per cubic metre of air (mg/m^3) for dusts, gases, vapours and mists. They may also be expressed in parts per million (by volume) or gases and vapours.

When exposure levels have been determined, the hygienist will compare those with published exposure limits.

HYGIENE CONTROL STRATEGIES

Having determined the level of contaminant and compared the level to the TLV a control strategy must be implemented. It is normally recommended that corrective action be taken immediately if the measured concentrations exceed half of the TLV. There are two options:

- **Zero exposure policy**: This is usually impossible. However, some countries adopt this policy for known carcinogens.

- **Permit certain levels of exposure**: These levels are applied to the workplace environment. Part of the safety procedures may involve the workers having to wear personal protective equipment. Some substances can be absorbed through the skin and airborne levels will not indicate total exposure. In these cases, measures to prevent skin absorption must be put in place.

There are a number of possible control measures designed to ensure that the workforce is subjected to as little contamination as is reasonably practicable. These control strategies include:

Elimination

This simply means completely eliminating the potentially toxic material.

Substitution

This involves the substitution of materials or operations by safer alternatives.

- **Material substitution** involves substituting a toxic or flammable substance by one less toxic or less flammable, e.g.:

  ◊ Replacing asbestos with fibreglass.

  ◊ Replacing the solvent carbon tetrachloride with trichomethane or trichloromethane.

  ◊ Replacing benzene with toluene.

- **Process Substitution**. This can take a number of forms:

◊ Arc welding is now used to replace riveting, leading to a reduction in noise levels. It should be noted here that a new hazard is present (welding fumes) and control measures for these fumes should be put in place.

◊ Replacing metal with nylon parts in machines will help reduce noise.

◊ Paint dipping is less hazardous than paint spraying because the possibility of inhaling fumes is reduced.

◊ Applying water close to the dust source can reduce dust hazards. This is always done when removing asbestos lagging. This is usually done also when sweeping out dusty areas, e.g. a carpenter's shop.

Isolation

The process is carried out away from the work area, as for the processing of toxic chemicals.

Segregation or Enclosure

This strategy involves enclosing the process totally. Examples would be enclosing a noisy machine by a physical barrier of absorbent material or handling toxic substances with gloves in an enclosed box, or enclosing dusts and vapours thus preventing their escape to the rest of the workplace.

In some cases, a particular process may be carried out only at night when a minimal workforce is present.

Local Exhaust Ventilation

Where it is not practical to enclose the process totally, removing gases, vapours, dusts and fumes using extraction systems can contain contaminants. These systems trap contaminants close to their source by filtering or delivering them to the outside atmosphere, thus preventing exposure to nearby workers. When using this strategy, care should be taken to ensure that other employees and the surrounding community is not contaminated and that only clean air is returned to the work atmosphere.

Local exhaust ventilation should be used where welding and paint spraying are being carried out and ventilation systems should be maintained regularly.

Dilution or General Ventilation

Where it is not possible to extract the contaminant close to its source, dilution ventilation can be used where there are small quantities of low toxicity contaminants. Natural ventilation through open doors, windows, or fans or blowers is used to draw or blow in fresh air to dilute the contaminant. It should be used only for dispersing vapours and not for fumes and dust.

Personal Hygiene and Good Housekeeping

Personal hygiene and good housekeeping are necessary to ensure minimal contact with hazardous substances. Procedures should be laid down for immediate cleaning of spillages, safe disposal of waste and the regular cleaning of workstations. Adequate washing and eating facilities on site are also necessary together with instructions on hygiene measures required to prevent contamination.

Reduced Time Exposure

This is a technique used to reduce the effect of a toxic contaminant. It is not, however, a primary control mechanism. The individual is exposed for a limited period only, e.g. where high noise levels are present workers should be exposed only for short periods, the remainder of the shift being spent in a quiet area. For example, if the allowable exposure to noise is 90 dBA for eight hours, then if the level reaches 93 dBA only four hours exposure is permitted.

Training and Education

Because occupational health hazards cannot be seen, workers should be educated about them and know how they should be controlled.

PERSONAL PROTECTIVE EQUIPMENT IN THE WORKPLACE

Only when all other possibilities for making the workplace safe are exhausted, or for short-term solutions, should personal protective equipment be used. Having to use personal protective equipment is an admission of failure and should be viewed as such. However, helmets and safety shoes should always be worn where necessary and specialist personal equipment is required when working with chemicals, dusts, or in hot and noisy environments, and when welding. Management has the responsibility to specify when protective clothing and equipment are required and to provide the worker with the appropriate gear. Personal protective devices do nothing to reduce the hazard at source, so if they fail, the worker's protection is reduced and the risk increases dramatically. It is important also that the correct protection is given for a particular hazard.

In order to put in place a personal protection programme, it is necessary to know:

- **The nature of the hazard**: In the case of air contaminants, the type of chemical and its concentration must be known, in the case of noise, the sound level and frequency characteristics are required.

- **Performance information on the protective equipment**: The ability of the equipment to protect against hazard must be known. This information is usually provided by the manufacturer and will normally conform to a given standard. The British Standards Institute sets standards for particular equipment after rigorous testing has been carried out.

- **Acceptable exposure level**: The occupational exposure limits of the substance to be protected against must be known.

Types of Personal Protective Clothing

Overalls

In general, protective clothing ranges from overalls giving protection against dirt and grease to specialised outfits for complete protection against a specific risk (e.g. lead poisoning). This includes,

PVC garments for protection against acid and other chemicals, as-bestos suits for protection against fire, leather aprons to guard against sparks and hot metals, and rubber and PVC clothing for protection in wet situations. People working on or about moving machinery should wear close-fitting overalls. Sleeves should be clear of the wrists and be sufficiently close-fitting to prevent in-volvement with a moving part. Sleeves should tear easily if caught in machinery.

Waterproof Jacket and Trousers

These should be water-resistant, durable and unaffected by oil or grease. Oilskin jackets, like other clothes, should be free from ex-ternal belts or buckles, which can catch on projections. The jacket should be single-breasted with a fly front, and should have a mini-mum of four buttons to avoid loose fitting. The collar should be fitted with a press stud-fastening front to prevent water seeping down the neck. The jacket should be big enough to allow room to wear other garments underneath and the back should be cut in one piece to avoid seams. Ventilation eyelets should be fitted below the arm-hole. Oilskin trousers should be unlined and elasticised with button-fly fronts, with slits for access to pockets, and no turnups.

Head Protection

Several types of head protection are available:

• Updraft helmets — Gives protection against chemical and liq-uid sprays and acid droplets, etc.

• Welding helmets — Give protection against injurious radia-tions and hot particles of weld metal.

• Safety helmets — Safety helmets conforming to a national stan-dard should be provided for all staff where required and should be worn at all times. Visitors should also be required to wear a safety helmet. Care should be taken to ensure that the helmet is of the required standard and type for the work being carried out. Management can set an example by always wear-ing helmets in designated areas.

Protective Footwear

Every working day, accidents occur in industry that lead to both serious and minor foot injuries. Many of these accidents can be avoided by the wearing of boots and shoes having built-in steel toe-caps and reinforced soles. Soles should be oil-resistant and non-slip. Rubber boots may be obtained with a steel toe-box and reinforced sole for work carried out under wet conditions.

Skin Protection

A number of options are available for effective skin protection:

- Gloves — These are available in all types of materials ranging from asbestos to cotton, PVC, neoprene and nitrite.

- PVC is recommended for protection against petroleum products, caustic soda, and acids.

- For protection against heat and in welding, hand gauntlets should be made of asbestos.

- There are specific gloves available for particular chemicals and reference should be made to the literature to determine the correct type of glove to be used. The gloves should be inspected regularly and replaced if defective.

- Suitable barrier creams can also be used to protect the skin. They should be applied at suitable intervals throughout the shift. After work moisturising creams, which replenish the skin oil, should be applied.

Eye and Face Protection

Goggles and safety spectacles corresponding to the appropriate British Standard should be provided on site. Suitable goggles must be provided and used to protect the eyes of persons engaged in any of the following processes:

- Dry grinding.

- Cutting.

- Wire brushing of metal, stone, concrete by mechanical power.

- Welding.

- Handling of strong acids and corrosive liquid.

Spectacle frames must be rigid enough to hold the lens in proper position in front of the eyes. If the nose-bridge is not adjustable, frames should be available in sizes to fit faces of various shapes. They should be of simple design for easy cleaning and disinfection.

A wide variety of goggles is available but care should be taken to avoid some common shortcomings such as imperfect fit, limited vision, difficulty of adjustment, and a tendency to mist up when worn due to inadequate ventilation.

Face Shields

Lightweight face shields are available for eye and face protection and can be secured to the front of the safety helmet. Fibreglass polyester welding shields are available for welding, either hand-held or fitted to a safety helmet.

Welding is a particularly hazardous occupation and all body parts must be suitably protected when welding. In some cases, it may be necessary to use respiratory protection.

Respiratory Protective Equipment

Respiratory protective equipment should be used when toxic materials liable to produce dusts, gases or vapours are present. Personal respiratory protection should be used only when no other method of control is possible. Respiratory protection should be used only in the following circumstances:

- To enter a contaminated atmosphere for a short time for rescue or emergency repair work, e.g. a radioactive atmosphere.

- For short-term inspection, maintenance or repair of equipment located in a contaminated atmosphere.

- Changing a compressed gas cylinder.

- In conjunction with other control measures where ventilation is not sufficient e.g. stripping of asbestos insulation.

- For escape purposes.

The use of respiratory protection should be restricted because some contaminated air may still be inhaled even with the best respiratory equipment. Because the equipment is uncomfortable to wear and makes communication difficult, adequate training is necessary for its use. It should also be stressed that employees with respiratory difficulties should not use respirators. Respiratory equipment works by either filtering the contaminated material, i.e. dust and fibres, so that it does not reach the user, by absorbing gases into an absorbing machine or by providing fresh air from an alternative source. For dusts and fibres, the size range of the particles must be known. There are different types of respirators available including half-mask, which covers nose and mouth; full-face, which covers eyes, nose and mouth; a hood; or a full suit.

Leakages can occur through the filter material, e.g., dust, the exhaust valves in the case of gases and vapours and the face seal. The efficiency of respiratory protection in removing contaminants is known as the nominal protection factor (NPF). This is defined as the concentration of contaminant in the atmosphere divided by the concentration of contaminant inside the face piece. Therefore, to determine the degree of protection required, the concentration of contaminant in the workplace must be known together with maximum permitted concentration that can be inhaled.

There are disposable filtering face-masks available for some dust exposures with efficiencies ranging from NPF 5 to 10. They should be replaced after every shift. Masks containing a strip of gauze should be used only for large nuisance-type dust. Fine dust and vapours will penetrate the weave of the gauze.

Respirators

These may be disposable, with the filtering material/absorbing material often a chemical contained in a cartridge. The lungs of the wearer provide the necessary pressure required to pull the dust over the filter. These have a NPF of between 5 and 10. The correct cartridge for the dust in question must be used. Positive-pressure full-face units — covering noise, mouth and eyes — are also used (NPF 400). The motor, which attached to a belt, supplies filtering air and ensures a positive pressure on all items within the mask to reduce inward leakage to a minimum. These units come in the form of a hood or a full suit that restrict the air outflow at the waist, wrists and ankles. Dual-purpose respirators for gas/vapours and dusts are available also.

Fresh Air Breathing Apparatus

These are used primarily where the atmosphere is deficient in oxygen or where wetted asbestos must be removed. The equipment consists of a face piece or hood/helmet/blouse combination. The wearer breaths uncontaminated air drawn from the fresh air unit or supplied by filtered compressed air via an airline. Self-contained breathing apparatus (SCBA), similar to that worn by divers, is available and the air is supplied to a full-face piece from cylinders carried on the wearer's back (NPF 1000–2000).

It is important that the equipment fits the wearer. Beards and spectacles may affect the seal between the equipment and the skin. Heat stress can occur when working in hot or humid conditions or when stripping asbestos. Freedom of movement is also important, for example, with compressed air apparatus movement is restricted by the hose, which should not become entangled or kinked. Self-contained breathing apparatus removes this limitation but the gear is bulky and heavy. Therefore, it is important to select the correct equipment for the job in question. Any resistance to breathing by the wearer is a sign that the filters are clogged or that the airflow is being restricted. If the wearer suspects a problem, the area should be vacated immediately and the equipment checked outside. It should be remembered that the wearing of pumps/respirators may reduce the wearer's field of vision, which could lead to a hazardous situation, and that it makes communication is difficult.

Hearing Protection

There are two main types of hearing protection:

- Ear-plugs — inserted into the ear canal.
- Ear-muffs — covering the external ear.

Cotton wool should not be used as a protective device because it is practically useless and may lead to a false sense of security.

Disposable earplugs are made from glass fibre and polyure-thane foam. Reusable earplugs are made from semi-rigid plastic or rubber. They must never be interchanged and should be moulded to fit the individual ear. If not, leakage of noise will occur when the individual moves his or her jaw. The best protective device is the ear-muff, which covers the ear and is held in position by an adjustable headband. The acoustic seal is usually made of polyurethane foam. Ear-muffs are supplied with a graph showing how their attenuation (reduction of noise energy) varies with the frequency composition of the noise. It is important, therefore, to choose the correct ear-muffs for the noise to which exposure occurs. Noise helmets, with specially-shaped acoustic insulation materials, are available for persons exposed to the upper end of the dB scale i.e. above 115 dB(A). These help to insulate the bone structure of the skull and neck, which transmit high noise intensity to the ears.

As with other protective devices, hearing protection is only a compromise, not a solution. All protective devices are uncomfortable to wear, especially in hot conditions, and in some cases constant wearing can lead to ear infections. There is also the feeling of isolation as a result of being unable to communicate with fellow workers, which can lead to stress. Employees may also have difficulty when wearing muffs in determining from which direction a sound is coming, which in turn can lead to accidents. Finally, workers wearing muffs cannot be warned of danger in their vicinity.

Protection against Falls

The use of harnesses and belts is generally recommended as protection against falls. The main reason for the use of safety belts and harnesses is to limit the distance of any fall and minimise the injury risk. They are not suitable for effective fall prevention measures. Therefore, proper work platforms, guard-rails and toe-boards and safety nets must be provided. Only when their provision is impracticable should harnesses and belts be used. They should always be used when working at heights. There are a number of different harnesses/belts and fall-arrest devices available. When used, an important consideration is that the distance of fall is minimised. Therefore, the belt or harness should be fixed to the structure as high as possible above the working position. Fall-arrest devices allow the user freedom of movement. All the devices must be regularly inspected and maintained.

CHAPTER ROUND-UP

- Occupational health is concerned with the promotion and preservation of employee health at work. It deals with all dimensions of work and the work environment. An important distinction is made between prevention and cure. Occupational medicine deals with health problems caused by poorly controlled work hazards; occupational hygiene involves attempts to recognise, understand, anticipate and control hazards arising from the workplace.

- Ill health generally results from complex biological processes. These processes may take place over a long period and the same disease may have both occupational and non-occupational causes. Exposure to disease risks is not always apparent. These characteristics mean that the identification of health hazards and health risk assessment generally requires an expertise in, and the measurement of exposures.

- The main activities of the occupational health department involve health surveillance, such as primary and secondary monitoring; treatment services, such as first aid; specialist services and health promotion activities, such as education, counselling and welfare services.

- Occupational diseases generally arise from excessive exposure to workplace hazards. The causes of such hazards may be physical, such as heat, light, noise, vibration and dust; chemical, such as acid and alkalis, metals and gases; biological, either human-, animal- or plant-borne. They may also arise from ergonomic causes such as friction, repetitive movement and social causes such as psychological strain and isolation.

- Occupational hygiene generally involves the recognition, evaluation and control of environmental factors and stresses. A central component of occupational hygiene is the implementation of audits. These audits are generally used to examine all substances and identify those, which are hazardous to health. The occupational hygienist will also examine ill health complaints and sickness/absenteeism records. The route of entry into the body will also be examined.

Chapter 21

OCCUPATIONAL HEALTH:
SOME CONTEMPORARY ISSUES

INTRODUCTION

This chapter considers a number of contemporary issues in occupational health that currently receive attention in the literature. The 1980s/1990s witnessed a growth in workplace health promotion. This has resulted in the design of programmes geared toward the provision of advice and services linked to preventative medicine such as screening services, information and health education initiatives. Although general health promotion policies are increasing, many health-related issues are best dealt with by means of specific policies. This chapter will focus on some of these policy areas including:

- Back pain at work.

- Repetitive strain injury.

- AIDS in the workplace.

- Smoking, alcohol and substance abuse.

- VDUs and health problems.

- Violence and bullying at work.

- Employee assistance programmes and counselling.

- Workplace counselling activities.

BACK PAIN AT WORK

Nature of Lower Back Pain

The general statistical evidence demonstrates that lower back pain is the most common form of work-related musculo-skeletal disorder. Pain in the lower back may be sharp or dull, diffuse or localised. If the pain is acute and/or severe, it is commonly called lumbago. Pheasant (1991) reports that the pain may be limited to the mid-line of the back or it may extend outward on either side. It may also be associated with tingling in the feet and radiate into the groin and down the front of the thigh. Poor movement and problems with muscle systems are also common with lower back pain.

Beiring-Sorensen (1984) reported that most episodes of back pain are relatively short-lived and the recurrence rate is very high. He found that 60 per cent had another attack within one year. Some people, mostly middle-aged or older have regular attacks whereas others are never symptom-free. There is also evidence that sickness absence from back pain has increased considerably in the last ten years (Waddell, 1987; Pheasant, 1991).

Work-related Risk Factors and Lower Back Pain

The general research finding is that employees in heavy manual occupations are more likely to suffer from back pain. The research suggests that the prevalence of back pain for workers in heavy manual occupations is higher than for light work. Magora (1972) demonstrates that employees who frequently lift weights have a high prevalence of back pain, as have employees involved in a lot of bending actions. He also found that employees who either stand or sit continuously for long periods at work have a high prevalence, whereas those who are free to vary their posture and to stand or sit at will, have a very low prevalence. Vallfors (1985) confirms that employees with back problems are significantly less likely to have varied work tasks or the ability to choose their working positions. Frymoyer et al. (1983) demonstrate that employees with back problems are more likely to report stressful events at work, tend to have lower job satisfaction and a poor opinion of working conditions.

There is evidence to suggest that jobs involving lifting objects that weigh more than 25 lbs carry a three-fold increase of risk. This increases further if twisting actions are involved, particularly if the knees are straight (Kelsey, 1994). Frymoyer et al. (1983) also found that jobs involving lifting, carrying, pushing, pulling, bending or twisting all carried increased risk of back pain.

Manning et al. (1984) have investigated the types of events that are associated with the onset of episodes of back pain. They found that the most common accident factor is a loss of footing, an unexpected load or loss of balance. Non-accident factors associated with back pain include lifting and carrying, twisting and bending actions. There is also evidence to suggest that acute attacks of back pain seem to occur during the course of perfectly normal movements when the operator is not involved in the handling of loads. Beiring-Sorensen (1984) suggests that stooping, sitting and standing tend to aggravate symptoms whereas lying and walking have the effect of relieving symptoms.

Personal and Psychological Factors and Back Pain

There appears to be an association between tallness and back pain, although Pheasant (1991) suggests that the relationship is relatively weak. He argues that tall employees may be more at risk in some jobs than in others. Cody et al. (1974) found that, while physical fitness is a good predictor of risk in a job that is physically demanding, it may not be as effective for less demanding jobs.

Participation in sporting activities in childhood is generally found to be associated with a reduction in risk of back pain in later life, although Burton et al. (1989) report that adult sports participation is associated with increased risk. There is also evidence to suggest that men who suffer from back problems are also likely to report a number of other medical conditions such as headaches, chronic bronchitis and poor overall fitness.

Smokers are more likely to suffer from back problems than non-smokers. Frymoyer et al. (1983) found that the effects of smoking are dose-related. They reported that risk increases by about 20 per cent for every ten cigarettes smoked per day. Beiring-Sorensen (1984) reports that women's back problems that start during pregnancy are likely to be exacerbated by the process of childbirth and the physical effort involved in rearing children.

In terms of psychological factors, there is a small amount of evidence to suggest that employees with back problems have particular personality traits. Frymoyer et al. (1983) found that back pain patients were more likely to be anxious and to suffer from depression. Vallfors (1985) found that employees with chronic back pain were more likely to show signs of alcohol abuse, report lower job satisfaction and show more evidence of physical illness. He also found that a significant number of employees with back pain believe that work conditions prevented them from returning to work.

Table 21.1 summarises some of the key findings in respect of lower back pain in the workplace.

Table 21.1: Lower Back Pain: Personal Risk Factors

Strong Risk Factors	<ul><li>Previous history of low back pain.</li><li>Low overall fitness.</li><li>Low lifting strength — compared with task demands.</li><li>Low endurance of back muscles.</li><li>Smoking.</li><li>Motherhood.</li></ul>
Moderate Risk Factors (may be significant in extreme cases)	<ul><li>Hypermobility.</li><li>Spondylosis.</li><li>Spondylolisthesis.</li><li>Scoliosis and unequal leg length.</li><li>Weak back muscles, weak abdominal muscles, tight hamstrings (predict recurrence but not first attacks).</li></ul>
Weak or Very Weak Risk Factors	<ul><li>Stature.</li><li>Overweight.</li></ul>
Factors of No Predictive Risk Value	<ul><li>Lordosis or flat-back.</li><li>Abnormal vertebral numbers.</li><li>Spina bifida occulta.</li></ul>

WORK-RELATED MUSCULO-SKETELAL DISORDERS

There is significant evidence to support the claim that certain jobs will cause employees with a musculo-skeletal disorder (MSD) to experience pain at work. The disorder will be considerably amplified or exposed by the demands of the job. Certain disorders are more noticeable in some occupations than others, which can lead to the mistaken conclusion that they are caused by work characteristics, rather than by having been exposed by such disorders.

Armstrong et al. (1993) argue that musculo-skeletal pain is work-related if it is caused by work conditions. Kilbom (1988) suggests that the physical demands of a task combine with an employee's capacity to determine the level of musculo-skeletal stress that the individual experiences when carrying out work. Age, strength and fitness influence the individual's capacity. He suggests that physical pain combines with psychological stress to produce a level of musculo-skeletal strain.

Armstrong et al. (1993) have advanced Kilbom's ideas and developed a model of musculo-skeletal disorders with an emphasis on five variables: exposure, dose, primary responses, secondary responses and capacity (**Table 21.2**). They define exposure as work demands such as posture, force and repetition rate. Dose is defined in terms of the effect of this exposure on the body parts such as metabolic changes in the muscles, etc. Primary responses constitute changes in the shape of the tissue or other physical changes whereas secondary responses refer to pain. Capacity refers to the employee's ability to cope with the doses to which they are exposed. They suggest that capacity is not fixed, but may change with age, the acquisition of a skill, training, etc.

MSD covers a broad range of health problems. The main problems are back pain/injuries and work-related upper limb disorders (WRULDs), which are commonly known as "repetitive strain injuries", though RSI is a term many would quarrel with. MSD can also cover lower limb disorders. Where one lever meets another is known as a joint and the power to make these joints move comes from the muscle that joins one bone to another, travelling over the joint as it does so. Muscles can contract (pull) so each joint has two sets of muscles, one to bend and one to straighten the joint. Muscles are attached to bones by tendons where the force is concentrated and the blood supply is less than that going to the muscle proper so that repair after any damage is much slower. When assessing the risk in a manual handling situation, we must consider the three areas of excessive force, abnormal posture and speed of repetition.

The factors that increase the risk of MSD can be grouped under two headings: physical aspects of work and work environment and organisation. There are many common elements in that list.

Figure 21.1: Factors that Increase Risk of MSD and/or WRULDs

MSD Risk Factors	WRULDs Risk Factors
Physical	Poor posture.
Loads.	Highly repetitive movements.
Poor posture.	Forced hand applications.
Highly repetitive movements.	Hand-arm vibration.
Forceful hand applications.	Direct mechanical pressures on body tissues.
Direct mechanical pressures on body tissues.	Cold work environments.
Body vibrations.	*Work Organisation*
Work Environment/Organisation	Perception of work organisation.
Pace of work.	
Repetitive work.	
Time patterns.	
Payment systems.	
Monotonous work.	
Fatigue.	
Cold work environments.	
Perception of organisation.	
Psychological work factors.	

Neck and Shoulder Pain and Headaches

Like back pain, neck pain tends to be recurrent and can consist of muscle spasms and limitations of movement, and the neck may have a twisted appearance. Neck pain commonly radiates into the shoulder and down the arms with the result that muscular pains in the neck, shoulder and the upper parts of the back tend to merge into one another. Some employees with neck problems also report experiencing episodes of dizziness, fainting and vertigo.

Hall (1954) found that the number of employees with stiff neck problems is high and there is a considerable body of research suggesting that this is related to a number of risk factors:

- They appear to be more common in black populations than white.

- Neck problems are also common in employees who carry loads on their shoulders.

- They are also common among employees in occupations with much static muscle tensions, such as musicians and telephone operators.

Grieco (1986) suggests that jobs are more likely to be associated with neck pain when they require employees to fix their eyes on a single point while performing some task with the hands, and which, as a result, fix the posture of the head, neck and upper limbs. He also found that jobs that require a significant amount of concentration, and where the employee had little opportunity for moving around, were more likely to result in employees reporting neck pain. Waris (1980) found that those employees who perform electrical wiring tasks, and who work for long periods with their arms in a raised position, were more likely to experience neck pain.

Headaches are generally due to muscle tension and may involve the neck muscles. Tension headaches are generally stress-related and it appears that a wide range of factors may precipitate a headache, including glare, noise, flickering lights and high levels of visual concentration on the part of the employee.

Elbow, Forearm, Wrist and Hand Disorders

In general, these disorders are associated with the performance of repetitive short-cycle tasks of an industrial nature. There is, however, some debate about the level of repetition required to expose an employee to a significantly increased risk. Putz-Anderson (1988) suggests that the number of repetitions must be between 1500-2000 per hour and involve a cycle time of less than 30 seconds.

Figure 21.2 summarises some of the key conditions and the ergonomic variables involved.

Table 21.2: A Model of Musculo-skeletal Disorders

Element	Example	
Exposure	Physical Factors	• Workplace layout.
		• Tool design.
		• Size/shape/weight of work objects.
	Work Organisation	• Cycle times.
		• Paced/unpaced work.
		• Spacing of rest periods.
	Psychological Factors	• Job dissatisfaction.
		• Quality of supervision.
		• Future uncertainty.
Dose	Mechanical Factors	• Tissue forces.
		• Tissue deformations.
	Physiological Factors	• Consumption of substrates.
		• Production of metabolites.
	Psychological Factors	• Ion displacements.
		• Anxiety.
Primary Responses	Physiological Factors	• Change in substrate levels.
		• Change in metabolite levels.
		• Accumulation of waste products.
		• Change in pH.
		• Change in muscle temperature.
	Physical Factors	• Tissue deformation.
		• Increase in pressure.
Secondary Responses	Physical Factors	• Change in strength.
		• Change in mobility.
	Psychological Factors	• Discomfort.
Capacity	Mechanical Factors	• Soft tissue strength.
		• Bone density/strength.
	Physiological Factors	• Aerobic capacity.
		• Anaerobic capacity.
		• Homeostatic control.
	Psychological Factors	• Self-esteem.
		• Tolerance of discomfort.
		• Tolerance of stress.

Figure 21.2: Work-related Musculo-skeletal Disorders of the Neck, Shoulder and Upper Limbs

Synonymous Generic Terms

- Repetitive strain injuries (RSI).
- Cumulative trauma disorders (CTD).
- Occupational cericobrachial disorders (OCD).
- Occupational overuse syndrome (OOS).

Some Specific Clinical Conditions

- Supraspinatus (or rotator cuff) tendonitis.
- Thoracic outlet syndrome.
- Lateral epicondylitis (tennis elbow).
- Medical epicondylitis (golfer's elbow).
- Tenosynovitis, peritendintis (crepitans) (De Quervain's disease).
- Trigger finger.
- Carpal tunnel syndrome.
- Cangalia.

Some Less Specific Descriptive Terms

- Cervical syndrome.
- Tension neck, stiff neck, etc.
- Frozen shoulder.
- Occupational cramps (craft palsies).

Some Occupational Variants

- Gaoler's elbow.
- Hopper's gout.
- Data-processing disease.
- Washer-woman's thumb.
- Cowboy's thumb.
- Writer's cramp.
- Florist's cramp.
- Telegraphist's cramp.
- Musician's cramp.

Table 21.3: Upper Limb Musculo-skeletal Disorder: Ergonomic Risk Factors

Task Demand	Disorder
Repeated extension of wrist and/or fingers, e.g. repeated backhand throwing actions.	Tennis elbow.
Repeated "clothes wringing" action (flexion/extension with supination/pronation and power grip).	Tenosynovitis, esp. De Quervain's.
Repeated radial and ulnar deviation, especially with forceful grip, e.g. using a spanner.	Tenosynovitis, esp. De Quervain's.
Repeated pronation/supination with ulnar-deviated wrist, e.g. twisting with pliers.	Tenosynovitis, esp. De Quervain's; tennis elbow; carpal tunnel syndrome.
Repeated gripping actions with flexed wrist.	Tenosynovitis of finger flexors (trigger finger).
Repeated flexion/extension of wrist, especially if combined with pinch grip or power grip.	Carpal tunnel syndrome.
Prolonged pressure on elbow, especially if elbow is flexed.	Ulnar nerve entrapment at elbow.
Repeated application of force with hand, with wrist in extended position.	Ulnar nerve entrapment at wrist.
Tools causing radial deviation of wrist, especially if combined with extension and pronation.	Tennis elbow.
Tools with triggers — especially if handle is too large so that proximal interphalangeal joint is extended.	Tenosynovitis of finger flexors (trigger finger).

There is evidence to suggest that women tend to report a higher prevalence of such disorders than men. This holds even where both sexes are performing the same tasks. Buckle and Stubbs (1986), for example, found evidence of gender differences for carpal tunnel syndrome but not for tenosynovitis. The conditions also appear to be age-related. It tends to occur most often in the 40-50 age group, although other occupational factors may be involved. The general evidence suggests that, while body-build, hand-size and muscle strength are not significant risk factors, it tends to be more prevalent in employees returning to work after a lay-off and in new inductees. Kurppa et al. (1979) report that it doubles after the summer holidays. **Table 21.4** provides a summary of actions taken by employers to deal with MSD.

Table 21.4: MSD Solutions: Good Practice Examples

Title	Industry/ Workplace	Main Source of Problem	Main Intervention
Redesigning tram driver's position	Public transport	Poor driving position	Redesign of tram cab
Adapting a fork lift truck	Warehouse	Driving	Redesign
An intelligent lifting device for loading	Furniture manufacture	Heavy, unwieldy loads	Mechanical aid
Improved organisation of workstation for sewing of mattresses	Textile and furniture manufacture	Workstation layout/foot pedals	Changes to workstation and equipment
Avoid manual lifting using a "vacuum" device to lift meat	Food	Heavy lifting – carcasses	Lifting aid
Automating removal of protective plastic from stainless steel parts	Electro-domestic goods manufacture/ dishwasher	Repetitive, forceful task	Automation
Reducing manual effort in factory loading tasks	Manufacturing / chemical products	Heavy loads, awkward postures/sacks, barrels	Lifting aid, redesign of workplace layout
Improved seating and reduced lifting in garment manufacture	Textile manufacture	Seating, pedal operation, pushing heavy loads	Improved work station, equipment, transport methods
Removing repetitive risks form assembly of small components	Electro-domestic goods manufacture	Highly repetitive work	Mechanisation /changes to workstation & organisation
Ergonomics programme for SMEs	Small businesses / various sectors	MSD from various types of work	External service programme to introduce ergonomic changes

Technical devices to reduce manual handling and repetitive work in meat packing	Food	Frequent manual handling of heavy loads	Automation
Mechanical aids for handling glass panes	Glazing /construction	Heavy, dangerous, awkward loads	Mechanical hoists, carts
Improving seating and ergonomics in factory quality control work	Manufacturing / plastic goods	Repetitive work, stretching and reaching	Seating, workstation redesign
Ergonomics for junior schools	Schools	Poor furniture design	External service programme to introduce ergonomic equipment, training, information
Introducing adjustable workstations on a packing production line	Food	Repetitive work, seating and work-place layout	Changes to seating, workplace layout
Worker rehabilitation using voice recognition computer software: "talk yourself into a job" training programme	Office	MSD from display screen equipment use (mouse, keyboard)	Rehabilitation: Training on voice operated equipment and advice

Repetitive Strain Injury

There is a considerable degree of controversy about the use of the term "repetitive strain injury" (RSI) but it generally refers to work-related musculo-skeletal disorders of the neck, shoulder and upper limbs. The term, which originated in Australia, is referred to as cumulative trauma disorder (CTD) in the United States. It is also known as the "occupational overuse syndrome" (OOS). Some commentators do not believe in the existence of RSI in the medical sense. Ferguson (1987), for example, refers to it as a complex psycho-social phenomenon with elements of mass hysteria, while others see it as a metaphor for worker alienation.

Even those who believe in its existence cannot agree about its manifestations. These are some of the ones most frequently cited:

- The syndrome involves primarily lowly-paid female workers in "boring jobs".

- The jobs may be, but more often are not, repetitious.

- The complainant will often have concurrent domestic or other personal difficulties.

- Symptoms can be quite dramatic while often variable and irre-producible.

- The affected limb is often protected or supported.

- Symptoms are generally quite refractory, failing to show a sus-tained response to any form of intervention, pain-killers, physiotherapy, etc.

- The pain is generally regarded as being genuine rather than feigned.

- Physical examination is entirely normal apart from tender spots, which tend to vary in location from day to day.

- Physical disease or injury has not been found in such cases.

- Neither muscle strain nor repetition appear to play any part in the process.

The emerging consensus among medical experts is that the syn-drome is primarily attributable to psycho-social factors rather than to physical disease or injury. The condition has been given legal recognition in the UK.

Keyboard operators are less at risk than previously, since modern keyboards and workstations are better designed. Em-ployees who are piece-work-paid are also more at risk because of the incentive to work faster and not take breaks from particular tasks — taking breaks means a change of activity not necessarily a half-hour drinking coffee.

Median nerve entrapment (Carpal Tunnel Syndrome) has been associated with some jobs requiring a lot of forceful wrist move-ments and is due to compression of the median nerve as it passes through a tunnel with bones on three sides of the wrist, pressure here results in abnormal sensation and pain in the hand, some-times worse at night. Job rotation is often used to reduce the risk so that production-line staff change jobs half way through the day, using different muscle groups and allowing recuperation of the previously used parts.

Mullaly and Grigg (1988) propose three categories of RSI. Type 1 consists of well-known clinical entities and Type 2 of chronic pain without inflammation, degeneration or any signs of a neurological or systemic disease. In Type 3, an initial Type 1 situation acts as a focus for pain but this is amplified by psychological factors. Psychological processes are of some significance in the development and course of Types 2 and 3. This has led many commentators to suggest that an ergonomic intervention, which focuses on issues of posture and layout, will be insufficient on its own. Some intervention of a psychological and/or organisational nature may also be necessary.

Barton et al. (1992) criticise the use of the term RSI to describe pain in the arms or hands. They put forward three main arguments:

- They suggest that the term implies the existence of a physical condition with an identifiable physical cause, whereas the research evidence suggests that in the case of RSI such a cause is difficult to identify.

- The word "stress" is not used appropriately. In the mechanical sense, repetitive strain injury comes about as the result of excessive physical stress being imposed and it can be objectively confirmed by observing damage or change to the body. This is generally not the case with RSI.

- An injury is usually believed to occur as a result of a single event in which both cause and effect are closely related, whereas RSI appears to occur as a result of repetitive work over long periods.

Quinter and Elvey (1993) propose that much of what is described as RSI may really be peripheral nerve pain. This pain is the result of a disorder of the pain receptors and occurs independently of the employee's mental state. According to this perspective, RSI is a form of peripheral neuropathy in which damaged nerves can result in chronic pain by injecting abnormal discharge into the nervous system and by amplification and distortion of naturally generated signals. Butler (1991) uses the term "activity specific mechanosensitivity" to describe the situation where the employee may complain of pain only when carrying out small repetitive motions but is perfectly capable of carrying out a wide range of other activities. **Figure 21.3** presents a set of actions for dealing with work-related Carpal Tunnel Syndrome.

EYESTRAIN PROBLEMS IN THE WORKPLACE

There is an abundance of evidence that eyestrain is now a common problem in industry, primarily as a result of increased use of VDUs and the performance of demanding visual tasks for long periods of time. Pheasant (1991) suggests that eyestrain has three primary symptoms:

- An aching or throbbing sensation in, around and behind the eyes, including blurred vision, double vision and a difficulty in focusing.

- An inflammation of the eyes and lids, leading to hot, red and watery eyes.

- Frontal headaches and feelings of tiredness, irritability.

These symptoms primarily occur because of the overuse of the muscles in and around the eye, and it is therefore appropriate to state that visual fatigue is, in many ways, a special case of local muscular fatigue.

In terms of sources, the general literature suggests that any working activity or visual stimulus that imposes excessive demand upon the muscles of the eye is potentially a source of eyestrain. The most common problems are prolonged close work, poor lighting, inadequate task contrast, glare and ceiling reflections. These tend to make the employee over-accommodate or make constant changes in accommodation in order to bring them into focus. The symptoms of eyestrain or visual fatigue are short-lasting and rapidly reversible and it is generally accepted that the eyes cannot be permanently damaged. There is evidence that people living in non-industrial societies have fewer problems with myopia. Myopic problems tend to increase with educational level as a consequence of the increased amount of time spent reading.

Figure 21.3: Actions for Dealing with Work-related Carpal Tunnel Syndrome (CTS)

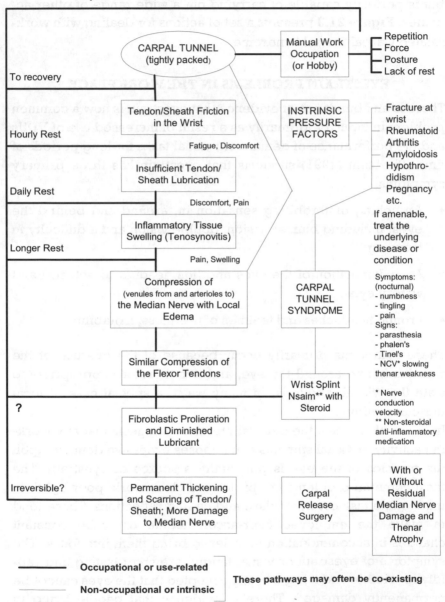

AIDS IN THE WORKPLACE

Acquired Immune Deficiency Syndrome (AIDS) and Human Im-muno-Deficiency Virus (HIV), the precursor to full-blown AIDS, are features of modern society. HIV can be transmitted through blood products, through unprotected sexual activity, by an infected mother to the unborn child and through intravenous drug use. HIV cannot be contracted through normal social contact and most workplace situations present no risk of cross-infection. An individual with the virus (HIV+) is normally able to attend work regularly and work performance is unaffected. A person living with full-blown AIDS may develop AIDS-related complex (ARC) and con-tract various illnesses and infections that will seriously impact on attendance and performance. This distinction between the two conditions was recognised in 1986.

Ignoring the HIV and AIDS issues until a case arises is not a sensible managerial option, as decisions taken under pressure may be inappropriate. Cases of HIV and AIDS raise different issues from those associated with other life-threatening illnesses. Distinc-tive HIV and AIDS issues include:

- Prejudice, which leads to discrimination.

- Anxiety and fear among employees about contracting the dis-ease.

- A lack of knowledge about the disease.

- A lack of sympathy towards AIDS sufferers because of stereo-typical assumptions and inaccurate perceptions about HIV transmission.

The advantage of investigating and addressing HIV and AIDS is-sues at work is an objectively defined managerial approach prior to a case occurring, in order to facilitate the handling of a case when it does. HIV and AIDS are emotive and emotional subjects, characterised by misinformation and stereotypical assumptions, and this may test the ability of the most objective manager to han-dle a case fairly and consistently. Banas (1992), in a frank and readable account of the difficulties of actually managing the em-ployment of staff who are living with AIDS, highlights the difficulties and the unpredictability of individual responses. HIV and AIDS are illnesses and an employee with an illness should be dealt with through the sickness and absence management policies and procedures. However, the distinctive issues relating to HIV and AIDS may justify further measures, including a specific policy, to ensure fair, reasonable and equitable treatment.

The language of the HIV and AIDS policy and the message it communicates are critical in setting the tone for the management of HIV and AIDS in the workplace. An analysis of AIDS policies by Goss and Adam-Smith (1994) identified the emergence of two distinct policy types:

- **The Defensive Policy:** this may include a strong introductory statement that discrimination against people affected will not be tolerated, but further investigation of the policy detail identifies a shift that introduces a 'sense of uncertainty' about the differential treatment of people with HIV and AIDS. Statements are ostensibly written in language that conveys protection for the AIDS sufferer, but in practice they are used for exclusion in order to 'defend' the organisation from AIDS sufferers.

- **The Constructive Policy:** this is more focused on the normalisation of HIV and AIDS as a lethal matter. As a positive consequence, it diverts attention from the stereotyping of and discrimination against the person living with AIDS.

There are many benefits to be gained from an employer approaching the issue of HIV/AIDS in a proactive manner. These include:

- Prevention of new infection among employees by educating them about how HIV is and is not transmitted.

- Informing managers and supervisors of the legal issues raised by HIV infection in the workplace.

- Preventing discrimination by fearful and ill-informed employees.

- Laying the groundwork and preparing managers and supervisors to consider requests from employees disabled by HIV infection.

- Facilitating improvements in morale and preventing fear and anxiety.

With regard to occupational hygiene, most organisations will not have to directly protect against the risks of HIV contamination, except for basic prophylactics in first aid situations. However, certain organisations, such as those involved in the provision of medical care, often require specific measures to prevent the spread of the HIV infection. In all cases, organisations should consider indirect hygiene steps (such as education programmes) to lessen the risk of employees contracting HIV outside the workplace. Education programmes may also have a secondary beneficial effect in reducing stress levels among the workforce, by removing fears and prejudices about the issue.

The most effective method for an organisation to treat employees with HIV or AIDS fairly is to implement a clear, non-discriminatory policy on the issue. A definite policy statement not only promotes equal opportunities, it also constitutes good management practice and makes economic sense. It can protect employee rights by providing confidentiality, and prevents discrimination in areas such as job security and promotion opportunities. It also gives managers clear guidelines on how to cope with the sensitivities involved, and can have positive repercussions for both employee relations and customer image.

Some organisations argue that AIDS does not merit this specific attention, especially where resources are tight, and argue that policies for non-occupational diseases are unnecessary. However, because of the sensitivity of the issue, it can create strong reactions, among both employees and the media, justifying the need for a policy. Medium- to large-scale organisations in particular need to prepare for the emergence of the issue, as sooner or later they are likely to have an employee with HIV or AIDS.

Aiken (1992) and the National AIDS Unit suggest that an HIV/AIDS policy should include the following elements to maximise its fairness:

- It should address HIV and AIDS separately, recognising that they are separate conditions, and provide appropriate responses to each.

- It should integrate the policy into other equal opportunity policies.

- It should not tolerate discrimination towards HIV or AIDS from any employee or any aspect of company activity.

- It should outline discipline and grievance procedures for those found breaching the terms of the policy.

- It should state that AIDS will be treated in the same manner as other progressive or debilitating illness.

- It should cover areas such as re-training, re-deployment, flexible working and compassionate leave.

- It should be reinforced by an equal opportunities stance on sexual orientation.

An effective policy will cover areas such as opportunities for redeployment, retraining, flexible working and compassionate leave. These provisions should also apply to employees infected with HIV.

In addition to these elements, a HIV/AIDS policy should contain a commitment to some form of educational programme for employees. As formal education programmes, in the form of seminars or workshops, can be both expensive and viewed with reluctance by staff, an alternative is to mail all employees with relevant information. Unfortunately, this method can lead to the issue becoming shrouded with secrecy, with staff perceiving the organisation to be sweeping AIDS under the carpet. It is, nonetheless, a useful way to introduce the issue, and ideally should be backed up with open information systems. These allow employees to improve their knowledge about HIV/AIDS, should they wish to do so.

Employees have a right to confidentiality in health matters and this should be respected in the case of HIV and AIDS. There is no strict obligation for an infected person to tell their employer. HIV and AIDS are not modifiable diseases and sufferers are advised by representative bodies not to reveal their illness. However, employees have a contractual duty of care and an infected employee in a "sensitive" job has a responsibility to ensure that risks of transmission are assessed and minimised. A sample HIV/AIDS policy is presented in **Table 21.5**.

Table 21.5: HIV/AIDS Policy Guidelines

An effective policy should:

- Address HIV and AIDS as separate conditions, because different issues are associated with each.

- Make an opening statement to specify the organisational attitude to HIV and AIDS and state that, as illnesses, any cases will be dealt with through the sickness procedures.

- Make clear that HIV-infected employees are able to work normally and that employees with full-blown AIDS who are no longer able to work normally, in line with all employees with long-term illness, will be considered for redeployment, retraining, flexible working, home working, reduced hours or compassionate leave. Ideally, the policy should extend these options to the carers of AIDS sufferers.

- Assert that discrimination against employees with HIV and AIDS is unlawful and will not be tolerated.

- State that applicants for employment will be assessed on their ability to do the job and that, in conformance with the spirit of the legislation, reasonable adjustments will be made where appropriate.

- Reassure infected employees of confidentiality and provide guidance on support and counselling services.

- Nominate organisational support workers so that the employee can elect to talk to the most appropriate person and not be forced to talk to their immediate manager.

- Commit to the HIV and AIDS education of employees and managers.

SMOKING IN THE WORKPLACE

The issue of smoking at work is a sensitive one, requiring tact and understanding on the part of management to avoid potentially serious employee relations conflicts. The arguments of both sides in the debate are strong. On the one hand, smoking, including passive smoking, has long been recognised as a serious health hazard, so non-smokers are justified when not wanting to be exposed to such a risk. On the other hand, the smoker may feel discriminated against by strict anti-smoking regulations, which can often appear as an attempt to restrict the smoker's individual freedom.

One of the most volatile issues for HR professionals today is a company's position on smoking. Growing information about the adverse effects of second-hand smoke have led some people to call for a ban on smoking in the workplace. The current trend of non-smoking employees is to file workers' compensation and disability claims and legal suits against companies where smoking is not restricted.

It is generally recommended that employees create ventilated smoking lounges to separate smokers from non-smokers. A growing number of organisations have developed restrictive policies ranging from the use of designated smoking areas to banning smoking in the workplace to requiring non-smoking as a condition of employment. The research findings illustrate that smokers in a non-smoking organisation reduce the number of cigarettes smoked per work shift and hence inhale decreased levels of nicotine and carbon monoxide. Thus, work-site smoking restrictions may promote meaningful reductions in tobacco exposure and consequent health risks.

The law generally requires employers, employees, and their unions to develop a policy on smoking, tailored to suit the needs of their workplace. Guidelines are provided on how best to achieve this, the main points of which are outlined in **Figure 21.5**. The process is broken down into stages of preparation, consultation, policy formulation, implementation, enforcement and monitoring.

Figure 21.4: Smoking in the Workplace: Summary of the Legal Provisions and Some Case Law

- The Safety, Health and Welfare at Work Act, 1989 requires employers to provide safe places of work, including the provision of a working environment which is effectively free from airborne contamination so far as is reasonably practicable. This means that if an employee is suffering from a respiratory condition it would not be reasonable to expect that person to continue working in a very smoky atmosphere which may make the condition worse.

- The Workplace Regulations (Part III of the Safety, Health and Welfare at Work (General Applications) Regulations, 1993 (SHAWAWR) require employers to make suitable arrangements to protect workers from discomfort caused by tobacco smoke in rest rooms or rest areas. It also requires employers to ensure that there is sufficient fresh air in enclosed places of work and to ensure that where ventilation systems are used that they are properly maintained.

- The Chemical Agents Regulations, 1994 require employers to assess the risks arising from working exposure to hazardous substances, and this may lead to the prohibition of smoking for certain occupations in the work area to minimise the risk of hand-to-mouth transfer of toxic material.

- The Tobacco (Health Promotion and Protection) Regulations, 1995 ban smoking in particular public buildings, state and semi-state premises, childcare facilities, waiting rooms in doctors' and dentists' practices, food preparation and storage areas, etc. In offices of state and semi-state organisations, smoking is banned in public offices, circulation spaces (stairs, corridors) and conference or meeting rooms. The Regulations also limit smoking in particular areas such as canteens, where at a minimum, 50% of the total area must be non-smoking (this may be reduced to 25% if special ventilation equipment is used and approved by the local Health Authority). The person in charge of the premises is required under the Regulations to ensure that such non-smoking areas are designated with appropriate signage.

- The Safety Health and Welfare at Work Act 1989, Section 6 requires that employers take reasonably practicable measures to ensure the health of employees. This provision suggests that employers should take steps to limit workplace smoking. However, it is generally taken that Section 6 does not require employers to ban smoking.

- No specific cases have yet been reported. However, two British cases are of relevance:
  - ◊ *Bland v. Stockport Borough Council* (English High Court, 1993): Bland claimed to have developed chronic bronchitis while working for Stockport Borough Council as a result of sharing an office with three other women who each smoked between 15-20 cigarettes a day. Bland claimed that her employer had failed to provide her with a place of work that was reasonably safe. The case did not however create a precedent because it was settled out of Court for stg£15,000 (€24,000).

  - ◊ *Dryden v. Greater Glasgow Health Board* (Scottish Employment Appeals Tribunal, 1992): Dryden had worked as a nurse in a hospital or many years and smoked about 30 cigarettes a day. In 1991, her employer decided to prohibit smoking in the hospital. She resigned and claimed constructive dismissal. The Tribunal ruled that the dismissal would have been unfair if her contract contained a term giving her a right to smoke. It did not contain such a term. The Tribunal held that the employer was entitled to implement a no smoking rule in order to protect the health of non-smoking employees.

Figure 21.5: Formulating a Smoking Policy: Some Guidelines

---

1. Preparation

• Treat the issue as a health and safety matter, stressing the positive rather than the negative aspects.

• Be informed — gather information on the policies of other companies.

• Assess the views of the workforce to ensure employees are involved.

• Make sure that action taken does not appear arbitrary, or viewed as taken against smokers themselves.

2. Consultation

• Involve employees and their representatives throughout policy formation implementation and development by gathering employee views by questionnaire or direct consultation.

3. Policy Formulation

• The policy should be clear about what actions are being taken, why they are being taken, and what are the penalties for non-compliance. The following issues should be considered:

◊ Decide on type of policy, e.g. total ban on smoking, partial ban, restrictions in certain areas, etc.

• The following objectives should be considered:

◊ there is no future for smoking in public places, including workplaces, and the policy should be flexible enough to develop into defining the workplace as a non-smoking area.

◊ smokers should be segregated from non smokers if smoking is to be permitted in work areas and/or in rest areas.

◊ smoking must be prohibited if it creates a significant fire risk (flammable materials) or in connection with work with hazardous substances or food.

◊ smoking must be prohibited in areas defined by the Regulations.

◊ priority should be given to the needs of non-smokers who do not wish to breathe tobacco smoke.

• If the policy is to permit smoking in designated areas, consider the following:

◊ smoking areas should be signed, and all entry points to

the premises indicate that smoking is permitted only in such designated areas.

◊ smoking areas are commonly available to all smoking staff, and non-smoking staff do not need to enter. Smoking by managers in their own offices is prohibited!

◊ smoking areas are ventilated separately and to a high level, so that they are under negative pressure and contaminated air does not leak into adjacent work areas. Air ventilated should not form part of general recirculation.

◊ a complaints procedure.

◊ disciplinary action.

◊ rationale for policy, e.g. legal, fire safety, hygiene, or product image reasons.

4. Implementation

• Timing — a realistic period should be allowed for both policy development and implementation, to allow smokers to adjust their smoking patterns. In each case, three months is a reasonable time period for medium to large enterprises.

• Consistency — the policy must be implemented evenly across the organisation.

• Briefing — all employees should be thoroughly informed of the policy to be implemented.

• Facilities may also be made available to help smokers adjust to the new policy, such as information on controlling or, indeed, giving up the habit if they wish to do so.

5. Enforcement and Monitoring

• To a large extent, employees will enforce the policy through self-regulation. However, if breaches do occur, procedures outlined in the policy should be applied consistently. Reviews should also take place to encourage feedback and to promote equity in awkward situations.

Smoking as a health and safety issue is very sensitive in organisations with high proportions of smokers and any policy formulation effort will require discussion on issues such as individual freedom, fire hazards, cleaning costs, time lost for smoking breaks and action for non-compliance. An effective policy on smoking will typically try to explain the reason for the policy, specify where employees can and cannot smoke, and state the penalties for violation. Some policies also address the issues involved in resolving disputes between smokers and non-smokers. **Figure 21.6** presents an example of a smoking policy.

While some organisations have implemented strategies to stop smoking, this is often not given explicit recognition in many smoking policies. Examples of strategies include access to "quit" programmes, the distribution of health promotion and life-style literature and the provision of medical interventions such as smokers' patches. Human resource managers and safety specialists are usually involved in formulating smoking policies and the subsequent application of discipline or counselling strategies.

Workforce attitudes towards smoking at work should be considered and it is essential to seek the opinions of the employees in developing policy. A joint working party is a useful way of examining the policy options and the composition of this group should include representatives of management and employees who are smokers and non-smokers. The group needs clear terms of reference to enable it to draw conclusions and make recommendations to management.

Figure 21.6: Sample Smoking Policy

Sample Policy

Subject: Workplace smoking

Purpose: to protect the health of all employees, avoid conflicts between smoking and non-smoking workers, and ensure accommodation for non-smokers' preferences when necessary.

Guidelines:

- Smoking is permitted outdoors or in designated sections of the cafeteria and employee lounges and break areas.

- Smoking is prohibited in all meeting rooms, classrooms, rest rooms, hallways, lifts and other common-access areas.

- Employees who do not smoke have the right to post a no smoking sign on their desk or at their workstation and co-workers who smoke must honour these requests. Employees who have objections to smoke in their work area must submit a written statement to their supervisor outlining the basic reasons for their objections along with possible solutions to the problem.

- Work units or departments may formulate smoking policies for their work areas designed to accommodate the preferences of smokers and non-smokers. All employees in a unit shall be allowed to vote on any such policy. If differences cannot be resolved, the manager of the unit or department will be responsible for attempting to fashion a reasonable accommodation, such as ventilation modifications, the use of filtering devices such as air purifiers or cleaners or the relocation of work stations. The cost of purchasing filtering devices will be borne by employees who request them.

- Supervisors who receive a written statement of objections to smoking from a worker will meet with the employee to discuss possible accommodation. Employees should be asked if devices such as air purifiers or filters would satisfy their objections. The supervisor should consider the feasibility of separating the workstations of smokers and non-smokers if this would resolve the problem. If no mutually acceptable solution can be found, the supervisor must accommodate the non-smoker by designating the work area as a non-smoking zone.

- Employees may enrol in either a work-site smoking-cessation programme or outside programmes sponsored by local agencies and organisations. The work-site programme will be free of charge to participants and one-half of the time spent in the sessions will be paid time. The company will reimburse employees for three-quarters of the cost of participating in an off site smoking-cessation programme. Employees who successfully quite smoking for a one-year period will be eligible for a one-time £50 bonus.

- The company will be responsible for supplying all no smoking signs, notices and postings used on the premises.

- Violators of the smoking restrictions set forth in this policy will be subject to the standard disciplinary penalties, i.e. first offences will elicit a verbal warning, second offences a written warning, etc.

Smoking Policy Options

Four basic options are available to the organisation in terms of a smoking policy.

Smoking in Designated Areas

This can be an effective option, particularly when a policy is first introduced. It allows for a pragmatic and progressive approach, which, coupled with health education, can enable the organisation to work toward more extensive coverage. Specific issues are associated with this option:

- What do designated areas mean? If smoking is allowed in enclosed personal space, for example, individual offices, this may be seen as unfair and divisive because only more senior employees are likely to have their own enclosed space.

- Designated areas may be distant from the individual's place of work and taking time off for smoking may adversely affect productivity. Tensions may be created in employee relations with non-smokers feeling aggrieved about the perceived preferential treatment of smokers.

- Designated areas need ventilation to avoid the recirculation of air to non-smoking areas. Designated areas can magnify the problem of litter, a polluted atmosphere and fire risk.

Smoking at Designated Times

This allows for a relatively smoke-free work environment during specific periods of the day. Key issues can be identified and agreed with the non-smoking population and, with tolerance and education, this may be implemented. However, it concentrates the problem and can be stressful for non-smokers, if smokers all smoke at the same time. It is very much a compromise option.

Freedom for Individual Work Areas to Decide

This may appear to be a fair and reasonable option, but the organisational status of the smoker may put non-smokers under pressure to accept a smoking environment, or vice versa. The basis for the decision needs to be specified and can present difficulties; will it be a simple majority, a certain percentage of the employees affected, or consensual?

A Total Ban

This creates problems for smokers who find it difficult to curtail or cease smoking. The reasonableness of a total ban could be challenged because of a 'custom and practice' right to smoke at work. Therefore, a reasonable period of notice, or perhaps three months or more, may be necessary to allow smokers to adjust to the new working arrangements. Failure to give reasonable notice may lead to allegations of unfairness and ultimately to constructive dismissal if the employee feels unable to continue working. A total ban raises enforcement issues and consideration should be given to how infringements of the policy will be dealt with, as disciplinary action may be necessary. Smokers are innovative in creating refuge areas when faced with smoking bans and the risk of fire and litter pollution increases if employees congregate and smoke in remote or obscure places.

Some smokers would prefer not to smoke but, because of the addictive properties of nicotine, find it difficult or even impossible to cease. A reasonable employer will acknowledge this and offer support. Support mechanisms that can help smokers to adjust and to change behaviour include health education, counselling or self-help groups, and assistance in reducing nicotine dependence, through the provision of patches or chewing gum.

Regular and well-publicised support sessions for smokers send a strong message to the workforce that the organisation is committed to a healthy, smoke-free environment and also that it is supportive of employees who are adjusting to the new policy.

The following steps should be observed when developing a smoking policy.

- Top management should make a commitment to the development of a smoking policy.

- Pertinent state and local laws should be reviewed.

- Unions should be involved (if applicable).

- The smoking policy should be tailored to particular work situations or stations.

- A committee of smokers and non-smokers from a cross-section of the workforce should be formed.

- The workforce should be surveyed to determine attitudes toward smoking and toward possible smoking policies.

- A proposed policy should be circulated throughout the workplace. Enforcement of policy violations on a consistent basis will encourage employee compliance.

ALCOHOL AND DRUG-RELATED PROBLEMS

A common cause of absenteeism in industry is connected with employees suffering from alcohol and other drug-related problems. This form of absenteeism can occur at any level within the organisation, and can be costly to employers in terms of disruption, poor morale, reduced output and safety problems.

It is estimated by IBEC that at least one in ten employees may suffer from alcohol abuse at some stage, with male employees being three times more likely to be at risk than female employees. O'Brien and Dufficy (1988) estimate that some 75 per cent of problem drinkers and 25 per cent of problem drug abusers are male employees. The problem can manifest itself in even the smallest of organisations and management should always have a planned procedure to aid employees experiencing difficulties.

O'Brien and Dufficy (1988) argue that there are numerous benefits to be gained from adopting a systematic approach to substance abuse. They highlight benefits such as fewer accidents, less time-off as a result of alcohol and drug-related sickness, better work relationships, improved decision-making and greater quality and quantity of production.

Means (1990) suggests that the development of a policy on substance abuse can take one of two approaches:

- A disease model that is primarily driven by considerations of organisational performance. There is the assumption that substance abuse leads to poor performance, hence the need to implement a policy that emphasises prevention and treatment.

- A legal and social responsibility model, primarily driven by a legalistic rationale, while at the same time demonstrating concern for disease and performance. There is the assumption that poor performance may be an indicator of substance abuse and, therefore, requires a remedy that will prevent legal problems and promote social gain.

Means suggests the following guidelines when formulating a policy:

- The organisation should produce a written policy that deals specifically with alcoholism alone.

- All employees should know this policy and it should clearly set out as a positive policy aimed at helping the substance abuser to recover.

- The organisation should develop specific procedures covering such issues as the handling and referral of employees experiencing problems and line managers ensuring compliance with procedures.

- The policy should include an effective referral system. It should incorporate provisions relating to qualified substance diagnostic facilities.

- The policy should have an effective medical record-keeping system underpinning it. This record-keeping system should assure confidentiality to the individual employee, while at the same time having the capacity to provide evidence on the success of the policies. **Figure 21.7** presents an example of an alcohol policy.

However, management must note the pitfalls when handling employees with a substance-abuse problem, as the issue has wide-ranging disciplinary and industrial relations implications, and often causes a great deal of stress for the employees involved. Nonetheless, properly handled, the situation can have positive outcomes for employees, acting as the first step towards their rehabilitation.

To avoid conflict over the issue, it is important to remember that dealing with the problem is a management responsibility, and that a consistent procedure for handling employees must be in place. IBEC suggest that this should consist of four main steps, as shown in **Figure 21.8**.

Figure 21.7: A Sample Alcohol Policy

This policy has been developed in consultation with employee representatives and has the full support of management. This policy applies to all employees and to contractors working on organisation premises. Alcohol consumption or possession in the workplace is prohibited. The breaking of this rule will result in disciplinary action.

The organisation has a duty to protect all employees and others, and alcohol misuse or addiction may affect employee health, safety and performance. The purpose of this policy is to protect employees from the dangers of alcohol and to encourage those with a problem to seek help. The organisation recognises that alcohol dependency may be an illness and can be treated in the same way as any other long-term illness.

The organisation is committed to supporting and assisting in the treatment of those with an alcohol problem. Help is available from your manager, the occupational health department or through the Employee Assistance Programme. The employee has a right to confidentiality in all aspects of health care.

The employee is entitled to occupational sick pay while undergoing recognised and agreed treatment and has the right to return to work following effective treatment, subject to the approval of the occupational health practitioner. Employees will be supported during treatment. However, where treatment is unsuccessful and the employee is not able to return to their job, suitable alternative employment will be sought, but if it is not available, termination of employment on the grounds of ill health may need to be considered.

Figure 21.8: Handling Employees with Alcohol and Drug-related Problems: Some Guidelines

---

1. **Identify possible problems among employees**

    Common indicators are:

    *   Regular absences from work, often with a variety of excuses.
    *   Poor time-keeping and missed deadlines.
    *   Poor work performance.
    *   Disimproved personal appearance.
    *   Disimprovement in personal relationships with colleagues.
    *   Uncharacteristic irritability and/or depression.
    *   Money problems — continued borrowing from colleagues.
    *   Obvious signs of substance abuse at work.

2. **Confirm that a suspected employee has a problem**

    Gather facts, not rumours, about the following:

    *   Work performance — examine quality, behaviour, time-keeping, absenteeism.
    *   Conduct interviews with the relevant supervisors.
    *   Analyse medical data for any deteriorations that are substance abuse-related.

3. **Act on the problem**

    If there is substantial hard evidence to show that the employee may have a problem, then interview the employee as soon as possible, taking the following into account:

    *   Give the employee the opportunity to have a colleague/ representative present.
    *   Present all of the gathered evidence to the employee regarding poor performance.
    *   Allow the employee to put forward an explanation for the poor performance.
    *   If the explanation is unsatisfactory, advise on the seriousness of the situation, and management's unwillingness to let it continue.
    *   Directly state to the employee the belief that they are suffering from a substance-abuse problem, and suggest appropriate referral to professional help.
    *   If the employee acknowledges the problem, written clarification should be provided regarding:

◊ specific performance improvement criteria.

◊ potential disciplinary consequences if these are not met.

◊ agreement to referral for professional help, where appropriate.

- If the employee denies the problem, then they should be advised of the disciplinary consequences, and a continued denial will result in the procedure moving forward to the final stage.

4. Disciplinary Action

This should take the form outlined in the company rule book or, in its absence, according to custom and practice. When carrying out disciplinary action, management should note that:

- It may be helpful to provide a list of sources of professional help.

- The issue has serious industrial relations repercussions, and the employee has the right to refer the issue to:

◊ a Rights Commissioner.

◊ the Labour Relations Commission/Labour Court.

◊ the Employment Appeals Tribunal.

A major issue in the American context relates to the testing for controlled substances. This issue has not received a significant degree of attention in Ireland or the UK. Testing for controlled substances is mandatory for federal employment in the US and is becoming increasingly common in the private sector, especially amongst larger employers. Brookler (1992) suggests a range of guidelines for mandatory testing:

- An employee who tests positive should be referred to an employee assistance programme (EAP).

- If the employee occupies a sensitive position, the individual should be removed immediately from that position.

- It is recommended that it should be at the employer's discretion whether the employee is returned to that position.

- The severity of action taken will depend on the circumstances of each case.

Before a company initiates drug testing, the following questions should be addressed: Why do we want this programme? Do we have a problem with drugs in our company? What will we do with the results of drug tests? Can our current discipline policy handle violations of this policy? How much will the programme cost? Can we afford it? Will it affect morale? Should it be a punitive or rehabilitative programme? Only after these questions are answered satisfactorily should a company consider implementing drug testing.

Companies use five approaches to drug testing: pre-employment screening, random testing of current employees, "reasonable cause" testing in response to performance problems, return-to-duty testing after drug treatment or suspension, and post accident testing. Science makes it possible to ascertain if a person has ingested a controlled substance, and more and more companies are joining the ranks of those who at least test applicants for the presence of drugs. An American survey found that 77 per cent of the companies responded test all new hires for drugs in pre-employment physical examinations. Surprisingly, workers are quite tolerant of testing. The survey found 60 per cent of those questioned supported random drug testing of current employees with no probable cause.

Two questions that science has not yet been able to answer, however, are exactly how much of a controlled substance an individual must ingest to be impaired and just what *impaired* means. For example, most countries have set a 0.10 per cent blood alcohol level to establish impairment by alcohol; a similar standard does not exist for controlled substances. While some employers declare that a drug test result showing any amount of a controlled substance will be grounds for rejecting an applicant or discharging a worker, other employers have set some level as the threshold for an assumption that the employee is impaired. Computerised tests are now available to help employers determine whether or not workers in safety-related jobs are impaired. One test operates like a video game and takes less than a minute to determine eye-hand co-ordination and reaction time. **Figure 21.9** presents an example of an actual policy.

Figure 21.9: Policy on Drugs and Alcohol at Work

[Delete inappropriate statements]

1. This organisation is committed to providing a safe and comfortable working environment within its building(s) and this requires a clear statement of corporate policy on alcohol and drug misuse.

2. Every line manager is responsible for ensuring that this policy is implemented.

3. Alcohol consumption on the premises is

    *   Prohibited to all staff, visitors, contractors and others, within the site boundary including car parks and other external areas.

    *   Permitted only in specified places and at specified times as may be agreed in writing by senior staff, for example associated with a pre-Christmas toast to staff, etc.

4. Alcohol consumption must be managed by all staff such that:

    *   No member of staff presents for work under the influence of alcohol, nor consumes alcohol during the working day (including when off-site during lunch breaks, etc).

    *   No member of staff presents for work under the influence of alcohol, and if alcohol is consumed off-site during the working day (such as during lunch breaks, etc) this is in moderation.

        Alcohol consumption in breach of the above restrictions is strictly prohibited, risks the safety and comfort of other staff and visitors, and will be regarded as a disciplinary matter.

5. Drug misuse by staff is strictly prohibited such that:

    a) No member of staff may present for work under the influence of misused drugs, nor may any member of staff misuse drugs during the working day (on the premises or off-site).

    b) Drug misuse in breach of the above restrictions is strictly prohibited, risks the safety and comfort of other staff and visitors, and will be regarded as a disciplinary matter.

6. All staff are required to bring this policy to the attention of visitors and contractors, and to report to their line manager if they see anyone consuming alcohol or misusing drugs, or who appears to be under the influence of either.

7. To supplement the restrictions of this policy, the Company also wishes to offer assistance to members of staff who may have developed a problem with either drugs or alcohol. To facilitate

> this, information on organisations available to assist shall be periodically circulated, posted on notice boards, etc.
>
> 8. Although the company will not tolerate criminal behaviour, it is possible for additional assistance to be offered to anyone identified as having an "alcohol (and/or drugs) problem". For anyone so identified, from sickness absence records, self-reporting and other means, the following shall apply:
>
>   a) The work undertaken by the person shall be reviewed, seeking to identify causes of stress which may be reduced.
>
>   b) The company may make available confidential counselling or other support to assist the person concerned to recover his/her control.
>
>   c) It should be noticed that if drug misuse and/or alcohol consumption reduces performance to unacceptable levels — in terms of safety, sickness absence or other factors — this may prove to be grounds for dismissal if counselling or other treatments are unsuccessful.

EMPLOYEE ASSISTANCE PROGRAMMES

Employee assistance programmes (EAPs) are a growing form of employee benefit that provide help to employees for a variety of problems. Many organisations use EAPs to treat job stress, alcoholism, and other forms of drug abuse, marital and emotional difficulties and financial problems. Recent research reveals that employees turned to EAPs because of corporate restructuring and downsizing. Many EAPs are also equipped to handle problems related to AIDS and workplace violence. In addition, EAPs can be designed to provide physical help with controlling blood pressure, weight and smoking.

The general goal of an EAP is to provide treatment for employees who are having problems so that they can return to normal, productive functioning on the job. While the vast majority of EAPs are in large organisations, even small businesses are getting involved with EAPs through consortiums with other small businesses. Most EAP referrals are based on an assessment of job performance and referrals by supervisors, although many employees also volunteer to attend EAPs. EAP staff often provide training for managers and supervisors on making "constructive confrontations" with their employees regarding work-related deficiencies.

Supervisors are thus exempted from trying to diagnose the causes of a problem. Getting at the cause of the performance problem is left to professionals (e.g., people with graduate degrees in psychology and social work), who are trained to make such diagnoses and treat people accordingly. Most EAPs are based on the principle of voluntary participation. Labour unions generally support drug counselling and EAPs but oppose coercion to participate in such programmes as a condition of employment, as well as opposing drug testing of any kind.

EAPs therefore represent an effective tool to assist managers in restoring poor work performance that is affected by personal and/or social problems. Such programmes work by using poor performance as a means of problem identification and referring the employee to sources of professional help for assessment and rehabilitation.

An EAP is a systematic, organised and continuing provision of counselling, advice and assistance, provided or funded by the employer and designed to help employees and their families with problems arising from work-related or external sources.

In the Irish and UK context, EAPs tend to have two main objectives:

- To help the employee who is distracted by a range of personal problems, be they emotional, stress, relationships, alcohol, drug, financial or legal-related, to cope.

- To assist the organisation in the identification and elimination of performance problems in employees whose job performance is adversely impacted by personal problems.

In terms of the essential elements that distinguish an EAP, Davis and Gibson (1994) and Lee and Gray (1994) suggest the following as core elements:

- A systematic survey of the organisation to determine the nature, causes and extent of problems perceived by individuals.

- A continuing commitment on the part of top management to provide counselling, advisory and assistance services, to problem employees on a no-blame and no-cost, totally confidential basis.

- An effective programme of promotion and publicity of the EAP within the organisation.

- A systematic education and training programme on the philosophy, goals and methods used within the EAP programme.

- A procedure for contact with the EAP and referral to counselling.

- An outline of problem assessment procedures, including issues of confidentiality, time scales, counsellor training and expertise and diagnosis of services.

- A protocol explaining the extent of short-term counselling, long-term treatment and assistance.

- An outline of how the EAP programme links with other services in the organisation and community.

- A procedure for follow-up and monitoring of employees subsequent to their use of the EAP service.

- A mechanism for the feedback of activities.

- A procedure to evaluate individual and organisational benefits.

These characteristics help to make EAPs distinct from other forms of workplace counselling.

A key issue in the operation of the EAP is the selection and placing of the EAP within the organisation. The wrong choice of the person to administer the programme may do more harm than good, and the programmes should be placed at the highest level within the organisation. If an external programme is used, the service provider must be able to demonstrate a high code of professional standards and ethics.

An EAP will provide the following benefits:

- Assist employees and their families in resolving personal problems that may have a negative influence on work performance.

- Provide managers/supervisors/unions with a professional resource for the resolution of performance problems caused by employees' personal or health problems.

- Manage and improve the quality of health care of employees and the company.

- Develop prevention activities for employee health care.

The type of EAP chosen will depend on many factors, including size of organisation, structure, culture and resources available. Indeed, in many large organisations, a pilot programme is carried out initially. Costs and benefits can then be evaluated prior to enlargement and extension.

Whatever type of programme is chosen, the investment will be considerable, particularly in the early stages where education and promotion will be expensive. Therefore, it is important for management to be able to evaluate the ratio of costs to benefits. There are three dimensions to this:

Direct Financial

Various statistics show the cost/benefit ratio ranges from 2:1 to an outstanding 13:1; the higher figure is said by Stern (1990) to be achievable where employees are referred by supervisors as a direct result of poor performance.

One of the most comprehensive and visible studies carried out on EAPs, according to Stern, is that which was carried out on behalf of MacDonnell Douglas Corp. In this case, the EAP administrator was told in 1985 that he could enlarge the programme, provided that he could show "a demonstrated return on investment". As a result, a study was designed and conducted by an outside consulting group and was completed in 1988. The study focused solely on money saved in reduced health claims and lower absenteeism rates of EAP "graduates". The results showed that the company saved at least four dollars for every dollar spent, representing estimated total savings of $5.1 million from an investment of $1.3 million over a three-year period. This return is considered conservative in that it did not include savings resulting from lower labour replacement costs as a result of reduced employee turnover (Stern, 1990). A study by Gaela et al. (1982) found that 85 per cent of poor performers were judged to be no longer "poor" after the EAP. The rate of improvement for all participants was 86 per cent. There was a significant decrease in the number of accidents in which these individuals were involved. Absenteeism also decreased, as did visits to the medical department. In short, at least for this sample of employees, the EAP was a great success.

Indirect Financial Benefits

Along with lower staff replacement costs, indirect financial benefits would also include management time costs. Steddon (1990) states that some managers spent around 65 per cent of their time trying to deal with people problems instead of running the business. **Figure 21.10** presents a sample EAP policy.

Figure 21.10: A Sample EAP Policy

Policy and Procedure

Policy Statement: An organisation shall adopt a written policy statement on alcoholism and other problems covered by the EAP. The chief executive and, where appropriate, union head will sign this and it will reflect management and labour attitudes and agreements as to the Programme's objectives. The policy should state that alcoholism is a disease responsible to treatment and rehabilitation and specifying the responsibilities of management, union representatives, and employees as they related to the Programme. The EAP need not in any way alter management responsibility or authority or union prerogatives. Participation in the EAP will not affect future employment or career advancement, nor will participation protect the employee from disciplinary action for continued substandard job performance or rule infractions.

Confidentiality: Written rules will be established specifying how records are to be maintained, for what length of time, who will have access to them, which information will be released to whom, and under what conditions, and what use, if any, can be made of records for research, evaluation and reports. Client records maintained by an EAP should never become part of the personnel file.

Procedures for Individuals referred by Management and/or Union Representatives: Each EAP will prepare written procedures for action initiated by management and/or union representatives. This will provide an assessment by EAP staff, evaluation by professionals, referral for treatment, feedback to and from the referral source and follow-up at least monthly for a minimum of one year.

Procedures for Voluntary use of the Programme by Employees/Family Members: Procedures for individuals who refer themselves will provide for assessment by EAP staff, evaluation by profes-

---

sionals, referrals for treatment and follow-up. The programme will initiate no contact with management concerning individuals who refer themselves, consistent with confidentiality regulations.

Administrative Functions

Organisational Position of the EAP: Operation of, or responsibility for, the EAP should be positioned at an organisational level high enough to insure the involvement of senior management and/or union leadership in sustaining the Programme.

Physical Location of the EAP: The physical location of the EAP should facilitate easy access while ensuring confidentiality.

Record Keeping System: Each EAP will have a record keeping system carefully designed to protect the identity of the client, while facilitating case management and follow-up and providing ready access to statistical information.

Relation of the EAP to Medical and Disability Benefit Plans: There should be a review of medical and disability benefits to ensure that plans adequately cover appropriate diagnosis and treatment for alcohol, drug, and mental health problems. Where feasible, coverage should include outpatient and day treatment care. The EAP staff should be familiar with provision of the medical and disability benefit plans so that they can advise clients clearly as to the extent, nature and cost of the recommended treatment and reimbursement available.

Malpractice/Liability Insurance: The organisation should conduct a legal review of all aspects of the Programme. The purpose is to ensure that there should be adequate protection for all EAP staff and the organisation against possible malpractice/liability claims.

Qualifications of EAP Staff: The EAP staff should combine:

- Appropriate managerial and administrative experience.

- Skills in identifying problems, interviewing, motivating, referring client and, where appropriate, in counselling or related fields, as well as experience and expertise in dealing with alcohol-related problems.

Education and Training

Communicating EAP Services to Employees and their Families: It is important that employees and their families are informed about the organisation's EAP and that the services it offers are continually updated by various educational techniques, regarding its existence and availability. Information about the EAP should be made available to all new employees and their families.

Employees' Education: An organisation should have major commitment to ongoing education about alcohol and alcoholism. Additional efforts should be made to educate employees about other recognised problem areas.

Orientation of Management and Union Representatives: Management and union representatives should be thoroughly informed about their key role in utilising the EAP services. Orientation for management and union representatives should be updated regularly.

Resources

Resource File on Providers of Assistance: Each EAP should maintain current information about alcoholism treatment services and other resources. These include Alcoholics Anonymous (AA) Al-Anon, Alateen and other self-help groups, appropriate health care, community services and other professionals.

Evaluation

Programme Review and Evaluation: There should be periodic review of the programme to provide an objective evaluation of operation and performance.

Staff Performance Evaluation: There should be an annual evaluation review of EAP staff performance.

WORKPLACE COUNSELLING

Traditionally, counselling was narrowly viewed as a reactive device in response to specific employee problems. There is now an increased awareness of the value of counselling skills in a business context. It is advocated as a positive intervention that helps organisations and employees to overcome problems and difficult situations and it promotes the emotional and physical well-being of the employees. Indeed, research shows that employees often report improved mental and physical well-being in comparison to that experienced before the counselling intervention. Summerfield and Van Oudtshoorn (1995) suggest that counselling is firmly rooted in good management practices and should not be used merely as a device to overcome specific problems.

The increase in the provision of counselling services in Irish companies may be linked to changes in management style and the way work is organised. In modern organisations, empowered team-oriented structures may benefit from the introduction of a counselling service that can promote a culture of continuous improvement by helping overcome learning blockages in order to realise development goals. There may be many motives for providing a counselling service; these can range from organisational self-interest, to a purely altruistic motivation that has the welfare of the employee in mind. Research by Highley and Cooper (1995) in the UK illustrates the rationale advanced by employers for the provision of a counselling service. The findings illustrate that the most frequently cited reasons are to provide support to staff members and to create a positive image of a caring employer. Helping employees adapt to organisational change and to cope with stress were also cited less frequently. The motives expressed by organisations introducing a counselling service were also economic, where the role of the counsellor is to maintain the employees' well-being so that absenteeism and turnover are controlled and do not adversely affect productivity.

Benefits of Workplace Counselling

It is intuitively appealing that both the organisation and employees benefit from the provision of counselling. However, there have been very few evaluations of the impact of workplace counselling. Sonnenstuhl and Trice (1986) suggest that this may be attributed to several factors, namely, the expense and time consuming nature and the issue of confidentiality. Organisations that provide workplace counselling put forward anecdotal evidence for the direct benefits they have experienced. These include:

- Enhanced work performance through employee well-being motivation and morale, which can foster commitment and loyalty to a firm.

- Enhanced work performance achieved through lower absenteeism rates, turnover, stress-related illnesses and accidents.

- Facilitates effective change management, fostering a culture of employee empowerment, continuous improvement and self-development.

- Conveys a positive image of the organisation as a caring firm.

- Indirect benefits may include the effective and efficient accomplishment of management functions, as employees' personal/social problems can distract a manager's attention from accomplishing the organisational objectives.

- Counselling has the potential to rehabilitate employees, allowing their work to contribute to the effectiveness of the organisation.

Approaches to Counselling

There are a number of approaches in which employers can provide counselling and related services. Employers may choose to set up a counselling service within the organisation, whereby qualified counsellors are employed by the organisation. Alternatively, counselling services can be contracted out to an external counselling specialist; this counselling agency acts as an intermediary between the organisation and the employees. There are advantages and disadvantages associated with both internal and external counselling and these vary depending on the context in which they are provided (Carroll and Walton, 1997). The greatest advantage of contracting out a counselling service is the perception of greater confidentiality by employees, which may result in a more open discussion and counselling session with the employee.

Some organisations, such as Intel, the ESB, Waterford Crystal and Hewlett Packard, provide an integrated model of internal and external counselling whereby management and HRM specialists may provide counselling services as well as working in partnership with external counsellors. There is controversy on what issues of counselling managers and human resource specialists should provide. Wells and Spinks (1997) suggest that the counselling that can be undertaken by managers should be confined to narrow bounds, related directly to work. They suggest that disciplinary counselling, grievance counselling and performance counselling is suitable/appropriate for a manager to tackle.

Figure 21.11: Advantages of Internal and External Counselling

Advantages of External Counselling	Advantages of Internal Counselling
• The counsellor is not immersed in organisational politics. • It can challenge the paradigm of the organisation. • A wide range of issues covered. • Individual's confidentiality may be secured. • Set up and development cost minimised. • Specialist expertise that could be lacking in the organisation. • The organisation is not responsible for malpractice of counsellors.	• The counsellor may have a greater appreciation of the culture, policies and procedures of the organisation. This may facilitate greater understanding of problems. • The counsellor is a visible face, an insider. • The counsellor has flexibility to adapt to clients' needs. • Greater control and accountability of the counselling programme. • The counselling service may have greater credibility. • The counsellor can provide a multiplicity of roles including trainer, welfare officer, home-visitor, information giver, personal adviser, organisational change agent, in addition to the traditional counselling role with individual clients.

Problems experienced by the employee may exceed the existing experience of managers and, in this situation, the employee should be given access to advice, information and support form another source.

There is an onus on management to monitor employee behaviour that may signal the need for counselling. Sidney and Phillips (1990) propose indicators for the provision of counselling:

• People not performing to their usual standard.

• Tardiness.

• Inability to communicate clearly.

- Inability to act as part of a team.

- Unusual or changed behaviour.

- Inability to take or make decisions.

- Change in personal circumstances.

- Change in work circumstances.

When to Use Counselling

There are many diverse issues encountered in present-day employment that could benefit from counselling. Problems arise both in a formal work context and also in a social sense. Problems can also be caused by the work organisation acting on the individual. Employees also experience problems that are principally non-work-related but that may have an impact on the employee's work performance. A number of these issues may affect employees at any one time and some work-related problems may exacerbate some non-work issues. The types of work and non-work issues that counselling may address are presented in **Figure 21.12**.

Figure 21.12: Types of Work and Non-Work Issues that Counselling may Address

Work-related Issues	Non-work-related Issues
<ul><li>Discipline.</li><li>Redundancy.</li><li>Stress.</li><li>Performance appraisal.</li><li>Grievance and disciplinary handling.</li><li>Relocation stress.</li><li>Change management.</li><li>Career advice.</li><li>Sexual harassment.</li><li>Retirement.</li></ul>	<ul><li>Marital and relationship problems.</li><li>Bereavement.</li><li>Suicide.</li><li>Disability or chronic sickness.</li><li>AIDS.</li><li>Mental health.</li><li>Substance abuse.</li><li>Alcohol abuse.</li></ul>

VISUAL DISPLAY UNITS AND HEALTH ISSUES

Poor ergonomic designs of VDUs and workstations have often led to occupational health problems. Symptoms include mental and visual fatigue, headaches, musculo-skeletal problems, nervous conditions and a general increase in the levels of stress encountered by operators. However, these problems are not an inevitable result of the use of VDUs, but rather conditions caused by poor work organisation or job design. The key to avoiding these problems is the use of sound ergonomic principles in the design of workstations, and the proper organisation of work. The important points are presented in **Figure 21.13**.

VDUs and Specific Health Risks

VDUs have often been the mythical cause of serious health problems. However, there is no evidence of any serious health risks from VDUs when they are used properly. Nonetheless, certain problems can arise if the ergonomic guidelines listed above are not followed. The remainder of this section examines specific areas of concern in respect of VDUs.

Figure 21.13: Ergonomic Principles in the Design of Work Stations

Work Station Equipment

- Display screen characters — well-defined, clearly-formed, adequate size and spacing.
- Image — stable, no flickering / instability.
- Adjustable brightness and contrast.
- Screen tilt.
- Adjustable base for screen (e.g. table).
- Screen free of reflective glare.
- Keyboard separate and tiltable.
- Space in front of keyboard for wrists during rests in typing.
- Matt surface on keyboard to avoid glare.
- Appropriate key arrangement.
- Clear symbols on keys.
- Work desk sufficiently large, made from low-reflecting material.

- Flexible arrangement of all equipment on desk made possible.
- Adjustable document holder.
- Work chair — height adjustable seat and back adjustable in both height and tilt.
- Footrest if desired.

Work Station Environment

- Sufficient space to adjust and vary posture.
- Lighting — satisfactory lighting, appropriate contrast.
- Reflections and glare removed by suitable systems of adjustable coverings.
- Noise — avoid distractions, speech undisturbed.
- Heat — excess heat from work station causing discomfort.
- Radiation — to be reduced to negligible levels with the exception of the visible part of the electromagnetic spectrum.
- Adequate level of humidity.

The Interface

- Software suitable for task.
- Easy to use and adaptable to the user's level of knowledge/experience; no quantitative or qualitative checking facility may be used without the knowledge of users.
- Such systems must provide feedback to users.
- Principles of software ergonomics to be applied.

Work Organisation

- A range of VDU activities should be provided where possible to prevent boredom (which can give rise to stress or fatigue).
- Work breaks should be designed to allow alteration of VDU activities to integrate non-VDU work.
- Rest pauses are essential in continuous VDU work and should be taken before the onset of fatigue and not as a recuperative period. Short frequent pauses seem more effective than occasional longer ones in reducing stress and fatigue.

Visual Fatigue

There is no solid evidence to suggest that VDUs damage sight. Although the short-term effects of eye strain may be observed among some employees, this is often the result of poor ergonomics, or an existing eye condition. Often the cause is muscle imbalance between the eyes, or simply the deterioration of eyesight due to ageing. Pheasant (1991) reports that studies demonstrate a prevalence of eyestrain of between 70-90 per cent for employees who do repetitive data entry and other screen-based clerical tasks. Laubli and Grandjean (1984) found that the prevalence of eyestrain increases as a linear function of the number of hours the employee spends at the terminal each day.

Dermatitis and Skin Rashes

A very small number of individuals using VDUs suffer from facial dermatitis. Although the phenomenon is not fully understood, it appears that the main causal factors are static electricity produced by the VDU, and often the low-humidity atmosphere surrounding the workstation. Such problems can be easily minimised by the installation of anti-static materials and humidifiers. Knave et al. (1985) found a skin rash prevalence of 35 per cent in VDU users compared with 5 per cent in other employees. The areas most affected are the cheekbones, followed by the forehead, neck, arms and hands. In general, the symptoms are mild and disappear when the worker is away from the workplace. There is some disagreement about what causes skin rashes but it appears to be related to a combination of very low humidity and electrostatic effects.

Radiation

There is no evidence as yet to show that radiation emissions from VDUs are of a harmful level. Indeed, they are well below accepted international standards for continuous occupational exposure.

Epilepsy

VDUs do not affect epilepsy, so most people with epilepsy can safely carry out VDU work. However, certain individuals who suffer from rare photosensitive epilepsy can have attacks triggered by flickering light sources. These individuals usually discover their epilepsy during their early teens while watching TV, or being affected by strobe lights, long before they come into occupational contact with VDUs. Such individuals require medical advice before operating VDUs.

Musculo-skeletal Disorders

The evidence suggests that data entry employees experience a high incidence of work-related aches and pains in the neck, shoulders and upper arms. Hunting et al. (1981), for example, found that the prevalence of such pains was: neck 11 per cent, shoulder 15 per cent, right arm 15 per cent, right hand 6 per cent. In another study by Ryan and Bampton (1988), 44 per cent of employees reported that they experienced pain or discomfort in the neck and shoulders more than three times a week and 39 per cent in the forearms or hands. DeMattoe (1985) reports that the prevalence of lower back pain steadily increases with the number of hours per day of VDU use. English et al. (1989) report that VDU users and other keyboard users were statistically over-represented in a sample of patients attending orthopaedic clinics with musculo-skeletal disorders. The right forearm and hand of data entry workers were affected much more frequently than the left.

In terms of why these problems arise, the evidence suggests that the working posture of VDU users is generally more constrained than the postures of employees doing non-repetitive tasks at an office desk. This constrained posture may result from the visual demands of the task. Stammerjohn et al. (1981), for example, found that VDU users who reported musculo-skeletal problems were also more likely to report problems of glare and flicker from the screen, and other studies show that they are also more likely to have eyestrain and headaches than those who do not use VDUs.

Stress

Pheasant (1991) suggests that the fragmented nature of some VDU-based tasks makes them inherently more stressful than other types of work. Grandjean (1987) concluded that while VDU users as a whole are no more stressed than other employees, VDU operators engaged in certain fragmented repetitive tasks show clear evidence of raised levels of stress. They were more likely to report lower levels of job satisfaction, negative mood states and problems such as sleep disturbances and gastrointestinal problems.

VDUs and Pregnancy

This is an area of much contention and concern. The possibility that the use of VDU may harm the unborn child is one that has not been conclusively decided. In the United States in the mid-1980s, the question arose when a number of miscarriages and birth defects were reported in groups of women working with VDUs during their pregnancy. However, the empirical evidence does not support a relationship. McDonald et al. (1986) found no significant difference in the reported frequency of miscarriages between women who did, and those who did not, work with VDUs, and Ericson and Kallen (1986) found no association between adverse pregnancy outcomes, such as birth defects, low birth weights, etc. and exposure to VDUs. In contrast, Goldhaber et al. (1988) found a significantly increased incidence of miscarriage in women who reported using VDUs for more than 20 hours per week during the first three months of pregnancy. This study has raised the possibility of a connection that there is a link between miscarriage and heavy VDU use during early pregnancy, and there is much speculation as to why this might be the case. The range of explanations focuses on stress, the length of time sitting in fixed positions and the effects of radiation on the body.

VIOLENCE AND BULLYING AT WORK

Violence has infiltrated all aspects of life: home, community, school and work. The workplace appears to be no safe haven from the threat or reality of violence, and research suggests that both the frequency and severity of work-related violence are increasing. Workplace violence, often perpetrated by disgruntled employees, has reached epidemic proportions. Estimates world-wide indicate that more than 1.90 million violent workplace crimes occur each year with half of these infractions caused by employees or former employees. About 10 per cent of these violent workplace crimes involve offenders armed with handguns. Criminologists call the trend in workplace homicide the fastest growing form of murder in America at present.

There is clear evidence of an increase in violence and bullying in the workplace in Ireland. In 1995, six per cent of all reported accidents in Irish workplaces were due to violence. It is estimated that up to five times as many incidents of violent crime occur as are reported (Hough and Mayhew, 1983). The Health and Safety Authority now requires that employers address this issue in safety statements.

Defining Violence at Work

The Health and Safety Authority defines violence at work as situations where individuals are verbally abused, threatened or assaulted in circumstances relating to their work. The European Commission, on the other hand, has defined violence at work as:

> ... incidents where persons are abused, threatened or assaulted in circumstances relating to their work, involving an implicit or explicit challenge to their safety, well-being or health.

There is evidence that employers may perceive violence differently. Research evidence suggests that many employers regard only physical attack with a weapon as constituting violence, but the experts agree that violence at work does not involve only physical attacks but also includes threats of attack or plain abuse.

Violence can occur at many levels within the organisation. **Figure 21.14** presents a conceptualisation of violence (Burroughs and Jones, 1995).

Although no method exists that can perfectly predict a violent employee, the research makes it possible to construct a profile of the typical perpetrator. While violent employees may not have all of the profile characteristics, most have a majority of them (Burroughs and Jones, 1995) — see **Figure 21.15**.

Figure 21.14: Levels of Workplace Violence

Moderately Injurious	Highly Injurious
• Property damage, vandalism. • Sabotage. • Pushing, fistfights. • Major violations of company policy. • Frequent arguments with customers, co-workers or supervisors. • Theft.	• Physical attacks and assaults. • Psychological trauma. • Anger-related accidents. • Rape. • Arson. • Murder.

Figure 21.15: Primary and Secondary Characteristics of the Perpetrator

Primary Characteristics	Secondary Characteristics
• White middle-aged male. • Holds a white- or blue-collar position, possibly as department head, manager or supervisor. • History of violence towards others. • Abuses illicit drugs. • Weapon owner and/or served in the military. • Extremely withdrawn, a "loner". • Few interests outside of work. • Constantly disgruntled, a 'troublemaker'. • Perceives unfairness, injustice, or malice in others.	• Overreacts to corporate changes. • Suffers form interpersonal conflict. • Recently fired or laid off, or perceives soon will be. • Argumentative/uncooperative. • Extremist opinions and attitudes. • Makes sexual comments or threats of physical assault. • Disobeys company policies and procedures/has difficulty accepting authority. • May sabotage equipment and/or property. • Steals.

Note: Most individuals prone to violence will possess a majority of these traits.

The Causes of Violence

Three sets of variables appear to be important in terms of explaining the occurrence of violence.

The Attacker

Four characteristics of the attacker appear to be important:

- **Personality**: History of violence/aggressive personality. Some aggressive personalities attribute aggressive behaviour to others even when there was no such intent. The attacker often comes to speedy conclusions and selectively recalls any behaviour that could possibly be interpreted as non-friendly or aggressive. Confused mental states/psychiatric illness.

- **Alcohol and drugs**: Alcohol is a factor in many assaults, e.g. casualty departments, discos and public transport.

- **Violent expectations**: Sometimes members of the public will approach situations prepared for confrontation. Disputes over housing, social security or finance may result in attackers using violence to intimidate or vent their frustrations.

- **Immaturity**: Younger people may be less restrained in their behaviour, especially when gathered in groups.

The Victim

It is argued that the victim may be able to influence the occurrence of violent behaviour. By being sensitive to changes in the potential assailant's body language, they may be able to avert confrontation.

The Work Environment

Some dimensions of the work environment appear to be important:

- **Lone workers**: Isolation from colleagues may put employees at increased risk and make them more vulnerable to violence.

- **Job location**: This can affect an employee's risk of becoming a victim of assault, as certain areas may have higher rates of violent crime. Employees who are mobile should be aware of locations that have a history of violent incidents. Known high-risk areas should be identified to employees.

- **Cash**: Handling cash means that robbery may be a possibility, even if only small amounts are handled. The local crime prevention officer of the Gardaí is readily available to provide advice to help reduce this risk.

- **Waiting**: Employees who provide a public service often deal with persons who have been waiting in a queue for some time, with rising frustration.

- **Time**: There are certain times of the day that are more dangerous than others, such as after pubs close or when opening or closing times of premises in which cash is kept. **Table 21.6** presents an analysis of employees most at risk.

Table 21.6: Employees Most at Risk of Violence

Handling money or valuables	• Cashiers. • Delivery staff. • Transport workers. • Bank and post office staff. • Commissionaires. • Security staff. • Shop assistants.
Providing care, advice or training	• Nurses. • Ambulance staff. • Social workers. • Teachers. • Housing Office staff.
Carrying out inspection or enforcement duties	• Traffic wardens. • Ticket inspectors. • Park keepers.
Working with mentally disturbed, drunk or potentially violent people	• Prison Officers. • Landlords. • Mental health workers.
Working alone	• Home visitors. • Taxi drivers. • Domestic repair workers.

Violence Prevention Strategies

Taking specific actions to prevent workplace violence can create a security-conscious organisational culture, thereby potentially reducing a company's exposure to violent employee crime. Prevention strategies may involve screening potential employees, communicating the company's commitment to non-violence through policies and procedures, training and educating supervisors and employees, employee assistance programmes, building a threat management team, and implementing specific security measures.

Redeployment Screening

Organisations can reduce the potential for violent accidents and negligent hiring claims by using comprehensive pre-employment screening procedures. Such procedures can usually detect service-oriented employees with strong interpersonal skills, as opposed to excessively violent and aggressive workers. Scientifically-based paper-and-pencil tests can serve as a baseline assessment for measuring future changes in an employee's behaviour. To obtain credible information about a high-risk applicant, a valid measure of violent potential that complies with professional guidelines should be chosen. One such test, the Personnel Selection Inventory (PSI), measures the likelihood that an applicant is not prone to abusive, argumentative, or hostile workplace behaviour. Research shows that well-validated instruments like the PSI can detect applicants who possess a history of violent behaviour who, once hired, may become counterproductive employees.

The ideal pre-employment screening programme will combine testing with employment verification (if there's a gap in work history, find out why) reference checks, criminal record checks, drug testing, and structured interviews. Interviewers should be educated to ask questions that may elicit responses indicating a candidate's likelihood for future violent outbursts. It is useful to design a standard assessment form to ensure candidates are compared consistently.

Policies and Procedures

By sending a strong message about the company's commitment to workplace safety, employees will feel more secure about reporting statements or behaviours that they perceive as threatening. One way to encourage such reports is to require employees to read and sign a "Zero Tolerance for Violence Policy", prohibiting the use of weapons, harassment, and verbal or physical threats on the job. Under this policy, employees will feel obligated to notify the human resource or security department regarding threats or violent encounters.

Some companies offer a confidential hot-line through which reports can be made. A zero tolerance policy will be effective only if the HR or security departments have the reputation for promptly handling matters seriously and with concern for all employees involved. As part of this policy, security procedures (e.g. visitors should wear ID badges) and planned escape routes should be identified, and emergency phone numbers should be published. Employees can refer to these important policies and procedures to know exactly what is expected of them.

Training and Education

Most employees do not become violent without displaying some early warning signs or symptoms. Therefore, employees and supervisors should learn to recognise and respond to highly stressed individuals and violent incidents and use non-confrontational response techniques to defuse potential problems. Supervisors must learn to recognise workers who display signs of extreme stress and whose work deteriorates significantly. Employees who begin to display irresponsible and inappropriate behaviours such as chronic absenteeism and lateness, grievances and complaints, and overt anger and resentment also should be monitored.

Management can help ease a frustrating work environment by giving employees a mechanism to voice their grievances without fear of reprisal. When possible, managers should take action to resolve the complaints. Establishing trust, co-operation, creativity, and internal teamwork will encourage mutual respect and allow for the development of team problem-solving skills. Basic interpersonal skills such as listening, giving positive encouragement, and learning to be prepared for change should be part of any programme.

Employee Assistance Programmes (EAPs) provide specific programmes designed to help employee deal with personal problems. EAPs are a resource that allow intervention with violent employees, but they are only one way in which human resource departments can help. Training and education programmes should incorporate stress management, active coping techniques, and drug abuse awareness. Employers can make educational materials available to employees and their families to help them identify and handle harassment, domestic abuse, substance abuse, and other emotional problems. Companies can even provide voluntary self-defence training and classes in personal safety and security to reach employees how to reduce their chances of being victimised.

Companies where violence has previously occurred must be especially aware of situations that could lead to employee anger or frustration, because that workplace is already perceived by employees as unsafe. Workplace violence should be an ongoing topic of company meetings, workshops, newsletters and new-hire orientation classes.

Termination of Employees

Handling layoffs and terminations is a highly sensitive area that requires special training because certain employees may become hostile after dismissal. A person charged with this responsibility needs to remain neutral when disciplining or terminating employees. In return, employees should have the opportunity to submit written grievances or appeals about their termination or any other pertinent issues. Consideration should be made as to how the dismissal is conducted. Some managers recommend using only one room during the process. The affected individual should remain in the room while meeting with the manager, HR representative, and outplacement counsellor. This prevents the person from moving around the building and possibly causing a scene.

After a dismissal, confidential psychological counselling should be offered as well as outplacement services such as vocational counselling and job search or résumé-writing assistance. It is critical that key, identification badges, and access cards are collected.

Threat Management Teams

The literature suggests that in addition to formal policies and procedures, companies need to form a threat management team. A threat management team is responsible for translating workplace violence policies into action, with particular emphasis on prevention. Typically this team is staffed with individuals from both inside and outside the company, including an HR professional, psychologist, lawyer, security guard, and a key front–line manager who is capable of supervising a tense situation. A strong negotiator can also be part of the team.

The first task of the team is to conduct an initial risk assessment to determine whether a threat is serious enough to justify deployment of the team and its resources. Risk assessment involves collecting personnel data to identify past and present problems with the employee posing the threat. Based on such assessment, the team then develops an initial action plan. This phase involves mobilising the resources needed to intervene in the situation and planning additional steps.

The team should outline the scope of the activities and operations that it will cover and set criteria for convening and reporting incidents to law enforcement and the media. Before extreme violence hits, the team must establish a relationship with local police and designate a spokesperson to deal with press reports. A formal procedure for investigating threats must also be defined. Some companies bring in an expert to evaluate the threat objectively and to guide action after the investigation.

Threat management teams also plan escape routes, co-ordinate medical and psychological care of injured victims, train employees to administer emergency aid to victims, and organise transportation for employees who are in no condition to drive following an incident. Employees and their families must be kept informed during the crisis and immediately thereafter. Therefore, a team member will be responsible for telephoning families to provide updates of victims' conditions, answer payroll or use of sick leave questions, and other necessary matters. Primary and refresher training criteria should be set for all team members. It is recommended that a company develop crisis scenarios against which the threat management team can practice its response. The team can also prepare news releases and potential question-and-answer lists before a crisis occurs.

Security

Workplace violence can be prevented in some cases by employing security measures. Often these are used to protect employees and employers from violent people outside the organisation (e.g. former employees). In this area, much can be accomplished at little cost. For example, a threat management team member can arrange regular police check-ups and rearrange offices and furniture to provide escape routes that are accessible to employees who, because of their positions, may be obvious targets of disgruntled persons. Limited and controlled access, security awareness briefings, surveillance cameras, and silent alarms can all help reduce employee vulnerability. Making high-risk areas visible to more people and installing good external lighting are two more strategies. In short, the company should make it difficult for anyone to engage in violence.

Some Work Considerations

Porteous (1997) argues that responses to violence need to be informed with a careful collection of facts and their systematic analyses. It is generally accepted that most violence arises through an escalation process. Much violence can therefore be avoided if staff are well-trained in recognising the warning signs.

The first step in establishing a preventative policy is to find out whether there is a problem. Four ways to find out suggest themselves:

1. Consider whether the organisation's operations or even some of them are in the "most at risk" category.

2. Look at the organisation's accident records and see which were the results of violence.

3. Record all incidents.

4. Classify these incidents.

The results of such an analysis should reveal if there is a problem, and, if there is, whether it is global within the organisation or manifests itself in certain areas of activity. Cox (1987) described three levels of intervention to tackle the problem:

- Firstly, prevention should deal with the problem by organisation and work design or through staff training. It should seek to remove or reduce exposure to potentially violent situations and/or their detrimental effects on staff.

- Secondly, timely reaction should deal with the problems as they arise, ensuring a rapid and appropriate response.

- Third, rehabilitation should deal with the aftermath of violence through enhanced staff support to help employees cope with and recover from incidents.

Wood (1996) emphasises training "staff to recognise a situation that might give rise to violence". Such situations are not limited to availability of cash or drugs. People's tempers become frayed when they are kept waiting, when queues for services are not organised in an orderly manner. Nurses and social workers who call to see patient/clients in their homes can be at risk, because often the patient/client has a grudge against authority and attacks the visitor as a representative of that authority.

Training, it is suggested, requires that the potential victim of violence should be able to recognise that an attack might occur, by understanding body language and by being able to defuse a situation. Self-defence training might be offered.

Security measures should be taken. Car parks and isolated areas should be well lit. Where cash or drugs are carried, access should be made difficult. Home visitors should carry personal alarms. **Figure 21.16** presents some considerations for employers.

Figure 21.16: Violence at Work — Organisational Considerations

- **Risk Assessment**: This is fundamental to establishing the threat of violence and to identifying appropriate managerial responses. The complex interplay between the nature of the work, the characteristics of the work situation, the work environment itself and the personal characteristics of staff contribute to defining the violence risk.

- **The Nature of Work**: There is evidence that this contributes to the risk of violence. Public sector and service sector organisations have a higher violence risk. Local authority employees, advisers to job seekers, social welfare officers, teachers, nurses, and others who provide public services come into contact with the public in sometimes frustrating and confrontational situations. The combination of frustration, anger and an inability of the employee to meet 'customer demands' can lead to loss of temper (customer rage) and increase the risk of violence. Jobs that involve cash handling also carry higher risk and bank staff, post office staff and retail sales staff, are at risk from theft and associated violence.

- **The Work Situation Itself**: Characteristics of the work represent a major contribution to the likelihood of violence. Occupations where staff work alone, such as nurses, social workers and bus and taxi drivers, present particular challenges and need special consideration. Employees who work outside normal hours may be at greater risk and work systems should ensure that staff are not permitted to work without adequate security arrangements.

- **The Work Environment**: Characteristics of both the internal and external work environment contribute to the risk of violence. The internal environment needs to be assessed for the availability of 'weapons', such as items of equipment, and the need for protective devices such as screens and alarms. The geographical location of the employer's premises and the incidence of local crime influence the external environment. Therefore, systems for the safety of employees entering and leaving the building may be required.

- **The Personal Characteristics of the Individual**: The evidence suggests that some employees are better equipped to deal with confrontational and potentially violent situations, but all staff should be trained to recognise potentially difficult situations and to respond accordingly. A survey of interactions between staff and customers can indicate triggers of frustration and anger and causes of violent exchanges. An analysis of these incidents informs managerial action, which may include changes in systems of work, the reduction of waiting time or the provision of a more amenable customer environment. Employees who are adequately trained to assess and control violent situations are less likely to be the victims of attack than employees who are unable to manage emotional exchanges, or cannot provide relevant information, or who lack skills and confidence in difficult encounters with customers.

Bullying in the Workplace

Bullying represents another dimension of violence in the workplace and it is on the increase. An MSF survey conducted in Ireland and the UK in 1994 revealed the following (Costigan, 1998):

- 30 per cent of respondents thought bullying to be a significant problem.

- 72 per cent of respondents reported that their employer had no policy for dealing with bullying.

- Organisations most susceptible to bullying included firms where workers had high workloads, where a macho competitive culture existed, where there is rapid change and uncertainty and where personnel management is poorly developed.

A later study in 1997 (Costigan, 1998) by the Irish Nurses Organisation (INO) revealed that:

- More than 9 of 10 nurses reported having been victims of bullying.

- Three in 10 were bullied by nurses of the same grade and 23 per cent said a member of the medical team was their harasser. Others who experienced bullying included: ward sisters, theatre sisters, unit nursing officers, assistant matrons and directors of nursing.

- Approximately 3 per cent of respondents were subjected to threatening behaviour and actual assaults also took place.

- The most common form of bullying (87 per cent) was verbal. An identical number reported incidents of psychological bullying.

A recent survey undertaken into the extent and nature of bullying in the civil service and semi-state sector reported in the *Revenue Group Journal* (Foran, 1999) revealed the following statistics (in the survey, bullying was defined into three areas: physical, verbal and psychological):

- 69 per cent of respondents indicated that bullying occurs within their offices.

- 81 per cent indicated that they had personally been bullied, while 19 per cent indicated they were aware of others being bullied.

- The vast majority of bullying reported was of a psychological nature and accounted for 57 per cent. Verbal accounted for 40 per cent and physical accounted for 3 per cent.

- Just under half of the people who were bullied reported the incident(s).

- Of those who did report the incident(s), 70 per cent indicated that they were not resolved.

- Colleagues (22 per cent), immediate supervisors (23 per cent), middle management (44 per cent) and higher management (11 per cent) bullied individuals.

- Bullying was more widespread in the civil service (85 per cent) than in the semi-state sector (15 per cent).

In 1998 Dr. Mona O'Moore of the Anti-Bullying Centre, Trinity College Dublin, was commissioned to undertake a detailed study of the extent, nature and effects of workplace bullying in schools and colleges throughout Ireland. Her findings were:

- 31 per cent of TUI members are bullied occasionally, 12 per cent are bullied often, 33 per cent witnessed bullying at work in the past 12 months and 23 per cent had been bullied over the past 12 months.

- With regard to the effects of bullying, the following were reported: disturbed sleep, 60 per cent; loss of confidence, 56 per cent; feeling helpless, 54 per cent; headaches/migraine, 36 per cent; emotionally drained, 34 per cent; suicidal, 5 per cent.

- Reasons for bullying as cited by respondents: arrogance, 92 per cent; envy, 88 per cent; poor management style, 87 per cent; to force victim out, 73 per cent; for fun, 50 per cent.

- Types of bullying included: lack of acknowledgement of good work done, 70 per cent; shouting and obscenities, 60 per cent; withholding of information, 58 per cent; constant work overload, 33 per cent; isolated/socially excluded, 30 per cent; physical abuse, 4 per cent.

The Health and Safety Authority (2001) published a major report on the nature of workplace bullying in Ireland. **Table 21.7** presents a summary of the main findings.

Table 21.7: The Nature of Workplace Bullying in Ireland

Bullying incidence levels: Of the workforce involved in the task force study 7% of employees record themselves as being victims of bullying in the six months prior to the survey. Women are 1.8 times more likely to be bullied than men. Employees are 3.6 times more likely to be bullied than the self-employed.
Age: There is no definitive evidence emerging from the study that bullying levels are correlated with age but the survey did find that the highest bullying rates exists among the 26-35 and 36-45 year olds. The higher levels appear to decrease at the age of 46.
Educational attainment: The surveys tested educational attainment as a predictor of the levels of bullying recording. It was found that educational attainment is positively related to the levels of bullying recorded. This suggests that the level of self-recorded bullying increases with the increased level of education achieved. The relationship is most apparent in the male employee group, although not as clearly defined among female employees. The findings suggest that compared to men who left school at the junior/intermediate certificate level, men who attained a third level qualification were 55% more likely to be the recipients of bullying in the workplace. Women with a third level qualification recorded a 40% greater chance of being bullied.
Social class: There was no evidence to suggest that bullying varied over social groups.
Industrial sector and public/private sectors: The survey revealed that the sectors that recorded the highest levels of bullying were the Public Administration/Defence (14%), Education (12%) and Health/Social Work (10%). The lowest levels recorded were in the Construction, Retail/Wholesale and Transport and Communications sectors. The Agriculture sector was extremely low. It was suggested that the levels recorded in these sectors may be indicative of the educational background of the people working in these sectors. Risk of bullying was strongly linked to high levels of educational attainment; it was also linked to gender.
Organisation size: Bullying is indeed linked to the size of the organisation.
Nature of employment tenure: The incidence of bullying is linked to the nature of the employment tenure of the employees. Employees in permanent employment situations recorded the lowest levels of bullying. The level increased for those employed on a temporary/contract basis and was higher again for those in casual work.
Corporate/managerial changes: The incidence of bullying is strongly related to organisational, structural and personnel changes within organisations. There was a higher level of bullying reported among organisations where a change in management or manager had taken place. A change in technology used had a less apparent effect on the rate of bullying. The risk of bullying is greater among males than females.

Frequency of bullying: The frequency rates of bullying do not show a lot of disparity between males and females. Of the respondents in this study, 39% said they experienced bullying only occasionally, 22% said it occurred several times each month, 19% said it happened several times each week and the remaining 20% said it happened almost every day.
Nature of bullying: The most frequently experienced form of bullying was verbal abuse/insults: 81% of respondents admitted to being victims of verbal abuse/insults; 35% of respondents who experienced bullying were victims of exclusion; 3.3% were victims of sexual harassment; 1.8% experienced physical abuse.
The perpetrators of bullying: The respondents who were victims of bullying recorded the perpetrator of bullying as: 81% of perpetrators were from a single type within the workplace; 45% bullied reported that a single supervisor/manager was the perpetrator; 43% bullied reported that a single colleague was the perpetrator.
Individual victim or as a group of victims: 56% recorded that the bullying was targeting a larger group of employees; 44% felt that it was individual victimisation.
Responses to bullying: Victimised employees' responses suggest that informal discussion of the bullying was more likely than formal workplace discussions. Victims of bullying were most likely to discuss the bullying with family (67%), a friend (71%), or a work colleague (77%). Only 51% recorded that they spoke with a supervisor or manager at work. Only 10-15% recorded that they used the organisational processes of personnel, union, staff or grievance procedures. Females were more likely to discuss the problem with family or friends than males. 11% admitted that they had quit their work after being the victim of bullying and 14% considered leaving the workplace entirely.
Staff-management relationships: A large percentage of the respondents who reported that they had experienced bullying considered the relationship between themselves and their manager to be a negative one. This trend applied to both men and women.
Levels of stress and sense of control over life: There was a large difference in stress levels recorded between those who were bullied and those who were not. The levels of stress experienced by the victims of bullying were far more likely to experience stress that there counterparts who were not bullied. Those employees who were victims of bullying were far more likely to feel that they could no longer achieve control over their own future compared to other employees. This trend applied equally to both men and women.

Source: The Health and Safety Authority (2001), *Dignity at Work: The Challenge of Workplace Bullying.* Report of the Task Force on the Prevention of Workplace Bullying.

Defining Bullying

The Collins English Dictionary defines a bully as one who "hurts, persecutes or intimidates weaker people". Bullying then is a form of harassment, a misuse of power to persistently criticise, humiliate and undermine an individual's ability (Spiers, 1996). The

Health and Safety Authority (HSA) defines bullying in the workforce as repeated verbal, psychological or physical aggression conducted by one individual/group on another individual/group. The HSA makes the distinction between isolated incidents of such behaviour and incidents that are on-going. While it is inevitable that there will be personality clashes when a number of individuals come together, it is important to note that the resulting conflicts do not constitute bullying behaviour. It is equally important though not to assign a potential bullying situation to the common euphemism of personality clashes.

People generally tend to define bullying in terms of its manifestations rather than its precise meaning. According to Randall (1997), bullying is the "aggressive behaviour arising from the deliberate intent to cause physical or psychological distress to others". This definition comments on the intent to cause distress, but does not comment on frequency or repetition of the intent. Randall posits that aggressive behaviour does not have to be repeated to constitute bullying behaviour. More often than not it is the fear of repetition of aggressive behaviour that is important and not the frequency.

Costigan suggests that, in cases of bullying, individuals are persistently criticised, threatened, humiliated or ridiculed. She makes no mention of the intent to cause distress but rather focuses on the persistent exposure of victims to bullying behaviour. This is akin to Field's definition of bullying: "behaviour which consistently undermines another's confidence, reducing feelings of self-worth or self-esteem" (1996:51). Field states that one of the greatest challenges in recognising bullying behaviour is being able to differentiate between poor interpersonal skills and bullying (1996:47). It is important when trying to do so that the intent and regularity of the offensive behaviour is noted. Only by doing this is bullying behaviour detected. Field presents an expansive list of bullying behaviours. He believes that everyone will at some stage exhibit characteristics of bullying behaviour, but the bully will exhibit the behaviours continuously and relentlessly. Some of the methods used by bullies include:

• Refusal to be specific about criticisms.

- Removal of status and authority, especially in a devious manner.

- Being tasked with additional responsibility, but not being informed.

- Isolation, cold-shouldering, snubbing, blocking promotion, or showing favouritism.

- Threats of disciplinary action for minor incidents but refusal to discipline other staff for similar or more serious disruptive behaviour.

- Humiliation, especially being shouted at in front of others.

- Changing a person's job description without consultation and then imposing it without the right of reply.

- Limiting communication to memo, email or via a third party in lieu of speaking directly.

- Holding meetings which the purpose of, and attendance at, is significantly at variance with what you have been led to believe.

- Being difficult with respect to requests for time off, flexible working hours, etc.

- Talking about an individual, in their presence.

Essentially, bullying is a form of harassment and can best be described as any form of unwanted attention, be it physical, verbal or psychological, which seeks to make an individual feel intimidated, offended or isolated. Bullying behaviour towards an individual will result in that person's confidence and self-esteem being undermined (Costigan, 1998).

Characteristics of the Bully and the Victim

The Bully

The research on bullying constantly reiterated that bullies themselves have low self-confidence and self-esteem and, because of this, they fear that their inability to properly fulfil their work duties will be discovered. So they take steps to ensure this does not happen.

According to Field (1996, 4) bullies are "dead weights, who blame others for their mistakes". Individuals who bully often experience feelings of inadequacy and insecurity and these feelings are personified when confronted with someone who is more popular, efficient or better qualified than them. In effect, the aforementioned qualities remind the bully of the things they would like to be and are not. Costigan (1998, 40) identifies tendencies which bullies exhibit:

• Always need to be in control.

• Blame everyone but themselves.

• Make life difficult for those they dislike.

• Refuse to delegate because they believe no one else can be trusted.

• Never admit they are wrong.

• Appear charming to outsiders and superiors.

• Can be emotionally unbalanced and prone to bouts of ferocious anger.

In essence, bullies are very insecure people whose only means of feeling powerful is to issue threats or exert oppression over their victims. Why they feel it is necessary to abuse their power can, in some way, be related to childhood or early adult experiences that left them feeling powerless or which led them to believe that they are the centre of the universe.

Earlier work by Adams (1992) focused on early childhood experiences and how these affected an individual's ability to express or cope with anger. Worth mentioning in regard to a person's control over their anger is the difference between appropriate and inappropriate anger.

Where a parent's expression of anger is totally out of proportion to an incident, this can leave a child feeling frightened and with a sense of injustice. The anger they feel is taken inside themselves as the parent does not allow the child to express that anger. Subjected to this type of discipline on an ongoing basis, a child will develop feelings of frustration and powerlessness. This could later be manifested in the manner in which the adult expresses anger. The most obvious example is of someone "flying off the handle".

This link is further explored by Randall (1997:4) who defines bullying as "the aggressive behaviour arising from the deliberate intent to cause physical or psychological distress to others". By way of explanation of this type of behaviour, Randall puts forward the theory that bullies are not born but rather created through "complex social process and faulty learning" (1997:74). It is widely accepted that the behaviour of primary carers, e.g. parents, forms the model upon which a child's subsequent behaviour is determined. Thus, in terms of behaviour and attitudes, a child will take on the characteristics of parents and in turn, display this behaviour in subsequent relationships. Randall posits that bullies discover in childhood that aggressive/manipulative behaviour can achieve the desired result — for example, the attention of the parent. Thus encouraged, the bullies go on to adulthood using this type of behaviour to get their own way. For example, as a child, the bully may have tried in vain to form a good relationship with an authoritative type or remote parent. Alternatively, a child brought up in a violent home will have had to develop aggression as a form of self-defence. Being undermined or made to feel insignificant as a child, the bully goes on to adopt manipulative type behaviours in the belief that this is the only way in which they will be in control of a complex situation.

Costigan (1998:40) also acknowledges that patterns laid down in childhood have a profound effect on the way in which an individual interacts with others. She views bullies as individuals who feel a sense of power when they humiliate others and that this perverse sense of gratification most certainly stems from childhood experiences of being constantly criticised or being wrongly accused of something over which they had no control.

Costigan further argues that bullies may have psychopathic tendencies, i.e. an inability to realise the effect their actions have on others. Psychopathic bullies have a very strong sense of self-righteousness, and believe that their wishes should come first (Adams, 1992:80). This may stem from learned childhood behaviour where the child's needs were consistently put after those of an authoritarian parent. The child grows up with an incessant desire for their needs to be met. Once in a position of power, the, by now, bully threatens or intimidates others into conforming to his/her wishes.

The Victim

According to Costigan (1998), there are two primary reasons as to why certain individuals are targeted for bullying; being too conscientious about one's job or being some way vulnerable and thus an easy target for ridicule or threats. Costigan presents a profile with regard to both types of victim as follows:

Table 21.8: Types of Victims of Bullying

Conscientious Victim	Vulnerable Victim
• High achiever. • Efficient, organised and diligent. • Highly intelligent and knowledgeable. • Confident, out-spoken and possessing superior social skills. • Higher qualifications. • Over-enthusiastic about work. • Popular among colleagues. • Attractive and youthful. • Creative with natural flair.	• Different from most staff members with regard to age, marital status, social background, sexual orientation or physical characteristics, including disability. • Vulnerable due to recent bereavement, break-up of a relationship, maternity leave or prolonged sickness. • Poor social skills, timidity and shyness.

Field (1996), in his analysis of why certain people are targeted, gives a more insightful view. He focuses on the bullied person's qualities, and distinguishes between introvert victims and extrovert victims. Examples of these qualities are presented in the following table.

Table 21.9: The Qualities/ Characteristics of Bullies Persons

The Bullied Person: General Qualities	Variations	
	Introvert Type	*Extrovert Type*
Honest, trustworthy and reliable. Sensitive and always thinking of others, a strong sense of conscience. Good organiser, a giver, obliging and willing to please. Long-term thinker, likes to do a good job and likes to feel valued. Tolerant, modest and good-humoured.	Quiet, silent, pensive, studious, excellent memory, eye for detail, meticulous, strongly analytical, shrewd, observant.	Outgoing, gregarious, tends to lead the conversation, very strong sense of injustice, builds group rapport easily.

While the problem of being bullied may rest solely with the bully, there are some researchers who have sought to explore the theory that maybe in some instances, the victim, either passively or pro-vocatively, unwittingly attracts the unwanted attention of the bully. This paradigm is presented in the work of both Adams (1992) and Randall (1997). (Neither Costigan nor Field examines this perspective).

In order to appreciate why one person is bullied and not an-other, Adams (1992:96) points to the importance of understanding how "residues from one's past may be operating in the present". Adams posits that different relationships at work can only be under-stood when pitched against a re-creating of earlier, similar type re-lationships. If, for example, an individual was subjected to bullying as a child — whether by a parent or by peers — and this individual subsequently encounters a colleague or manager displaying similar traits to the bully, the response elicited from the victim can be pro-found. All the old childhood feelings of self-doubt, fear, anxiety, worthlessness and injustice resurface. In attempting to deal with the problem of bullying, the adult may revert to childhood mechanisms in trying to deal with their current aggressor. It may be that the victim's response will be to try to pacify the bully, or ignore the problem in the hope that it will "go away". This response however, is more likely to increase the likelihood of an attack, because the bully will feel that they "can get away with it". According to Adams, the unwillingness of a victim to confront an aggressor amounts to "collusion with the aggressor" (1992:102).

Randall (1997:89) further substantiates this theory. His viewpoint is that "what happens to them (the victim) at work is often no more than an extension of what happened to them in school or at home when they were children". Thus, a child subjected to anger or rejection by parents learns to be passive in order to avoid tension or further rejection. The child proceeds into adulthood, carrying with them this fear of reprimand or confrontation. Unfortunately, it is exactly this type of submissive behaviour that can attract attention from a bully.

Randall also discusses provocative victims (1997:94). These are individuals who, unconsciously, provoke anger in others. People who, for example, talk excessively and seem uninterested in others can be infuriating. This behaviour, according to Adams (1992, 105) may actually be a re-creation of an earlier relationship where, as a child, the victim tried in vain to seek attention so as to bolster their self-confidence. Alternatively, the provocative victim can elicit an aggressive response from others by their silence. Individuals who do not share their feelings or thoughts with colleagues may invoke in them a sense of rejection. This may lead to provocation of an individual, simply to get some sort of response.

Both these passive and provocative characteristics discussed by Randall and Adams were the focus of a study by Aquino et al. (1999). The study focused on victim characteristics rather than those of the perpetrator, in an attempt to understand why some people become targets for bullying. They termed this approach the victimology approach and identified predictors of victimisation based on an employee's level of negative affectivity and self-determination. In the study, negative affectivity (NA) is defined as "a high-order personality variable describing the extent to which a person experiences high levels of anger, hostility, fear and anxiety". The researchers offered two arguments regarding the effects of NA on the likelihood of victimisation:

- People with high NA actively provoke others to be aggressive towards them by reacting with hostility to perceived identified threats.

- People with high NA passively present themselves as potential targets because they exhibit characteristics such as insecurity, distress and anxiety, which make them appear weak and submissive.

Their findings concluded that NA was positively related to victimisation. This would appear to give weight to Randall's and Adams' proposition.

A second victim characteristic examined in the study, self-determination, was found to be indicative of the likelihood of being victimised. Self-determination to an "individual's internal perceived locus of causality". This refers to the extent to which an individual perceives they can exercise control over their environment. When people experience high levels of self-determination, they perceive they can exercise control over their environment and thus will be more assertive in defending themselves against harassment. People who are low in self-determination feel powerless and assume the role of the passive, anxious victim, thereby attracting the attention to potential aggressors. The findings showed that individuals with higher levels of self-determination were less likely to be victims of bullying.

Effects of Bullying on Individuals and the Organisation

On the Individual

A person who is exposed to repeated forms of bullying tactics will experience a range of effects: emotional, cognitive and physiological. The most serious effects documented in various readings are fear, anxiety and depression. Subjected to bullying on an ongoing basis, an individual will feel isolated and rejected. While colleagues may be aware that bullying is taking place they may avoid supporting the victim for fear of reprisal. At the extreme, prolonged periods of bullying can result in the individual becoming depressed and suicidal (Adams, 1998:62).

According to IBEC Guideline 20 (*Harassment/Bullying in the Workplace*) the following are symptoms experienced by victims of bullying:

Table 21.10: Symptoms Felt by Victims of Bullying

Physiological Symptoms	Psychological Symptoms
• Headaches.	• Depression.
• Nausea/butterflies in the stomach.	• Mood swings.
	• Acute anxiety.
• High blood pressure.	• Panic attacks.
• Loss of appetite.	• Crying.
• Fatigue.	• Loss of self-esteem.
• Sleeplessness.	

These symptoms are manifested in an individual's behaviour through withdrawn personality, irritated and distracted behaviour and an increased reliance on alcohol, cigarettes and drugs.

On the Organisation

A climate of fear and resentment is not conducive to a productive working environment. Organisations that choose to ignore hostility in the work environment over a protracted period will suffer reduced productivity and low employee morale. Thus, bullying will have a detrimental effect on the organisation as a whole. Individuals who are in a constant state of fear and anxiety do not perform to the best of their ability and the consequences for the organisation include increased absenteeism, high staff turnover and a tarnished corporate image. Employers should also remember that there are high costs associated with legal proceedings, should they choose to ignore the problem in the hope that it will sort itself out. A further cost, in the form of a social cost, includes difficulty in attracting new staff and loss of business.

Despite the lack of statistics to confirm in monetary terms the effects of bullying, both the HSA and the IPD draw attention to the potential loss that could be suffered by organisations. The effects of bullying on the organisation, emphasised by the HSA, are:

• Increased absenteeism.

- Low motivation.

- Reduced productivity.

- Reduced efficiency.

- Faulty decision-making.

- Poor industrial relations.

Similarly, the IPD warns organisations that to ignore bullying or intimidation in the workplace will reinforce the cycle, resulting in an unpleasant working environment. The consequences may include a lack of commitment on behalf of employees, low morale, feelings of tension and hostility leading to lower productivity and poor customer services (Costigan, 1998:75). With regard to absenteeism and lower productivity, research carried out at the University of Manchester Institute of Science and Technology has shown that in the UK, some 40 million working days are estimated to be lost each year because of bullying at work. This is more than 160 times the number of days lost through strikes (*Business and Finance*, April, 1996).

Costigan (1998:74) comments on a study by the Institute of Social Research at the University of Michigan, USA into the cause of reduced productivity. This study revealed that:

> ... managers and supervisors who promoted co-operative and supportive relationships at work, and who gave employees the opportunity for self-fulfilment, creativity and economic security, tended to achieve the highest productivity, lowest cost and highest levels of employee motivation.

This style of management is the antithesis of the style often used to threaten or coerce workers, namely boss management. This will be addressed in the following section.

Strategies to Address Bullying in the Workplace

Anti-Bullying Policy. It is essential that any organisation, regardless of its size or nature, has in place a policy identifying areas of the workplace where bullying behaviour has been a problem or is likely to be a problem. Such a policy should contain a clear definition of bullying and should convey that bullying is perceived as unacceptable behaviour and will be treated as a disciplinary offence. The policy should also set out the support, counselling and rehabilitation available for those being bullied and for those carrying out the bullying behaviour. In this way, bullies can avail of training to change their behaviour and thus prevent the cycle being perpetuated. The contents of such a policy should include:

- Commitment from the top down.

- Be draw up by both management and unions.

- Recognition that any type of bullying behaviour is an offence.

- Uniform application to employees, regardless of their status within the organisation.

- Assurance the individual(s) of confidentiality.

From any employee's perspective, it should be remembered that the absence of an anti-bullying policy would mean that an employer could be open to a successful claim, even when that employer has no knowledge of the harassment taking place. Similarly, the presence of a policy would be taken into account by third parties, e.g. Labour Court, to determine whether the employer had done everything to prevent the bullying arising.

As well as establishing/expanding an anti-bullying policy, IBEC recommend that employers should:

- Ensure the policy is circulated to all staff, and that it is included in the induction programme for new staff.

- Set standards of behaviour by treating all staff and customers with respect.

- Ensure that confidentiality is maintained. This will assure those employees who may be unforthcoming in making a complaint in the first place.

- Should provide an independent counselling service to help rebuild damaged confidence and self-esteem.

Figure 21.17 presents a sample policy on bullying and harassment in the workplace.

Figure 21.17: Sample Safety Policy in relation to Bullying and Harassment in the Workplace for Inclusion in the Safety Statement

---

The following are the responsibilities of the manager/ supervisor:

• Communicate to all staff that bullying or harassment by any member of the organisation regardless of status will not be tolerated.

• Identify any areas or locations in the workplace under your control where bullying or harassment have been a problem and prioritise for corrective action.

• All identified victims will be offered counselling.

• Bullies or harassers will be offered training to change their behaviour (if they are not to be dismissed)

• Ensure all managers, supervisors, and safety representatives under your control, are trained in how to recognise signs that a person is being bullied and the various forms of bullying.

• All staff members are to be provided with information on the various forms of bullying and on what is deemed unacceptable behaviour.

• Inform all staff under your control of the complaints procedure and on likely disciplinary action taken if a complaint is proved.

The following are the responsibilities of the organisation:

• Instigate corrective action in areas that have been prioritised (such action might include the use of special surveillance equipment, private investigators, etc.)

• Arrange the training of all managers, supervisors and safety representatives on how to recognise signs that a person is being bullied, and the various forms of bullying.

• All persons dealing with complaints are properly trained in such matters

• In general try to foster an anti-bullying culture in the workplace.

• Arrange for the provision of a counsellor for victims of bullying or harassment.

• Arrange for training of proven bullies to change their behaviour.

• Maintain statistics on the incidence and type of bullying.

The following are the responsibilities of all employees:

- Be aware of behaviour that is deemed unacceptable

- Make efforts to ensure that bullying and harassment is not occurring in the workplace.

- Where you personally observe incidents of bullying or harassment, ask the bully to desist from his/her actions and make a note of the incident.

- Advise the victim of the complaints procedures and offer any assistance in this regard.

- In general, try to foster an anti-bullying culture into the workplace.

Complaints Procedure

The organisation will usually have a special complaints procedure for dealing with bullying and harassment, that is outside the normal safety channels. The person who deals with such complaints must ensure that each complaint is dealt with in a fair and efficient manner and has appropriate independence and status to deal with allegations at every level in the organisation.

- Employees who are being bullied or harassed should, in the first instance, ask the instigator to desist or, if they feel unable to do this, they should ask a colleague to do it for them. A record of each incident should be noted.

- Should the bullying or harassment continue, a complaint should be made to the employee's immediate supervisor/manager or another supervisor.

- Alternatively, a specifically named individual will deal with any complaints against an individual in the strictest of confidence.

- Once any such complaint is revived, it will be investigated immediately and prompt feedback will be provided.

- Steps will be taken to ensure that any person making such a complaint is not victimised as a result of making such a complaint.

- All alleged bullies or harassers will be given ample and fair opportunity to defend themselves. If it is determined that the seriousness of the complaint will warrant a disciplinary procedure, a written statement from both the parties will be required.

- It is hoped that the majority of cases will be resolved amicably; however, where a complaint is proven, an individual will go through the standard company disciplinary procedures and receive a penalty ranging from a verbal warning up to and including dismissal for series offences of bullying and harassment.

It is unlikely that the safety representatives will get involved in dealing directly with incidents of bullying or harassment. However, they should be able to provide advice to employees in relating to the complaints procedure.

Management Practices

The motivations for bullying are so complex that it would be unrealistic to expect managers to completely eliminate harassment in the workplace. However, according to Randall (1997, 107), by displaying a commitment to anti-harassment policies and being aware of signs of bullying, management can endeavour to protect employees from hostility and harassment. In this regard, it is important that management encourage frank and open lines of communication. This cannot be achieved as long as there is a gulf between management and workers. This is not to say that there should be no lines of authority or no clear hierarchy. Instead, management should encourage team-work in an effort to promote a sense of unity among workers, thereby discouraging isolation of any one individual. If bullying does take place despite this approach, at least employees will be aware of management's commitment to deal with the situation and will not be intimidated or ashamed at the prospect of seeking help.

The importance of frank and open lines of communication emphasised by Randall was found to be a significant factor in deterring bullying in a study by Varian (1996). This study found that an authoritative way of setting conflicts, poor flow of information and poor possibilities to influence matters concerning one's job proved to be important characteristics of a work environment that promotes bullying.

In his review of management practices and the role they play in preventing or minimising bullying, Randall also highlighted the importance of managers appreciating that an employee's quality of work, and the environment in which they do it, is heavily associated with their sense of worth and fulfilment (1997, 108). To this end, negative changes in the psychological well-being of staff may well indicate that the worker is being subjected to harassment. It is essential in this regard that managers suitably equip themselves with the knowledge and skills to enable them to spot the warning signs and take a firm line against the bully. Quite often it is the case that managers are promoted on technical expertise and do not have any sound training in people skills, if any at all. This will be discussed later.

Employee Selection

Quite often individuals with anti-social personalities are selected simply on the basis of fulfilling some requisite technical requirement. No consideration is given to, or means of assessing, that person's ability to work within a team or to lead a team. This shortcoming of the selection process can be due to the interview panel being made up of a number of people (and sometimes people from outside the organisation) who may have no real interest in interpersonal relationships and their impact on employees' ability to work together harmoniously. To overcome this, Randall (1997) suggests the following:

- Multiple interviews so that several opinions on the applicant's ability to work with a team can be obtained.

- A thorough background check before interviews take place rather than making appointments 'subject to good references'.

- Possibly the use of psychological tests to determine the basic personality traits of the applicant. This practice can provide invaluable information but should not be weighted too heavily in the overlap with the selection process.

Giving greater consideration to the process of selecting a potential employee/manager may be more time-consuming but in the long run, be more cost-effective. This cost-effectiveness would transpire in lower absenteeism and thus greater productivity and also, the avoidance of employer liability should an employee be successful in a case of bullying.

Training for Managers in Human Resource and Related Areas

As mentioned earlier in this section under both management practices and employee selection, managers are usually promoted on the basis of expertise in a specific discipline, e.g. accounting, economics or science. Individuals can become leaders of sizeable teams, having no training in, or understanding of, group dynamics. Although efforts are made in management training, Costigan (1998, 91) reports that management courses tend to concentrate on areas such as finance and business environment subjects, with little emphasis on human resources management and entrepreneurial development. A later study in 1997 (*White Paper on Human Resources Development,* published by the Department of Enterprise and Employment), and also reported in Costigan, confirmed this lack of management training.

Costigan suggests the following in an effort to promote better employee-management relations so that bullying can be more easily detected and solutions are more readily available:

* Developing a policy of training for those in supervisory/ managerial positions in the theories and practices of HRM.

* Training in basic communication skills, conflict resolution, assertiveness skills and stress management.

* Training in people skills, which serve to highlight the importance of maintaining open, clear and honest communication with staff at all levels.

* Training in basic counselling skills.

As well as providing training for managers, Reach (1996) suggests that employees themselves evaluate the results of the training through regular appraisals. In this way, important feedback on the quality of the training and on deficits and problems can be obtained, thus allowing corrective action to be taken to improve the training.

Engaging supervisors/mangers in this type of training has a double benefit. First of all, it will obviously equip them with the necessary tools to deal with a bullying situation, which is the main objective of the training. More importantly though, undertaking training in the aforementioned areas may serve to highlight to managers/supervisors the consequences of their actions in the day-to-day performance of their duties. For example, it may well be the case that a manager/supervisor shows favouritism to certain employees or excludes others from activities. While this may not be entirely intentional, such behaviour over a period of time can result in an individual becoming distanced and isolated from other workers. This vulnerability may well be a contributory factor in a potential bullying situation.

CHAPTER ROUND-UP

- Within an HRM approach to health and safety, a key component relates to causes of occupational health and welfare. Within HRM thinking, the role of occupational health and welfare has not received as much attention as other areas. This has occurred primarily from a concern to distance HRM from traditional personnel management.

- In the years ahead, the occupational health and welfare agenda is likely to focus on issues such as health promotion, alcohol and drug abuse, stress and counselling. It is now generally accepted that initiatives in all of these areas provide direct benefits to organisations in terms of cost savings and performance enhancement. It is also suggested that such initiatives will seek to individualise the employment relationship.

- Acquired Immune Deficiency Syndrome (AIDS) emerged as an important concern for occupational health in the 1990s and is likely to remain a concern for some time to come. Since the early 1990s, the formulation of corporate AIDS policies has become more commonplace. Such policies are intended to deal specifically with HIV/AIDS and most contain a general statement of commitment to non-discrimination, employee educa-

tion, equitable benefits, guarantees of medical confidentiality
and assurances of continued employment.

• Substance abuse in the workplace has also become a major
  problem. Organisations are increasingly likely to face situations where employees experience drink- or drug-related
  problems. Companies are now implementing written policies
  dealing with alcoholism and substance abuse and the policies
  specify proceedings in terms of the handling and referral of
  employees experiencing such problems.

• Violence and bullying represent two contemporary occupational health topics in both the literature and organisation practice. There is evidence that both are frequent occurrences in
  many workplaces. Organisations have a range of strategies
  available to deal with violence and bullying, including training,
  discipline and counselling interventions.

Chapter 22

OCCUPATIONAL HEALTH: STRESS

INTRODUCTION

The word "stress" is derived from the Latin word *stringere,* which means to draw tight. In the modern context, it has come to mean a number of different things to different people and as a result is often misunderstood, and often cited in terms of both cause and effect.

Canadian endocrinologist Hans Selye (1936) defined stress as "the non-specific response of the body to any demand made upon it". More recently, it has been defined in terms of the demands of the environment and the individual's capabilities to meet these demands. This latter definition does confuse the issue as, in the first definition, stress is viewed purely in terms of the demands made upon the individual by the environment whereas, in the latter, stress is viewed as an intervening variable that cannot be observed directly. For the purposes of this handbook, "stress" will be viewed in terms of both the environmental conditions placed on individuals and their particular responses to those conditions.

Stress is, therefore, the reaction of the body to a threatening source and can emanate from two different areas within our lives: cataclysmic events and daily hassles.

This chapter considers the concepts of stress, burnout and post-traumatic stress disorder and then analyses some of the sources of stress in the modern organisation as a component of occupational health. The chapter concludes with a consideration of stress management.

STRESS, BURNOUT AND POST-TRAUMATIC STRESS DISORDER

In everyday usage, stress is generally construed as something unpleasant. It may be used to describe something environmental, such as a traffic jam, large crowds at a football match, or it may denote emotions aroused by an external problem such as anxiety, fear or frustration.

Further, we associate with stress certain physical symptoms, sweating hands, a stiffened neck, a tight stomach. When we shift to a scientific (or technical) meaning of stress, we find that pleasant, as well as unpleasant, events can cause illness, that positive as well as negative emotions can accompany stress. In the technical sense, stress can be considered from at least two perspectives.

Firstly, stress can be viewed as a trigger for a response. In this sense, it may be thought of as a cause. When stress is used in this way, it is commonly called a stressor. A stressor is any demand on mind and body. Secondly, stress can be thought of as an effect, called a stress response. The stress response is made up of psychological and biological patterns. Neither stressors, nor the stress response, exist in isolation, rather they both feed back on each other to produce the stress experience.

The terms stress, burnout and post-traumatic stress disorder have specific meanings in the literature. Job stress can be defined as a situation wherein job-related factors interact with an employee to change his or her psychological and/or physiological conditions such that the person is forced to deviate from normal functioning. Stress should be distinguished from a stressor, which is the object or event that causes the stress. For example, the notion that work with VDUs may be hazardous could be considered a stressor that may cause stress in some employees. Exposure to second-hand smoke, which may cause cancer, now serves as a stressor for many non-smoking employees. Stressors can be found in the physical environment due to lighting or noise problems, temperature, or polluted air. The research evidence reveals that these potential stressors can have an interactive effect such that, for example, temperature combined with a noisy environment may cause even greater stress than the two sources independently.

A relatively new term for one type of stress is burnout, which reflects an emotional reaction in people who often work in human services and work closely with people. Burnout is common among police officers, teachers, social workers and nurses. People who experience burnout may develop cynical attitudes towards their jobs and clients and may feel emotional exhaustion, de-personalisation, and a sense of low personal accomplishment or control. However, burnout is not inevitable in these jobs. The effects of burnout can be reduced using positive feedback about job performance.

Post-traumatic stress disorder (PTSD), or psychological trauma, is related to accidents in the workplace, fires, crashes or similar disasters. Employees who suffer from this syndrome often try to block out the experience. When this fails, they display symptoms such as sleeplessness, anger and jumpiness. Frost (1990) suggests that these symptoms can be emotionally crippling. There is strong evidence to suggest that the long-term problems associated with PTSD include heart disease, abnormal blood pressure and diabetes.

THE PHYSIOLOGY OF STRESS

While stress generally has negative connotations associated to it, the reality is that individuals can experience both positive and negative stress, and positive stress can improve their performance. These two types were identified by Selye (1936) as "eustress" and "distress" (the former is associated with positive and the latter with negative stress), with the particular event causing either of the above identified as a "stressor". Stress, therefore, in itself is not bad, and it can be necessary in order for people to perform well. There is an optimum stress level at which performance is maximised and this has been referred to as the "Yerkes–Dodson rule" (see **Figure 22.1**).

It points to the fact that an individual's level of arousal directly affects their performance of a given task. At low arousal levels, the nervous system is unresponsive, attention levels are low and individuals tend to slip in and out of consciousness. At the other extreme, performance is also sub-standard because the nervous system becomes over-responsive and an individual's behaviour becomes disorganised. It is at moderate levels of arousal that individuals function most effectively because the body is alert and performance is at an optimal level. The individual's level of arousal is of course dependent on a number of factors in the employee's environment, which include variables such as noise, lighting and sleep patterns.

Figure 22.1: The Yerkes–Dodson Rule

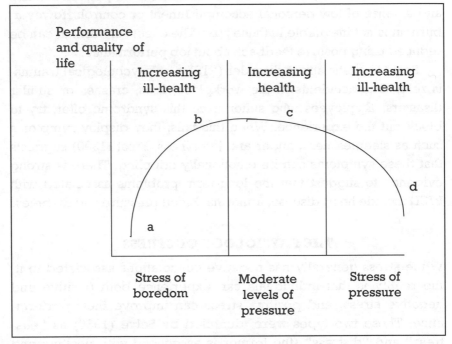

The "fight or flight" syndrome is the process the body experiences when confronted with a potentially stressful situation. It is directly connected to the autonomic system, a series of nerves that connect the brain and spinal cord to various organs within the body. It controls both the physiological and the psychological responses. The sympathetic system is concerned with answering the body's call to fight, i.e. increased heart rate, increased blood supply to the organs, stimulation of sweat glands, dilation of the pupils and the release of adrenalin and noradrenalin from the adrenal glands, while the parasympathetic system is responsible for emotions and the protection of the body which has its physical expression in reflexes such as sweating, quickened heart rate, blushing and digestive disturbance. The body can benefit from such activity where the stress is of a mild nature because it improves performance.

However, danger lies ahead if the body is consistently being put through this process. As a result of constant acute stress, it can cause permanent physical damage. The "fight or flight" action, in time, does not become possible and, therefore, problems arise as the individual is unable to escape from the stressor.

The General Adaptation Syndrome developed by Selye (1936) outlines the stages the body goes through when a stressor is encountered. This has three distinct stages: the alarm reaction stage; the resistance stage; and the exhaustion stage.

The alarm reaction stage is concerned with the initial shock to the system. Initially defences are down, but these are automatically raised once the threat has been identified. At this stage, the brain sends a biochemical "message" to the pituitary gland that secretes adrenocortitrophic hormones. This, in turn, causes the adrenal glands to secrete corticoids such as adrenalin and the result is a general "call to arms" of the body's systems.

The resistance stage is concerned with two responses: the body will either resist the stressor or adapt to the effects of the stressor. It is the opposite of the alarm reaction stage. Defences are now mobilised and the individual will either resist the stressor and return to their natural state or, where they are unable to resist, move on to the third stage.

The exhaustion stage is concerned with the effect of the stressor if the body is unable to adapt to its cause. A state of overload is reached and the body returns to the initial reaction stage with the result, perhaps, of damage to a particular bodily function or, in the extreme case, death.

The potential stressors encountered by the individual are dependant on a number of individual factors such as the individual's strength of constitution, psychological strength, degree of control and perception of the event and the effects of successful and unsuccessful adaptation. The long-term effect of stressors can also be seen in terms of greater vulnerability or increased resistance.

Symptomatic Relationships between Context, Vulnerability and Stressors

McLean (1965) developed a model of stress that sought to better understand its nature by looking at the environmental context, the individual's vulnerability to it and the situation of the stressor. The model hypothesises that a stressor is only able to produce stress when all of the three aforementioned factors overlap and this indicated a symptomatic response to their concurrence. The model makes no attempt to weight the factors in terms of their influence on a stressful situation occurring. It does, however, suggest that favourable individual characteristics might prevent a symptomatic stress response when the environmental context and the presence of a stressor would otherwise facilitate one and, similarly, if a favourable environmental context existed.

Person-Environment Fit

Another, more in-depth model to explain the consequences of stress is called the Person-Environment Fit Model, developed by Payne and Cooper (1988). The model emphasises the difference between the subjective and objective evaluation of the individual and their environment. Stress is induced by the subjective Person-Environment Fit, which is ultimately mediated by the individual's perceptions of the self and the environment. The logic of this model lies in the interaction of four variables: the objective environment–objective person, the objective environment–subjective environment, the objective person–subjective person, and the subjective environment–subjective person.

An example may explain this model. A garment worker may be expected to produce 40 pieces per hour (objective environment), whereas she believes she is required to produce 50 (subjective environment). She may actually be capable of producing 45 pieces (objective individual) but she thinks she can only produce 40 pieces (subjective individual). The example suggests that there is a good fit between the objective environmental demands and the objective person's ability, thereby reducing the possibility of a stressful situation. However, the worker's perception of the subjective environment (50 garments) and her own belief of her abilities (40 garments) would suggest that a potentially stressful situation will be encountered. In summary, the individual may encounter a stressful situation based on a poor subjective Person–Environment Fit. The model highlights the importance of the individual's subjective interaction with the environment.

These models place an emphasis on the individual and their environment, demonstrating that the nature of stress can be very subjective. This is also highlighted in Selye's General Adaptation Syndrome where individuals' own characteristics are considered important in determining the effect of a stressor.

SOURCES OF STRESS: INDIVIDUAL LEVEL

Figure 22.2 presents a model of stress, which forms the basis of the remainder of this chapter.

Figure 22.2: A Model of Organisational Stress

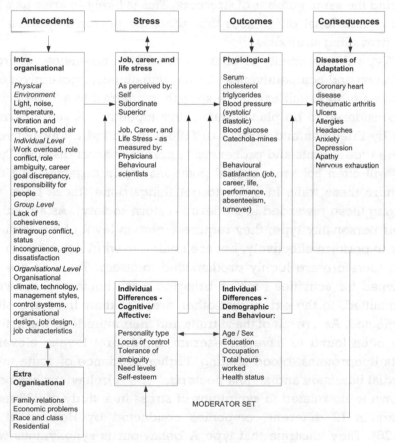

Source: Ivancevich J.M. & Matteson, M.T. (1980) *Stress and Work: A Managerial Perspective*, Glenview, IL: Foreman.

Personality Types

Personality traits such as feelings about locus of control, Type A/Type B characteristics, self esteem, extroversion/ introversion, intelligence, sex, social status and education can often influence the likelihood of work-induced stress.

A case has been made for the increased incidence of heart disease among Type A personalities. Seward (1990) points out that pre-existing psychiatric conditions may also effect the individual's perception of stress and the physiological and psychological outcomes. Research demonstrates that even people in the same jobs, working in the same environment, do not see their environment as having the same number of stressors. This is likely to arise as a result of individual differences that affect the person's appraisal of the prevailing stressors.

Type A personality is characterised by impatience, energy, ambition and competitiveness, haste, impatience, aggressiveness, hyper-alertness and explosive speech in contrast to a Type B who is considered to be placid, quiet, uncompetitive. A study carried out by Friedman and Rosenman (1964) identified a link between these type A traits and proneness to coronary heart disease. Type A's will often hold managerial positions within organisations that require these traits in order to get things done (these traits are among those rewarded in modern Western society). As a result of their personality type, they require a certain level of stress in order to perform effectively, but are unable to wind down and relax and therefore are highly predisposed to stress. Type As are renowned for activities such as bringing work home and are very committed, to the extent that other areas of their lives are often neglected. As a result of these traits and their attitude to work, they are often found to have high-serum cholesterol levels, elevated beta lipoproteins, blood clotting, higher incidence of acute myocardial infarction and angina pectoris. Type A behaviour has been shown to be related to symptoms of stress in a study of 236 managers in 12 different companies conducted by Howard et al. (1976). They illustrate that type A behaviour is synonymous with high blood, cholesterol and triglyceride levels and Type A managers are also less interested in exercise. This evidence has however been disputed by other researchers, who believe that there is no link between Type A behaviour and risk factors connected with coronary heart disease.

Locus of control is concerned with whether or not individuals perceive themselves as having control over their own destiny and it has been identified as having an effect on perceived stress. Individuals can be categorised into externals, those who believe that they have no control over their own destiny, and internals, those who believe that they do. Externals are perceived to be less able to cope with stressful situations and, therefore, are more predisposed to experience the physiological and psychological effects of stress than their internal counterparts. This is basically as a result of their belief that they are not in control of the situation. Internals believe that they do have control over what happens and, therefore, it follows logically that when they encounter a stressful situation they are confident of dealing with it and thus avoid the consequences of prolonged periods of stress (Krause and Stryker, 1984). Phares (1976) pointed out that internals exert greater effort to control their environment, exhibit better learning, seek new information more actively when that information has personal relevance, use information better, and seem more concerned with information rather than with social demands of situations. He also points out that the extremes on the internal/external continuum are much more predisposed to stress. The reason is that internals in the extreme, when confronted with a stressful situation, are overcome as a result of the personal responsibility they feel for the stressful occurrence and thus suffer from anxiety and depression. This view is supported by empirical research by Krause and Stryker (1984). They found that both moderates and internals were better suited to dealing with stressful life situations than their counterparts on the extreme end of the "internal" continuum.

Career Development

Overall "career stress" has been shown to be associated with low job satisfaction, burnout and poor performance (Ivancevich and Matteson, 1980). Career development is primarily concerned with security of tenure, obsolescence and retirement. Individuals have different concerns during different periods of life, with early career characterised by the pressure to achieve both in terms of responsibility and wealth. Cooper et. al. (1988) point out that this period is highly stressful because of the realisation that the work environment does not live up to the expectation of the individual and results in disillusionment.

Later in an individual's career, as fewer opportunities become available and energy levels are not as high, issues of job security may become potential sources of stress. Ivancevich and Matteson (1980) suggest that it can prove stressful as a result of the realisation that mobility has decreased and certain goals have not yet been attained.

People no longer enjoy the job security that once prevailed in society and more and more people find themselves moving not only between jobs but often between professions on a regular basis. Therefore, people now have to accept that they may have a portfolio of careers in their lifetime. However, with this come considerable levels of stress. Middle-aged workers have been, and will continue to be, acutely affected by this trend, given the fact that as one grows older career opportunities diminish for various reasons and, therefore, the threat to one's job takes on greater significance in the latter part of one's career. Arnold et al. (1995) outlined a number of symptoms of this career-crisis stage of middle-aged men, which included feelings of fear and disappointment, isolation, doubts about ability and a belief that old knowledge and skills were no longer relevant. Females also suffer stress as a result of career development issues. The most damaging health factors for females are those related to promotion, such as sex discrimination, male colleagues being treated more favourably and insufficient delegation of assignments.

Other factors to be considered include the issue of career frustration as a result of the decreasing number of managerial positions in business due to the practice of delayering in organisations. This leads to increased competition among prospective candidates and, eventually, greater degrees of frustration owing to the imbalance of positions to potential candidates. These restricted career opportunities are also prevalent outside organisations. Such frustration can spill over to the home environment (Culbert, 1974). Morris (1956) shows a causal link between being passed over for promotion and psychosomatic illness. Being overpromoted may lead to being overworked. This may mask inner insecurities with consequent psychosomatic complaints and, eventually, mental illness (Brook, 1973).

Social Dimension

Many factors outside the work environment can cause stress. Examples include financial commitments, or family problems and commitments, competing with commitments to the organisation. The conflict between family and work is probably the most frequently cited source of stress to many employees. This problem is somewhat paradoxical in that the home can play two different roles. On the one hand, it can be viewed as a refuge that provides support from the stressful work environment, while on the other it can be viewed as a source of stress in itself. Handy (1975) and Pahl and Pahl (1971) have investigated this issue extensively. Traditionally, the wife is viewed to have a supportive role while the husband is the " bread-winner" for the family. However, this view is over-simplistic and does not reflect the problems associated with the home/work interface. A wife who plays a supporting role may become bored and consequently jealous of her husband's career. The wife may object to her husband's inability, in terms of time, to consider her problems and retaliate by objecting to bringing work home. Increases in divorce rates among senior managers can be a consequence of their socially unskilled wives who are left at home and become bored.

The degree of social support outside the workplace influences the individual's reaction to stress. Individuals with a high level of support may initially view a situation as stressful, but due to this support, the development of stress is negligible, whereas an individual with a low social support system will not have that moderating factor and, therefore, suffer higher levels of stress.

Retirement

Retirement for most managers signifies a happy ending of the work relationship and a life of decreased responsibility and stress. Retirement has been described as a role-less state and the degree to which retirement proves stressful often depends on the degree to which the individual's career was a means to an end or an end in itself. For those who are forced into retirement, it may become one of the most stressful events in their lifetime. Cooper (1979), for example, found that those who retire early find the adjustment process difficult and suffer from loneliness and depression. The loss of the social outlet that work provides is a factor to be considered, along with the increased time spent in the home, which can often be a source of stress for those who are not ready and poorly prepared for early retirement. Finally, it must be noted that retirement in itself may prove stressful if the individual is not prepared financially.

Relationships at Work

Relationships at work are an important influence on any organisation's performance. Both the individual and the organisation benefit from good working relationships, while an atmosphere of distrust can lead to poor communication and low job satisfaction (French and Caplan, 1970). Poor interpersonal relationships in the workplace lead to stress and are most often found in environments that are highly pressurised and competitive. The effect can be seen in employees' lack of affiliation to the organisation and their colleagues, and the stressful consequences that are associated with this. The subordinate/supervisor relationship is possibly the most significant situation that leads to stress. A subordinate may expect more, in terms of management style and ability, from their supervisor, and this often leads to a situation where the subordinate suffers from the symptoms of stress. Buck (1972) cites the lack of participation in decision-making as being a source of stress among subordinates, arising primarily from high levels of supervision and low autonomy. Coch and French (1948) suggest involving employees in the decision-making process because this would have the effect of decreasing levels of stress, lowering absenteeism and staff turnover and, therefore, promoting good mental health amongst employees. The peculiarities of the situation will dictate to a considerable degree the effectiveness of such a participative approach to workforce management. Employees may not wish to be involved in the decision-making process and managers may not wish to relinquish their decision-making powers, which could have the effect of increasing stress in the workplace and diminishing the mental health of all employees.

Redundancy and Unemployment

Redundancies in organisations will generally be a source of stress for employees. Research demonstrates that employees in organisations where redundancies are imminent experience higher levels of blood pressure. For those made redundant, the pattern continues with the accompaniment of depression and low self-esteem. In a situation where redundancies are imminent, rumours abound, having the effect of heightening tension. Once redundancies are announced, a feeling of relief prevails because employees know where they stand. Feelings of lost status and failure emerge and a sense of loneliness and isolation begins to set in.

Once employees get over this initial period, they may find themselves in the job market again with a degree of optimism, only to find that they still carry the stigma of being made redundant, which may affect their confidence and thus their job prospects. The stress caused in such a situation will not only affect the individual but also family life, with the individual, perhaps, taking an ever-decreasing role in family life because of the family's and the individual's own negative view of themselves (Jahoda, 1979). The long-term unemployed face the added stress of not having a structure to their day, which can have the effect of making them pessimistic, distressed and apathetic to life in general. Fagin (1979) highlighted that individuals who suffered long stints of unemployment began to change many aspects of their lives such as social behaviour, while roles within the family may alter considerably. Other studies in the UK point out a type of justification process that the long-term unemployed use to delay the negative feelings associated with unemployment.

In a general context, unemployment is viewed among many medical practitioners and academics as posing a serious threat to the state of public health. Research demonstrates that the unemployed are more depressed and experience higher levels of strain than their counterparts who are in employment. Suicide rates are also higher among the unemployed. Warr and Jackson (1984) demonstrate that the negative health consequences of unemployment are felt in the first three months, thereafter stabilising, while there appears to be no difference between social classes in terms of reactions to unemployment; working class people, however, have shown greater anxiety with regard to financial difficulties (Fryer and Payne, 1986).

Those caught in the unemployment trap undoubtedly suffer from higher levels of stress. Financial insecurity not only hinders their freedom in the extrinsic sense that they are unable to buy the goods and services that they desire, but can also impact on more intrinsic security such as social status that may have been based originally on their financial position in society.

SOURCES OF STRESS: THE PHYSICAL ENVIRONMENT: THE JOB/ORGANISATIONAL LEVEL

Working Hours

Excessive working hours are directly related to deaths from heart disease. Breslow and Buell (1960) conducted a study of light industrial workers and concluded that individuals under the age of 45 who worked 48 hours or more a week had twice the probability of dying from heart disease than their counterparts who worked 40 hours per week. Not only do excessive working hours affect the physiology of individuals but they also affect their behaviour patterns. The medical profession is an occupational category that regularly suffers the consequences of excessive working hours, often of 30 hours or more without sleep. As a result, their performance and health deteriorates and their social activities become marginalised. They not only predispose themselves to high levels of stress, but also deprive themselves of one of the primary coping strategies, social support, to combat such stressful work circumstances.

Shift Work

Shift work contributes to stress in the workplace and affects both blood temperature, metabolic rate and behavioural factors such as sleep patterns, family and social life. Sutherland and Cooper (1987) found that shift work was a source of stress and that the greater the length of the shift the greater the stress experienced.

Sigman (1993) found a number of consequences that resulted from undertaking shift work. These include a constant state of disarray for the individual's body clock, higher levels of irritability than individuals working day shifts and lower levels of alertness. Loss of social contact is also cited as a consequence of shift work, while rotating shifts have been shown to increase the incidence of sleep deprivation.

Danger

People working in jobs that involve risk and danger are more susceptible to stress because the individual is constantly aware of potential danger and the body is pushed into the "fight or flight" state resulting in long-term physiological damage.

Work Overload

Work overload may take two forms: quantitative or qualitative. Having too much to do (quantitative) can lead to having to work long hours with consequent medical and social implications. Qualitative work overload correlates positively with increased heart rate and cholesterol levels (French and Caplan, 1972). Other effects of work overload include escapist drinking, absenteeism, low motivation and low self-esteem (Margolis et al., 1974). Work overload is most commonly associated with those in middle management and is attributed to the role they play within the organisation. Work overload for managers' emanates from two sources: demands made on managers by subordinates and demands made by senior managers. Managers are often required to cut costs and implement budgets, which have the effect of damaging relationships and losing the trust of subordinates. Recent years have witnessed a reduction in the number of middle line managers as a result of delayering policies. Those left behind are usually expected to take over the responsibilities of those who have been made redundant and, consequently, their workload increases dramatically.

Role Ambiguity

Role ambiguity occurs where the individual's role in the organisation is unclear. This can occur where the objectives and scope of the job are not clearly defined, with the effect that the individual is unclear as to what they are supposed to do, what they are supposed to be striving for, and to and for whom they are responsible. The studies of French and Caplan (1970) and Margolis et al. (1970) demonstrate that role ambiguity has the effect of lowering job satisfaction, satisfaction with life in general, increasing depression, lowering motivation and increasing blood pressure and heart rate.

Role Conflict

Role conflict arises when the individual is torn between two conflicting demands such as cost control and maintenance of service, or even between the demands of subordinates and superiors. The effects of this can be seen in increased levels of anxiety, a decrease in job satisfaction and also cardiovascular ill health (Ivancevich and Matteson, 1980). Parkington and Schneider (1979) report that where employees perceive management emphasising systems at odds with customer needs, higher role conflict and ambiguity are a consequence with a decrease in job satisfaction, poor customer service and increased propensity to leave. A significant relationship exists between role conflict and coronary heart disease among managerial employees (Shirom et al., 1973).

Boundary Roles

Roles that lie on the boundaries both between different departments within the organisation and the external environment are also considered to be highly stressful (Khan et al., 1964). The job will often entail a role that casts the individual into a situation where they must play the "middle person". The studies of Margolis et al. (1974) highlighted the problems faced by supervisors on a factory floor who cover the boundary between factory floor workers and the management. They were seven times more likely to develop ulcers than the factory floor workers.

Responsibility

The level/degree of responsibility is also viewed as a stressor. Stress can be experienced as a result of having either too much or too little responsibility for people. Managers have responsibility for things or people, with the latter proving to be particularly stressful as it requires greater interaction. Wardwell et al. (1964) found this was likely to lead to coronary heart disease in the form of diastolic blood pressure and high-serum cholesterol levels.

Repetitive Work

Repetitive work is often cited as a source of stress among operators. In many cases, this type of work is also associated with workers' posture and shift work. Cox (1985) points out that repetitive work amounts to a set of discrete activities that are repeated over and over again without any interruptions. People who work under such conditions often experience low job satisfaction levels as a result of their lack of autonomy and responsibility for the task.

The research demonstrates that those involved in repetitive work suffer poorer health than those involved in other occupations, particularly as a result of the shift work and night work associated with these types of jobs. Broadbent and Gath (1981) undertook a study of factory floor workers in a car manufacturing plant and found that workers disliked the job but were not shown to be unhealthy. Furthermore, those workers who were machine-paced experienced high levels of anxiety, while short work-cycles were shown not to have a link with job dissatisfaction or ill health compared to longer-cycles. They also found that people with obsessional-type personalities were more predisposed to suffer from stress if they were placed on a repetitive machine-paced job. Finally, the study showed that a higher proportion of employees in machine-paced jobs may be in need of psychiatric help than other employees. The study demonstrates that machine-paced work is the primary source of stress among factory floor workers and that, although people may not be dissatisfied with their job, this does not necessarily mean that they are not susceptible to stress.

Job Control

Job control relates to the opportunity for the significant use of judgement and discretion in a job. Karasek (1979, 1990) has undertaken major studies to see whether there exists a causal link between the degree of control experienced in a job and the levels of stress associated with it. The results showed that people who occupied jobs that enabled them to exercise judgement and discretion, combined with the job being demanding, showed greater job satisfaction and lower levels of depression than individuals in jobs that allowed little discretion and were not demanding. His later study highlighted that those who had greater control and higher participation in their jobs reported fewer health problems. Fisher (1985) identified that when white- and blue-collar workers are compared, the latter fare much worse in terms of job control. They are seen to suffer greater levels of stress as a result of a number of specific factors: less control over how their time is spent at work; less scope to modify the job they are carrying out because their jobs are well-defined and very systematic; less mobility; and less freedom to move from a job where they find the conditions stressful. Finally, he believes that there are fewer opportunities for social activity in their workplace due to the lack of discretion in their jobs.

New Technology

The last 20 years have witnessed an explosion in both the development and use of technology in the work environment. One of the most controversial technological issues, in terms of health and safety, is the visual display unit or VDU. Much has been written on this area and initially the threat that VDUs posed was believed to be that of danger resulting from the emission of radiation. Due to significant improvements in design, it is now agreed that there exists little or no risk from radiation for those who work on these machines on a daily basis. A new and more recent development, however, is a different threat to the health and safety of individuals who work with these machines on a continuous basis: repetitive strain injury (RSI). Other risks include damage to posture and anxiety (Mackay and Cox, 1984). RSI occurs when the operator has to maintain the same posture at a keyboard for long periods, placing the muscles in the arms and lower back under constant strain, which results in severe pain. Not all employees are frequent users of computers in the workplace and the study of Johansson and Aronsson (1984) found that infrequent users felt that computers helped them carry out their job more efficiently and effectively, while those who were frequent users suffered eye strain, headaches and pains in the arms and shoulders as a result of their long periods of interaction with the computer. Frequent computer breakdowns was also cited as a source of stress.

VDUs have many effects on individuals who interact with them on a daily basis. Mackay and Cox (1984) summarised these under three headings: underload, deskilling and control. They believe that the introduction of VDUs led to a decrease in the work-load that employees carried out primarily because simple clerical tasks were now computerised and, therefore, required less amounts of effort and work while still maintaining a high degree of repetition. Deskilling also occurs where new technology is introduced. Skills become redundant with the resultant effect of lessening the degree of challenge and interest in the job. Finally, those operating computers often feel a lack of control over the task they are carrying out. Some of the more modern computer systems monitor performance while the individual is operating the machine, thereby often leading to feelings of suspicion and resentment, and consequently fatigue and stress among operators. The operation of the computer may cause stress where programmes/systems break down or malfunction and leave operators feeling frustrated as they may not have the skills necessary to rectify the problem.

Position in the Company

There is a widely held belief among academics that stress is a function of the level at which the individual operates within a company. Cooper (1979) points out that lower and middle line managers suffer greater levels of stress than their more senior counterparts with resultant ill effects on health. Packard (1962) goes further and suggests that the most likely individual to suffer a heart attack is not the chief executive but the junior executive, who is seeking to further his or her career. Cooper's study demonstrates that those in senior positions enjoy managing people and appear to feel more pressure from large amounts of communication and consultation while being more satisfied when they are free from decision-making that involves consultation. Bureaucracy within the organisation is a form of stress and managers felt that their present jobs put greater demands on them in terms of time, with the effect of interrupting family life. Career progression was not a motivator because they had reached their career ceiling.

Middle line managers felt that dealing with personnel problems and new systems or methods was a major source of stress. Bureaucracy and the intrusion of work on family life were also perceived as a source of pressure. Furthermore, lack of opportunities was perceived as a source of stress. Other research demonstrates conflicting views on whether control over decision-making or lack of control is a source of stress. Schoonmaker (1969) found that making major decisions has the effect of causing ulcers while Wallis (1983) showed that decision-making, or the lack of it, can both be a source of stress.

Noise

Rule and Nesdale (1976) found noise levels to correlate positively to perceived job stressors. Noise can be defined as unwanted sound and is considered to be a health threat at levels in excess of 85dB or 90dB. This level does not, however, have to be breached for it to be a form of stress. Noise in the workplace may interfere with many aspects of the job at much lower levels and, therefore, careful consideration must be given to it when examining sources of stress. The response that an individual makes to noise is a subjective one and factors such as context must be considered as well as intensity.

For example, noise that contains speech, is much more annoying than continuous unstructured noise such as that of a machine, while the irritation of noise is considerable when one is trying to concentrate. Furthermore, noise construed as evidence for someone else's lack of consideration is the most stressful of all (Pheasant, 1991).

Temperature and Humidity

While temperature in itself may not be hazardous, in its extremes it may have a detrimental effect on the health of those who are subjected to work under such conditions. The effects include abnormalities of cardiac function, dehydration, exhaustion and collapse. Other effects of cold conditions include frost-bite and hypothermia. The effect of temperature on performance and health is not to be underestimated, as even minor deviations from the optimal temperature levels in any given situation can become a source of stress for individuals. It is very difficult to ascribe an "ideal" temperature to work in but a general rule is that those of a sedentary nature are generally most comfortable at around the 20-24° C. range with humidity running at 40-50 per cent.

EFFECTS OF STRESS

There are psychological, physiological, and behavioural consequences of stress. However, reactions to the same stressors vary greatly with the individual. Although individual reactions are difficult to predict, it is known that some people can handle tremendous amounts of stressors without any manifest stressful reactions. Other people fall apart, become violent, or turn to drugs or alcohol. Psychological stress may be manifested in anxiety, depression, irritability, and hostility and may also have physiological consequences such as high blood pressure, numbness, fatigue, and heart problems. Stress may also affect work performance, work attendance, and accident rates. These consequences can have profound (and costly) organisational consequences, including union organising, workers' compensation, poor work products, and legal problems.

The physiological effects of stress have a link with the "fight or flight" syndrome identified by Selye (1936) that results in the individual overcoming the stressor or the stressor overcoming the individual. Although this reaction of the body to a threat was required by early man to combat real or physical danger, this is not generally the case today, as the threat is usually symbolic and our existence not in any great or real danger. Unfortunately, the body does not realise that physical action is unwarranted and, at this stage, the mechanisms to combat the threat have begun and will take hours to undo.

Therefore, the danger lies in the fact that the body and its systems are put into this state of "alert" and, more often than not, are not required to take any specific action, or only take an action which will last for a minimal period of time but which takes the body a significant amount of time to climb down from.

Many illnesses and disorders such as coronary heart disease, strokes, indigestion, back pain, diabetes, cancer, asthma, migraine, tuberculosis, colitis, rheumatoid arthritis and psychological disorders such as anxiety, phobias, obsessions and depression as well as behavioural effects such as irritability, tiredness, apathy and loss of concentration are known to have links with stress (see **Figure 22.3**). These illnesses are of both a psychological and physiological nature. The essential difference lies in the fact that the former is related to changes in the state of one's body, while the latter relates to changes in one's state of mind and manifest themselves in mental and physical symptoms, while the behaviour affects the way individual carry on in their lives.

The psychological approach to stress emphasises the relationship between the person and his/her environment. In particular, it emphasises the importance of the individual's perception of the event and whether they feel they are able to cope with it. The psychological effects of stress manifest themselves in feelings such as depression, anxiety and exhaustion.

The mental health effects of stress exist on a continuum ranging from subjective symptoms that have a relatively mild effect on daily life, to significant psychiatric diseases with impairment of functions. These early subjective reports of stress will usually take the form of depression, anxiety and irritability and may be the first steps towards more severe symptoms. Behavioural changes can also be a result of stress and may take the form of marital discord, reduced participation in family activities and also changes in eating behaviour. The third style or area relating to the psychological effects of stress is overt psychological dysfunction and can take the form of clinical depression, anxiety disorders and also the compounding of existing physical conditions by psychological factors, which highlights the fact that both psychological and physiological effects of stress are not mutually exclusive.

Figure 22.3: Behavioural, Psychological and Physical Symptoms of Stress

---

Behavioural Symptoms of Stress

- Constant irritability with people.
- Difficulty in making decisions.
- Loss of sense of humour.
- Suppressed anger.
- Difficulty concentrating.
- Inability to finish one task before rushing into another.
- Feeling one is the target of other's animosity.
- Feeling unable to cope.
- Wanting to cry at the smallest problem.
- Lack of interest in doing things after return home from work.
- Waking up in the morning and feeling tired after an early night.
- Constant tiredness.

Psychological Symptoms of Stress

- Job dissatisfaction.
- Breakdown of relationships at home and work.
- Absenteeism.
- Low productivity.
- Anxiety about work and home.
- Depression and frustration.

Physical Symptoms of Stress

- Lack of appetite.
- Craving for food when under pressure.
- Frequent indigestion or heartburn.
- Constipation or diarrhoea.
- Insomnia.
- Tendency to sweat for no good reason.
- Nervous twitches, nail-biting, etc.
- Headaches.
- Cramps and muscle spasms.

- Nausea.
- Breathlessness without exertion.
- Fainting spells.
- Impotency or frigidity.
- Eczema.

Ailments Recognised to have Stress Backgrounds

- Hypertension: high blood pressure.
- Coronary thrombosis: heart attack.
- Migraine.
- Hay fever and allergies.
- Asthma.
- Pruritis: intense itching.
- Peptic ulcers.
- Constipation.
- Colitis.
- Rheumatoid arthritis.
- Menstrual difficulties.
- Nervous dyspepsia: flatulence and indigestion.
- Hyperthyroidism: overactive thyroid gland.
- Diabetes mellitus.
- Skin disorders.
- Tuberculosis.
- Depression.

Stress and Heart Disease

Table 22.1 outlines the effects of stress on bodily function. It has been well proven that heart attacks and high blood pressure have links to stress. Russek and Zohman (1958), for example, found that 91 per cent of a sample of coronary patients reported a period of prolonged stress preceding their heart attack, compared with 20 per cent of the control groups. While eating habits and lifestyle habits play an important role in bringing about such conditions, it is believed that stress plays a central role. Hypertension or high blood pressure has been shown to be directly related to stress, in that the condition is characterised by tension of the arterial vessels, which are controlled by the autonomic nervous system. Constant activation of the sympathetic nervous system, which is associated with those who suffer from stress, is believed to reduce the elasticity of the blood vessels and thus cause high blood pressure. As a result of this, individuals with high blood pressure are at a greater risk of suffering from heart diseases as a result of the increased workload that the heart must undertake in order to push blood through the arteries. Furthermore, in cases of acute stress the large amounts of fat released into the blood during the "fight or flight" response increased the individual's susceptibility to heart disease arising from the blockage of arteries, which provide oxygen to the heart muscle.

Stomach and Intestinal Problems

Stress can also have the effects of increasing the levels of acid in the stomach with the effect of creating ulcers. Irritable bowl syndrome is also believed to be associated with chronic stress.

Skin Disorders

Eczema, hives and acne have all been shown to have links with stress.

Cancer and the Immune System

The link between cancer and stress is a topic of considerable interest. Fox (1978) put forward the argument that cancer is triggered by the production of an agent or mechanism overcoming existing resistance of the body (carcinogenesis) the result of which is the development of a carcinogen that normally is insufficient to produce cancer.

Table 22.1: Effects of Stress on Bodily Functions

Part of Body	Normal (relaxed)	Under Pressure	Acute Pressure	Chronic Pressure (Stress)
Brain	Blood supply normal	Blood supply up	Thinks more clearly	Headaches and migraines, tremors and nervous tics
Mood	Happy	Serious	Increased concentration	Anxiety, loss of sense of humour
Saliva	Normal	Reduced	Reduced	Dry mouth, lump in throat
Muscles	Blood supply normal	Blood supply up	Improved performance	Muscular tension, pain
Heart	Normal rate and blood pressure	Increased rate, blood pressure	Improved performance	Hypertension and chest pain
Lungs	Normal respiration	Increased respiration rate	Improved performance	Coughs and asthma
Stomach	Normal blood supply and acid secretion	Reduced blood supply and increased acid secretion	Reduced blood supply reduces digestion	Ulcers due to heartburn and indigestion
Bowels	Normal blood supply and bowel activity	Reduced blood supply and increased bowel activity	Reduced blood supply reduces digestion	Abdominal discomfort and diarrhoea
Bladder	Normal	Frequent urination	Frequent urination due to increased nervous stimulation	Frequent urination, prosthetic symptoms
Sexual Organs	Male: (Normal) Female: Normal periods, etc.	Male: Impotence (decreased blood supply) Female: Irregular periods	Decreased blood supply	Male: Impotence Female: Menstrual disorders
Skin	Healthy	Decreased blood supply, dry skin.	Increased blood supply	Dryness and rashes
Biochemistry	Normal: oxygen consumed, glucose and fats liberated	Oxygen consumption up, glucose and fat consumption up	More energy immediately available	Rapid tiredness

Headache and Backache

Headaches are the result of tension in the face and scalp that stress has been shown to bring on, while migraines result from spasms of the blood vessels supplying the brain. The link with stress is not so clear, as many other variables are also connected to this form of headache. Backache can also be associated with stress as it often results from a muscle spasm, which is stress-induced.

The Musculo-skeletal System

Pheasant (1991) points out that musculo-skeletal pain and dysfunction commonly has a significant psychogenic component in its aetiology. A number of different physiological mechanisms can mediate this connection. Pain may be triggered in previously sensitised structures as the result of generalised muscle tension, which is brought about by stress. Many people concentrating on a demanding task often fidget less, thereby allowing areas of abnormal tension to be maintained. The mechanisms of local muscle fatigue have a strong neuro-psychological component and individuals under stress often prolong work beyond its normal limit and take shorter rests therefore allowing chronic fatigue states to develop (this will be dealt with in more detail in the next section). Finally, hyperventilation increases blood lactate; and conversely, deep relaxation decreases lactate below the ordinary resting levels (Benson, 1975).

Fatigue

Fatigue has the effect of decreasing the employee's ability and motivation to work. The body will suffer overall exhaustion as a result of prolonged heavy work, which depletes the body's energy reserves.

Chronic fatigue has the effect of making individuals feel tired, even after they may have had long periods of rest. Other symptoms include headaches, giddiness, palpitations, cold sweats, loss of appetite, dyspepsia, diarrhoea and constipation, which are all stress-related (Grandjean, 1988). Abnormal tiredness and lethargy may co-exist with some of the musculo-skeletal symptoms already outlined, such as the disease known as post-viral fatigue syndrome or ME (Yuppie Flu). This disease can debilitate some individuals to the extent that they could be considered clinically depressed, but there is some controversy within the medical profession about whether in fact this disease is of a physiological nature or purely psychological.

The psychological approach to stress emphasises the relationship between the person and their environment. Lazarus and Folkman (1966) highlight the importance of the individual's perception of both how they view the event and whether or not they feel they are able to cope with it. The psychological effects of stress manifest themselves in feelings such as depression, anxiety and exhaustion.

The mental health effects of stress exist on a continuum ranging from subjective symptoms that have a relatively mild effect on daily life, to significant psychiatric diseases with impairment of functions. These early subjective reports of stress will usually take the form of depression, anxiety and irritability and may be the first steps towards more severe symptoms. Behavioural changes can also be a result of stress and may take the form of marital discord, reduced participation in family activities and also changes in eating behaviour. The third type or area relating to the psychological effects of stress is overt psychological dysfunctioning and can take the form of clinical depression, anxiety disorders and also the compounding of existing physical conditions by psychological factors, which highlights the fact that both psychological and physiological effects of stress are not mutually exclusive.

COPING STRATEGIES

Coping strategies for dealing with stress exist both at a macro and micro level. The individual may use personal strategies of their own to offset the effects of work stress. The organisation can also implement strategies to reduce stress and to help employees to cope better. Strategies pertain to both the avoidance of stress and to coping with stress and it is important to make this distinction. There are many strategies open to the individual some of which are structured and others, which are not.

Figure 22.4 provides a framework of specific intervention programmes and the stress outcomes that they may be directed toward (Ivancevich et al., 1990).

Figure 22.4: Stress Management Interventions: Targets, Types and Outcomes

Targets of Stress Management Interventions	Types of Interventions	Outcomes
	Individual • Meditation. • Exercise. • Relaxation Techniques. • Cognitive Approaches. • Goal Setting. • Time Management.	**Individual** • Blood Pressure, Heart Rate, Catecholamines. • Quality of Life. • Anxiety, Depression, etc. • Psychosomatic Complaints.
	Organisational • Organisational Structure. • Job Design. • Selection and Placement Programmes. • Working Conditions. • Training and Development.	**Organisational** • Productivity Quality and Quantity. • Turnover. • Absenteeism. • Health Care Costs. • Accidents.
Situational Stressors (1) Cognitive Appraisal of Stressors (2) Coping Strategies (3)	**Individual/ Organisational Interface** • Job Demands – Person Style Fit. • Participation Preferences – Practices. • Autonomy Preferences – Practices. • Co-Worker Relationships.	**Individual/ Organisational Interface** • Job Performance. • Job Satisfaction. • Burnout. • Health Care Utilisation.

The three intervention targets in the figure correspond to: (1) changing the degree of stress potential in a situation by reducing the intensity or number of stressors present, (2) helping employees to modify their appraisal of potentially stressful situations, and (3) helping employees to cope more effectively with the consequences of stress. Stress management and reduction programmes are common in industry today. These include for example, programmes that emphasise exercise, nutrition, relaxation techniques, time management and self-awareness. Some organisations provide employees with breaks during which they can relax with New Age music, meditation, and stretches or increase their energy level by listening to a tape of empowering thoughts or getting up and moving to upbeat music. Other organisations have attempted to reduce physical stressors by redesigning the workplace. Role ambiguity and role conflict can often be reduced by interventions following a job analysis and survey research. Studies point to immediate supervisors as a primary source of stress among workers.

Individual Coping Strategies

When we look at coping, we find a great variation of responses to the identifiable stressor. Personality traits have been examined from the perspective of coping. Antonovesky has identified a sense of coherence as a key trait of survivors of World War II concentration camps. He found that people with a strong sense of coherence tend to make sense even of the worst situations. They have confidence that they can manage the stressor itself or their response to it. They were found to be better able to cope with distress from insoluble problems. A sense of coherence is similar to having a purpose in life. They have a sense of control, or "things are in control". However, there are a number of individual coping strategies.

Exercise can often be a very effective strategy for managing stress. Individuals who exercise regularly are often found to have less tension, a higher level of self-confidence and a healthier outlook on life. Folkins (1976) has also shown that individuals who do not exercise are generally more predisposed to stress and more likely to suffer from depression.

Relaxation is also an effective method for managing stress. It may take many differing forms such as yoga, visualisation, meditation, autogenics, massage and vacations and provides an escape from the daily life hassles that form the basis of people's stress and tension.

Managing time effectively is also a useful strategy. It allows the individual to prioritise activities and allocate their working day time in a systematic manner. By managing time more effectively, individuals find they are able to execute more activities and therefore the pressures of work overload can often be diminished.

Probably the most used and effective strategy is that of support groups. This may take the form of family or a close group of friends who provide social support, which helps alleviate the effects of stress. These are particularly helpful when stress has been induced as a result of a crisis in an individual's life. The group can often provide affection, approval and security that help the individual who may be suffering from some of the psychological symptoms of stress which were outlined earlier. They can also reduce the level of stress at source by ensuring that interpersonal relations are strong and therefore cannot form the basis of stressful situations (Williams and House, 1985).

Stress Resistance Resources

A growing emphasis is now placed on the role that resources play in the experience of stress. Key stress resistance resources include:

- **Material Resources:** these include money and all the things it can buy — food, clothes, shelter, health care and heating.

- **Physical Resources:** are the positive physical attributes of a person. Attributes like strength, health and energy and attractiveness can be helpful in coping with stressors.

- **Personal and Interpersonal Resources:** these include the "inner" strengths that help us cope with life events. One of the most important resources is that of self-esteem and acceptance of oneself. Ego identity refers to a stable and integrated sense of self; this enables one to keep in touch with social and cultural reality.

- **Informational and Educational Resources:** knowledge and education are most valuable resources. Knowledge and information, in this age of new technology, are sources of income and influence, and of having a sense of control over one's environment.

- **Cultural Resources:** our culture also provides us with a sense of coherence. This resource refers to the extent to which a person has an enduring sense of confidence that there is meaning to life. Beliefs about oneself and religious beliefs are part of this sense of meaning and general life philosophies.

How well employees are able to cope depends on several factors. A transactional view of stress and coping focuses on the dynamic relationship between the employee and the environment. Key coping resources include:

- **Health and Energy:** healthy robust individuals are better able to manage external and internal demands than frail, sick and tired people.

- **Positive Beliefs:** is a second important resource. The ability to cope with stress is enhanced when people believe they have the ability to bring about desired consequences and results.

- **Problem-solving Skills:** the ability to analyse a problem, to identify the pros and cons, to order and sort out information that can eliminate or alleviate a stressor.

- **Social Skills:** the ability to get others to co-operate can be an important source of stress management.

- **Social Support:** is closely related to social skills, and refers to the feeling that one is accepted, loved and valued by others. Social support is very important in coping with stress as well as in preventing stress. It can alleviate job stress by enhancing employee health through fulfilling psychological needs of approval, social contact, security, and affection. It reduces interpersonal conflict and tension and can act as a buffer against stress. Home and a spouse can act as social support and a retreat from the pressures of work. On the other hand, managers who spend long hours at work may be escaping from home pressures.

Organisational Coping Strategies

The work setting is the primary source of stress for many individuals and, although employees can use their own strategies to offset the effects of stress, the organisation has an important role to play in combating stress.

The conditions people work in, as well as the design of work and management style, have been shown to be sources of stress in the workplace. Stress can be avoided by ensuring that jobs are designed so that they avoid situations where individuals experience role conflict, role overload, role ambiguity and role underload. The environment within which employees work can be made more ergonomic by ensuring that work stations and environmental elements, such as lighting and heating, are of the optimal standard.

Organisational culture is indirectly related to stress levels. It may become a norm in organisations to work long hours and refrain from taking time off and, as a result, people suffer from stress. The culture may be used on a number of levels so as to provide a virtuous, rather than a vicious, circle in terms of stress. Cultures may promote the idea of a balance between work and home, thereby reducing the possibility of stress arising from this source. The culture may promote a norm where problems are shared, with a team approach to work in place. This would have the effect of reducing the level of stress associated with interpersonal relationships. Management style may also help promote a healthier workplace.

Lack of control and participation is often cited by employees as a source of stress. More self-directed employees may find this an effective method for preventing stress in the workplace and improving employee performance (Cobb, 1976). It should be noted, however, that while this may prove an effective strategy for many employees it may in itself become a source of stress for others.

Health promotion and stress management programmes instigated by organisations can also teach individuals who are suffering from stress how to deal with it. These are so-called collateral programmes, as they are reactive in nature and do not seek to reduce but rather to deal with stress.

Primary Prevention Strategies

The literature identifies primary prevention strategies that focus primarily on the organisational or work level. There is however limited research identifying their overall effectiveness as stress reducers. **Table 22.2** presents a summary of primary prevention strategies.

Table 22.2: Primary Prevention Strategies Available to the Organisation

---

Clear Company Objectives

Clear policies and procedures, including those that focus on well-being and safety, such as how to deal with stress, conflict, grievance, harassment and complaints.

A Structure which is Supportive of its Employees

Help or guidance needs to be available for all employees, particularly those new to the organisation or new to the role. This can be achieved by developing appropriate supervision, coaching or mentoring programmes.

A Consultative as Opposed to an Autocratic Culture

Managers should be approachable and trained in interpersonal skills, particularly listening skills. Communication needs to be effective up, down and across the organisation, with opportunities for staff to contribute suggestions to the functioning of their own job.

Appraisal

Opportunities for appraisal and feedback need to be provided. Although feedback should be provided on a continuously ongoing basis, there should be at least one annual structured appraisal with the manager to provide peer appraisal, upward appraisal and/or 360-degree feedback.

Appropriate Training and Development of Staff

Systematic training needs analysis should be conducted to identify strengths and areas for improvement.

Flexible Work Schedules

Consideration should be given to employees to allow an appropriate balance between home and work commitments. Examples could be flexibility for parents with young children.

Effective Recruitment Policies

These would ensure that the skill set for a particular role has been clearly defined and that applicants for the roles are being correctly assessed to ensure there is an appropriate match or that they are capable of developing the skills. Organization should examine whether they have the correct assessment tools available and should consider whether there is a need for a professional assessment centre, for psychometric testing or for training their interviewers.

STRESS, THE SAFETY STATEMENT AND
RISK ASSESSMENT PROCESSES

Stress should normally be included in the safety statement and it is desirable to articulate a general policy on stress at work. This policy should establish ways in which the organisation will deal with stress and stress-related issues. This policy can then be incorporated into the general safety statement and it functions should include the following: the establishment of standards and the demonstration of commitment to manage stress; the communication of commitments to employees and the provision of a framework within which to judge activities. The policy itself may follow the guidelines set out in **Figure 22.5**.

Risk assessment should be used as part of the overall approach to stress. A risk assessment can provide valuable information on the intensity of stress, its primary sources and possible preventative and/or remedial strategies that can be implemented by the organisation. It needs to be tailored to each organisation, so that it addresses the specific issues relevant to it and its employees. Because perceived stress changes from day-to-day and from week-to-week, an assessment will provide only a snapshot at a particular time of the health and well-being of the organisation and the workforce.

It is not essential that an occupational psychologist should conduct the assessment. In some cases managers can conduct the assessments. If a manager conducts an assessment, important criteria are whether the assessor can be objective, be accepting of critical feedback, and be willing to change.

Figure 22.5: Model Extract from the Safety Statement regarding Stress at Work

---

1. This organisation accepts that some work activities have the potential to cause stress, particularly at busy times. The formal terms of many employees' contracts on hours is 9.00am to 5.00pm with one hour for lunch although most employees are expected to work such hours as may be necessary to get the job done, and care is taken in recruitment policy to ensure that each person's workload is reasonable.

2. Managers, when performing risk assessments on the activities of their department, will pay special attention to potential risks from stress and signs of stress at work and these risks will have to be noted.

3. This organisation has an arrangement with an Employee Assistance Scheme, which offers confidential and individual counselling and other advice to employees, who may need it.

4. Any individual with clear stress-related problems shall receive appropriate counselling and help from the organisation and shall be encouraged to make use of the Employment Assistance Scheme but it is understood that this is not an alternative to looking at the cause of the stress and, if work-related, seeking to alter the structure and working arrangements of the job.

5. Following action to reduce the risks, they shall be reassessed. If the risks remain unsustainable by the employee concerned, efforts shall be made to reassign that person to other work for which the risks are assessed as tolerable.

6. If it is not possible to reassign the worker to work that the employee concerned is capable of carrying out, the procedures for long-term ill health shall be applied in accordance with the organisation's policy on such matters and employment law.

7. The organisation will provide and maintain a suitable, smoke-free room for individuals to take breaks from their work activity at appropriate times. The timing and duration of such breaks are at the discretion of the line manager.

The manager can check some or all of the following as part of the risk assessment process:

• During assessment of work activities, the line manager can check shift patterns, especially if they involve night work —

are they reasonable and are the individuals working those shifts suitable for this sort of work?

- Check legal position if they are clearly not suitable: manual handling — exposure to these risks can lead to stress — ventilation, space allocation, and lighting. Are appropriate standards being adhered to?

- Any work liable to cause fatigue, physical or mental work involving long hours on a day-to-day basis. Is the worker routinely working late/taking work home to perform a job that should be do-able in a reasonable working day?

- Any work in which the taking of rest breaks may be a problem.

- Any work which could pose a stress hazard to an employee.

- Check absence records and, if any are higher than the average of five working days a year lost, look for signs of stress.

CHAPTER ROUND-UP

- This chapter considered a major contemporary occupational health issue of occupational stress. Contemporary organisations are characterised by self-induced stress, where individuals pushed themselves towards the edge to achieve personal success and material gain. It is also a time of imposed stress as managers and other employees attempt to survive in competitive times.

- Stress is any force that places a psychological or physical factor beyond its range of stability, producing strain within the individual. Knowledge that stress is likely to occur constitutes a threat to the individual. A threat can cause strain because of what it signifies to the individual. Stress can also be defined to include burnout and post-traumatic stress disorder. It is suggested that occupations differ in terms of stresses and risks to health.

- Certain stresses and strains are associated with different aspects of organisational life. These include role overload, role complexity, role ambiguity, boundary roles, responsibility for people, machine-paced and repetitive work, decision latitude and job control, shift work, new technology in the form of VDU work, hierarchical level, work relationships, career development, redundancy and unemployment, early retirement, and personality factors including locus of control.

• A number of remedies to prevent or counteract stressful situations are available to both individuals and organisations. These range from psychotherapy and meditation to nutritional balance in intake of food, regular exercise, a balanced personal and social existence and social support. Preventative health management is also important. These include health promotion programmes, including workplace wellness programmes.

• It is generally considered that legal actions under employers' duty of care resulting from stress are not only possible but likely. Stress at work has increased and, with it, potential for claims is considerable. Recent case law establishes the precedent that an employee who suffers stress at work can successfully sue their employer under the duty of care principle.

BIBLIOGRAPHY

Adam, C.S. (1965) *Inequity in Social Exchange: Advances in Experimental Social Psychology*, New York: Academic.

Adams, A., (1992) "Bully at Work Contributes Significantly to Workplace Stress", in *Industrial Relations Review and Report*, November.

Adams, A., (1992) "Holding out Against Workplace Harassment and Bullying", in *Personnel Management*, Vol. 24, No. 10, October.

Adams, A., (1992) *Bullying at Work: How to Confront it and Overcome it*, Virago Press, London.

Adams, J. (1976) "Issues for a Closed Loop Theory on Motor Learning" in G. Stelmach (ed) *Motor Control Issues and Trends*. New York: Academic.

Adams, L. and Zucherman, D (1991) "The Effect of Lighting Conditions on Personal Space Requirements", *Journal of General Psychology*, 118, 335-40.

Adams, S. and Trucks, L. (1976) "A Procedure for Evaluating Auditory Warning Signals" in Proceedings of the 6th Congress of the International Ergonomics Ass. and Technical Program for the 20th Annual Meeting of the Human Factors Society, Santa Monica, CA: Human Factors Society, pp. 166-172.

Adler, A. (1941), "The Psychology of Repeated Accidents in Industry", *American Journal of Psychiatry*, 98:99-101

Aiken, L. (1992) *Psychological Testing and Assessments*, ninth edition, London: Allyn and Bacon.

Akerstedt, T. and Torsvall, T. (1981) "Shift Work: Shift-Dependent Well-Being and Industrial Differences". *Ergonomics*, 24, 265-273

Alderfer, C.P. (1972) *Existence, Relatedness and Growth: Human Needs in Organisational Settings*, New York: Free Press.

Alexander, M., Cox, S. and Cheyne, A. (1995) *UK Offshore Safety Culture*, Paper presented at the "Understanding Risk Perception" Conference, Aberdeen, February.

Allport, G.W. (1960) *Personality and Social Encounter*, Berkeley, CA: Beacon Press.

Allport, G.W. (1965) *Letters from Jenny*, New York: Harcourt, Brace and World.

American Industrial Hygiene Association (1992) *Guidelines on Industrial Hygiene*, Washington: AIHA.

Amis, H. and Booth, R.T. (1991) *Monitoring Health and Safety Management*, London: Institution of Occupational Safety and Health.

Andersson, G.B.T. (1986) "Loads on the Spine During Sitting", in *The Ergonomics of Working Postures*, London: Taylor and Francis.

Anonymous (1998) "The Bully Leaves School and Heads for the Office", in *Management Today*, February.

Anonymous (1999) "Illness and Absence due to Workplace Bullying", in *Employers' Platform*, September.

Aquino, K., Grover, S., Bradfield, M., and Allen, D., (1999) "The Effects of Negative Affectivity, Hierarchical Status, and Self-Determination on Workplace Victimisation", in *Academy of Management Journal*, Vol. 24, Issue 3, June.

Arbous, A. G. and Kerrich, J. E. (1951): 'Accident Statistics and the Concept of Accident Proneness', *Biometrics*, 7, (4), 340-42.

Argelis, M., Dores, G. and Quin, T. (1974) "Job Stress: An Unlisted Occupation — A Hazard", *Journal of Occupational Medicine*, 16, 10, 654-61.

Armstrong, T.J., Buckle, P.D., Fine, L.J., Hagberg, M., Jonssen, B., Kilbom, A., Kourinkal, P., Silverstein, B.A., Sjogaard, G. and Viikari-Jantura, E.R.A. (1993) "A Conceptual Model for Work-Related Neck and Upper Limb Musculoskeletal Disorders", *Scandinavian Journal of Work Environment and Health*, 19: 73-84.

Arnold, J., Cooper, C.L. and Robertson, I.T. (1995), *Work Psychology: Understanding Human Behaviour in the Workplace*, second edition, London: Pitman.

Athearn, J.L. and Pritchett, S.J. (1984) *Risk and Insurance*, St. Paul, MN: West Publishing.

Ayoub, M.M. (1973) "Work Place Design and Posture", *Human Factors*, 15, 265-268.

Barber, P. (1987) *Applied Cognitive Psychology, An Information Processing Framework*, London: Methuen

Bardana, E.J., Montanaro, A. and O'Hallaren, M.T. (1988) "Building Related Illness — A Review of the Available Scientific Data", *Clinical Reviews in Allergy*, 6, 61-89.

Barnes, G.R., Benson, A.J. and Prior, A.R.J. (1978) "Visual — Vestibular Interaction in the Control of Eye Movement", *Aviation, Space and Environmental Medicine*, 49, 557-64.

Barnes, R.M. (1963) *Motion and Time Study*, New York: Wiley

Barrington Consumer Report (1983) *Report of the Commission of Inquiry on Safety, Health and Welfare at Work*, Dublin: Government Publications.

Bartlett, F.C. (1950) "Programme for Experiments of Thinking", *Quarterly Journal of Experimental Psychology*, 2, 145-52.

Barton, N.J., Hooper, G., Noble, J. and Steel, W.M. (1992) "Occupational Causes of Disorders in the Upper Limb", *British Medical Journal*, 304:309-311.

Baxter, C.E. (1987) Low Back Pain and Time of Day: A Study of the Effects on Psychophysical Performance. Ph.D. Thesis, University of Liverpool.

Beacham, J. (1976) *The Cost of Accidents Within the Port Industry*, London: Manpower Services Commission.

Beck, U. (1992) *Risk Society: Towards a New Modernity*, London: Sage.

Beirinq-Sorensen, F. (1984) "Physical Measurements at Risk Indicators for Low Back Trouble over a One-year Period", *Spine*, 9: 106-119.

Bell, C.R., Crowder, M.J. and Walters, J.D. (1976) "Effects of Job Enrichment and Task Goals on Satisfaction and Productivity: Implications for Job Design", *Journal of Applied Psychology*, 61, 4, 379-394.

Bellingar, T. and Slocum, A. (1993) "Effect of Protective Gloves on Hand Movement: An Exploratory Study", *Applied Ergonomics*, 24, 244-50.

Bem, D.J. (1967) "Self-Perception: An Alternative Interpretation of Cognitive Dissonance Phenomena", *Psychological Review*, 74, 3, 183-200.

Benson, H. (1975) *The Relaxation Response*, New York: William Marrow.

Berry, A. (1991) "Management Development", Manchester Business School Research Newsletter, 13, 5.

Bird, F.E (1966) *Damage Control*, New York: American Management Association

Bird, P.F. (1977) "Digilux Touch-Sensitive Panel in Displays for Man–Machines Systems", IEE Conference Publication, No 150, London: IEE.

Blake, M.J.F. (1971) "Temperament and Time of Day" in W.P. Colquhoun (ed) *Biological Rhythms and Human Performance*. London: Academic.

Bohle, P. and Tilley, A.J. (1989) "The Impact of Night Work on Psychological Well Being", *Ergonomics*, 32, 1089-1099.

Bouma, H. (1980) "Visual Reading Processes and the Quality of Text Displays", in E. Grandjean and E. Vigliani (eds) *Ergonomic Aspects of Visual Display Terminals*, London: Taylor and Francis.

Boyle, A. J. (1980): "'Found Experiments" in Accident Research: Report of a Study of Accident Rates and Implications for Future Research', *Journal of Occupational Psychology*, 53, (1), 53-64.

Bradley, J.W. (1967) "Tactual Coding of Cylindrical Knobs", *Human Factors*, 9, 483-96.

Bradley, J.W. (1969) "Glove Characteristics Influencing Control Manipulability", *Human Factors*, 11, 21-36.

Brand, J.L. and Judd, K.W. (1993) "Angle of Hard Copy and Text Editing Performance", *Human Factors*, 35, 57-69.

Branton, P. (1983) "Ergonomic Research Contribution to the Design of the Passenger Environment", paper presented to the Institute of Mechanic Engineers Symposium on Passenger Comfort, London.

Branton, P. and Grayson, G. (1967) "An Evaluation of Train Seats by an Observation of Sitting Behaviour", *Ergonomics*, 10, 35-41.

Brenner, S.N. (1977) "Are the ethics of business changing?", *Harvard Business Reviews*. January-February, 57-71.

Breslow, J. and Buell, T. (1960) "Mortality from Coronary Heart Disease and Physical Activity of Work in California", *Journal of Chronic Diseases*, 11, 615-25.

Bridger, R.S. (1995) *Introduction to Ergonomics*, New York: McGraw Hill.

Briscoe T. (1995) "Is Health and Safety an Industrial Relations Issue?" From a Recent Talk to the Irish Association of Industrial Relations in Dublin.

Broadbent, D. and Gath, G. (1981) "Ill-Health on the Line: Sorting Out Myth from Fact" *Employment Gazette*, March, 157-160.

Broberg, E. (1984) "Use of Census Data Combined with Occupation and Accident Data", *Journal of Occupational Accidents*, 6: 147-153.

Brook, A. (1973) "Mental Stress at Work", *The Practitioner*, 210-500-506.

Brookes, M.J. (1972) "Office Landscape: Does it Work?", *Applied Ergonomics*, 3, 224-36.

Brookler, R. (1992) "Industry Standards in Workplace Drug Testing", *Personnel Journal*, April, pp. 123-32.

Brooks, L.R. (1968) "Spatial and Verbal Components in the Act of Recall", *Canadian Journal of Psychology*, 22, pp. 349-368.

Brown, J., Peterson, R., and Peterson, T. (1959) cited in Sanders, M.S. and McCormick, E.J., *Human Factors in Engineering and Design*, New York: McGraw-Hill.

Brunswic, M. (1984) "Ergonomics of Seat Design", *Physiotherapy*, 70, 39-43.

Buck, V. (1972) *Working Under Pressure*, London: Staples Press.

Buckle, P.W. and Stubbs, D.A. (1986) "Musculo-Skeletal Disorders (and Discomfort) and Associated Work Factors", in Corlett et al. (1972).

Burge, S., Hedge, A., Wilson, S., Bass, J.H. and Robertson, A. (1987) "Sick Building Syndrome: A Study of 4373 Office Workers", *Annals of Occupational Hygiene*, 31, 493-504.

Burroughs, S.M. and Jones, J.W. (1995) "Managing Violence: Looking out for Trouble", *Occupational Health and Safety*, 34-37).

Burrows, A.A. (1965) "Control Feel and the Dependent Variable", *Human Factors*, 7, 413-21.

Burton, A.K., Tilletson, K.M. and Troup, J.D.G. (1989) "Variation in Lumbar Saggital Mobility with Low Back Trouble", *Spine*, 14, 584-590.

Buswell, G.T. (1935) *How People Look at Pictures*, Chicago: University of Chicago Press.

Butler, D.S. (1991) *Mobilisation of the Nervous System*, Edinburgh: Churchill Livingstone.

Byrne, D., Baskett, G.D. and Hodges, L. (1971) "Behavioural Indicators of Interpersonal Attraction", *Journal of Applied Social Psychology*, 1, 137-49.

Byrne, R. (1994) *A Guide to Safety. Health and Welfare at Work Regulation.* Dublin: NIFAST.

Canter, D. and Donald, I. (1990), "Accident by Design: Environmental Attitudinal and Organisational Aspects of Accidents", Culture Space History, Proceedings of the 11th International Conference of the International Association for the Study of People and their Physical Settings, Ankara, Turkey, 8-12 July 1990.

Card, S.K., English, W.K. and Burr, B.J. (1978) "Evaluation of Mouse, Rat-Controlled Isometric Joystick, Step Keys and Text Keys for Text Solution on a CRT", *Ergonomics*, 21, 601-613.

Carpentier, J. and Cazamian, P. (1977) *Night Work: Its Affects on the Health and Welfare of the Worker*, Geneva: International Labour Office.

Catovic, A., Kosovel, Z., Catovic, E. and Muftic, O. (1989) "A Comparative Investigation of the Influence of Certain Arm Positions on Hand Pinch Grips in the Standing and Sitting Positions of Dentists", *Applied Ergonomics*, 20, 109-14.

Cattell, R.B. (1965) *The Scientific Analysis of Personality*, Harmondsworth: Penguin.

CBI (1991) *Developing a Safety Culture*, London: CBI.

Chapanis, A. (1960) "Human Engineering" in C.D. Fagle, W.H. Higgins and R.N. Roy (eds,) *Operations Research and Systems Engineering*, Baltimore, MD: The Johns Hopkins University Press.

Chapanis, A. (1976) "Engineering Psychology" in M.D. Dunnette (ed) *Handbook of Industrial Psychology*, Chicago: Rand McNally.

Cherns, A. (1976) "The Principals of Sociotechnical Design", *Human Relations*, 29 787-792.

Chiringelli, L. (1980) "Collection of Subjective Opinions on the Use of VDUs", in E. Grandjean and E. Vigliani (eds) *Ergonomic Aspects of Visual Display Terminals*, London: Taylor and Francis.

Chokkar, J.S. and Wallin, J.A. (1984) "A Field Study of the Effect of Feedback Frequency on Performance", *Journal of Applied Psychology*, 69, 524-30.

Clarke, (1951) "The Limiting Hand Skin Temperature for Unaffected Manual Performance in the Cold", *Journal of Applied Psychology*, 45, 193-4.

Clarke, R. (1993) *Contract*, London: Sweet and Maxwell

Cobb, S. (1976) "Social Support as A Moderator of Life Stress", *Psychosomatic Medicine* 38 300-314.

Coch, L. and French, J.R.P. (1948) "Overcoming Resistance to Change", *Human Relations*, 1, 512-32

Cochran, D.J., Albin, I.J., Riley, M.W. and Bishu, R.R. (1986) "Analysis of Grasp Force Degradation with Commercially Available Gloves", Proceedings of the Human Factors Society 1986, Human Factors Society.

Cody, L.D., Bischoff, D.P., O'Connell, E.R., Thomas, P.C. and Allen, J.H. (1974) "Strength and Fitness and Subsequent Back Injuries of Firefighters", *Journal of Occupational Medicine*, 21, 269-279.

Coe, J.B., Cuttle, K., McCledon, W.C., Warden, N.J. and Yurner, P.J. (1980) "Visual Display Units", Report W/1/80 Wellington: New Zealand Press.

Coleshaw, S.R.K., Van Someren, R.N.M., Wolff, A.H., Davis, H.M. and Keatinge, W.R. (1983) "Impaired Memory Registration and Speed of Reasoning Caused by Low Body Temperature", *Journal of Applied Psychology: Respiration, Environmental and Exercise Physiology*, 55, 27-31.

Colquhoun, W.P. (1971) "Evaluation of Auditory, Visual and Dual-made Displays for Prolonged Sonar Monitoring in Repeated Sessions", *Human Factors*, 17,425-37.

Colquhoun, W.P. (1975) "Accidents, Injuries and Shiftwork", paper presented to NIOSH Symposium on Shiftwork and Health, Cincinnati, OH.

Connaughton, M. (1998) "Implications of Employment Law: Organisation of Working Time", Graphite HRM Ltd, Dublin.

Connaughton, M. (1998) "Wrestling with the Minefield of Working Time Restrictions", Graphite HRM Ltd, Dublin.

Connaughton, M.G. (1998) "Organisation of Working Time Act, 1997" in *Handling Employment Law Issues 1998: A Practical and Comprehensive Guide*, Vol. 1, University Industry Centre, UCD, Belfield, Dublin.

Cooper, C.L (1979) *The Executive Gypsy: The Quality of Managerial Life*, London: Macmillan.

Cooper, C.L., Cooper, R.D., and Eaker, L.H. (1988) *Living with Stress*, London: Penguin.

Cooper, M.D. (1998) *Improving Safety Culture. A Practical Guide*, Chichester: Wiley.

Corlett, E.N., Hutcheson, C., deLugan, M.A. and Rogozenski, J. (1972) "Ramps or Stairs: The Choice using Physiological and Biomechanical Criteria", *Applied Ergonomics*, 3, 195-201.

Costigan, L. (1998) *Bullying and Harassment in the Workplace*, Columba Press, Dublin.

Courtney, A.J. (1994) "Hong Kong Chinese Direction-of-Motion Stereotypes", *Ergonomics*, 37: 417-426.

Cox T. (1985) "The Nature and Management of Stress", *Ergonomics*, 28, 1155-1163

Cox, S. (1996) "Maximising Performance: The Impact of Positive Safety Culture". Paper presented at the 5th Offshore Installation Managers Conference, April, Aberdeen.

Cox, S. and Cox, T. (1991) "The Structure of Employee Attitudes to Safety: A European Example", *Work and Stress*, 5, 93-106.

Cox, S. and Cox, T. (1996) *Safety, Systems and People*. Oxford: Butterworth-Heinemann.

Cox, S. and Flin, R. (1998) "Safety Culture: Philosopher's Stone or Man of Straw?" *Work and Stress* (Special issue on safety culture), 12 (3) 189-201.

Cox, S., Cheyne, A.J.T, and Alexander, M. (1997) "Safety Culture in Offshore Environments". Paper presented at the International Ergonomics Association Annual Conference, June, Tampera, Finland.

Cox, S., James, J.E., Cheyne, A.J.T., and Oliver, A. (1998) "Safety Culture: The Prediction of Commitment to Safety in Manufacturing Industry", *British Journal of Management*, 9 (3), 3-11.

Cox, S.J. and Tait, N.H.S. (1991) *Reliabilty, Safety and Risk Management: An Integrated Approach*, Oxford: Butterworth.

Cox, T. (1987) "Stress Coping and Problem Solving", *Work and Stress*, 1, 4-14.

Cribb, J. (1992) "Big Cost of Sick Buildings", *Australian*, 4 April, p. 49.

Crook, M.A. and Langdon, E.J. (1974) "The Effects of Aircraft Noise in Schools around London Airport", *Journal of Sound and Vibration*, 12, 221-32.

CSO Labour Force Survey (1993), Dublin: CSO.

Culbert, S. (1974) *The Organisation Trap,* New York: Basic Books.

Dainoff, M.J. (1982) "Occupational Stress Factors in Visual Display Terminal (VDT) Operation: A Review of Empirical Research", *Behaviour and Information Technology*, 1, 141-76.

Damon, A., Stoudt, H.W. and McFarland, R.A. (1971) *The Human Body in Equipment Design*, Cambridge, MA: Harvard University Press.

Davis, A. and Gibson, L. (1994) "Designing Employee Welfare Provision", in J.R. Berridge and C.C. Cooper (eds.) The Employee Assistance Programme: Its Role in Organisational Coping and Excellence, *Personnel Review*, Vol. 23, No. 7, pp. 33-45.

Davis, D.R. (1958) "Human Errors and Transport Accidents", *Ergonomics*, 2, 24-3.

Dawson, S. (1991) "Managing Safety Offshore. Offshore Operations Post Proper Alpha", London, 6-8 February (Paper 13) London: Marine Management (Holdings) Ltd.

Dawson, S., Willman, P., Bamford, M. and Clinton, A. (1983), *Safety at Work: The Limits of Self-Regulation*, Cambridge: Cambridge University Press.

Dawson, S.,William, Pl, Clinton, A, Bamford, M. (1988) *Safety at Work: The Limits of Self-Regulation*, Cambridge, England: Cambridge University Press.

De Bobes, L. (1986) "The Psychological Factors in Accident Prevention", *The Work Environment*, Melville, New York.

De Wall, M., Van Riel, M.P.J.M., Snijders, C.J. and Van Wingerden, J.P. (1991) "The Effect of Sitting Posture of a Desk with a 10 degree Inclination for Reading and Writing", *Ergonomics*, 34, 575-84.

Deatherage, B.H. (1972) "Auditory and Other Sensory Forms of Information Presentation", in H.P. Van Cott and R.G. Kinkade (eds) *Human Engineering Guide to System Design*, Washington, DC: US Government Printing Office.

Dedobbeleer, N. and Beland, F. (1991) "A Safety Climate Measure for Construction Sites", *Journal of Safety Research*, 22, 97-103.

DeGreen, K.B. (1972) "Systems Theory, Macroergonomics and the Design of Adaptive Organisations" in *Human Factors in Organisational Design and Management*, North Holland, NY: North Holland.

Deloitte and Touche (1996) "Report on the Economic Evaluation of Insurance Costs in Ireland", Dublin: Department of Enterprise and Employment.

DeMattoe, B. (1985) *Terminal Shock: The Health Hazards of VDUs*, NTC Press.

Denenberg, H.S., Eilers, R.D., Melone, J.J. and Zelten, R.A. (1974) *Risk and Insurance*, Englewood Cliffs, NJ: Prentice Hall Inc.

Denison, D. (1996) "What is the difference between Organisational Culture and Organisational Climate? A Native's Point of View on a Decade of Paradigm Wars", *Academy of Management Review*, 21 (3) 619-654.

Deves, L. (1989) "Policy and Action in Occupational Health: A Question of Ideology", *Journal of Occupational Health and Safety*, Vol. 5, No. 2, pp. 11-121

Dewar, M.E. (1977) "Body Movements When Climbing a Ladder", *Ergonomics*, 1, 347-55.

Diamond, J. (1991) "Pearl Harbour and the Emperor's Physiologists", *Natural History*, 12: 5-7.

Dickson, G. (1989) "Risk Management: What does the Future Hold?", *Journal of Society of Fellows*, London: Chartered Insurance Institute, Vol. 4, July.

Donald, I. and Canter, D. (1993) "Psychological Factors and the Accident Plateau", *Health and Safety Information Bulletin*, 21 (5), 5-8.

Donald, I. And Canter, D. (1994) "Employee Attitude and Safety in the Chemical Industry", *Journal of Loss Prevention in the Process Industries*, 7, 203-208.

Donald, I. and Young, S. (1996) "Managing Safety and Attitudinal-Based Approach to Improving Safety in Organisations", *Leadership and Organisational Development Journal*, 17 (4), 17-25.

Donald, T. and Carter, D. (1993) "Psychological Factors and the Accident Plateau" *Health and Safety Information Bulletin*, Vol. 215, 5-8, November.

Douglas, M. (1966) *Purity and Danger: An Analysis of Concepts of Pollution and Taboo*, London: Routledge and Kegan Paul.

Douglas, M. (1992) *Risk and Blame*, London: Routledge.

Doyle, D., (1998) "Managers May Very Often be Bullies", in *Business and Finance*, November 5.

Dunbar, H.F., Wolfe, R.P. and Rioch, J. (1936) "The Psychic Component in Fracture" Part 1 *American Journal of Psychiatry*; 93; 649-79.

Dunbar, R.L. (1975) "Manager's Influence on Subordinate Thinking about Safety", *Academy of Management Journal*, 18, 364-369.

Dunne, E. (2000): *The Psychology of Working Safely*, Dublin: Blackhall Publishing

Eason, K.D. (1991) "Ergonomic Perspectives on Advances in Human-Computer Interaction", *Ergonomics*, 34, 721-42.

Eiro, (1998) "The EU Parental Leave Agreement and Directive: Implications for National Law and Practice", European Foundation for the Improvement of Living and Working Conditions, January.

Eklund, J.A.E. (1988) "Organisation of Assembly Work: Recent Swedish Examples" in E.D. Megaw (ed) *Contemporary Ergonomics*, London: Taylor and Francis, pp 351-356.

Ellis, H.D. (1982) "The Effects of Cold on the Performance of Serial Choice Reaction Time and Various Discrete Tasks", *Human Factors*, 21, 161-8.

Embrey, D.E. (1992) "Incorporating Management and Organisational Factors into Probabilistic Safety Assessment", *Reliability Engineering and System Safety*, 38, 199-208.

English, C.J., Maclaren, W.M., Court-Brown, C., Hughes, S.P.F., Breter, R.W., Wallace, W.A., Graves, R.J., Pethick, A.J. and Soutar, C.A. (1989) "Clinical Epidemiological Study of Relations between Upper Limb Soft Tissue Disorders and Repetitive Movements at Work", Report No. TM/88/19, Institute of Occupational Medicine, Edinburgh.

Ericson and Kallen (1986) "An Epidemiological Study of Work with Video and Pregnancy Outcome, A Register Study" *American Journal of Industrial Medicine*, 9, 447-457.

European Foundation (1997) *Health and Safety within the European Community*, Brussels: European Foundation.

Evans, D. and Ginsburg, A. (1985) "Contrast Sensitivity Predicts Age-Related Differences in Highway Sign Discriminability", *Human Factors*, 27, 637-642.

Evans, G.W. and Howard, R.B. (1973) "Personal Space", *Psychological Bulletin*, 80, 334-44.

Eysenck, H.J. (1987) "Speed of Information Processing, Recreation Time and the Theory of Intelligence", in P.A. Vernon (ed) *Speed of Information Processing and Intelligence* (pp 21-67) Norwood, NJ: Ablex.

Fagin, L.H. (1979) "The Experience of Unemployment (I): The Impact of Unemployment", *New Universities Quarterly*, Winter, 48-64.

Fahy, D., (1998) "Parental Leave Rules are Miserly, says SIPTU", in *The Irish Times*, 08, 07, 98.

Farmer, E. and Chambers, E.G. (1926) "A Psychological Study of Individual Differences in Accident Rates" Report No. 38 Industrial Fatigue Research Board, Medical Research Council, 1-46.

Fellows, G.L. and Freivalds, A. (1991) "Ergonomics Evaluation of a Foam Rubber Grip for Tool Handles", *Applied Ergonomics*, 22, 225-30.

Fennell, C. and Lynch, I. (1994) *Labour Law in Ireland*, Dublin: Gill and Macmillan.

Ferguson, D.A. (1987) "RSI: Putting the Epidemic to Rest", *Medical Journal of Australia*, 147, 213-214.

Festinger, L. (1957) *A Theory of Cognitive Dissonance*, New York: Harper and Row.

Field, T. (1996) *Bully in Sight: How to Predict, Resist, Challenge and Combat Workplace Bullying*, Oxfordshire: Wessex Press.

Fielder, F.E., Bell, C.H. Jr., Chemers, M.M., and Patrick, D. (1984) "Increasing Mine Productivity and Safety Through Management Training and Organisational Development: A comparative Study", *Basic and Applied Social Psychology*, 5, 1-18.

Fishbein, P.M. and Ajzen, I. (1975) *Belief, Attitudes, Intention and Behaviour: An Introduction to Theory and Research*, Reading, MA: Addison-Wesley.

Fisher, S. (1985) "Control and Blue-Collar Work", in C.L. Cooper and M.J. Smith (eds) *Job Stress and Blue-Collar Work*, Chichester: Wiley.

Fitch, J.M., Templer, J. and Corcoran, P. (1974) "The Dimensions of Stairs", *Scientific American*, 231, 82-90.

Fitts, P.M. and Jones, R.E. (1947) "Analysis of Factors Contributing to 460 'Pilot-Error' Experiences in Operating Aircraft Controls", Report on Aeronautical Laboratory, Wright Patterson Air Force Base, Dayton, OH.

Fitzgerald, J. (1973) "The IAM type Aircrew Lumbar Support: Fitting, Manufacture and Use", Aircrew Equipment Group Report No. 304, Institute of Aviation Medicine, Farnborough, Hampshire.

Floyd, W.F. and Ward, J.S. (1969) "Anthropometric and Physiological Considerations in School, Office and Factory Setting", *Ergonomics*, 12, 132-9.

Folkard, S. and Monk, T.H. (1979) "Shiftwork and Performance", *Human Factors*, 21, 483-92.

Folkard, S. and Monk, T.H. (1985) *Hours of Work: Temporal Work Factors in Work-Scheduling*, Chichester: John Wiley.

Folkard, S., Monk, T.H. and Chobban, M.C. (1978) "Short and Long Term Adjustment of Circadian Rhythms in 'Permanent' Night Nurses", *Ergonomics*, 21, 785-99.

Foot, F. and Hook, C. (1999) *Introducing Human Resource Management*, London: Longman.

Foran, M. "Sticks and Stones", in *The Revenue Group Journal*, October, (1999).

Fowler, R.L., Williams, W.E., Fowler, M.G. and Young, D.D. (1968) "An Investigation into the Relationship between Operator Performance and Operator Panel Layout for Continuous Tasks", Ohio: USAF AMRL-TR-68-170.

Fox, B.H. (1978) "Premorbid Psychological Factors", *Journal of Behavioural Medicine*, Vol. 1 (I).

Fox, J.G. (1983) "Industrial Music", in D.J. Oborne and M.M. Gruneberg (eds) *The Physical Environment at Work*, Chichester: John Wiley.

Fox, W.F. (1967) "Human Performance in the Cold", *Human Factors*, 9, 203-20.

French, J.R.P. and Caplan, R.D. (1970) "Psychological Factors in Coronary Heart Disease", *Industrial Medicine*, 39, 383-397.

French, J.R.P. and Caplan, R.D. (1972) "Organisational Stress and Individual Strain" in A. Marrow (ed) *The Failure of Success*, New York: Amacom.

Freud, S. (1938) *The Basic Writings of Sigmund Freud*, New York: Modern Library

Fried, M.L. and DeFrazio, V.T. (1974) "Territoriality and Boundary Conflicts in the Subway", *Psychiatry*, 37, 47-59.

Friedman, M. and Rosenman, R.H. (1964) *Type A Behaviour and Your Heart*, New York: Knopf.

Frost, B. (1990) "Fireman Awarded £34,000 for Trauma after King's Cross", *The Times*, 19 December, p. 3.

Fryer, D. and Payne, R. (1986) "Being Unemployed", in C.L. Cooper and I.T. Robertson (eds) *International Review of Industrial and Organisational Psychology*, Chichester: John Wiley.

Frymoyer, J.W. (1988) "Back Pain and Sciatica", *New England Journal of Medicine*, 318, 219-300.

Frymoyer, J.W., Pope, M.H., Clements, J.H., Wilder, D.G., MacPherson, B. and Ashikaga, T. (1983) "Risk Factors in Low Back Pain", *Journal of Bone and Joint Surgery*, 65A, 213-218.

Fynes, B., Morrissey, T., Roche, W.K., Whelan, B.J., and Williams, J. (1996) *Flexible Working Lives: The Changing Nature of Working Time Arrangements in Ireland*, Dublin: Oak Tree Press.

Gawron, V. (1982) "Performance Effects of Noise Intensity, Psychological Set, and Task Type and Complexity", *Human Factors*, 24, 225-243.

Ghiringhelli, L. (1980) "Collection of Subjective Opinions on the Use of VDUs", in E. Grandjean and E. Vigliani (eds) *Ergonomic Aspects of VDTs*, London: Taylor and Francis.

Gilsbreacht, G.G., Arnett, J.L., Vela, E. and Bristow, G.K. (1993) "Effect of Task Complexity on Mental Performance During Immersion Hypothermia", *Aviation, Space and Environmental Medicine*, 64, 206-11.

Glendon, A.I. and McKenna, E.F. (1995) *Human Safety and Risk Management: A Psychological Perspective*, London: Chapman and Hall.

Goldhaber, M.K., Polen, M.R. and Hiatt, R.A. (1988) "The Risk of Miscarriage and Birth Defects among Women Who Use VDTs during Pregnancy", *American Journal of Industrial Medicine*, B, 695-706.

Gopher, D., Olin, M., Badhih, Y., Cohen, G., Donchin, Y., Bieski, M. and Gotev, S. (1989) "The Nature and Causes of Human Errors in a Medical Intensive Care Unit", Proceedings of the 32nd Annual Meeting of the Human Factors Society. Santa Monica, CA: Human Factors Society .

Grandjean, E. (1973) *Ergonomics in the Home*, London: Taylor and Francis.

Grandjean, E. (1987) *Ergonomics in Computerised Offices*, London: Taylor and Francis.

Grandjean, E. (1988) *Fitting the Task to the Man — A Textbook of Occupational Ergonomics*, London: Taylor and Francis.

Grandjean, E., Hunting, W., and Hedernann, M. (1983) "VDT Workstations Design: Preferred Settings and their Effects", *Human Factors*, 25, 161-75.

Green, M.R. and Serbein, O.N. (1983) *Risk Management: Text and Cases*, Virginia: Reston Publishing.

Greenford, B. (1991) "Perceptions of Risk Management in the United Kingdom and Republic of Ireland and South Africa", Report of Insurance Economists, University of Nottingham.

Greenwood, M., Woods, H.M. and Yule, G.U. (1991) "The Incidence of Industrial Accidents Upon Individuals, with Reference to Multiple Accidents", Industrial Fatigue Research Board, Report No. 4, London.

Grieco, A., (1986) "Sitting Posture: An Old Problem and a New One", *Ergonomics*, 29, 345-362.

Griffin, M.J. (1976) "Vibration and Visual Activity" in W. Tempest (ed) *Infrasound and Low Frequency Vibration*, London: Academic.

Griffin, M.J. (1990) *Handbook of Human Vibration*, London: Academic.

Hackman, J.R. and Oldman, G. (1976) "Motivation Through the Design of Work: Test of a Theory", *Organisational Behaviour and Human Performance*, 16, 250-79.

Hale, A. and Glendon, I. (1987) *Individual Behaviour in the Control of Danger*, Amsterdam: Elsevier.

Hall, E.T. (1976) "The Anthropology of Space: An Organising Model", in H.M Proshansky, W.H. Ittleson and L.R. Rivlin (eds) *Environmental Psychology*, second edition, New York: Holt, Rinehart and Winston.

Hammett, J. (1994) "The Changing Work Environment: High Technology and the Baby Boomers Challenge Management to Adopt", *Employment Relations Today*, 11 (3) 297-304.

Hammond, J. (1978) *Understanding Human Engineering, An Introduction to Ergonomics*, Newton Abbot, UK: David and Charles.

Handy, C. (1975) "Difficulty of Combining Family and Career", *The Times*, 22nd September, p. 16.

Hanna, J.M. and Brown, D.A. (1979) "Human Heart Tolerance: Biological and Cultural Adaptions", *Yearbook of Physical Anthropology*, 22: 163-186.

Hannabuss, S. (1998) "Bullying at Work", in *Library Management*, Vol. 19, No. 5.

Hansen, C. P. (1989): 'A Causal Model of the Relationship among Accidents, Biodata, Personality and Cognitive Factors', Journal of Applied Psychology, 74(1), 81-90.

Hansen, C.P. (1988) "Personality Characteristics of the Accident Involved Employee", *Journal of Business and Psychology*, 2: 346-65.

Hart, B., (1982) "Working Time: A Review of Problems and Policies within a Collective Bargaining Framework", IIM/LMP 82-26, Wissenschaftszentrum, Berlin.

Hayward, M.G. and Keatinge, W.R. (1981) "Roles of Subcutaneous Fat and Thermoregulatory Reflexes in Determining Ability to Stabilise Body Temperature in Water", *Journal of Physiology*, 320, 229-51.

Healy, A.F. (1975) "Temporal-Spatial Patterns in Short-Term Memory", *Journal of Verbal Learning and Verbal Behaviour*, 14: 481-495.

Heglin, H. (1973) *NAVSHIPS Display Illumination Design Guide, Vol. 2: Human Factors* (NELC-TD223) San Diego: Naval Electronics Laboratory Centre.

Heider, F. (1958) *The Psychology of Interpersonal Relations*, New York: Wiley.

Heinrich, H.W. (1950) *Industrial Accident Prevention: A Scientific Approach*, New York: McGraw-Hill.

Heinrich. H.W. (1930) *Unsafe Acts and Conditions*, New York: McGraw -Hill.

Helmreich, R.L., Fooushee H.C., Benson, R., and Russini, W. (1986) "Cockpit Resource Management: Exploring the Attitude–Performance Linkage", *Aviation, Space and Environmental Medicine*, 57, 1198-1200.

Helmreich, R.L., Wilhelm, J.A., Gregorisch, S.E., and Chidester, T.R. (1990) "Preliminary results from the Evaluation of Cockpit Resource Management", *Environmental Medicine*, 61, 576-579.

Herzberg, F. (1966) *Work and the Nature of Man*, Cleveland, OH: World

Hill, J.M. and Trist, E.L. (1953) "A consideration of industrial disputes as a means of withdrawal from work situation", *Human Relations*, 6, 357-80.

Hofmann, D.A. and Stetzer, A. (1996) "A Cross-Level Investigation of Factors Investigating Unsafe Behaviours and Accidents", *Personnel Psychology*, 49, (2), 307-340.

Hofmann, D.A., Ladd, D., Stetzer, A., and Cart, J.S. (1995) A Review of Organisational Safety Interventions and a Discussion of Future Directions. Manuscript in Preparation.

Hofmann,D.A., Jacobs, R., and Landy, R.L. (1995) "High Reliability Process Industries: Individual, Micro, and Macro Organisational Influences on Safety Performance", *Journal of Safety Research*, 26, 131-149.

Hogan, P.M. (1987) "The Legal Status of Administration Rules and Circulars", Dublin: Round Hall Press.

Holland J.L., (1985) *The Self Directed Search: Professional Manual*, Odessa, TX: Psychological Assessment Resources Inc.

Hough, L.M. and Mayhew, P. (1983) *The British Crime Survey*, London: HMSO.

Howard, J.H., Cunningham, D.A. and Rechnitzer, P.A. (1976) "Health Patterns Associated with Type A Behaviour. A Managerial Population", *Journal of Human Stress*, March, 24-31.

Hoyos, G.G. and Zimolong, B. (1988) *Occupational Safety and Accident Prevention: Behavioural Strategies and Methods in Advances in Human Factors*, Amsterdam: Elsevier.

HSA Annual Reports (1993–1995), Health and Safety Authority, Dublin.

Hsu, S.H. and Peng, Y. (1993) "Control/Display Relationship of the Four-Burner Stove: A Re-examination", *Human Factors*, 35: 745-749.

Humphreys, J. (1998) "Budget failed women on issues of child care", Quinn, in *The Irish Times*, July 12.

Hunt, J. (1999) "Every Society and Organisation has its Bullies", in *The Irish Times*, August 30.

Hunting, W., Laubli, T. and Grandjean, E. (1981) "Postural and Visual Loads at VDT Workstations, Part 1, Constrained Postures", *Ergonomics*, 24, 917-931.

Hurst, N.W., Bellamy, L.J., Guyer, T.A.W., and Astley, J.A. (1990) "A Classification Scheme for Pipework Failures to Include Human and Socio-Technical Errors and their Contribution to Pipework Failure Frequency", *Journal of Hazardous Materials*, 26, 159-186.

IBEC (1986) "Developing a Safety Culture", Dublin: IBEC.

IBEC (1999) "Guideline 20: Harassment/Bullying in the Workplace", in *Personnel Policies and Procedures Guidelines*, Dublin: IBEC.

Ivancevich, J.M. and Matteson, M.T. (1980) *Stress at Work*, Chicago, IL: Scott, Foresman and Co.

Ivancevich, J.M., Matteson, M.T., Freedman, S.M. & Phillips, J.S. (1990) "Worksite Stress Management Interventions", *American Psychologist*, 252-261.

Jahoda, M. (1979) "The Impact of Unemployment in the 1930 and the 1970s", *Bulletin of the British Psychological Society*, 32, 309-14.

Jenkins, W.D. (1947) "The Tactual Discrimination of Shapes for Coding Aircraft-Type Controls", in P.M. Fitts (ed) *Psychological Research on Equipment Design*, Columbus, OH: USAF Research Report No. 19.

Johansson, G. and Aronsson, G. (1984) "Stress Reactions in Computerised Administrative Work", *Journal of Occupational Behaviour*, 5, 159-81.

Johnson, G. and Scholes, K. (1997) *Exploring Corporate Strategy*, London: Macmillan.

Jones, J. W. and Wuebeker, L. (1985) 'Development and Validation of the Safety Locus of Control Scale', *Perceptual and Motor Skills*, 61, 151-61.

Jung, C.G. (1965) *Memories, Dreams, Reflections*, New York: Random House.

Jungermann, A., Schutz, H. and Thuring, M. (1988) "Mental Models in Risk Assessment: Informing People about Drugs", *Risk Analysis*, Vol. 8, pp. 147-55.

Kak, A.V. and Knight, J.K. (1980) "Text Formatting Effects in Speed Reading", Proceedings of the 24ᵗʰ Human Factors Society Meeting, Baltimore, MD: HFS.

Kales, R.W., Hohenemeer, C. and Kasperson, D.Y. (1985) *Previous Progress: Managing the Hazards of Technology*, New York: Westview Press.

Karasek, R. (1070, 1000) "Job Demands, Job Decision Latitude and Mental Strain: Implications for Job Redesign", *Administrative Science Quarterly*, 24, 285-306.

Katz, D. (1960) "The Functional Approach to the Study of Attitudes", *Public Opinion Quarterly*.

Katz, G. (1985) *Industrial and Organisational Psychology*, New York: Wiley.

Kelley, H.H. (1971) *Attribution in Social Interaction*, Morristown, NJ: General Learning Press.

Kelly, M.L. (1955) "A Study of Industrial Inspection by the Method of Paired Comparisons", *Psychological Monographs*, 69 (394) 1-16.

Kelman, H.C. (1961) "Processes of Opinion Change", *Public Opinion Quarterly*, 25, 57-78.

Kelsey, J.L., Githens, P.B., O'Connor, T., Weil, V., Cologero, J.A., Holford, T.R., White, A.A., Walter, S.D., Ostrield, A.M. and Southwick, W.O. (1994) "Acute Prolapsed Lumbar Invertebral Disc. An Epidemiological Study with Special Reference to Driving Automobiles and Cigarette Smoking", *Spine*, 9, 608-613.

Kerkhoff, G. (1985) "Individual Differences in Circadian Rhythms" in Folkard and Monk (1985), pp 29-32.

Kerr, W. (1957) "Complementing Theories of Safety Psychology", *Journal of Social Psychology*, 45, 3.9.

Khalil, T.N. and Kurucz, C.N. (1977) "The Influence of 'Biorhythm' on Accident Occurrence and Performance", *Ergonomics*, 20, 389-98

Khan, R.L., Wolfe, D.M., Quinn, R.P., Snoek, J.D. and Rosenthal, R.A. (1964) *Organisational Stress*, New York: Wiley.

Kilbom, A. (1988) "Intervention Programmes for Work-Related Neck and Upper Limb Disorders, Strategies and Evaluation", in Designing a Better World, Proceedings of the 10ᵗʰ International Congress of the I.E.A.

Klapp, S. and Netcik, J. (1988) "Multiple Resources for Processing and Storage in Short-term Working Memory", *Human Factors*, 30 (5), 617-632.

Kloman, H. (1990) "Reshaping the Discipline", *Risk Management*, April.

Knave, B.G., Wibom, R.I., Bergqvist, V.O., Carlsson, L.L.W., Levin, M.I.B., and Nylen, P.R. (1985) "Work with Video Display Terminals among Office Employees II, Physical Exposure Factors", *Scandinavian Journal of Work Environment and Health*, 11, 467-474.

Knight, F.H. (1921) *Risk, Uncertainty and Profit*, Boston: Houghton Mifflin.

Knights, D. and Vurdubakis, T. (1993) "Calculation of Risk: Towards an Understanding of Insurance as a Moral and Political Technology Accounting", *Organisations and Society*, Vol. 18, Nos. 7/8, pp. 729-64.

Kobrick, J.L. and Fine, B.J. (1983) "Climate and Human Performance" in D.J. Oborne and M.M. Grunenberg (eds) *The Physical Environment in Work*, Chichester: John Wiley.

Kocvhanskha, J.T. and Rase, D.A. (1996) "Designing a Competency Based Human Resource Organisation", *Human Resource Management*, 35 (1) 19-33.

Kohn, A. (1993) "Why Incentive Plans Cannot Work", *Harvard Business Review*, Sept-Oct, 1993, 54-63.

Koller, M., Kundi, M. and Cervinka, R. (1978) "Field Studies of Shift Work in an Australian Oil Refinery, I :Health and Psyghologial Well-Being of Workers Who Drop Out of Shift Work", *Ergonomics*, 2: 835-847.

Komaki, J., Barwick, K.D., and Scott, L.R. (1978) "A Behavioural Approach to Occupational Safety: Pinpointing and Reinforcing Safe Performance in a Food Manufacturing Plant", *Journal of Applied Psychology*, 63 (4), 434-445.

Kopelman, R., Brief, A. and Guzzo, R. (1990) "The Role of Climate and Culture in Productivity", in B. Schneider (ed) *Organisational Climate and Culture*, Oxford: Jossey Bass.

Koretz, G. (1996) "Parental Leave: Healthier Kids (leave from work so parents can care for children)", in *Business Week*, January 18.

Kozlowski S.W.J. and Jutls, B.M. (1987) "An Exploration of Climates for Technical Updating and Performance", *Personnel Psychology*, 40, 539-563.

Krause, N. and Styker, S. (1984) "Stress and Well-Being: The Buffering Role of Locus of Control Beliefs", *Social Science and Medicine*, 18, 783-790.

Krutssonn, A., Aherstedt, J., Jonsson, B.G. and Orth-Comer, K. (1987) "Increaesd Risk of Ischaemic Heart Disease in Shift Workers", *Lancet*, July 12, pp. 89-92.

Kurppa, K., Waris, P. and Rokkanen, M.D. (1979) "Peritendinitis and Tenosynovitis — A Review", *Scandinavian Journal of Work Environment and Health*, Supplement 3, 19-24.

Lampert, U. (1974) "Age and the Predisposition to Accidents", *Archives des Maladies Professionelles*, 62, 173.

Latham, G.P. and Locke, E.A. (1979) "Goal Setting: A Motivational Technique that Works", *Organisational Dynamics*, 8 (2) 68-80.

Laubli, T. and Grandjean, E. (1984) "The Magic of Control Groups in V.D.T. Field Studies", in Grandjean (1984), pp. 105-112.

Laubli, T., Hunting, W. and Grandjean, E. (1982) "Visual Impairments in VDU Operators Related to Environmental Conditions", in E. Grandjean and E. Vigliani (eds), *Ergonomics Aspects of Visual Display Terminals*, London: Taylor and Francis.

Lazarus, R.S. (1971) *Personality*, New York: Prentice Hall.

Lazarus, R.S. and Folkman, S. (1966) *Psychological Stress and the Coping Process*, New York: McGraw Hill.

Lee and Moray (1992) "Trust, Control Strategies and Allocations of Function in Human-Machine Systems", *Ergonomics*, 35, 1243-70.

Lee, C. and Gray, J.A. (1994) "The Role of Employee Assistance Programmes" in C. Cooper and S. Williams (eds.) *Creating Healthy Work Organisations*, Chichester: Wiley.

Lee, R.T. and Ashforth, B.E. (1990) "On the Meaning of Maslach's Three Dimensions of Burnout", *Journal of Applied Psychology*, December, 743-747.

Lee, T.R. (1995) "The role of Attitudes in Safety Culture and how to change them", Paper presented at the Conference "Understanding Risk Perception", Aberdeen, February.

Levenson, H., Hirschfield, M.L. and Hirschfield, A.S. (1980) "Industrial Actions and Recent Life Events", *Journal of Occupational Medicine*, 22. 53-57

Licklider, J.C.R. (1961) "Audio Warning Signals for Air Force Weapon Systems", Technical Report WADD TR60-814, Wright-Patterson AFB, Ohio.

Liebman, M. (1970) "The Effects of Sex and Race Norms on Personal Space", *Environmental Behaviour*, 2, 208-46.

Light, D. and Keller, S. (1979) *Sociology*, New York: Knopf, p. 564.

Little, K.B. (1965) "Personal Space", *Journal of Experimental Social Psychology*, 1, 237-47.

Loader, H.R. (1987) "Report on the Status, Salary and Conditions of Service of Full Members of AIRMIC", London: AIRMIC.

Locke, E. and Latham, G.P. (1990) *A Theory of Goal-Setting and Task Performance*, Englewood Cliffs, NJ: Prentice Hall.

Locke, E.A. (1968) "Toward a Theory of Task Performance and Incentives", *Organisational Behaviour and Human Performance*, 3, 157-189.

Luthans, D. (1995) *Organisational Behaviour*, St Paul, MN: West.

MacCrimmon, K. and Wehrung, O.A. (1986) "Characteristics of Risk Taking Executions", *Management Science*, Vol. 36, No. 4, pp. 422-35.

Mackay, C. and Cox, T. (1984) "Occupational Stress and Health: Some Current Issues" in C.L. Cooper and I.T. Robertson (eds) *International Review of Industrial and Organisational Psychology*, Chichester: Wiley.

Mackay, G.M., Defoneka, C.P., Blair, I. and Clayton, A.G. (1969) "Causes and Effects of Road Accidents", Dept. of Transportation, University of Birmingham.

Magora, A. (1972) "Investigations of the Relation between Low Back Pain and Occupation III. Physical Requirements; Sitting, Standing and Weight Lifting", *Industrial Medicine*, 41, (12) 5-9.

Mandal, A.C. (1976) "Work Chair with Tilting Seat", *Ergonomics*, 19, 157-64.

Mandal, A.C. (1981) "The Seated Man (Homo Sedens)", *Applied Ergonomics*, 12, 19-26.

Manning, D.P., Mitchell, P.G. and Blanchfield, L.P. (1984) "Body Movements and Events Contributing to Accidental and Non-Accidental Back Injuries", *Spine*, 9, 734-739.

Margolis, B.L. and Kroes, W.H. (1970) "Work and the Health of Man", in J. O'Toole (ed) *Work and the Quality of Life*, Cambridge, MA: MIT Press.

Margolis, B.L., Kroes, W.H. and Quinn, R.P. (1974) "Job Stress: An Unlisted Occupational Hazard", *Journal of Occupational Medicine*, 16, 10, 654-661.

Marsh, T.W., Robertson, I.T., Duff, A.R., Cooper, M.D. and Weyman, S. (1995) "Improving Safety Behaviour Using Goal Setting and Feedback", *Leadership and Organisational Development Journal*, 10 (1), 24-32.

Maslow, A.H. (1954) *Motivation and Personality*, New York: Harper and Row.

Matin, E. (1974) "Saccadic Suppressed: A Review and Analysis", *Psychological Bulletin*, Vol. 81, pp. 899-914.

Mayo, E. (1933) *The Human Problems of an Industrial Civilization*, London: Macmillan

McAfee, R.B. and Winn, A.R. (1989) "The Use of Incentives/Feedback to Enhance Work Place Safety: A Critique of the Literature", *Journal of Safety Research*, Vol. 20, No. 1, pp. 7-19.

McBride, G., King, M.G. and James, J.W. (1965) "Social Proximity Effects on GSR in Adult Humans", *Journal of Psychology*, 561, pp. 153-7.

McCann, K.B. (1996) "Corporate Culture is the Key to Safety", Liberty Feature Article, Microsoft Internet.

McCarthy, B. (1994) "Work and Mind: Searching for Our Celtic Legacy", *Irish Journal of Psychology*, 15 (2) 372-390.

McCarthy, J. (1987) "A Study of EAP Programmes in Cork", unpublished thesis.

McCarthy, J. (1994) "Dealing with Employers' Liability Proceedings Creating a 'No Claims' Culture" *IRN Report*, Dublin.

McCormick, E.J. (1995) *Industrial Psychology*, Englewood Cliffs, NJ: Prentice Hall.

McCormick, E.S. (1970) *Human Factors Engineering*, New York: McGraw Hill.

McIntyre, D.R. and Bates, B.T. (1982) "Effects of Rung Spacing on the Mechanics of Ladder Ascent", *Journal of Human Movement Studies*, 8, 55-72.

McKenna, E. (1994) *Business Psychology and Organisational Behaviour*, New Haven, NJ: Lawrence Erlbaum Associates Publishers.

McKenna, F. P. (1983): 'Accident Proneness: A Conceptual Analysis', *Accident Analysis and Prevention*, 15, (1), 65-71.

McLean (1965) "Brightness Contrast, Colour Contrast and Legibility", *Human Factors*, 7, 521-6.

McMahon, B.M. and Binchy, W. (1990) *Irish Law of Torts,* second edition, Dublin: Butterworth.

McMurray, R.N. (1973) "The Executive Neurosis", in R.L. Noland (ed) *Industrial Mental Health and Employee Counselling*, New York: Behavioural Publications.

Mead, P.G. and Sampson, P.B. (1972) "Hand Steadiness During Unrestricted Linear Arm Movements", *Human Factors*, 14, 45-50.

Means, R. (1990) "Alcohol, Alcohol Problems and the Workplace" in Dovgan, K. and Means, R. (eds.) *Alcohol and the Workplace*, Bristol: SAUS.

Mearns, K. and Flin, R. (1999) "Assessing the State of Occupational Safety: Safety Culture or Safety Climate", *Current Psychology*, 18 (1), 15-28.

Mearns, K., Flin, R., Fleming, M. and Gordon, R. (1997) *Human and Organisation Factors in Offshore Safety*, OTH 87 543. Suffolk: HSE Books

Mearns, K., Flin, R., Gordon, R. and O'Connor, P. (1997) Factoring the Human into Safety: Translating Research into Practice. Research Paper. Department of Psychology, University of Aberdeen.

Meenan, F., (1999) "Working Within the Law: A Practical Guide for Employers and Employees", 2nd ed., Oak Tree Press, Dublin.

Mehr, R.I. (1986) *Fundamentals of Insurance*, Homewood, IL: Irwin.

Meister, D. (1987) *Behavioural Analysis and Measurement Methods*, New York: Wiley.

Middlemist, R.D., Knowles, E.S. and Matter, C.F. (1976) "Personal Space Invasions in the Lavatory: Suggestive Evidence for Arousal", *Journal of Personality and Social Psychology*, 33, 541-6.

Miller, G.A. (1956) "The Magical Number Seven, Plus or Minus Two. Some Limits on our Capacity for Processing Information", *Psychological Review*, 63: 81-97.

Miller, G.R. (1972) *An Introduction to Speech Communication*, 2nd ed., Indianapolis, IN: Bobbs-Merrill.

Minister, D. (1987) *Behavioural Analysis and Measurement Methods*, New York: Wiley.

Minors, D.S. and Waterhouse, J.M. (1985) "Introduction to Circadian Rhythms", Ch. 1, in Folkard and Monk (1985) pp 1-14.

Mischel, W. (1986): *Introduction to Personality*, 4th ed., New York: Holt, Rinehart & Winston.

Mital, A. (1991) "Handtools: Injuries, Illnesses, Design and Usage" in A. Mital and W. Karwowski (eds) *Workspace, Equipment and Tool Design*, Amsterdam: Eslevier.

Mital, A., Ford, H.F. and Khaledi, H. (1987) "A Biochemical Evaluation of Staircase Riser Heights and Tread Depths during Stair-Climbing", *Clinical Biomechanics*, 2, 162-4.

Mitler, M.M., Carskadon, M.A. and Czeisler, C.A. (1988) "Catastrophes, Sleep and Public Policy: Consensus Report", *Sleep*, 11: 100-109.

Moffat, G., (1998) "The Regulation of Working Time: A European Odyssey", Warwick: Papers in Industrial Relations.

Moran, E. and Volkwein, J. (1992) "The Cultural Approach to the Formation of Organisational Climate", *Human Relations*, 45 (1) 19-47.

Morgan, C.T., Cook, J.S., Chapanis, A. and Lund, M. (1963) *Human Engineering Guide to Equipment Design*, New York: McGraw Hill.

Morris, J.N. (1956) "Job Rotation", *Journal of Business*, October, 268-273.

Morton and Provins (1960) "Finger Numbness after Acute Local Exposure to Cold", *Journal of Applied Psychology*, 15, 149-54

Mossholder, K.W., and Bedeian, A.G. (1983) "Cross-Level Inference and Organisational Research: Perspectives on Interpretation and Application", *Academy of Management Review*, 8, 547-558.

Mudd, S.A. (1961) "The Scaling and Experimental Investigation of Four Dimensions of Pure Tone and their Use in an Audio-Visual Monitoring Problem", Unpublished Ph.D. Thesis, Lafayette, IN: Purdue University.

Mullaly, J. and Grigg, L. (1988) "RSI: Integrating the Major Theories", *Australian Journal of Psychology*, 40: 19-33.

Mulligan, B., McBride, D. and Goodman, L. (1984) "A Design Guide for Nonspeech Auditory Displays", (SR-84-1) Pensacola, FL: Naval Aerospace Medical Research Laboratory.

Murray-Bruce, D. (1982) "Promotions the Healthy Banker", *Journal of the Institute of Bankers*, December, 199-200

Murrell, K.F.H (1971) *Ergonomics: Man in his Working Environment*, London: Chapman and Hall.

Murrell, K.F.H. (1969) "Beyond the Panel", *Ergonomics*, 5, 147-53.

Myers, I.B. (1962) *The Myer-Briggs Type Indicator*, Palo Alto, CA: Consulting Psychologists Press.

Nagel, D.C. (1988) "Human Error in Aviation Operation" in E. Weiner and D. Nagel (eds) *Human Factors in Aviation*. pp 263-303. New York: Academic Press.

Nemecek, J. and Grandjean, E. (1973) "Noise in Landscaped Offices", *Applied Ergonomics* 4, 19-22

Newbold, E.M. (1926) "A Contribution to the Study of the Human Factor in the Causation of Accidents", Industrial Health and Research Board, Report no. 34, London.

Newell (1992) "The Myth and Destructiveness of Equal Opportunities: The Continued Dominance of the Mothering Role", *Personnel Review*, 21 (4): 37-47.

Niskanen, T. (1994) "Safety Climate in Road Administration", *Safety Science*, 17, 237-255.

Norman, D.A. (1988) *The Psychology of Everyday Things*. New York: Basic Books.

O'Brien, O. and Dufficy, H. (1988) "Alcohol and Drug Policies" in Dickenson, F. (ed.) *Drink and Drugs at Work*, London: IPM.

O'Moore, M. (1999) "Illness and Absence due to Workplace Bullying", *Employers Platform,* September.

Oborne, D.J (1975) "An Investigation of Passenger Comfort with Particular Reference to the Effects of Vibration", Ph.D. Thesis, University of Wales.

Oborne, D.J. (1995) *Human Factors in Design and Development, Ergonomics at Work*, New York: Wiley.

Oborne, D.J., Branton, R., Leal, F., Shipley, P. and Stewart, T. (1993) *Person Centred Ergonomics: A Bratonic View of Human Factors*, London: Taylor and Francis.

O'Connell, S., (1996) "Management Beating the Bully", in *Business and Finance*, April 30.

Ostberg, O. (1980) "Accommodation and Visual Fatigue in Display Work" in Grandjean and Vigliani, 11. 41-52.

Ostberg, O.N., Warell, B. and Nordell, L. (1984) "Comfortable: A Generic Desk for the Automated Office", *Behaviour and Information Technology*, 3, 411-416.

Ostrom, L., Wilhelmsen, C. and Kaplan, B. (1993) "Assessing Safety Culture", *Nuclear Safety*, 34, 163-172.

O'Sullivan, R., (1999) "Task Force Set to Prevent Bullying in the Workplace", *The Irish Times*, September 22.

Owsley, C., Sekuler, R. and Siemen, D. (1983) "Contrast Sensitivity Throughout Adulthood", *Vision Research*, 23, 689-699.

Packard, V. (1962) *The Pyramid Climbers*, New York: McGraw Hill.

Pahl, J.M. and Pahl, R.E. (1971) *Managers and their Wives*, London: Allen Lane.

Parker, S.K. and Wall, T.D. (1996) "Job Design and Modern Manufacturing", in P. Warr (ed) *Psychology and Work*, 4th ed., London: Penguin.

Pat-Cornell, M.E., (1990) "Organisational Aspects of Engineering System Safety: The Case of Offshore Platforms", *Science*, 250, 1210-1217.

Patterson, M.L. and Sechrest, L.B. (1971) "Interpersonal Distance and Impression Formation", *Journal of Personality*, 38, 161-6.

Patterson, M.L., Mullens, S. and Romano, J. (1984) "Compensatory Reactions to Spatial Intrusion", *Sociometry*, 34, 121-4.

Patterson, R. (1982) *Guidelines for Auditory Warning Systems on Civil Aircraft*, (CAA Paper 82017), London: Civil Aviation Authority.

Payne, R. and Cooper, C.L. (1988) *Causes, Coping and Consequences of Stress at Work*, Chichester: Wiley.

Pearcy, M.J. (1993) "Twisting Mobility of the Human Back in Flexed Postures", *Spine*, 18: 114-119.

Peck, D. and Whitlow, D. (1975) *Approaches to Personality Theory*, London: Methuen.

Perrow, C. (1984) *Normal Accidents Living with High Risk Systems*, New York: Basic Books.

Peters, T.J. (1987) *Thriving on Chaos*, London: Heinemann.

Pfeffer, I. (1956) *Insurance and Economic Theory*, Homewood, IL: Irwin.

Phares, E. (1976) *Locus of Control in Personality*, Morristown, NJ: General Learning Press.

Pheasant, S.T. (1986) *Bodyspace*, London: Taylor and Francis.

Pheasant, S.T. (1987) *Ergonomics: Standards and Guidelines for Designers*, pp 7317, London: British Standards Institution.

Pheasant, S.T. (1988) "User-Centred Design" in Nicholson and Ridd, pp. 73-96.

Pheasant, S.T. (1991) *Ergonomics, Work and Health*. London: Taylor and Francis.

Pheasant, S.T. (1991) *Lifting and Handling — An Ergonomic Approach*, Teddington, Middlesex: National Back Pain Association.

Pheasant, S.T. and O'Neil, D. (1975) "Performance in Gripping and Turning — A Study in Hand/Handle Effectiveness", *Applied Ergonomics*, 6, 205-8.

Pidgeon, N.F. (1991) "Safety Culture and Risk Management in Organisations". *Journal of Cross-Cultural Psychology*, 22, 129-140.

Pidgeon, N.F. (1995) "Risk Construction and Safety Culture in Managing High-Risk Technologies". Paper prepared for International Workshop on Institutional Vulnerabilities and Resilience in Public Administration, Crisis Research Centre. Leiden, The Netherlands.

Porteous, M. (1997) *Occupational Psychology*, London: Prentice Hall.

Porter, J.M., Gyi, D.E. and Robertson, J. (1992) "Evaluation of a Tilting Computer Desk", in E.J. Lovesy (ed.) *Contemporary Ergonomics*, London: Taylor and Francis.

Porter, L.W. and Lawler, E.E. (1968) *Managing Motivation, Attitudes and Performance*, Homewood, IL: Irwin.

Porter, S. (1988) "Accident Proneness: A Review of the Concept", *International Review of Ergonomics*, 2, 177-206.

Potter, M., Dubreuil, A. and Mond, H. (1969) "The Effects of Sitting Posture on the Volume of the Foot", *Ergonomics*, 12, 753-758.

Poulton E.C. (1978) "Increased Vigilance with Vertical Vibration at 5hz: An Alerting Mechanism", *Applied Ergonomics*, 9, 73-6

Poulton, E.C., Hunt, E.M., Carpenter, A. and Edwards, R.S. (1978) "The Performance of Junior Hospital Doctors following Reduced Sleep and Long Hours of Work", *Ergonomics*, 21: 279-296.

Powell, P.I., Hale, M., Martin, J. and Simon, M. (1971) *2000 Accidents*, London: National Institute of Industrial Psychology.

Putz-Anderson, V. (ed) (1988) *Cumulative Trauma Disorders — Manual for Musculosketal Diseases of the Upper Limbs*, London: Taylor and Francis.

Pykko, I., Farkkila, M., Tiovanen, J., Korhonen, D. and Hyvarinen, J. (1976) "Transmission of Vibration in the Hand-Arm System with Special Reference to Changes, Compression, Force and Acceleration", *Scandinavian Journal of Work Environment and Health*, 29,311,325

Quinter, J.L. and Elvey, R.L. (1993) "Understanding 'RSI': A Review of the Role of Peripheral Neural Pain and Hyperalgesia", *The Journal of Manual and Manipulative Therapy*, 1:99-105.

Randall, P. (1997) *Adult Bullying: Perpetrators and Victims*, Routledge, London.

Rasmussen J. (1979) "Notes on Human Error Analysis Prediction" in G. Apostalalkis and C. Volta (eds) *Synthesis and Analysis and Prediction in Reliability Studies*, New York: Plenum.

Rasmussen, J. (1982) "A Taxonomy for Describing Human Malfunction in Industrial Installation", *Journal of Occupational Accidents*, 4, 311-333.

Ray, P.S. and Frey, A., (1999) "Validation of the Safety Behaviour Index", *Professional Safety*, 44 (7), 25-30.

Rayner, K. (1977) "Visual Attention in Reading: Eye Movements Reflect Cognitive Processes", *Memory and Cognition*, 5, 443-8.

Rayner, K., Sereno, S.C., Morris, R.K., Schmauder, A.R. and Clifton, C. (1989) "Eye Movements and On-line Language Comprehension Processes", *Language and Cognitive Processes*, 4, 21-49.

Rayner, S. and Cantor, R. (1987) "How Far is Safe Enough? The Cultural Approach to Social Technological Choice", *Risk Analysis*, Vol. 7, pp. 3-9.

Reason, J. (1990) *Human Error*, Cambridge: Cambridge University Press.

Reason, J.T. (1979) "Actions not as Planned: The Price of Atomisation" in G. Underwood (ed) *Aspects of Consciousness, Psychological Issues*, London: Academic Press.

Reason, J.T. (1997) *Managing the Risks of Organization Accidents*. Aldershot: Ashgate.

Reber, R.A. and Wallin, J.A. (1983) "Validation of a Behavioural Measure of Occupational Safety". *Journal of Organisational Behaviour Management*, 5, 69-77.

Reber, R.A. and Wallin, J.A. (1984) "The Effects of Training, Goal Setting and Knowledge of Results on Safe Behaviour: A Component Analysis", *Academy of Management Journal*, Vol. 27, No. 3, pp. 544-60.

Redmond, M. (1984) *Redmond's Guide to Irish Labour Law*, Dublin: Bridgefoot Press.

Resch, M. (1996) "Mobbing-Prevention and Management in Organisations", in *European Journal of Work and Organisational Psychology*, Vol. 5, No. 2.

Rey, R.P. and Meyer, J.J. (1980) "Visual Impairments and their Objective Correlates" in E. Grandjean and E. Vigliani (eds) *Ergonomic Aspects of Visual Display Terminals*, London: Taylor and Francis.

Ridley, J. (1995) *Safety at Work*, 3rd ed., London: Heinemann.

Rivas, F.J., Diaz, J.A. and Santos, R. (1993) "Valores Maximos de Esfuerzo Admisibles en los Puestos de Trabajo", *Prevención*, 87: 20-25.

Rolfe, J.M. and Allnutt, M.F. (1967) "Putting the Man in the Picture", *New Scientist*, 16 February, 401-6.

Rosa, R.R. and Bonnet, M.F. (1993) "Performance and Alertness on 8h and 12h Rotating Shifts at a Natural Gas Utility", *Ergonomics*, 36: 1177-1193

Roscoe and Couchman (1987) "Improving Visual Performance through Volitional Focus Control", *Human Factors*, 29, 311-325.

Rotter, J.B. (1966) "Generalised Expectancies for Internal versus External Control of Reinforcement", *Psychology Monographs*, 80, 1, 609.

Rouse, W.B. and Rouse, S. (1983) "Analysis and Classification of Human Error", *IEEE Transactions on Systems, Man and Cybernetics*, SMC 13 (4), 539-49.

Rousseau, D. and Wade-Bernzoni, K.A. (1994) "Linking Strategy and Human Resource Practices: How Employee and Customer Contracts are Created", *Human Resource Management*, 33 (3) 463-89.

Rousseau, D.M. (1985) "Issues of Level in Organisational Research: Multilevel and Cross-Level Perspectives". I Cummings, L.L. and Staw, B.M. (eds.) *Researching Organisational Behaviour*, 7, 1-37, Greenwich, CT: JAI Press.

Rousseau, D.M. (1988) "The Construction of Climate in Organisational Research", in C. Cooper and I.T. Robertson (eds.) *International Review of Industrial and Organisational Psychology*. Chichester: Wiley.

Rousseau, D.M. (1990) "New Hire Perceptions of their Own and their Employers' Obligations: A Study of Psychological Contracts", *Journal of Organisational Behaviour*, 11, 389-400.

Rousseau, D.M. and Parks, J.M. (1993) "The Contracts of Individuals and Organisations", in Cummings, L.L. and Staw, B.M. (eds.) *Research in Organisational Behaviour*, 15, (1) AI Press, Greenwich, CT p. 1-43.

Rowe, W.B. and Morris, N.M. (1986) "On Looking into the Black Box: Prospects and Limits in the Search for Mental Models", *Psychological Bulletin*, 100, 349-63.

Rummer, K., Berggrund, V., Jernberg, P. and Ytterbom, U. (1976) "Driver Reaction to a Technical Safety Measure — Studded Types", *Human Factors*, 18, 443-454.

Russek, H.I. and Zohman, B.L. (1958) "Relative Significance of Heredity, Diet and Occupational Stress in CHD of Young Adults", *American Journal of Medical Sciences*, 235, 266-275.

Ryan, G.A. and Bampton, M. (1988) "Comparison of Data Process Operation with and without Symptoms", *Community Health Studies*, 12, 63-68.

Rys, M. and Konz, S. (1994) "Standing", *Ergonomics*, 37, 677-87.

Saarela, Saari, J. and Aaltonen, M. (1989) "The Effects of an Information Safety Campaign in the Shipbuilding Industry", *Journal of Occupational Accidents*, Vol. 10, pp. 255-66.

Sah, A.P. (1989) "Personality Characteristics of Accident Free and Accident Involved Indian Railway Drivers", *Journal of Personality and Clinical Studies*, 5, 203-6.

Sanders, M. and Shaw, B. (1988) *Research to Determine the Contributions of System Factors in the Occurrence of Underground Injury Accidents*, Pittsburgh, PA: Bureau of Mines.

Sanders, M.G., Halcomb, C.G., Fray, J.M. and Owens, J.M. (1976) "Internal-External Locus of Control and Performance on a Vigilance Task", *Perceptual and Motor Skills*, 42, 939-43.

Sanders, M.S. and McCormick, E.J. (1992) *Human Factors in Engineering and Design*, 7th ed., New York: McGraw Hill.

Savinar, J. (1975) "The Effect of Ceiling Height on Personal Space", *Man Environment Systems*, 5, 321-4.

Scannell, Y. (1995) *Environmental and Planning Law*. Dublin: Round Hall.

Schneider, B. (1975) "Organisational Climate: Individual Preferences and Organisational Realities Revisited". *Journal of Applied Psychology*, 60, 459-465.

Schneider, B. (1990) "The Climate for Service: An Application of the Climate Construct" in Schneider B. (ed) *Organization Climate and Culture* (383-412). San Francisco: Jossey-Bass.

Schneider, B. (1990) *Organisational Climate and Culture*, San Francisco: Jossey Bass.

Schneider, B. and Gunnarson, S. (1996) "Organisational Climate and Culture: The Psychology of the Work Place", in J. James, B. Steffy and D. Bray (eds) *Applying Psychology in Business*: Mass: Lexington.

Schoonmaker, A.N. (1969) *Anxiety and the Executive*, New York: American Management Association.

Seedy, N.P. and Chapman, A.J. (1987) "Industrial Accidents" in Cooper, C.L. and Robertson I.T. (eds.), *International Review of Industrial and Organisational Psychology* (201-227), Chichester: Wiley.

Seidel, H. and Heide, R (1986) "Long Term Effects of Whole Body Vibration: A Critical Survey of the Literature", *International Archives of Occupational and Environmental Health*, 58, 12-6.

Sell (1977) "Ergonomics as Applied to Crane Cabs", in J.S. Weiner and H.G. Maule (eds) *Human Factors in Work, Design and Production*: London: Taylor and Francis.

Selye, H. (1936) *The Stress of Life*, New York: McGraw Hill.

Seminara, J.L., Gonzales, W. and Parsons, S. (1977) *Human Factors Review of Nuclear Power Plant Control Room Design* (EPRI NP-309) Palo Alto, CA: Electric Power Research Institute.

Shaw, L. and Sichel, H.S. (1971) *Accident Proneness: Research in the Occurrence, Causation and Prevention of Road Accidents*, Oxford: Pergamon.

Sheldon, W.H. (1954) *A Guide for Somatotyping and the Adult Male at All Ages*, New York: Harper.

Shepherd, A. (1993) "An Approach to Information Requirements Specification for Process Control Tasks", *Ergonomics*, 36, 1425-1437.

Shibolet, S., Lancaster, M.C. and Danon, Y. (1976) "Heat Stroke: a Review", *Aviation, Space and Environmental Medicine*, 47, 280-301.

Shirom, A., Eden, D., Silberwasser, S. and Kellerman, J.J. (1973) "Job Stress and the Risk Factors in Coronary Heart Disease among Occupational Categories in Kibbutzim", *Social Science Medicine*, 7, 875-892.

Shoenberger R.W. (1970) "Human Performance as a Function of Direction and Frequency of Whole Body Vibration", Army Medical Research Laboratories Report, Ohio, AMRL-TR-70-7

Sigman, A. (1993) "Working Shifts on the Red-Eye", *Personal Management Plus*, October, p. 19.

Simons, A.K. and Schmitz, W.A. (1958) "The Effect of Low Frequency, High Amplitude Whole Body Vibration on Human Performance", Washington DC : Office of the Surgeon General, Research and Development Division.

Singleton, W.T. (1982) *The Body at Work: Biological Ergonomics*, London: Cambridge University Press.

Sinha, S.P. and Sinha, S.P. (1991) "Personal Space and Density as Factors in Task Performance and Feeling of Crowding", *Journal of Social Psychology*, 131, 831-7.

Skinner, B.F. (1953) *Scientific and Human Behaviour*, New York: Macmillan.

Skinner, B.F. (1974) *About Behaviourism*, New York: Knopf.

Slappendal, C., Laird, I., Kawachi, I., Marshall, S. and Cryer, C. (1993) "Factors Affecting Work-Related Injury among Forestry Workers: A Review". *Journal of Safety Research*, 24, 19-32.

Slovic, P., Fischhoff and Lichtenstein, S. (1978) "Accident Probabilities and Seat Belt Usage: A Psychological Perspective", *Accident Prevention and Analysis*, 10, 281-285.

Smith, H.P. (1979) "A Simulator Study of the Interaction of Pilot Workload with Errors, Vigilance, and Decisions" (NASA TM-78482). Moffett Field, CA: NASA-Ames Research Centre.

Sommer, H.C. and Harris, S.C. (1970) "Combined Effects of Noise and Vibration on Mental Performance as a Function of Time of Day", Ohio Army Medical Research Laboratories Report , ARML-TR — 70 -36.

Sommer, R. (1969) *Personal Space: The Behaviour Basis of Design*, New York: Prentice-Hall.

Spiers, C., (1996) "Bullying at Work: The Cost to the Business", in *Training Officer*, Vol. 32, No. 8, October.

Spillane, R. and Deves, L. (1987) "RSI: Pass Pretence or Patienthood?" *Journal of Industrial Relations*, March, pp. 41-9.

Stager, P. and Hameluck, D. (1986) "Contrast Sensitivity and Visual Detection in Search and Rescue", Toronto, ON: Defence and Civil Institute of Environmental Medicine.

Stammerjohn, L., Smith, M.J. and Cohen, B. (1981) "Evaluation of Work Station Design Factors in VDT Operations", *Human Factors*, 23, 401-412.

Starr, S.J., Thompson, C.R. and Shute, S.J. (1982) "Effects of Video Display Terminals on Telephone Operators", *Human Factors*, 23, 401-12.

Stein, R.T. (1982) "Using Real-Time Simulations to Evaluate Managerial Skills", *Journal of Assessment Centre Technology*, 5, 9-15.

Stewart-Buttle, C., Marras, W.S. and Kim, J.Y. (1993) "The Influence of Anti-Fatigue Mats on Back and Leg Fatigue", in *Proceedings of the Human Factors and Ergonomics Society, 37th* Annual Meeting, Human Factors and Ergonomics Society, 769-73.

Stranks, J. W. (1994b) *Human Factors and Safety*, London: Pitman.

Stranks, J.W. (1994a) *The Handbook of Health and Safety Practice*, London: Pitman.

Stubbs, D.A., Buckle, P.W., Hudson, M.P., Rivers, R.M. and Worrington, R.N. (1983) "Back Pain in the Nursing Profession: Part 1, Epidemiology and Pilot Methodology", *Ergonomics*, 26, 755-65.

Suchman, E. (1961) "On Accident Behaviour", in *Behavioural Approaches to Accident Research*, Washington, DC: Association for the Aid to Crippled Children.

Sutherland, V. and Cooper, C.L. (1987) *Man and Accidents Offshore*, London: Lloyds.

Swain, A. and Guttman, H. (1983) "Handbook of Human Reliability Analysis with Emphasis on Nuclear Power Plant Application", Final Report (Nureg/CR-1278) Washington, DC: Nuclear Regulatory Commission.

Taylor, D.J. and Pocock, S.J. (1972) "Mortality of Shift and Day Workers 1956-68", *British Journal of Industrial Medicine*, 29: 201-207.

Taylor, W. (1974) "The Vibration Syndrome: Introduction" in W. Taylor (ed) *The Vibration Syndrome*, London: Academic Press.

Teisinger J., (1972) "Vascular Disease Disorders Resulting from Vibrating Tools", *Journal of Occupational Medicine*, 14, 129-133.

Tillman, W.A. and Hobbs, G.E. (1949) "The Accident Prone Automobile Driver", *American Journal of Psychiatry*, 106: 321-31.

Timbal, J., Londe, M. and Boutelier, C. (1976) "Mathematical Model of Man's Tolerance to Cold Using Morphological Factors", *Aviation, Space and Medicine*, 47,958-64.

Trice, H.M. and Roman, P.M. (1972) *Spirits and Demons at Work: Alcohol and Other Drugs on the Job*, New York: New York School of Industrial and Labour Relations, Cornell University.

Turner, B. and Pidgeon, N. (1997) *Man-Made Disasters*, London: Butterworth.

Turner, B., Pidgeon, N., Blockley, D.and Tort, B. (1989) "Safety Culture: Its Importance in Future Risk Management". Position Paper for Second World Bank Workshop on Safety Control and Risk Management, Karlstad, Sweden.

Tynan, M. (1998) "Employers' Group Criticises Extensions to Parental Leave", *The Irish Times*, 31 December.

Tynan, M. (1998) "Severe Criticism of Bill on Parental Leave", *The Irish Times*, 9 June.

Vallfors, B. (1985) "Acute, Subacute and Chronic Low Back Pain — Clinical Symptoms, Absenteeism and Working Environment", *Scandinavian Journal of Rehabilitation Medicine*, Suppl. 11, 1-98.

Valsamakis, A.C., Vivian, R.W. and duToit, G.S. (1992) *The Theory and Principles of Risk Management*, Durban: Butterworths.

Van Nes, F.L. (1968) "Space, Colour and Typography on Visual Display Terminals", *Behaviour and Information Technology*, 5: 99-118.

Varita, M. (1998) "The Sources of Bullying: Psychological Work Environment and Organisation Climate", in *European Journal of Work and Organisational Psychology*, Vol. 5, No. 2.

Verhaegen, P., Vanhalst, B., Derycke, H. and Van Hoeke, M. (1976) "The Value of Some Psychological Theories of Industrial Accidents", *Journal of Occupational Psychology*, 1, 39-45.

Voke J. (1982) "Colour Vision Problems at Work", *Health and Safety at Work*, January, 27-28.

Vroom, V.H. (1964) *Work and Motivation*, New York: Wiley.

Waddell, G., (1987) "A New Clinical Model for the Treatment of Low Back Pain", *Spine*, 12, 632-644.

Waller, R.A. (1968) "Office Acoustics Effect on Background Noise", *Applied Acoustics*, 2 121-80

Wallis, C. (1983) "Stress: Can We Cope?", *Time*, 6 June, 44-52.

Wardwell, W.I., Hyman, M. and Bahnson, C.B. (1964) "Stress and Coronary Disease in Three Field Studies", *Journal of Chronic Disease*, 17, 73-74.

Waris, P. (1980) "Occupational Cervicobrachial Syndromes — A Review", *Scandinavian Journal of Work Environment and Health*, 6 Suppl. 3, 3-14.

Warner, H.D. and Mace, K.C. (1974) "Effects of Platform Fashion Shoes on Brake Response Time", *Applied Ergonomics*, 5, 143-6.

Warr, P.B. and Jackson, P.R. (1984) "Men Without Jobs: Some Correlates of Age and Length of Unemployment", *Journal of Occupational Psychology*, 57, 77-85.

Warrick, (1947) "Direction of Movement in the Use of Control Knobs to Position Visual Indicators" in P.M. Fitto (ed.) *Psychological Research on Equipment Design*, Ohio U.S Army Air Force Aviation Program Research Dept., Report no.19.

Weaver, S. (1972) cited in Stranks, J.(1994) *Human Factors and Safety*, London: Pitman.

Weidman, B. (1970) "Effect of Safety Gloves on Simulated Work Tasks", AD 738981, Springfield, VA: National Technical Information Service.

Weisz, A.Z., Goddard, C. and Alen, R.W. (1965) "Human Performance Under Random and Sinusoidal Vibration", Ohio: Aerospace Medical Research Laboratories, Report AMRL-TR-65-209.

Wetherall, A. (1981) "The Efficacy of Some Auditory Vocal Subsidiary Tasks as Measures of the Mental Load on Male and Female Drivers", *Ergonomics*, 24, 197-214.

White, A.A. and Panjabi, M.M. (1978) *Clinical Biomechanics of the Spine*, Philadelphia, PA: Lippincott.

White, J.P.M. (1993) *Civil Liability for Industrial Accidents*, Dublin: Oak Tree Press.

Whitlock, F.D., Stou, J.R., and Rekhdahl, R.J. (1977) "Crisis, Life Events and Accidents", *Australian and New Zealand Journal of Psychiatry*, 11, 127-32.

Wickens, C., Sandry, D. and Vidulich, M. (1983) "Compatibility and Resource Competition Between Modalities of Input, Central Processing and Output", *Human Factors*, 25, 227-248.

Wickens, C.D. (1992) *Engineering Psychology and Human Performance*, 2nd ed., New York: Harper Collins.

Wilde, G.J.S. (1982) "The Theory of Risk Homeostasis: Implications for Safety and Health", *Risk Analysis*, 2, 209-225.

Wilkins, C., Sandry, D. and Vidulich, M. (1988) "Fluorescent Lighting, Headaches and Eyestrain", paper presented at National Lighting Conference.

Williams, R.D. and House, J.S. (1985) "Social Support and Stress Reduction", in C.L. Cooper and M.J. Smith (eds) *Job Stress and Blue-Collar Work*, Chichester: Wiley.

Williamson, A., Feyer, A.M., Carins, D. and Biancotti, D. (1997) "The Development of a Measure of Safety Climate: The Role of Safety Perceptions and Attitudes". *Safety Science*, 25 (1-3), 15-27.

Williamson, A.M., Gower, C.G.I. and Clarke, B.C. (1994) "Changing the Hours of Shiftwork: A Comparison of 8 and 12 hour Shift Rosters in a Group of Computer Operators", *Ergonomics*, 37: 287-298.

Willis (1966) "Initial Speaking Distance as a Function of the Speaker's Relationship", *Psychonomic Science*, 5, 221-2.

Wilson, J.R. (1989) "Mental Models: Theory and Application in Human Factors", *Human Factors*, 31 (6), 617-634.

Winfield, T. and Jolowicz, M. (1990) *Law of Tort*, 13th ed., London: Sweet and Maxwell.

Winsemius, W. (1965) "Some Ergonomic Aspects of Safety", *Ergonomics*, 8, 151-162.

Wolcott, J.H., McMeekin, R.R., Burgin, R.E. and Yanowitch, R.E. (1977) "Correlations of General Aviation Accidents with Biorhythm Theory", *Human Factors*, 19, 382-93.

Wolford, G. and Hollingworth, S. (1974) "Lateral Masking in Visual Information Processing", *Perception and Psychophysics*, 16, 315-20.

Woodson (1981) *Human Factors Design Handbook*, New York: McGraw Hill.

Wuebeker, L. J., Jones, J. W. and Dubois, D. (1985): 'Safety Locus of Control and Employee Accidents', *Technical Report: The St Paul Companies*, St Paul MN.

Wyndham, C. H. (1966) "A Survey of the Casual Factors in Heat Stroke and of their Prevention in the Gold Mining Industry", *Journal of the South African Industry of Mining and Metallurgy*, 1, 245.85

Yarbus, A.L. (1967) *Eye Movements and Vision*, New York: Plenum.

Yeats, P. (1998) "Cassells Concerned at Parental Leave Delay", *The Irish Times*, 29 May.

Yeats, P. (1998) "EU Permission Sought to Postpone Directive", *The Irish Times*, 18 May.

Young, L.R. and Sheena, D. (1975) "Survey of Eye Movement Recording Techniques", *Behaviour Research Methods and Instrumentation*, 7, 397-429.

Zabetakis, R. (1977) cited in Stranks, J. (1994) *Human Factors and Safety*, London: Pitman.

Zohar, D. (1980) "Safety Climate in Industrial Organisations: Theoretical and Applied Implications", *Journal of Applied Psychology*, 65 (1) 96-102.

Zuboff, S. (1988) *In the Age of the Smart Machine: The Future of Work and Power*, New York: Basic Books.

INDEX

Also available from
OAK TREE PRESS

Insurance Law in Ireland:
Volume 1
€60 pb : ISBN 1-86076-066-X

Volume 2
€95 pb : ISBN 1-86076-233-6
€60 pb : ISBN 1-86076-235-4

Volume 1 of **Insurance Law in Ireland** is a comprehensive analysis of the law relating to general insurance in Ireland. Focusing on the legal aspects that arise in the day-to-day practice of insurance, its broad scope covers Intermediaries and the Law; Duty of Disclosure; General Principles of Insurance; Policy Conditions and Interpretation; Motor Insurance; Liability Insurance; Material Damage; and Business Interruption. It is an essential reference.

Volume 2 of **Insurance Law in Ireland** identifies recent developments in Insurance Law in England and analyses them in the context of Irish Insurance Law and practice, recognising that judicial decisions in the English Courts are not binding on the Irish Courts but are, and have always been, of very persuasive authority. It also deals with many issues that were either not addressed at all or needed to be dealt with in greater detail.

To order:
Email: orders@oaktreepress.com
Telephone: 1890 313855 **Fax:** 021 4313496

Also Available from
OAK TREE PRESS

Casebook of Irish Insurance Law
John A Campbell & Michael Corrigan
€75 hb : ISBN 1-872853-31-5
€50 pb : ISBN 1-872853-30-7

In this comprehensive casebook, Michael Corrigan and John Campbell have gathered together all the significant insurance decisions of the Irish courts over the past 150 years. An invaluable reference for students, agents and others in the insurance industry. Winner of the Sargison Memorial Award for its significant contribution to insurance learning in Ireland.

Civil Liability for Industrial Accidents
John PM White
€540 hb, 3 Volume set, boxed : ISBN 1-86076-198-4

This uniquely comprehensive work in three volumes provides an in-depth and up-to-date analysis of all aspects of employers' liability at common law and the statutory regime of protection of workers' safety and health. Extending to 4,300 pages, Dr White's work is an indispensable reference in the library of every practising lawyer.

Medical Negligence Actions
John PM White
€100 hb : ISBN 1-86076-017-1

This book offers a complete statement of the law and practice relating to medical negligence cases — from the initial taking of instructions by the plaintiff's solicitor, through the complexities of discovery and interrogatories, to a comprehensive treatment of the principles and rules governing the liability of medical practitioners and hospital proprietors. It also includes a unique and invaluable set of precedent letters and pleadings.

To order:
Email: orders@oaktreepress.com
Telephone: 1890 313855 **Fax:** 021 4313496